INTRODUCTION TO
CHEMICAL ENGINEERING THERMODYNAMICS

McGRAW-HILL SERIES IN CHEMICAL ENGINEERING

Max S. Peters, *Consulting Editor*

EDITORIAL ADVISORY BOARD

BUILDING THE LITERATURE OF A PROFESSION

Fifteen prominent chemical engineers first met in New York more than 30 years ago to plan a continuing literature for their rapidly growing profession. From industry came such pioneer practitioners as Leo H. Baekeland, Arthur D. Little, Charles L. Reese, John V. N. Dorr, M. C. Whitaker, and R. S. McBride. From the universities came such eminent educators as William H. Walker, Alfred H. White, D. D. Jackson, J. H. James, Warren K. Lewis, and Harry A. Curtis, H. C. Parmelee, then editor of *Chemical & Metallurgical Engineering*, served as chairman and was joined subsequently by S. D. Kirkpatrick as consulting editor.

After several meetings, this first Editorial Advisory Board submitted its report to the McGraw-Hill Book Company in September, 1925. In it were detailed specifications for a correlated series of more than a dozen texts and reference books which have since become the McGraw-Hill Series in Chemical Engineering.

Since its origin the Editorial Advisory Board has been benefited by the guidance and continuing interest of such other distinguished chemical engineers as Manson Benedict, John R. Callaham, Arthur W. Hixson, H. Fraser Johnstone, Webster N. Jones, Paul D. V. Manning, Albert E. Marshall, Charles M. A. Stine, Edward R. Weidlein, and Walter G. Whitman. No small measure of credit is due not only to the pioneering members of the original board but also to those engineering educators and industrialists who have succeeded them in the task of building a permanent literature for the chemical engineering profession.

THE SERIES

INTRODUCTION TO
Chemical Engineering Thermodynamics

J. M. SMITH

Professor of Chemical Engineering
Northwestern University

H. C. VAN NESS

Professor of Chemical Engineering
University of California

Second Edition

INTERNATIONAL STUDENT EDITION

McGRAW-HILL BOOK COMPANY, INC.

New York   St. Louis   San Francisco
London   Mexico   Sydney   Toronto

KŌGAKUSHA COMPANY, LTD.

Tokyo

INTRODUCTION TO CHEMICAL ENGINEERING THERMODYNAMICS

INTERNATIONAL STUDENT EDITION

Exclusive rights by Kōgakusha Co., Ltd. for manufacture and export from Japan. This book cannot be re-exported from the country to which it is consigned by Kōgakusha Co., Ltd. or by McGraw-Hill Book Company, Inc. or any of its subsidiaries.

V

Library of Congress Catalog Card Number 58-11192

TOSHO PRINTING CO., LTD., TOKYO, JAPAN

PREFACE

The purpose of this edition, like that of the first, is to present an introductory treatment of thermodynamics from a chemical engineering viewpoint. A primary consideration in both editions has been a presentation that is easily understood by the average undergraduate student and also rigorous enough to provide a firm foundation for more advanced work.

The justification of a separate text for chemical engineers rests upon the same reasoning as it did a decade ago when the first edition was published. The thermodynamic principles applied to problems in any field of engineering are the same. However, the teaching of these principles, which are often abstract, is more effective if advantage can be taken of the student's interest in his own chosen engineering area. Thus, applications indicating the usefulness of thermodynamics in chemical engineering, even in an introductory course, not only help maintain the student's interest but also give him a clearer understanding of the fundamentals themselves.

The arrangement of the material in the book is essentially unchanged from the first edition. The treatment of the basic definitions and the first law in the first two chapters has been rewritten and enlarged. The objective of this revision is to offer a more complete explanation of first concepts in order that the student may obtain a sound footing before continuing his exploration of thermodynamics.

The chapters on the pressure-volume-temperature behavior of fluids, heat effects, the second law, and thermodynamic properties of fluids have been rewritten to introduce new data and to achieve greater clarity of presentation. The increased importance of fluid mechanics in chemical engineering has required considerable revision of the chapter on flow of fluids, particularly the part concerned with the Bernoulli equation. The treatment of power production has been enlarged to include more complete discussion of the gas turbine and an introduction to the thermodynamic analysis of rocket motors and other jet-propulsion systems.

The thermodynamic analysis of processes, originally at the end of the chapter on the second law, has been enlarged considerably and placed in Chapter 11, near the end of the text. This material demonstrates the application of the second-law principle in evaluating the efficiency of energy utilization in practical processes. Coming near the end of the book, it provides a review and summary of the most important concepts of thermodynamics.

The rather complete treatment of phase and chemical-reaction equilibria included in the first edition has been retained in the second, because these areas are still of vital importance to chemical engineers. However, both chapters have been completely rewritten in order to bring the material up to date and to make the more complex passages clearer. Special attention has been accorded to the subject of the standard states since this is always a difficult concept to explain.

The length of the book is about the same as that of the first edition. Space for the enlarged treatment of principles and the new developments in thermodynamics has been obtained by deleting out-of-date and less significant material. Hence, the complete text can be covered in a two-semester course. It may be used for a one-semester offering by omitting some of the application chapters at the end.

As a whole, the book is probably best suited for the third or fourth year of undergraduate work. However, the first five chapters have been used by the authors in the introductory sophomore course in chemical engineering. The chief purpose here is to introduce the subject of "heat balances" from a thermodynamic viewpoint.

Many persons have aided in the revision of the first edition. Acknowledgment is due particularly to those teachers using the book who have given their comments and suggestions. Professors E. W. Comings and R. Curtis Johnson and the staff at Purdue University offered many valuable suggestions based upon direct experience. Finally, much is owed to those teachers of thermodynamics, B. F. Dodge, W. N. Lacey, and H. C. Weber, who stimulated the authors' interest in the subject.

J. M. Smith
H. C. Van Ness

CONTENTS

LIST OF SYMBOLS

The nomenclature in use throughout the book is given in the following list. Special symbols which appear from place to place are defined where they occur.

English Letter Symbols

A Area

A Work function or Helmholtz free energy $= E - TS$

A Amagat compressibility factor

a Acceleration

a Activity

C Number of components

C_p Molal heat capacity at constant pressure

C_v Molal heat capacity at constant volume

c_p Specific heat at constant pressure

c_v Specific heat at constant volume

D Diameter

E Internal energy

F Force

F Free energy, *i.e.*, Gibbs free energy $= H - TS$

$\bar{F}_i$ Partial free energy of component i in solution

$\Delta F°$ Standard free-energy change for a chemical reaction

f Fugacity of a pure substance

$\bar{f}_i$ Fugacity of component i in solution

G A thermodynamic state function in general

g Local acceleration of gravity

g_c Dimensional constant with the value 32.1740 $(\text{lb}_m/\text{lb}_f)$ (ft/sec^2)†

H Enthalpy $= E + pV$

$\bar{H}_i$ Partial enthalpy of component i in solution

$\Delta H°$ Standard heat of a chemical reaction

† lb_m denotes pounds of mass; lb_f, pounds of force.

x

ΔH_f°	Standard heat of formation
ΔH_c°	Standard heat of combustion
K	Phase-equilibrium constant
$K_a,\ K_p,$ etc.	Chemical-reaction equilibrium constants
L	Length
M	Molecular weight
m	Mass
n	Number of moles
P	Number of phases
p	Pressure
p_c	Critical pressure
p_r	Reduced pressure
p_i	Pure-component pressure of component i in a gaseous solution
$\bar{p}_i$	Partial pressure of component i in a gaseous solution; defined by $\bar{p}_i = y_i p$
p'	Vapor pressure
Q	Heat
R	Universal gas constant (see Table 3-1 for values)
S	Entropy
s	Distance
T	Absolute temperature, °K or °R
T_c	Absolute critical temperature
T_r	Reduced temperature
T_o	Absolute temperature of the surroundings
t	Temperature, °C or °F
u	Velocity
V	Variance or degrees of freedom
V	Total volume
V_i	Pure-component volume of component i in a gaseo solution
$\bar{v}_i$	Partial volume of component i in solution
v	Molal or specific volume
v_c	Critical volume
W	Work
W_s	Shaft work associated with a flow process
x_i	Mole fraction of a component in solution in general and mole fraction of component i in a liquid phase in particular
y_i	Mole fraction of component i in a gaseous phase
z	Height above a datum plane
Z	Compressibility factor $= pv/RT$
Z_c	Critical compressibility factor $= p_c v_c/RT_c$

Greek Letter Symbols

α Residual volume $= RT/p - v$

α, β, γ Constants in the equation $C_p = \alpha + \beta T + \gamma T^2$

γ Ratio of molal heat capacities of gases $= C_p/C_v$

γ Activity coefficient $= \bar{f}_i/x_i f_i$

δ Constant in the equation $pv^\delta = $ constant

Δ Indicates a finite change in the quantity it precedes, *i.e.*, the final value minus the initial value

η Joule-Thomson coefficient

μ Chemical potential $= \bar{F}_i$

μ Viscosity

ρ Density

ϕ Fugacity coefficient $= f/p$ or $\bar{f}_i/x_i p$

Notes

1. ° used as a superscript designates a standard state.

2. * used as a superscript designates the zero-pressure state or the ideal-gas state at any pressure.

3. When it is necessary to denote the total value of any extensive property (except volume) so as to distinguish it from the molal or specific property, a solid line will be used under the symbol, for example, $\underline{H}$, $\underline{S}$, etc.

CHAPTER 1

INTRODUCTION

1-1. The Scope of Thermodynamics. By derivation, the word "thermodynamics" means heat power, or power developed from heat. However, such a restriction on its meaning has long since disappeared. In its broader sense, thermodynamics is the science which deals with the transformations of energy of all kinds from one form to another. The general restrictions within which all such transformations are observed to occur are known as the first and second laws of thermodynamics. These laws cannot be "proved" in the mathematical sense. Rather, their validity rests upon experience.

The value of thermodynamics lies in the fact that these laws and certain accompanying definitions have been given mathematical expression. This has led to the development of a consistent network of equations from which a wide range of practical results and conclusions may be deduced. The universal applicability of this science is shown by the fact that it is employed alike by physicists, chemists, mechanical engineers, chemical engineers, and metallurgists. In each case the basic principles are the same, but the applications differ. The chemical engineer must be able to cope with a particularly wide variety of problems, among the most important of which are the determination of heat and work requirements of physical and chemical processes, the calculation of the work obtainable from power cycles, and the determination of equilibrium conditions for both chemical reaction and mass transfer between phases.

Certain limitations on the thermodynamic method should be made clear at the beginning. Thermodynamic considerations by themselves are not sufficient to allow the calculation of the *rates* of chemical or physical processes. Rates depend on both driving force and resistance, and while driving forces may be calculated from thermodynamics, the determination of resistances is not possible by such methods. Moreover, thermodynamics is of no help in determining the mechanisms of either physical or chemical processes. Although this may be regarded as a limitation on the thermodynamic mode of analysis, it is also a major advantage, for it means that the detailed mechanism by which a process occurs need not be known. Thus the thermodynamic approach permits the evaluation of the energy effects of a process, either physical or chemical, solely from a knowledge of the initial and final conditions. The advantage of this is that the results for a complicated process may be evaluated by considering the same change to occur by the simplest process which can be devised.

A practical limitation sometimes results from the lack of sufficient data to allow effective use of thermodynamics. The numerical results of a thermodynamic analysis are accurate only to the extent that the required data are accurate. The chemical engineer must work with a large number of chemical substances, and, unfortunately, adequate data are known for only a relatively few. Thus he must learn to estimate results when only meager data are available.

In spite of these limitations, the science of thermodynamics is remarkable in the number and variety of conclusions that can be reached by starting with only two basic laws. All else results from either definition or deduction. Thus, in order to apply the thermodynamic method, one must develop the ability to proceed logically from one deduction to the next, making use always of precisely defined terms. The remainder of this chapter and much of the next will therefore be devoted to the definition of terms.

1-2. Fundamental Quantities. From a scientific point of view, we know only what our senses tell us, and they can experience but a limited number of things. Among these are time, distance, mass, force, and temperature. These quantities represent fundamental concepts. They are known only from our experience. However, in order to give them quantitative meaning, standard units of measurement are essential. The definitions of such units were entirely arbitrary in the beginning, but during the course of time certain units have become universally accepted as standards.

1-3. Time. The fundamental unit of time θ is the second, defined as $1/86,400$ part of a mean solar day. The primary standard, which may be checked at will, is the average interval required for a complete rotation of the earth. All other units of time are defined in terms of this primary standard.

1-4. Distance. The fundamental unit of distance or length s or L is the meter, defined as the distance between two marks on a platinum-iridium bar at $0°C$, kept in a vault at Sèvres, near Paris, France. All other units of length are defined in relation to this primary standard. The foot, for example, is defined as 0.3048006 meter.

1-5. Mass. The fundamental unit of mass m is the kilogram. The primary standard is a lump of platinum-iridium also kept at Sèvres, France. All other units of mass are defined in relation to this primary standard. The most commonly used unit of mass in the English engineering system of units is the pound *mass* (lb_m), which is defined as

0.4535924 kg. It should be understood that mass is the measure of *quantity of matter.* It is also the measure of the property of matter known as inertia. While mass is related to weight, the two terms must be distinguished, for weight refers to the *force* exerted by gravity on mass. At a particular location weight is proportional to mass, but the proportionality factor changes from place to place. Although the weight of an object varies from place to place, its mass remains invariant.

Secondary standards of both mass and length are maintained in various parts of the world. For example, duplicates of the standard kilogram and the standard meter are preserved by the National Bureau of Standards in Washington, D.C.[1]

1-6. Force. The concept of force F is probably best introduced with reference to Newton's second law of motion. The fundamental equation which expresses this law states that force is proportional to the product of mass and acceleration, or

$$F = \frac{1}{g_c} (m)(a) \tag{1-1}$$

where $1/g_c$ is the proportionality constant and a is acceleration. Equation (1-1) provides a relationship among the four fundamental quantities, time, distance, mass, and force, which must be valid regardless of the system of units employed. If the units of time, distance, and mass are defined first as in Secs. 1-3 to 1-5, it is only necessary to select a unit for force, and then g_c is determined by Eq. (1-1). In the absolute system of units used in scientific work, it is customary to define the unit of force so that g_c is unity. Thus when time is measured in seconds, distance in centimeters, and mass in grams, the unit of force is taken as the dyne, defined as that force which will cause a mass of one gram to accelerate 1 cm/sec². Substitution of these values in Eq. (1-1) gives

$$1 \text{ dyne} = \frac{1}{g_c} (1 \text{ g})(1 \text{ cm/sec}^2)$$

Thus

$$g_c = 1 \text{ (g-cm)}/(\text{dyne-sec}^2)$$

The units of g_c may be viewed in two ways. If the dyne is regarded as an independent unit, g_c has the units just given. However, if the dyne is regarded merely as an abbreviation for the composite unit gram-centimeter per second squared, then g_c is considered unitless. If this latter view is adopted, Eq. (1-1) may be written

$$F = ma$$

since g_c is unity and dimensionless.

[1] For an extensive compilation of conversion factors between units, see Units of Weight and Measure, *Natl. Bur. Standards (U.S.), Misc. Publ.* 214, July 1, 1955.

Chemical engineers in the United States commonly employ a set of units, known as the English engineering system, which uses both pounds *force* and pounds *mass*. In this book these two units will be distinguished by using the abbreviations lb_f and lb_m. Since these units of force and mass are defined without reference to Eq. (1-1), g_c is not unity. Its value may be determined by considering what is meant by the unit of a pound *force*.

The pound *mass* represents a given amount of material and was defined in Sec. 1-5 as equivalent to 0.4535924 kg. The pound *force* is the force exerted by gravity on one pound *mass* of material under conditions where the acceleration of gravity has its standard value of 32.1740 ft/sec². Thus one pound *mass* will be given an acceleration of 32.1740 ft/sec² by a force of one pound *force*. Substitution of these values in Eq. (1-1) gives

$$1 \ lb_f = \frac{1}{g_c} \ (1 \ lb_m)(32.1740 \ \text{ft/sec}^2)$$

It is seen from this equation that g_c has a value of 32.1740 and units of $(lb_m/lb_f)(\text{ft/sec}^2)$ in the English engineering system. Thus in this system g_c is a dimensional constant having a numerical value equal to the standard acceleration of gravity, but having different units.

It should be clear from the preceding discussion that the pound *force* and the pound *mass* are not the same quantity and that they cannot be canceled against one another. When an equation contains both the units of pounds *force* and pounds *mass*, the dimensional constant g_c must also appear in the equation to make it dimensionally correct.

The term *weight* is properly used to indicate the force of gravity on a body, while mass designates the quantity of matter in a body. This distinction is not always made, however, and standards of mass are often referred to as "weights." Moreover, the use of a balance to compare masses is frequently called "weighing." Thus, one must learn to recognize whether force or mass is meant when the word weight is used.

Example 1-1. What would be the weight or force of gravity in pounds *force* on an object having a mass of 12.00 lb_m at a place where the local acceleration of gravity is 32.000 ft/sec²?

Solution. By Eq. (1-1),

$$F = \frac{ma}{g_c} = \frac{mg}{g_c}$$

or

$$F = \frac{(12.00)(32.000)}{32.174} = 11.94 \ lb_f$$

Example 1-2. A spring scale is calibrated so as to read pounds *mass* at a location where the acceleration of gravity has its standard value of 32.174 ft/sec². If the scale is used at a place where the acceleration of gravity is 32.300 ft/sec², what is the mass of an object which "weighs" 15.00 lb according to this scale?

Solution. The spring scale registers pounds *force.* Thus the force of gravity on the object is 15.00 lb$_f$. By Eq. (1-1),

$$m = \frac{Fg_c}{g} = \frac{(15.00)(32.174)}{32.300} = 14.94 \text{ lb}_m$$

$$\left(F = \frac{g}{g_c} \, m \right)$$

In most engineering work accuracy of the order indicated in the preceding problems is neither necessary nor practical, and in such cases the ratios g/g_c and g_c/g are taken as unity. However, there are times when high accuracy is essential.

1-7. Temperature. The definition of a temperature scale is not so simple as might be supposed. The most common method of measuring temperature T is with a liquid-in-glass thermometer. This method uses the property of expansion of fluids when they are heated. Thus a uniform tube, partially filled with mercury, alcohol, or some other substance, can readily be used to indicate degree of "hotness" simply by measurement of the length of the fluid column. However, numerical values can be assigned to the various degrees of "hotness" only by arbitrary definition. For the centigrade or Celsius scale, the ice point (freezing point of water saturated with air at standard atmospheric pressure) is defined as zero and the steam point (boiling point of pure water at standard atmospheric pressure) as 100. Hence a thermometer may be given a numerical scale by immersing it in an ice bath and making a mark for zero at the fluid level, and then immersing it in boiling water and making a mark for 100 at that fluid level. The distance between the two marks is divided into 100 equal spaces called degrees. Other spaces of equal size may be marked off below zero and above 100 to extend the range of the thermometer. How good will such a temperature-measuring device be? This depends on the fluid used in the thermometer. All thermometers, regardless of fluid, will read the same at zero and 100 if they are calibrated by the method described, but at other points the readings will not usually correspond because fluids vary in their expansion characteristics. An arbitrary choice could be made, and for many purposes this would be entirely satisfactory. However, it is more reasonable to make the choice of a standard thermometric fluid in some logical way.

The method which has been adopted makes use of the gas thermometer, an instrument in which a gas serves as the thermometric fluid. The essential features of the constant-pressure gas thermometer are shown in Fig. 1-1. In this apparatus a gas sample is confined over mercury in the thermometer bulb. The thermostat is first filled with a mixture of ice and water. As the gas contracts, mercury is injected into the apparatus, and when thermal equilibrium has been reached, a final adjustment is made so that the mercury levels in the manometer and in the thermometer bulb are the same. In this way atmospheric pressure is maintained on the gas in the bulb. At this mercury level the scale is marked zero to indicate the ice point. A similar procedure is followed when the thermostat is filled with boiling water, and the scale is marked 100. The length between these two marks is then divided into 100 equal divisions or degrees. Divisions of the same size may be laid off both above and below this range to extend the scale. In this way it is possible to construct a gas thermometer to operate at atmospheric pressure. A simple

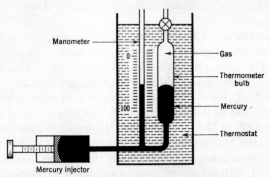

Fig. 1-1. Simple gas thermometer.

modification can be made to allow this thermometer to operate at other pressures. It is only necessary to connect the open end of the manometer to a vessel maintained at constant pressure either above or below atmospheric.

If such a thermometer is filled with various gases, using an amount of each so that the zero point is constant, one finds that the readings are nearly independent of the kind of gas used. Moreover, this becomes more and more nearly true as the pressure is lowered below atmospheric, and at zero pressure it is exactly true. Thus, a gas thermometer operating at a pressure approaching zero gives identical readings for all gases and is therefore a logical choice for a standard thermometer. Of course, no thermometer can actually operate at zero pressure, but it is not difficult to extrapolate to this condition.

The zero-pressure state of a gas perhaps deserves some discussion. As the pressure on a gas is decreased, the individual molecules become more and more widely separated. The actual volume of the molecules themselves becomes a smaller and smaller part of the total volume occupied by the gas. Furthermore, the forces of attraction between molecules become ever smaller because of the increasing distances between them. In the limit, as the pressure approaches zero, the molecules become separated by infinite distances. Therefore their actual volume becomes infinitesimal compared with the total volume occupied by the gas, and the intermolecular forces of attraction approach zero. A gas which meets these conditions is known as _an ideal gas._ Thus the temperature scale established with the zero-pressure gas thermometer is usually known as the ideal-gas temperature scale. The properties of an ideal gas will be considered in more detail in Chap. 3.

While the ideal-gas temperature scale is the logical one to adopt as the primary standard, it is not practical for everyday use because of the complicated nature of gas thermometry. For a detailed discussion of this subject, the excellent work of Keyes[1] is available. The _practical_ temperature scale presently accepted as the standard is known as the "International Temperature Scale of 1948." Every effort has been made to define this scale in such a way that it is a close approximation to the ideal-gas temperature scale. It is based on the following invariant reference points, each of which is defined for standard atmospheric pressure:[2]

Oxygen point (boiling point of O_2)	$-182.970°C$	
Ice point (freezing point of H_2O)	0.000	} fundamental
Steam point (boiling point of H_2O)	100.000	
Sulfur point (boiling point of S)	444.600	
Silver point (freezing point of Ag)	960.8	
Gold point (freezing point of Au)	1063.0	

Between these points, temperatures are defined according to the readings of specified temperature-measuring devices which are calibrated at these reference points by standard procedures. These devices and their ranges of use are as follows:

Platinum resistance thermometer	$-190-660°C$
Platinum vs. platinum–10% rhodium thermocouple	$660-1063°C$
Optical pyrometer	Above $1063°C$

The temperature scale determined in this way is so close to the ideal-gas temperature scale that the two may be considered identical for all practical purposes.

So far, only the centigrade system of temperature measurement has been considered. The other temperature scales are defined in terms of it. The Fahrenheit scale, which is commonly used by engineers, is defined by the equation

$$t°F = 1.8(t°C) + 32 \qquad (1-2)$$

Thus the ice point on this scale is 32° and the steam point is 212°. It should be noted also that one centigrade degree is equivalent to 1.8 Fahrenheit degrees.

Two other temperature scales used in scientific work deserve special

[1] F. G. Keyes, "Temperature, Its Measurement and Control," Chap. I, Reinhold Publishing Corporation, New York, 1941.

[2] H. F. Stimson, The International Temperature Scale of 1948, _Natl. Bur. Standards, J. Research,_ **42**, 211 (1949).

consideration because they involve the concept of an absolute lower limit of temperature. For the present let it suffice to say that accurate measurements place this limit at $-273.16°C$, or $-459.69°F$. Since this temperature represents a lower limit, it is only natural that temperature scales have been defined which assign zero to this limit. Two such *absolute* scales are in common use. On the *Kelvin scale* the size of the degree is the same as the centigrade degree, but all temperatures are 273.16 degrees higher. On the *Rankine scale* the size of the degree is the same as the Fahrenheit degree, but all temperatures are 459.69 degrees higher. For most engineering work these numbers are rounded off to 273 and 460. The relationships among the four scales are shown in Fig. 1-2. Temperature in degrees Rankine is always 1.8 times the temperature in degrees Kelvin. When temperature is referred to without qualification in any discussion of thermodynamics, absolute temperature is implied.

Example 1-3. The accompanying table lists the specific volumes of water, mercury, hydrogen at 1 atm, and hydrogen at 100 atm for a number of temperatures on the International Temperature Scale. Assume that each of these substances is to be used as the fluid in a thermometer, calibrated by the method described at the ice and steam points. To determine how good these thermometers are, calculate what they will read at the true temperatures for which data are given.

°C	Specific volume, cm³/g			
	Water	Mercury	H₂ at 1 atm	H₂ at 100 atm
-100	....	....	7,053	76.03
0	1.00013	0.073554	11,125	118.36
50	1.01207	0.074223	13,161	139.18
100	1.04343	0.074894	15,197	159.71
200	1.1590	0.076250	19,266	200.72

Solution. In calibrating thermometers by this method, one assumes that each degree can be represented by the same length on the thermometer scale for a given thermometer. This is equivalent to the assumption that each degree of temperature change is accompanied by the same change in volume or specific volume of the thermometric substance used. Thus if water is used as the thermometric fluid, its change in specific volume in going from zero to 100°C is 1.04343 − 1.00013 = 0.04330 cm³. If it is assumed that this volume change is divided equally among the 100 degrees between zero and 100, then the volume change per degree should be 0.000433 cm³/°C. If this assumption is not valid, then the thermometer will give incorrect readings when compared with the International Temperature Scale. In the case of water, its *actual* change in specific volume in going from zero to 50°C is 1.01207 − 1.00013 = 0.01194 cm³. Since each "degree" on the water thermometer has been taken to represent 0.000433 cm³, the number of these degrees represented by a volume change of 0.01194 cm³ is 0.01194/0.000433, or 27.6 degrees. Thus the water thermometer will read 27.6 degrees when the actual temperature is 50°C.

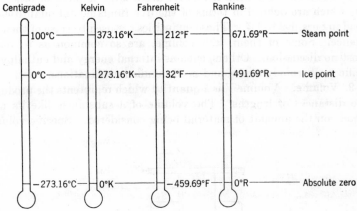

FIG. 1-2. Relations among temperature scales.

At 200°C, the actual specific volume of water is 1.1590 cm³, and its volume change in going from zero to 200°C is

$$1.1590 - 1.00013 = 0.1589 \text{ cm}^3$$

Thus the water thermometer will read

$$\frac{0.1589}{0.000433} = 368 \text{ degrees}$$

when the true temperature is 200°C. The accompanying table gives all the results obtained by similar calculations.

°C	Reading			
	Water	Mercury	H_2 at 1 atm	H_2 at 100 atm
−100	.....	.....	−100.0	−102.3
0	0	0	0	0
50	27.6	49.9	50.0	50.4
100	100	100	100	100
200	368	201	199.9	199.2

It will be noted that each thermometer reads the true centigrade temperature at zero and 100 because each was calibrated at these points. At other points, however, the readings may differ from the true values of the temperature. Water is seen to be a singularly poor thermometric fluid. Mercury, on the other hand, is good, which accounts for its widespread use in thermometers. Hydrogen at 1 atm makes a very good thermometric fluid, but is not practical for general use. Hydrogen at 100 atm is not as good because it behaves less like an ideal gas.

1-8. Secondary Quantities. There are a large number of other variables which are defined in terms of the five fundamental quantities discussed in Secs. 1-2 to 1-7. These quantities are used because of their convenience. Some of them, like volume, are so common as to require almost no discussion. Others, such as internal energy and enthalpy, are specific to thermodynamics and need detailed explanations.

1-9. Volume. Volume V is a quantity which represents the product of three distances or lengths. The volume of a substance, like its mass, depends on the amount of material being considered. Specific volume v

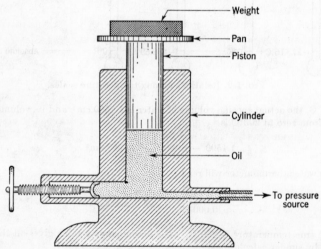

FIG. 1-3. Dead-weight gauge.

on the other hand is defined as volume per unit mass or volume per mole of material and is, therefore, independent of the total amount of material considered. Density ρ is the reciprocal of specific volume.

1-10. Pressure. The pressure p of a fluid on a surface is defined as the normal force exerted by the fluid per unit area of the surface. If force is measured in pounds and area in square inches, the units of pressure are pounds *force* per square inch, or psi. The primary standard for pressure measurement is based directly on this definition. A known force is balanced by a fluid pressure acting on a known area. The pressure by definition is the force divided by the area, or $p = F/A$. The apparatus used for measuring pressures by this method is known as a dead-weight gauge. A simple design is shown in Fig. 1-3. The piston is carefully fitted to the cylinder so that the clearance is small. "Weights" are placed on the pan until the pressure of the oil, which tends to make the piston rise, is just balanced by the force of gravity on the piston and all that it supports. The force of gravity is given by Eq. (1-1) as $F = mg/g_c$, where m is the mass of the piston, pan, and "weights," and g is the local acceleration of gravity. The pressure of the oil is, then,

$$p = \frac{F}{A} = \frac{mg}{Ag_c}$$

where A is the cross-sectional area of the piston. Gauges in common use, such as Bourdon gauges, are calibrated by comparison with the dead-weight gauge.

Pressures are also frequently measured in terms of the height of a column of fluid under the influence of gravity. Thus mercury manometers are used to give pressure readings in inches or millimeters of mercury. Such values are converted to force per unit area by multiplying the height of the column by its density. This relationship is developed by considering the force exerted by gravity on the mercury column. According to Eq. (1-1)

$$F = \frac{1}{g_c} (m)(g)$$

where g is the local acceleration of gravity. The mass m of the column of mercury is given by the equation

$$m = (A)(h)(\rho)$$

where A is the cross-sectional area of the column of mercury, h is its height, and ρ is its density. These equations may be combined to eliminate m, giving

$$\frac{F}{A} = p = (h)(\rho) \frac{g}{g_c}$$

It will be noted that the term g/g_c appears in this equation. It must be included to make the equation strictly correct, both numerically and dimensionally. However, g and g_c are almost always nearly equal; so this term has little effect on the numerical value of the pressure. It is therefore frequently omitted, and one must tacitly assume that pressure is given in pounds *force* per unit area even though ρ is given in pounds *mass* per unit volume. Since the density of mercury is a function of temperature, the pressure to which a given height of a mercury column corresponds depends on its temperature. If the temperature is not stated, it is assumed to be 0°C.

Another commonly used unit of pressure is the atmosphere, which corresponds to the force of gravity acting on the air above the earth's surface. Since this is a variable quantity, it is customary to employ a *standard* atmosphere, equal to 14.696 lb$_f$/sq in. or 29.921 in. of mercury at 0°C in a standard gravitational field.[1]

---

[1] In Europe, a different atmosphere is sometimes used. It is defined as 10^6 dynes/sq cm and is equivalent to 0.9869 atm. This quantity is called a *bar* in the United States.

Most pressure gauges give readings which represent the difference between the pressure being measured and the pressure of the surrounding atmosphere. These readings are known as "gauge" pressures, and can be converted to total or *absolute* pressures by adding the barometric pressure. Absolute pressures must be used in thermodynamic calculations. Gauge pressures exist only because gauges give readings of this kind. This is true also of vacuum gauges, which are almost always calibrated in inches of mercury vacuum. Thus a "27-in." vacuum referred to a "30-in." barometer indicates an absolute pressure of 3 in. of mercury, or 3 in. Hg.

Since the most common unit of pressure measurement in the United States is pounds *force* per square inch, it is convenient to have an abbreviation for this unit. In this book *psia* will refer to pounds *force* per square inch absolute, and *psig* will indicate pounds *force* per square inch gauge.

Example 1-4. A dead-weight gauge with a ½-in.-diameter piston is being used to measure pressures very accurately. In a particular instance it balances with a mass of 13.476 lb_m on it (including the piston and pan). If the local acceleration of gravity is 32.000 ft/sec², what is the gauge pressure being measured? If the barometric pressure is 14.593 psi, what is the absolute pressure?

Solution. The force of gravity on the piston, pan, and "weights" is

$$F = \frac{mg}{g_c} = \frac{(13.476)(32.000)}{32.174} = 13.403 \ lb_f$$

$$p = \frac{F}{A} = \frac{13.403}{(\frac{1}{4})(\pi)(\frac{1}{2})^2} = 68.261 \ psig$$

Absolute pressure = 68.261 + 14.593 = 82.854 psia

Example 1-5. A mercury manometer at 80°F reads 23.82 in. The local acceleration of gravity is 32.10 ft/sec². To what pressure in atmospheres does this height of mercury correspond?

Solution

$$p = (h)(\rho)\frac{g}{g_c}$$

At 80°F the density of mercury is 13.53 g/cm³ or (13.53)(62.43)/1728 lb_m/in.³

$$p = \left[\frac{(23.82)(13.53)(62.43)}{1728}\right]\left(\frac{32.10}{32.174}\right) = 11.62 \ psi \ or \ 0.790 \ atm$$

Example 1-6. A mercury manometer is used to measure a *vacuum*. It reads 27.38 in. Hg at 70°F. The local acceleration of gravity is 32.10 ft/sec². The barometric pressure is 14.77 psi. What is the absolute pressure in pounds per square inch absolute?

Solution. The mercury-manometer reading represents a pressure *below* atmospheric. This pressure must be converted to pounds per square inch and subtracted from 14.77 to obtain the absolute pressure. This could be done exactly as it was in Example 1-5. However, another method will be demonstrated. One converts the measured mercury height to the height it would have at the standard conditions of 0°C and standard gravity. These corrections are easily understood if it is recognized that the height of a column of mercury corresponding to a given pressure is inversely proportional both to its density and to the acceleration of gravity.

At 70°F: $\rho = 13.543$ g/cm³
At 0°C: $\rho = 13.595$ g/cm³

Therefore the height of mercury after being corrected to 0°C and standard gravity is

$$h = (27.38) \left(\frac{13.543}{13.595}\right) \left(\frac{32.10}{32.174}\right) = 27.22 \text{ in. Hg}$$

Since 29.92 in. Hg at 0°C and standard gravity is equivalent to 14.7 psi,

$$p = 14.77 - (27.22) \left(\frac{14.7}{29.92}\right) = 14.77 - 13.37 = 1.4 \text{ psia}$$

1-11. Work. Work W is done whenever a force acts through a distance. The quantity of work done is defined as the product of the force and the distance through which it moves, and in the English engineering system it is expressed in foot-pounds *force.* If the force is constant, then $W = Fs$. If the force is variable, the equation for work is expressed in terms of differentials:

$$dW = F \, ds \tag{1-3}$$

This equation must be integrated if the work for a finite process is required.

In engineering thermodynamics the most important type of work is that which accompanies a change in volume of a gas. Consider the compression or expansion of a gas in a cylinder by the movement of a piston. The force exerted by the piston on the gas is equal to the product of the piston area and the pressure of the gas. The distance through which the piston moves is equal to the volume change of the gas divided by the area of the piston. Equation (1-3) therefore becomes

$$dW = (pA) \, d \, \frac{V}{A}$$

or, since A is constant,

$$dW = p \, dV \tag{1-4}$$

Integrating,

$$W = \int_{V_1}^{V_2} p \, dV \tag{1-5}$$

Equation (1-5) is the general expression for the work done as a result of a finite compression or expansion process. This kind of work can be represented as an area on a pressure-vs.-volume $(p\text{-}V)$ diagram, such as is shown in Fig. 1-4. In this case a gas having an initial volume V_1 at a pressure p_1 is compressed to a pressure p_2 and a volume V_2 along the path shown from 1 to 2. This path relates the pressure which exists at any point during the process to the volume. The work required for the process is given by Eq. (1-5) and is represented on Fig. 1-4 by the area under the curve all the way down to zero pressure.

1-12. Energy. The concept of energy developed slowly over a period of several hundred years and culminated in the establishment of the general principle of conservation of energy about 1850. The germ of this principle as it applies to mechanics was present in the work of Galileo (1564–1642) and Isaac Newton (1642–1726). Indeed, it follows almost automatically from Newton's second law of motion once the quantitative definition of work as the product of force and distance is formulated. Unfortunately, no such concept existed until 1826, when it was introduced by the French mathematician J. V. Poncelet at the suggestion of G. G. Coriolis, a French engineer. At that time, and indeed for some years thereafter, the science of mechanics was characterized by a looseness in the definition of terms. The word "force" (or the Latin *vis*) not only was used in the sense described by Newton in his laws of motion, but also was applied to the quantities which we now define as work and potential and kinetic energy. This ambiguity confused the thinking of generations of physicists and precluded for some time the development of any general principle of mechanics beyond Newton's laws of motion.

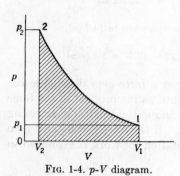

FIG. 1-4. p-V diagram.

With the definition of work as a quantitative and unambiguous physical entity, it is possible to develop several very useful relationships. If a body of mass m is acted upon by the force F, its acceleration is related to the force by Eq. (1-1). During a differential interval of time, the body moves through the differential distance ds. The work done by the force F acting through this distance is given by Eq. (1-3) as

$$dW = F \, ds$$

but by Eq. (1-1)

$$F = \frac{ma}{g_c}$$

Thus

$$dW = \frac{ma}{g_c} \, ds$$

If u is velocity and θ is time, the acceleration is given by the expression

$$a = \frac{du}{d\theta}$$

Hence

$$dW = \frac{m}{g_c} \frac{du}{d\theta} ds$$

This may also be written

$$dW = \frac{m}{g_c} \frac{ds}{d\theta} du$$

Since the definition of velocity is

$$u = \frac{ds}{d\theta}$$

then

$$dW = \frac{m}{g_c} u \, du$$

This equation may now be integrated for a finite change in velocity from u_1 to u_2:

$$W = \frac{m}{g_c} \int_{u_1}^{u_2} u \, du = \frac{m}{g_c} \left(\frac{u_2^2}{2} - \frac{u_1^2}{2} \right)$$

or

$$W = \frac{mu_2^2}{2g_c} - \frac{mu_1^2}{2g_c} = \Delta \frac{mu^2}{2g_c} \qquad (1\text{-}6)$$

The two quantities $mu^2/2g_c$ on the right-hand side of Eq. (1-6) have been given several names, but the term *kinetic energy*, introduced by Lord Kelvin[1] in 1856, is now universally used. Thus, by definition,

$$KE = \frac{mu^2}{2g_c} \qquad (1\text{-}7)$$

The importance of this quantity was recognized by Thomas Young, an English physicist, who in 1807 called it simply *energy*, the first recorded instance of the use of this word. Equation (1-6) shows that the work done *on* a body in accelerating it from an initial velocity u_1 to a final velocity u_2 is equal to the change in kinetic energy of the body. Conversely, if a moving body is decelerated by the action of a resisting force, the work done *by* the body is equal to its change in kinetic energy. The use of g_c in the preceding equations is particularly to be noted. In the absolute system of units often used in scientific work, g_c is unity, and kinetic energy becomes $\frac{1}{2}mu^2$. In the English engineering system, however, g_c has the value 32.1740 and the units $(\text{lb}_m/\text{lb}_f)(\text{ft}/\text{sec}^2)$. Thus the unit of kinetic energy in this system of units is

$$KE = \frac{mu^2}{2g_c} = \frac{(\text{lb}_m)(\text{ft}^2/\text{sec}^2)}{(\text{lb}_m/\text{lb}_f)(\text{ft}/\text{sec}^2)} = \text{ft-lb}_f$$

[1] Lord Kelvin, or William Thomson (1824–1907), was an English physicist who, along with the German physicist Rudolf Clausius (1822–1888), laid the foundations for the modern science of thermodynamics.

This is the unit of work. That this should be so is clear from Eq. (1-6). Without the inclusion of g_c, the equation would not be dimensionally consistent.

If a body of mass m is raised from an initial elevation z_1 to a final elevation z_2, an upward force at least equal to the weight of the body must be exerted on it, and this force must move through the distance $z_2 - z_1$. Since the weight of the body is the force of gravity on it, the minimum force required is given by Eq. (1-1) as

$$F = \frac{1}{g_c} ma = \frac{1}{g_c} mg$$

where g is the local acceleration of gravity. The minimum work required to raise the body is then

$$W = F(z_2 - z_1) = m \frac{g}{g_c} (z_2 - z_1)$$

or

$$W = mz_2 \frac{g}{g_c} - mz_1 \frac{g}{g_c} = \Delta \frac{mzg}{g_c} \qquad (1\text{-}8)$$

It is seen from Eq. (1-8) that the work done *on* the body in raising it is equal to the change in the quantity $mz(g/g_c)$. Conversely, if the body is lowered against a resisting force equal to its weight, the work done *by* the body is equal to the change in the quantity $mz(g/g_c)$. Equation (1-8) is similar in form to Eq. (1-6), and both show that the work done is equal to the change in a quantity which describes the condition of the body in relation to its surroundings. In each case the work performed can be recovered by carrying out the reverse process and returning the body to its initial condition. This observation leads naturally to the thought that, if the work done on a body in accelerating it or in elevating it can be subsequently recovered, then the body by virtue of its velocity or elevation must contain the ability or capacity to do this work. This concept has proved so useful that the capacity of a body for doing work has been given the name *energy*, a word derived from the Greek and meaning "in work." Hence the work of accelerating a body is said to produce a change in its *kinetic energy*, or

$$W = \Delta(\text{KE}) = \Delta \frac{mu^2}{2g_c}$$

and the work done on a body in elevating it is said to produce a change in its *potential energy*, or

$$W = \Delta(\text{PE}) = \Delta \frac{mzg}{g_c}$$

Thus potential energy is defined as

$$\text{PE} = mz \frac{g}{g_c} \qquad (1\text{-}9)$$

This term was first proposed in 1853 by the Scottish engineer William Rankine (1820–1872), and it also has come into universal use.

In considering physical processes, an attempt is naturally made to find or to define quantities which remain constant regardless of the changes which occur. One such quantity, early recognized in the development of mechanics, is mass. The great utility of the law of conservation of mass as a general principle in science suggests that further principles of conservation would be of comparable value. Thus the development of the concept of energy logically led to the principle of its conservation in mechanical processes. If a body is given the capacity to do work when it is elevated, it seems reasonable to suppose that the body will conserve or retain this capacity until it actually performs the work of which it is capable. It follows that, if an elevated body is allowed to fall freely, it should gain in kinetic energy what it loses in potential energy so that its capacity for doing work remains unchanged. Hence it should be possible to write for a freely falling body the equation

$$\Delta(\text{KE}) + \Delta(\text{PE}) = 0$$

or

$$\left(\frac{mu_2^2}{2g_c} - \frac{mu_1^2}{2g_c}\right) + \left(\frac{mz_2g}{g_c} - \frac{mz_1g}{g_c}\right) = 0$$

The validity of this equation has been confirmed by countless experiments. Success in application to freely falling bodies led to the generalization of the principle of energy conservation to apply to all purely mechanical processes. Ample experimental evidence to justify this generalization was readily obtained.

Other forms of mechanical energy besides kinetic and gravitational potential energy are possible. The most obvious is probably potential energy of configuration. When a spring is compressed, work is done by an external force. Since the spring can later perform this work by expanding against a resisting force, the spring possesses capacity for doing work. This is potential energy of configuration. Energy of the same form exists in a stretched rubber band or in a bar of metal deformed in the elastic region.

To increase the generality of the principle of conservation of energy in mechanics, it is convenient to look upon work itself as a form of energy. This is clearly permissible because it has been shown that both kinetic- and potential-energy changes are equal to the work done in producing them. However, work is energy in transit and is never regarded as residing in a body. When work is done and does not appear simultaneously elsewhere, it is converted into another form of energy.

It has been found helpful in thermodynamics to regard the body on which work is done or which is doing work as separate and distinct from its surroundings. The body or assemblage on which attention is focused is called the *system*. All else is called the *surroundings*. When work is done, it is done by the surroundings on the system or vice versa, and thus transfers energy from the surroundings to the system or the reverse. It is only during this transfer that the form of energy known as work exists. In contrast, kinetic and potential energy reside with the system. Their values, however, are measured with reference to the surroundings, *i.e.*, kinetic energy depends on velocity with respect to the surroundings and potential energy depends on elevation with respect to the surroundings. *Changes* in kinetic and potential energy are independent of the reference or datum level.

Example 1-7. An elevator with a mass of 5000 lb_m rests at a level 25 ft above the base of an elevator shaft. It is raised to 250 ft above the base of the shaft, where the cable holding it breaks. The elevator falls freely to the base of the shaft and strikes a strong spring. The spring is designed to bring the elevator to rest by means of a catch arrangement that holds the elevator at the position of maximum spring compression. Assuming the entire process to be frictionless, and taking the ratio of g/g_c to be unity, calculate:

(a) The potential energy of the elevator in its initial position relative to the base of the shaft

(b) The work done in raising the elevator

(c) The potential energy of the elevator in its highest position relative to the base of the shaft

(d) The velocity and kinetic energy of the elevator just before it strikes the spring

(e) The potential energy of the compressed spring

(f) The energy of the system consisting of the elevator and spring (1) at the start of the process, (2) when the elevator reaches its maximum height, (3) just before the elevator strikes the spring, and (4) after the elevator has come to rest

Solution. Let subscript 1 designate the initial conditions; subscript 2, conditions when the elevator is at its highest position; and subscript 3, conditions just before the elevator strikes the spring.

(a) By Eq. (1-9),

$$(PE)_1 = mz_1 \frac{g}{g_c} = (5000)(25)(1) = 125,000 \text{ ft-lb}_f$$

(b) $$W = \int_{z_1}^{z_2} F\, ds = \int_{z_1}^{z_2} \frac{mg}{g_c}\, ds = m\frac{g}{g_c}(z_2 - z_1)$$

$$= (5000)(1)(250 - 25) = 1,125,000 \text{ ft-lb}_f$$

(c) $$(PE)_2 = mz_2 \frac{g}{g_c} = (5000)(250)(1) = 1,250,000 \text{ ft-lb}_f$$

It should be noted that $W = (PE)_2 - (PE)_1$.

(d) $$\Delta(KE)_{2\to 3} + \Delta(PE)_{2\to 3} = 0$$

or

$$\frac{mu_3^2}{2g_c} - \frac{mu_2^2}{2g_c} + \frac{mz_3 g}{g_c} - \frac{mz_2 g}{g_c} = 0$$

Therefore,

$$\frac{u_3^2}{2(32.174)} - 0 + 0 - (250)(1) = 0 \qquad \frac{\Delta m u^2}{2g_c} + \frac{\Delta m z g}{g_c}$$

$$u_3^2 = (250)(2)(32.174)$$

$$u_3 = 127 \text{ ft/sec}$$

Since the total energy of the elevator does not change during its fall, its kinetic energy just before it strikes the spring must equal its potential energy at its maximum elevation. Thus

$$(KE)_3 = 1,250,000 \text{ ft-lb}_f \quad = (PE)_2$$

(e) $$\Delta(PE)_{\text{spring}} + \Delta(KE)_{\text{elevator}} = 0$$

Since the initial potential energy of the spring and the final kinetic energy of the elevator are zero, the final potential energy of the spring must equal the kinetic energy of the elevator just before it strikes the spring. Thus the final potential energy of the spring is 1,250,000 ft-lb$_f$.

(f) If the elevator and the spring together are taken as the system, the initial energy of the system is the potential energy of the elevator, or 125,000 ft-lb$_f$. The total energy of the system can change only if work is transferred between it and the surroundings. As the elevator is raised, work is done on the system by the surroundings in the amount of 1,125,000 ft-lb$_f$. Thus the energy of the system when the elevator reaches its maximum height is $125,000 + 1,125,000 = 1,250,000$ ft-lb$_f$. Subsequent changes occur entirely within the system, with no work transferred between the system and the surroundings. Hence the total energy of the system must remain constant at 1,250,000 ft-lb$_f$. It merely changes form from potential energy of position (elevation) of the elevator to kinetic energy of the elevator to potential energy of configuration of the spring.

This example serves to illustrate the application of the law of conservation of mechanical energy. It will be recalled that the entire process was assumed to occur without friction. The results obtained are exact only for such an idealized process, and would be approximations for the process as it actually occurs.

During the period of development of the law of conservation of mechanical energy, heat was not generally recognized as a form of energy, but was considered to be an indestructible fluid, called "caloric." This concept was so firmly established that no connection was recognized between the heat developed by friction and the established forms of energy. Indeed, caloric was endowed with the most extraordinary properties in order to explain the phenomena observed in connection with heat. With the caloric theory of heat, the law of conservation of energy was limited in application to frictionless mechanical processes. Such a limitation is no longer required, for heat like work is now considered as energy in transit. This idea that heat is energy being transferred gained acceptance during the years following 1850, largely on account of the classic experiments of J. P. Joule (1818–1889), a brewer of Manchester, England. These experiments will be considered in detail in Chap. 2, but first it will be helpful to examine some of the characteristics of heat.

1-13. Heat. It is known from experience that a hot object brought in contact with a cold object becomes cooler whereas the cold object becomes warmer. Clearly, something is transferred from the hot object to the cold, and that something is called heat Q. From early times men have speculated about the nature of heat, and two theories developed by the Greek philosophers have been in contention until modern times. As previously mentioned, the one most generally accepted until the middle of the nineteenth century was that heat is a weightless and indestructible substance called "caloric." The other theory represented heat as connected in some way with motion, either of the ultimate particles of a body or of some medium permeating all matter. This latter view was held by Francis Bacon, Newton, Robert Boyle, and other scientists of the seventeenth century. Without the concept of energy this view could not be exploited, and by the middle of the eighteenth century the materialistic or caloric theory of heat gained ascendancy. However, a few men of science did retain the other view, notably Benjamin Thompson[1] (1753–1814) and Sir Humphry Davy (1778–1829). Both submitted experimental evidence contrary to the caloric theory of heat, but their work went unheeded. Moreover, the steam engine, an excellent example of the conversion of heat into work, had been perfected by James Watt (1736–1819) and was in common use at the time.

One notable advance in the theory of heat was made by Joseph Black (1728–1799), a Scottish chemist and a collaborator of James Watt. Prior to Black's time no distinction was made between heat and temperature, just as no distinction was made between force and work. Temperature was regarded as the measure of the quantity of heat or "caloric" in a body, and a thermometer reading was referred to as a "number of degrees of heat." In fact, the word *temperature* still had its archaic meaning of *mixture or blend*. Thus a given temperature indicated a given mixture or blend of caloric with matter. Black correctly recognized temperature as a property which must be carefully distinguished from quantity of heat. In addition, he showed experimentally that different substances of the same mass vary in their *capacity* to absorb heat when they are warmed through the same temperature range. Moreover, he was the discoverer of *latent* heat. In spite of the difficulty of explaining these phenomena by the caloric theory, Black supported this theory throughout his life. Here the matter rested until near the middle of the nineteenth century.

Among the early champions of the energy concept of heat were Mohr, Mayer, and Helmholtz in Germany; Colding, a Dane; and especially James P. Joule in England. Joule presented the experimental evidence

---

[1] Better known as Count Rumford. Born in Woburn, Mass., unsympathetic to the American cause during the Revolution, he spent most of his adult life in Europe. For an account of his extraordinary activities, see "An American in Europe" by Egon Larsen, The Philosophical Library, Inc., New York, 1953.

which conclusively demonstrated the energy theory, and thus made possible the generalization of the law of conservation of energy to include heat. The concept of heat as a form of energy is now universally accepted and is implicit in the modern science of thermodynamics.

One of the most important observations about heat is that it *always* flows from a higher temperature to a lower one. This leads to the concept of temperature as the driving force for the transfer of energy as heat. More precisely, the rate of heat transfer from one body to another is proportional to the temperature difference between the two bodies; when there is no temperature difference, there is no net transfer of heat. It is important to note that in the thermodynamic sense heat is never regarded as being stored within a body. Like work, it exists only as energy in transit from one body to another, or between a system and its surroundings. When energy in the form of heat is added to a body, it is stored not as heat but as kinetic and potential energy of the atoms and molecules making up the body. It is not surprising, therefore, that the energy theory of heat did not develop until the atomic theory of matter was well established.

In spite of the transient nature of heat, it is inevitably thought of in terms of its effects on the body from which or to which it is transferred. As a matter of fact, the traditional definitions of the quantitative units of heat are based on the temperature changes of a unit mass of water. Thus the *calorie* was long defined as that quantity of heat which must be transferred to one gram of water to raise its temperature one degree centigrade. Likewise the *British thermal unit,* or *Btu,* was defined as that quantity of heat which must be transferred to one pound *mass* of water to raise its temperature one degree Fahrenheit. While these definitions are helpful for the visualization of heat quantities and are satisfactory for most engineering calculations, they lack the precision necessary for exact work. They depend on the accuracy of experiments made with water and are thus subject to change with each increasingly accurate measurement. Moreover, they depend on the particular degree of temperature rise chosen, because the amount of heat required to raise the temperature of water one degree varies slightly with temperature. This has led in the past to the use of many "calories" and to considerable confusion. This difficulty has been largely avoided in modern times by recognizing the calorie and Btu for what they are, namely, units of energy, and by defining them arbitrarily in terms of other energy units for which much more precise standards are available. Two such defined calories are presently in use, the international steam-table calorie (or I.T. calorie) and the thermochemical calorie. The I.T. calorie forms the basic unit for all steam tables now in use, whereas the thermochemical calorie is used for all thermochemical calculations. Fortunately, they differ by less than one part per thousand and do not need to be distinguished except for very precise calculations. In terms of the most common engineering unit of energy

$$1 \text{ I.T. calorie} = 3.08797 \text{ ft-lb}_f$$

and

$$1 \text{ thermochemical calorie} = 3.08595 \text{ ft-lb}_f$$

The Btu is defined so that

$$1 \text{ I.T. calorie/gram} = 1.8 \text{ Btu/lb}_m$$

The Btu is thus equivalent to 778.156 ft-lb$_f$. For a more complete discussion of the units of energy, the work of Rossini[1] should be consulted. In this book no distinction will be made between the I.T. calorie and the thermochemical calorie. Reference will be made simply to the *calorie*, and the following approximate relationships between energy units will be employed:

$$1 \text{ Btu} = 252 \text{ calories} = 778 \text{ ft-lb}_f$$

PROBLEMS

1. (a) What is the value of g_c and what are its units in a system in which the second, the foot, and the pound *force* are defined as in Secs. 1-3, 1-4, and 1-6 and the unit of mass is taken as the slug? The slug is defined as that mass which is accelerated 1 ft/sec^2 by a force of 1 lb$_f$.

(b) What is the value of g_c and what are its units in a system in which the second, the foot, and the pound *mass* are defined first and the unit of force is taken as the poundal? The poundal is defined as that force required to accelerate 1 lb$_m$ 1 ft/sec^2.

2. Using the data of Example 1-3 for the specific volumes of H$_2$ at 100 atm, check the results given for the readings of a thermometer filled with hydrogen at 100 atm.

3. Pressures up to 3000 atm are to be measured with a dead-weight gauge. The piston diameter is to be $\frac{1}{8}$ in. What is the approximate total mass of the "weights" which must be provided for use with this gauge?   *Ans.* 541 lb$_m$.

4. A mercury manometer at 70°F reads 14.37 in. The local acceleration of gravity is 32.120 ft/sec^2. The barometer (brass scale) also at 70°F reads 29.21 in. of mercury. What is the absolute pressure being measured in pounds per square inch absolute? [For the method of correcting the barometer to 0°C, see J. H. Perry (ed.), "Chemical Engineers' Handbook," 3d ed., p. 365, McGraw-Hill Book Company, Inc., New York, 1950.]   *Ans.* 21.30 psia.

5. A gas is confined in a cylinder by a piston, 2 in. in diameter, on which rests a "weight." The mass of the piston and weight together is 8 lb$_m$. The local acceleration of gravity is 32.00 ft/sec^2. Assume standard atmospheric pressure.

(a) What is the force exerted on the gas by the atmosphere, the piston, and the weight in pounds *force*, assuming no friction between the piston and cylinder?

(b) What is the pressure of the gas in pounds *force* per square inch?

(c) If the gas in the cylinder is heated, it will expand, pushing the piston and weight

---

[1] Frederick D. Rossini, "Chemical Thermodynamics," John Wiley & Sons, Inc., New York, 1950.

upward. Assuming that enough heat is supplied to raise the piston and weight 8 in., calculate the work done by the gas in raising the piston and weight. What is the change in potential energy of the piston and weight? Give your answers in foot-pounds *force*.

6. An automobile having a mass of 3000 lb is traveling at 55 miles/hr. What is its energy in foot-pounds *force*? In Btu? How much work must be done to bring it to a stop?

7. A 1-lb mass initially at rest falls in a vacuum under a constant gravitational force.

(*a*) What is its downward velocity as a function of distance from the starting point?

(*b*) Explain how the law of conservation of energy is involved in this problem.

8. The turbines in a hydroelectric plant are fed by water falling from a height of 100 ft. Assuming 95 per cent efficiency for converting the potential to electrical energy, and 10 per cent loss of resulting power in transmission, how many tons of water per hour are needed to keep a 100-watt light bulb burning? *Ans.* 1.55 tons.

9. A spring scale is calibrated to read pounds *mass* at a location where the local acceleration of gravity is 32.400 ft/sec². (That is, 1 lb_m placed on the scale will give a scale reading of 1, 2 lb_m will give a reading of 2, etc.) If the scale is moved to a location where g is 32.000 ft/sec², what will be the mass in pounds *mass* of an object which, when placed on the scale, gives a reading of 20.000? Justify your method of calculation. *Ans.* 20.25 lb_m.

10. The piston areas of dead-weight gauges are sometimes difficult to determine with sufficient accuracy by direct measurement. One method used for this purpose is to balance the gauge with a known mass of "weights" when a known pressure is exerted on the gauge. In a particular instance, a gauge for use at high pressures balanced under a mass of 57.43 lb_m (including piston and pan) when the pressure exerted was the vapor pressure of CO_2 at 0°C. This pressure is known to be 34.40 atm abs. If g is 32.38 ft/sec² and the barometric pressure is 29.68 in. Hg, what is the area of the piston?

11. The first accurate measurements of the properties of gases at high pressures were made by E. H. Amagat in France between 1869 and 1893. Before developing the dead-weight gauge, he worked in a mine shaft and used a mercury manometer for pressure measurement. He reached a pressure of 430 atm. If g is 32.10 ft/sec² and if the temperature of the mercury manometer is 20°C, what height of manometer is required to attain this pressure? *Ans.* 1079 ft.

CHAPTER 2

THE FIRST LAW AND OTHER BASIC CONCEPTS

2-1. Joule's Experiments. During the years 1840 to 1878, J. P. Joule[1] carried out careful experiments on the nature of heat and work. These experiments are fundamental to an understanding of the concept of energy and, hence, the first law of thermodynamics.

In their essential elements Joule's experiments were simple enough, but he took elaborate precautions to ensure accuracy. In the most famous series, he placed measured amounts of water in an insulated container, and agitated the water with a rotating stirrer. The amount of work done on the water by the stirrer was accurately measured, and the temperature changes of the water were carefully noted. It was found that a definite amount of work was required per unit mass of water for every degree of temperature rise caused by the stirring. In modern units, this figure is approximately 778 ft-lb, of work for every pound *mass* of water raised one degree Fahrenheit. When water has had its temperature raised in this way, it can readily be returned to its original condition by extracting heat from it. The amount is equal approximately to one Btu for every pound *mass* of water cooled one degree Fahrenheit. Thus Joule was able to show that a quantitative relationship exists between work and heat and, therefore, that heat is a form of energy rather than a substance, as had been previously supposed.

2-2. Internal Energy. In experiments such as those conducted by Joule, energy is added to the water as work, but is extracted as heat. The question arises as to what happens to this energy between the time it is added to the water as work and the time it is extracted as heat. It is only logical to believe that this energy is contained within the water in some form. This form of energy is defined as internal energy E.

Although it is not necessary in classical thermodynamics to know more than this about the nature of internal energy, it may be profitable to consider the question briefly. The internal energy of a substance does not include any energy that it may possess as a result of its position or movement *as a whole*. Rather it refers to the energy of the molecules making

---

[1] For a fascinating account of Joule's celebrated experiments, see T. W. Chalmers, "Historic Researches," Chap. II, Charles Scribner's Sons, New York, 1952.

up the substance.   The molecules of any substance are believed to be in ceaseless motion and therefore to possess kinetic energy not only of translation but also in many cases of rotation and vibration.   The addition of heat to a substance increases this molecular activity, and thus causes an increase in its internal energy.   Work done on the substance can have the same effect, as was shown by Joule.

In addition to kinetic energy, the molecules of any substance possess potential energy resulting from the forces of attraction existing among them.   On a submolecular scale there is energy associated with the electrons and nuclei of atoms and bond energy resulting from the forces which hold atoms together as molecules.   It has not been possible to determine the total internal energy of a substance, and hence absolute values are unknown.   However, this is not a disadvantage in thermodynamic analysis since only *changes* in internal energy are required.

The designation of this form of energy of a substance as *internal* distinguishes it from potential and kinetic energy which the substance may possess because of its position or motion *as a whole*, and which can be thought of as *external* forms of energy.

2-3. Formulation of the First Law of Thermodynamics.   The recognition of heat and internal energy as forms of energy suggests a generalization of the law of conservation of energy (as discussed in Sec. 1-12) to include these forms of energy as well as the forms known as work and external potential and kinetic energy.   Indeed, the generalization can be extended to still other forms, such as surface energy, electrical energy, and magnetic energy.   This generalization was at first no more than a postulation, but without exception the vast number of observations of ordinary processes made since 1850 support it.[1]   Hence it has achieved the stature of a law and is known as the first law of thermodynamics.   It

---

[1] Processes involving nuclear reactions are not included in the term "ordinary processes."   Such processes require the use of the Einstein equation relating energy and mass:

$$E = \frac{c^2 m}{g_c}$$

where c is the velocity of light.   Since the term c^2 is very large, a small quantity of mass can be transformed into an enormous amount of energy.   For example, in the usual engineering units c is approximately 10^9 ft/sec, and 1 lb_m is equivalent to

$$E = \frac{(10^{18})(1)}{32.2} = 3.1 \times 10^{16} \text{ ft-lb}_f$$

Thus the laws of conservation of energy and mass cannot be thought of as existing separately, where nuclear reactions are concerned, but must be combined to state that energy and mass together are conserved.   The principles of nuclear physics are, however, beyond the scope of this book, and they are not involved in the ordinary applications of chemical engineering thermodynamics.

may be stated formally in many ways; one of these is as follows: *although energy assumes many forms, the total quantity of energy is constant, and when energy disappears in one form it appears simultaneously in other forms.*

In the application of the first law to a given process, it is convenient to divide the sphere of influence of the process into two parts, the *system* and its *surroundings.* The part in which the process occurs is usually taken as the system. Everything not included in the system is considered to constitute the surroundings. The system may be of any size depending on the particular conditions, and its boundaries may be real or imaginary, rigid or nonrigid. Frequently a system is made up of a single substance; in other cases it may be very complicated. In any event, it is helpful to formulate the equations of thermodynamics with reference to some well-defined system. The advantage of this procedure is that it allows one to focus attention on the particular process being examined and on the equipment and material directly involved in the process.

However, it should be made clear at the outset that the first law applies to the system *and* surroundings, considered together, and not, in general, to the system alone. In its most basic form, the first law may be written:

$$\Delta(\text{energy of the system}) + \Delta(\text{energy of surroundings}) = 0 \quad (2\text{-}1)$$

In the system, energy changes in various forms may occur, *e.g.*, changes of internal energy, potential and kinetic energy of the system as a whole, or potential and kinetic energy of finite parts of the system. Likewise, the energy change of the surroundings may consist of increases or decreases of energy in various forms.

In the thermodynamic sense, heat and work refer to energy *in transit* across the boundary between the system and surroundings. These forms of energy can never be stored. It is incorrect to speak of heat or work as being contained in a body or system. Energy is stored in its potential, kinetic, and internal forms. These forms of energy reside with material objects and exist because of the position, configuration, and motion of matter. The transformations of energy from one form to another and the transfer of energy from place to place often occur through the mechanisms of heat and work.

Thus it is usually convenient in applying the first law to select the system in such a way that all energy passing across the boundary between the system and its surroundings is transferred in the forms of heat and work. If no other energy transfer occurs, then the total energy change of the surroundings must be equal to the energy transferred to or from it as heat and work. Hence the second term of Eq. (2-1) may be replaced by an expression representing the heat and work crossing the boundary between the system and the surroundings, *i.e.*,

$$\Delta(\text{energy of surroundings}) = \pm Q \pm W$$

The choice of signs to be used with Q and W will depend on the convention as to which direction of transfer shall be regarded as positive.

The first term of Eq. (2-1) may be expanded to show energy changes in various forms. If the mass of the system is constant and if only internal-, kinetic-, and potential-energy changes are involved,

$$\Delta(\text{energy of the system}) = \Delta E + \Delta(\text{KE}) + \Delta(\text{PE})$$

With these substitutions, Eq. (2-1) becomes

$$\Delta E + \Delta(\text{KE}) + \Delta(\text{PE}) = \pm Q \pm W \qquad (2\text{-}2)$$

where ΔE, $\Delta(\text{KE})$, and $\Delta(\text{PE})$ represent changes in internal, kinetic, and potential energy of the system, respectively. The signs to be used on the right-hand side of Eq. (2-2) must now be decided upon. The usual convention is to regard heat as positive when it is transferred to the system from the surroundings. On the other hand, work is usually regarded as positive when it is transferred from the system to the surroundings. With this understanding, Eq. (2-2) becomes

$$\Delta E + \Delta(\text{KE}) + \Delta(\text{PE}) = Q - W \qquad (2\text{-}3)$$

In words, Eq. (2-3) states that the total energy change of the system is equal to the heat added to the system minus the work done by the system. The equation applies to the changes which occur in a constant-mass system over a period of time.

In many applications of the first law, the system undergoes no change in external potential or kinetic energy, but only changes of internal energy. For these nonflow processes, the first law (Eq. 2-3) becomes

$$\Delta E = Q - W \qquad \text{Batch process} \qquad (2\text{-}4)$$

Equation (2-4) applies to processes involving *finite* changes in the system. For *differential* changes this equation is written

$$dE = dQ - dW \qquad (2\text{-}5)$$

Equation (2-5) is useful when it is necessary to express E, Q, or W as functions of variables which change during a process, and many applications will be found for it. The limitations of Eqs. (2-4) and (2-5) are that they may be applied to systems of constant mass which undergo changes in internal energy only.

The units used in Eqs. (2-3), (2-4), and (2-5) must be the same for all terms. Any energy units may be used. Those most commonly employed by engineers are the foot-pound *force*, the Btu, and the calorie.

In the application of the preceding equations it is important that the system be clearly defined. The most advantageous choice of a system for solving a particular problem is not always obvious but must be learned from experience. The illustrative examples throughout this chapter should serve as a guide.

2-4. The Thermodynamic State and State Functions. It is necessary in thermodynamics to distinguish between two types of quantities: those which depend upon path and those which do not. Actually, both types are in everyday use. Consider, for example, an automobile trip from New York to San Francisco. The straight-line distance between these two cities is fixed, it does not depend on the path or route taken to get from one to the other. On the other hand, such measurements as miles traveled and gasoline consumption definitely depend on the path. So it is in thermodynamics; both types of quantities are used.

There are many examples of quantities which do not depend on path. Among these are temperature, pressure, and specific volume. We know from experience that fixing two of these quantities automatically fixes all other such properties of a homogeneous substance and, therefore, determines the condition or *state* of the substance. For example, nitrogen gas at a temperature of 70°F and standard atmospheric pressure has a definite specific volume or density, a definite viscosity, a definite thermal conductivity; in short it has a definite set of properties. If this gas is heated or cooled, compressed or expanded, and then returned to its initial conditions of 70°F and standard atmospheric pressure, it will be found to have exactly the same set of properties as before. These properties do not depend on the past history of the substance or on the path it has followed in reaching a given state. They depend only on the immediate conditions, however reached. Such quantities are known as *point functions* or *state functions.* When two of them are fixed or held at definite values for a homogeneous substance, it is said that the *thermodynamic state* of the substance is fixed.

For more complicated systems than a simple homogeneous substance, the number of properties or state functions which must be arbitrarily fixed in order to define the state of the system may be different from two. The method of determining this number for any system is the subject of Sec. 2-8.

The comprehension of this concept is vital to an understanding of thermodynamics because internal energy and a number of other thermodynamic functions (to be defined later) are quantities of this kind; *i.e.*, they are state functions and are, therefore, properties of the system. The values of state functions can always be represented as points on a graph, which suggests the synonymous term point function. It should be noted that the differential of a state function is spoken of as an infinitesimal change in the property, and is not referred to as a quantity. The integration of such a differential results in a finite difference between two values of the property.   For example,

$$\int_{p_1}^{p_2} dp = p_2 - p_1 = \Delta p \quad \text{and} \quad \int_{E_1}^{E_2} dE = E_2 - E_1 = \Delta E$$

Work and heat on the other hand are not state properties; they are dependent on the path followed.   They cannot be represented by points on a graph, but rather are represented by areas, as shown in Fig. 1-4. The differentials of heat and work are not referred to as changes, but are regarded as infinitesimal *quantities* of heat and work.   When integrated, these differentials give not a finite change but a finite quantity.   Thus

$$\int dQ = Q \quad \text{and} \quad \int dW = W$$

It can readily be demonstrated experimentally that processes which accomplish the same change in state by different paths require, in general, different amounts of work and heat.   However, *it can be just as easily shown for these same processes that the algebraic difference*[1] *between the heat and work quantities is constant.*[2]   This gives experimental justification to the statement that internal energy is a state function.   Equation (2-4) will yield the same value of $Q - W$ and hence of ΔE regardless of the path followed, provided only that the change in the system is always from the same initial state to the same final state.

Another difference between state functions and heat or work is brought out by the fact that a state function represents an instantaneous property of a system and always has a value.   Work and heat appear only when changes are caused in a system by a process, which requires time. Although the time required for a process cannot be predicted by thermodynamics alone, nevertheless it should be made clear that, whenever heat is transferred or work is accomplished, the passage of time is inevitable.

It is largely because internal energy is a state function that it is valuable for calculating the heat and work requirements of physical and chemical processes.   The same is true of the other thermodynamic functions yet to be considered. . Heat and work quantities are essential for the design of such equipment as heat exchangers, evaporators, distillation columns, pumps, compressors, turbines, internal-combustion engines, etc. It would be impossible to tabulate all possible Q's and W's for all possible processes.   But the state functions, such as internal energy, are properties of *matter*.   Once measured, they can be tabulated for use in calculating Q and W for *any* process through the unifying principles known as the laws of thermodynamics.   The measurement, correlation, and use of the state functions will be considered in detail in later chapters.

The first-law equations may be written for systems of any size and com-

---

[1] The sign convention must be followed here as elsewhere.
[2] For a system of constant mass.

plexity, and the values used for Q, W, and the energy terms will then refer to the entire system. The values of certain properties, such as volume and internal energy, depend on the size of the system considered, *i.e.*, on the quantity of material involved. They are known as *extensive* properties of the system. Properties such as temperature and pressure do not involve the amount of material in any way, and they are known as *intensive* properties.

In many applications it is convenient to write the thermodynamic equations for a unit amount of material, either a unit mass or a mole, which is representative of the entire system. In this way it is possible to deal with volume, internal energy, and other extensive properties on a unit basis. In this case, they too become intensive properties. Thus, although volume is an extensive property, specific volume (or density) is an intensive property, independent of the quantity of material actually present. Similarly, internal energy per mole or per unit mass is also an intensive property. When written for a representative unit of the system, the symbols E, Q, and W in Eqs. (2-4) and (2-5) represent these quantities of a unit basis. Although Q and W are then the heat and work terms for a unit quantity, it must be remembered that they are not properties of the system. If a total quantity is required, it is easily calculated by multiplying the quantity on a unit basis by the total mass or total moles of the system.

Example 2-1. Consider 1 lb_m of water going over a 100-ft waterfall at a location where the local acceleration of gravity is 32.00 ft/sec². It may be assumed that no energy is exchanged between the pound of water and its surroundings.

(a) What is the potential energy of the water at the top of the falls with respect to the base of the falls?

(b) What is the kinetic energy of the water just before it strikes the bottom, and what is its potential energy?

(c) After the pound of water has entered the river below the falls, what change has occurred in its state?

Solution. (a) The pound of water will be taken as the system. Its boundaries are imaginary. Its potential energy at the top of the falls is given by Eq. (1-9):

$$PE = mz\frac{g}{g_c} = (1)(100)\left(\frac{32.00}{32.17}\right) = 99.5 \text{ ft-lb}_f$$

(b) The form of the first law which applies to this process is given by Eq. (2-3). In this case no energy is exchanged between the system and surroundings. Hence Q and W are zero. Therefore,

$$\Delta(PE) + \Delta(KE) + \Delta E = 0$$

During the falling process, no mechanism exists for the conversion of potential or kinetic energy into internal energy. Therefore it is assumed that $\Delta E = 0$. Thus the equation describing this process is

$$\Delta(PE) + \Delta(KE) = 0$$

At the base of the falls the potential energy of the water becomes zero.   Thus $\Delta(PE) = 0 - 99.5 = -99.5$ ft-lb$_f$.   By this equation,

$$\Delta(KE) = -\Delta(PE) = 99.5 \text{ ft-lb}_f$$

If it is assumed that the initial kinetic energy of the water at the top of the falls is negligible, its kinetic energy just before it strikes the bottom is

$$(KE)_2 - 0 = 99.5$$

or

$$(KE)_2 = 99.5 \text{ ft-lb}_f$$

(c) The last step of this process is also covered by Eq. (2-3).   Again Q and W are zero, but in this case there is no change in potential energy, that is, $\Delta(PE) = 0$.   If it is assumed that the final kinetic energy of the river below the falls is negligible, $\Delta(KE) = 0 - (KE)_2 = -99.5$.   Equation (2-3) now gives

$$\Delta E = 99.5 \text{ ft-lb}_f$$

Thus the over-all result of the process is an increase in the internal energy of the water by 99.5 ft-lb$_f$/lb$_m$.   The conversion of kinetic energy to internal energy occurs through the mechanism of turbulence, which is equivalent to the stirring of Joule's experiments.   This change in internal energy is manifested in a temperature rise of the water.   Since energy in the amount of 778 ft-lb$_f$/lb$_m$ is required for a temperature rise of 1°F, the temperature rise caused by an increase in internal energy of 99.5 ft-lb$_f$/lb$_m$ is

$$\frac{99.5}{778} = 0.13°\text{F}$$

Example 2-2.   A gas is confined in a cylinder by a piston.   The initial pressure of the gas is 100 psia, and the volume is 0.20 ft³.   The piston is held in place by latches in the cylinder wall.   The whole apparatus is placed in a total vacuum.   What will be the energy change of the apparatus if the retaining latches are removed so that the gas suddenly expands to double its initial volume where the piston is again held by latches?

Solution.   Since the question concerns the entire apparatus, the system will be taken as the gas, piston, and cylinder.   No work is done during the process since no force external to the system moves, and no heat is transferred through the vacuum surrounding the apparatus.   Hence Q and W are zero, and the total energy of the system remains unchanged.   Without further information it is impossible to say anything about the distribution of energy among the parts of the system.   This may well be different than the initial distribution.

Example 2-3.   If the process described in Example 2-2 is repeated not in a vacuum but in air at standard atmospheric pressure, what will be the energy change of the apparatus?   Assume the rate of heat exchange between the apparatus and the surrounding air to be slow compared with the rate at which the process occurs.

Solution.   The system will be chosen exactly as before, but in this case work is done by the system in pushing back the atmosphere.   This work is given by the product of the force exerted by the atmospheric pressure on the piston and the distance the piston moves.   If the area of the piston is A, the force is

$$F = p_{atm}A$$

The distance moved by the piston is equal to the volume change of the gas divided by the area of the piston, or

$$s = \frac{V}{A}$$

The work done by the system on the surroundings is, therefore,

$$W = Fs = p_{atm} \Delta V$$

According to the sign convention this work is positive.

$$W = (14.7)(144)(0.40 - 0.20) = 423 \text{ ft-lb}_f$$

Heat transfer between the system and surroundings is also possible in this case, but the problem will be worked for the instant after the process has occurred, before appreciable heat transfer has had time to take place. Thus Q is assumed to be zero. Therefore,

$$\Delta(\text{energy of the system}) = Q - W = 0 - 423 = -423 \text{ ft-lb}_f$$

or

$$\Delta(\text{energy of the system}) = -\frac{423}{778} = -0.544 \text{ Btu}$$

The total energy of the system has *decreased* by an amount equal to the work done by the system on its surroundings.

2-5. Enthalpy. In addition to internal energy there are a number of other special thermodynamic functions. Any number of such quantities might be arbitrarily defined, but experience has shown that only a few are necessary. One of the most useful is considered in this section, and others will be introduced in later chapters. The reasons for defining these quantities will emerge as they are used in practical applications.

Enthalpy (en-thal'-py), perhaps the most widely used of the thermodynamic functions, is given the symbol H. It is explicitly defined for any system by the mathematical expression

$$H = E + pV \tag{2-6}$$

where E = internal energy of system
p = absolute pressure of system
V = volume of system

The units of the terms of this equation must, of course, be consistent. The product pV has the units of energy, as does E. Thus enthalpy H also has the units of energy. The most common unit for the pV product is the foot-pound *force*, which results when pressure is given in pounds *force* per square foot and volume in cubic feet. This unit is usually converted to Btu by dividing by 778 for use in Eq. (2-6) because the most common engineering unit for E and H is the Btu.

Since E, p, and V are all state functions, any combination of them must also be a state function. Equation (2-6) shows that enthalpy is one combination of these quantities; therefore it too must be a point or state function.

In differential form Eq. (2-6) may be written

$$dH = dE + d(pV) \tag{2-7}$$

This equation applies whenever a differential change occurs in the system. Since all its terms are state functions, it may be readily integrated to give

$$\Delta H = \Delta E + \Delta(pV) \tag{2-8}$$

This equation is applicable whenever a finite change occurs in the system.

Equations (2-6) to (2-8) may be written for any amount of material, though they are usually put on a unit mass or mole basis. In this case, the volume V becomes the specific volume v. It is to be noted that H is an extensive property of the system, like internal energy and volume.

The enthalpy concept is particularly useful because the $E + pV$ group occurs frequently in problems of interest to engineers, e.g., flow problems. This is illustrated in Sec. 2-6. The calculation of a numerical value for ΔH is carried out in the following example.

Example 2-4. Calculate ΔE and ΔH in Btu for 1 lb$_m$ of water as it is vaporized at the constant temperature of 212°F and the constant pressure of 1 atm. The specific volumes of liquid and vapor H_2O at these conditions are 0.0167 and 26.80 ft³/lb$_m$, respectively. For this change, 970.3 Btu is added to the water as heat.

Solution. The pound of H_2O will be taken as the system since it alone is of interest here. It is convenient to regard the fluid as being contained in an imaginary cylinder by a weightless and frictionless piston. Since the pressure on the fluid is 1 atm, the cylinder and piston apparatus may be imagined to exist in an atmosphere at this pressure. During the process, 970.3 Btu is added to the water as heat, and it expands in the cylinder from a volume of 0.0167 ft³ to a volume of 26.80 ft³. This expansion causes the piston to move, and as it does so it does work in pushing back the surrounding atmosphere. As in Example 2-3, this work is given by

$$W = p_{atm} \Delta v = (14.7)(144)(26.80 - 0.0167) = 56,700 \text{ ft-lb}_f$$

or

$$\frac{56,700}{778} = 72.9 \text{ Btu}$$

Since $Q = 970.3$ Btu, Eq. (2-4) gives

$$\Delta E = Q - W = 970.3 - 72.9 = 897.4 \text{ Btu}$$

By Eq. (2-8),

$$\Delta H = \Delta E + \Delta(pv)$$

Since p is constant and equal to p_{atm},

$$\Delta H = \Delta E + p \, \Delta v = \Delta E + p_{atm} \, \Delta v$$

But $p_{atm} \Delta v = W$. Therefore,

$$\Delta H = \Delta E + W = Q = 970.3 \text{ Btu}$$

2-6. The Steady-state Flow Process.   The application of Eqs. (2-4) and (2-5) is restricted to nonflow (batch) processes in which only internal-energy changes occur.   Far more important industrially are processes which involve the steady-state flow of a fluid through equipment.   For such processes the more general first-law expression [Eq. (2-3)] must be used.   However, it may be put in more convenient form.   The term *steady state* implies that conditions at all points in the apparatus are constant with time.   For this to be the case, all rates must be constant, and there must be no accumulation of material or energy within the apparatus over the period of time considered.   Moreover, the total mass flow rate must be the same at all points along the path of flow of the fluid.

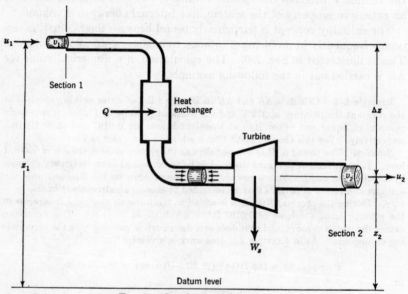

FIG. 2-1. Steady-state flow process.

Consider the general case of a steady-state flow process as represented in Fig. 2-1.   A fluid, either liquid or gas, flows through the apparatus from section 1 to section 2.   At section 1, the entrance to the apparatus, conditions in the fluid are designated by the subscript 1.   Thus, at this point the fluid has an elevation above an arbitrary datum level of z_1, an average velocity u_1, a specific volume v_1, a pressure p_1, an internal energy E_1, etc.   Similarly, the conditions in the fluid at section 2, the exit of the apparatus, are designated by the subscript 2.

The system will be taken as 1 lb_m of the fluid flowing, and we will consider the over-all changes which occur in this pound of fluid as it flows through the apparatus from section 1 to section 2.   Clearly, it may change in all three forms of energy taken into account in Eq. (2-3), *i.e.*, potential, kinetic, and internal.   By the definition of kinetic energy [Eq. (1-7)],

$$\Delta(\text{KE}) = \Delta \frac{mu^2}{2g_c} = \frac{\Delta u^2}{2g_c} = \frac{u_2^2 - u_1^2}{2g_c}$$

In this equation u represents the average velocity of the flowing fluid, defined as the volumetric flow rate divided by cross-sectional area.   The development of the expression $u^2/2g_c$ for kinetic energy in terms of the average velocity is considered in detail in Chap. 8.   Potential energy is defined by Eq. (1-9), and therefore

$$\Delta(\text{PE}) = \Delta \frac{mzg}{g_c} = \frac{g}{g_c} \Delta z = \frac{g}{g_c} (z_2 - z_1)$$

It should be noted that m is the mass of the system and that it has been taken as unity.   With these substitutions, Eq. (2-3) becomes

$$\Delta E + \frac{\Delta u^2}{2g_c} + \frac{g}{g_c} \Delta z = Q - W \qquad (2\text{-}9)$$

where Q and W represent *all* the heat added and work extracted per pound *mass* of fluid flowing through the apparatus.

At first thought it might seem that W is merely the shaft work W_s indicated in Fig. 2-1, but this is not the case.   The term *shaft work* is used to indicate work done by or on a piece of equipment through which the fluid flows.   Such work is usually transmitted by a shaft which protrudes from the equipment and which either rotates or reciprocates. Therefore, the term is taken to mean the work which is interchanged between the system and the surroundings through this shaft.   In addition to W_s there is work exchanged between the unit mass of fluid taken as the system and the fluid on either side of it.   The element of fluid regarded as the system may be imagined to be separated from the rest of the fluid by flexible diaphragms and to flow through the apparatus as a small cylinder of fluid which expands and contracts with changes in cross-sectional area, temperature, and pressure.   As illustrated in Fig. 2-1, a free body drawing of this cylinder at any point along its path will show pressure forces at its ends exerted by the adjacent fluid.   These forces move with the system and do work.   The force on the upstream side of the cylinder does work *on* the system.   The force on the downstream side is in the opposite direction and represents work done *by* the system on the surroundings.   From section 1 to section 2 these two pressure forces follow exactly the same path and vary in exactly the same manner. Hence, the net work which they produce between these two sections is zero.   However, the terms representing work done by these pressure forces as the fluid enters and leaves the apparatus do not, in general, cancel. In Fig. 2-1 the unit mass of fluid is shown just before it enters the apparatus. This cylinder of fluid has a volume v_1 equal to its specific volume at the conditions existing at section 1. If its cross-sectional area is A_1, its length is v_1/A_1. The force exerted on its upstream face is p_1A_1, and the work done by this force in pushing the cylinder into the apparatus is

$$W_1 = p_1A_1 \frac{v_1}{A_1} = p_1v_1$$

This represents work done *on* the system by the surroundings. At section 2 work is done *by* the system on the surroundings as the element of fluid emerges from the apparatus. As before, this work is given by the expression

$$W_2 = p_2A_2 \frac{v_2}{A_2} = p_2v_2$$

Since W in Eq. (2-9) represents *all* the work done *by* the 1 lb$_m$ of fluid, it is equal to the algebraic sum of the shaft work and the entrance and exit work quantities; that is,

$$W = W_s + p_2v_2 - p_1v_1$$

The combination of this expression with Eq. (2-9) to eliminate W gives

$$\Delta E + \frac{\Delta u^2}{2g_c} + \frac{g}{g_c} \Delta z = Q - W_s - p_2v_2 + p_1v_1$$

or

$$\Delta E + \Delta(pv) + \frac{\Delta u^2}{2g_c} + \frac{g}{g_c} \Delta z = Q - W_s$$

But by Eq. (2-8),

$$\Delta E + \Delta(pv) = \Delta H$$

Therefore,

$$\Delta H + \frac{\Delta u^2}{2g_c} + \frac{g}{g_c} \Delta z = Q - W_s \tag{2-10}$$

This equation is the mathematical expression of the first law for a steady-state flow process.[1] All the terms are expressions for energy per unit

[1] Equation (2-10), like Eq. (2-3), was developed for a constant-mass system. Equation (2-3) may be used for any process which is not steady flow, because a constant-mass system can always be found by selecting the system large enough. However, it is possible to generalize Eq. (2-3) to give an equation applicable to systems of variable mass (open systems) as well as to systems of constant mass (closed systems).

Equation (2-3) expresses the fact that the energy change of a constant-mass system is equal to $Q - W$. If the mass of the system changes, the energy change of the *system* over a differential time interval is

$$d[m(E + PE + KE)]_{sys}$$

where the energy quantities of the system are on a unit-mass basis. The energy

mass of fluid, and, of course, the same unit of energy must be employed for all terms when numerical calculations are made.   For example, the usual engineering unit for ΔH and Q is the Btu, while kinetic and potential energy and work are usually expressed as foot-pounds *force*.   Therefore the factor 778 ft-lb$_f$/Btu must be used with the appropriate terms to put them all in consistent units of either foot-pounds *force* or Btu. Since g and g_c usually have nearly the same numerical value, the ratio g/g_c is normally taken as unity.

For many of the applications considered in thermodynamics, the kinetic- and potential-energy terms are very small compared with the others and may be neglected.   In such a case Eq. (2-10) reduces to

$$\Delta H = Q - W_s \qquad (2\text{-}11)$$

This expression of the first law for a steady-state flow process is analogous to Eq. (2-4), $\Delta E = Q - W$, for a nonflow process.   It is clear that for a

---

added to the system during this time interval in the form of heat and work, that is, $dQ - dW$, goes partly to accomplishing the energy change of the system and partly to changing the energy of the streams carrying material to and from the system.   Equation (2-10) shows that the energy per unit mass carried by a flowing fluid is given by

$$H + \frac{zg}{g_c} + \frac{u^2}{2g_c}$$

Hence the difference between the total energy of outflowing and inflowing streams during a differential time interval is

$$\Delta \left[\left(H + \frac{zg}{g_c} + \frac{u^2}{2g_c} \right) dm \right]_{\text{flowing streams}}$$

where the energy terms are on a unit-mass basis and Δ indicates the difference between outflowing and inflowing streams.   Therefore the total energy change of both the system and the flowing streams as a result of the energy addition $dQ - dW$ is

$$d[m(E + \text{PE} + \text{KE})]_{\text{sys}} + \Delta \left[\left(H + \frac{zg}{g_c} + \frac{u^2}{2g_c} \right) dm \right]_{\text{flowing streams}} = dQ - dW \qquad (2\text{-}10a)$$

If the system expands or contracts, dW will include the work expended in pushing back the surrounding atmosphere.   Also for a finite time interval, this equation must be integrated.

The application of Eq. (2-10a) may be illustrated by considering a simple case in which the kinetic- and potential-energy changes for the system and the flowing streams are negligible.   Then Eq. (2-10a) reduces to the form

$$d(mE)_{\text{sys}} + \Delta(H\,dm) = dQ - dW$$

Suppose further that there is but one flowing stream, an inflowing one, connected to the system.   A practical example might be adding fluid to a tank through an inlet line.   Under this restriction, $\Delta(H\,dm)$ becomes $0 - H_1\,dm_1$, or simply $-H_1\,dm_1$, where H_1 is the enthalpy per unit mass of the inlet stream and dm_1 is the mass added to the system in the differential time interval.   The final form of the first law then is

$$d(mE)_{\text{sys}} - H_1\,dm_1 = dQ - dW$$

flow process it is the enthalpy change rather than the internal-energy change that is of importance, and this is a major reason for defining this special thermodynamic function.

Equations (2-10) and (2-11) are universally used for the solution of problems involving the steady-state flow of fluids through equipment. For most such applications information on the enthalpy must be available. Since H is a state function and a property of matter, its values

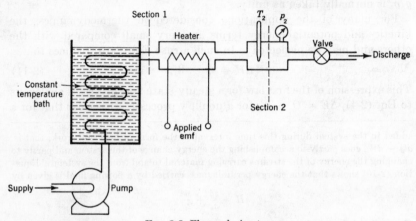

FIG. 2-2. Flow calorimeter.

depend only on point conditions. If values are once determined for given sets of conditions, they may be tabulated for subsequent use whenever the same sets of conditions are encountered again. Thus Eq. (2-10) may be applied to laboratory processes designed specifically for the measurement of enthalpy data.

One such process employs a flow calorimeter. A simple example of this device is illustrated schematically in Fig. 2-2. It is little more than an electrical heater immersed in a flowing fluid, and it is designed so that the kinetic- and potential-energy changes of the fluid from section 1 to section 2 are negligible. This is easily accomplished by having the two sections at the same elevation and by keeping the velocities small. Furthermore, no shaft work is accomplished between sections 1 and 2. Hence Eq. (2-10) reduces to

$$\Delta H = H_2 - H_1 = Q$$

Heat is added to the fluid from the electrical resistance heater, and the amount can easily be determined from the resistance of the heater and the current passing through it. The entire apparatus is well insulated. In practice there are a number of details which have to be considered, but in principle the operation of the flow calorimeter is simple enough.

Measurements of the rate of heat input and the rate of flow of the fluid allow the calculation of values of ΔH between sections 1 and 2.

As an example, consider the measurement of enthalpies of H_2O, both as liquid and as vapor. Liquid water is supplied to the apparatus by the pump. The constant-temperature bath might be filled with a mixture of crushed ice and water to maintain a temperature of 32°F. The coil which carries the test fluid, in this case, water, through the constant-temperature bath is made long enough so that the fluid emerges essentially at the bath temperature of 32°F. Thus the fluid at section 1 is always liquid water at 32°F. The temperature and pressure at section 2 are measured by suitable instruments. Hence values of the enthalpy of H_2O for various conditions at section 2 may be calculated by the equation

$$H_2 = H_1 + Q$$

where Q is the heat added by the resistance heater per pound *mass* of water flowing. It is seen that H_2 depends not only on Q but also on H_1. The conditions at section 1 are always the same, *i.e.*, liquid water at 32°F, except that the pressure varies from run to run. However, pressure has a negligible effect on the properties of liquids unless very high pressures are reached, and for practical purposes H_1 may be considered a constant. It has been pointed out that absolute values of internal energy are unknown. The same is true of enthalpy. Thus some arbitrary base must be selected before the numerical magnitude of enthalpy can be calculated. For water it is customary to set $H = 0$ for liquid water at 32°F. Values of H_2 may then be computed on this *basis* from calorimetric measurements since

$$H_2 = H_1 + Q = 0 + Q = Q$$

These results may be tabulated together with the corresponding conditions existing at section 2 for a large number of runs. In addition, specific-volume measurements may be made for these same conditions, and these too may be tabulated. Moreover, corresponding values of the internal energy of water may be calculated by Eq. (2-6), $E = H - pv$, and these numbers too may be tabulated. In this way tables of thermodynamic properties may be compiled for the entire useful range of conditions. The most widely used such tabulation is that for H_2O and is known as the "steam tables."[1] Tables for various other substances may be found in standard handbooks.[2] For substances other than water, the enthalpy may be taken as zero for other states than that of liquid at 32°F. The choice of a base point is not important as long as all measurements for a

---

[1] See Appendix.
[2] J. H. Perry, "Chemical Engineers' Handbook," 3d ed., p. 249, McGraw-Hill Book Company, Inc., New York, 1950.

particular substance are referred to it. The reason for this is that the equations of thermodynamics, such as Eq. (2-10), always include enthalpy *differences*, and these are independent of where the origin of values is placed. It should be noted that, once an arbitrary zero point has been selected for enthalpy, no arbitrary choice can be made for the internal energy, for the values of internal energy are then always directly calculable from the enthalpy by Eq. (2-6).

Tables of thermodynamic properties are needed for a variety of chemical engineering calculations. The consideration of methods to develop such tables in their entirety will be delayed until Chap. 7.

Example 2-5. For the flow calorimeter just discussed, suppose that the following data were taken for one run:

$$\text{Test fluid: water}$$
$$T_1 = 32°F$$
$$T_2 = 500°F$$
$$p_2 = 40 \text{ psia}$$
$$\text{Flow rate} = 0.437 \text{ lb}_m/\text{min}$$
$$\text{Rate of heat addition from resistance heater} = 562 \text{ Btu/min}$$

It was observed that the water was completely vaporized in the process. Calculate the enthalpy of steam at 500°F and 40 psia based on $H = 0$ for liquid water at 32°F.

Solution. If Δz and Δu^2 are negligible and if W_s and H_1 are zero,

$$H_2 = Q$$

$$Q = \frac{562}{0.437} = 1285 \text{ Btu/lb}_m$$

Therefore

$$H = 1285 \text{ Btu/lb}_m$$

for steam at 500°F and 40 psia.

Example 2-6. Water at 200°F is being pumped from a storage tank at the rate of 50 gal/min by a pump. The motor driving the pump supplies energy at the rate of 2 hp. The water passes through a heat exchanger where it gives up heat at the rate of 40,000 Btu/min and is delivered to a second storage tank at an elevation of 50 ft above the first tank. What is the temperature of the water delivered to the second tank?

Solution. This is a steady-state flow process for which Eq. (2-10) applies. Since the water is taken from one storage tank to another, its initial and final velocities are both essentially zero. Therefore, the term $\Delta u^2/2g_c$ may be neglected. In the absence of any data for the local acceleration of gravity, the ratio g/g_c will be taken as unity. All terms of Eq. (2-10) will be put in units of Btu per pound *mass*. At 200°F the density of water is 60.1 lb$_m$/ft³. Since 1 ft³ is equivalent to 7.48 gal, the mass flow rate is $(50/7.48)(60.1) = 402$ lb$_m$/min. One horsepower is equivalent to 33,000 ft-lb$_f$/min, and 778 ft-lb$_f$ is equivalent to 1 Btu. Thus

$$W_s = -\frac{(2)(33,000)}{(402)(778)} = -0.21 \text{ Btu/lb}_m$$

$$Q = -\frac{40,000}{402} = -99.50 \text{ Btu/lb}_m$$

$$\frac{g}{g_c} \Delta z = \frac{(1)(50)}{778} = 0.06 \text{ Btu/lb}_m$$

$$\frac{\Delta u^2}{2g_c} = 0$$

$$\Delta H + \frac{\Delta u^2}{2g_c} + \frac{g}{g_c}\,\Delta z = Q - W_s$$

Therefore

$$\Delta H = Q - W_s - \frac{g}{g_c}\,\Delta_z = -99.50 - (-0.21) - 0.06$$

$$\Delta H = -99.35 \text{ Btu/lb}_m$$

The enthalpy of water at 200°F is given in the steam tables as 167.99 Btu/lb$_m$.   Thus,

$$\Delta H = H_2 - H_1 = H_2 - 167.99 = -99.35$$

and

$$H_2 = 167.99 - 99.35 = 68.64 \text{ Btu/lb}_m$$

The temperature of water having an enthalpy of 68.64 Btu/lb$_m$ is given in the steam tables as 100.67°F.   Thus,

$$T_2 = 100.7°F$$

In this problem W_s and $(g/g_c)\,\Delta z$ are very small compared with Q, and for all practical purposes they could have been neglected.

2-7. Equilibrium.   _Equilibrium_ is a word denoting a static condition, the absence of change.   In thermodynamics it is taken to mean not only the absence of change but the absence of any _tendency_ toward change on a macroscopic scale.   Thus a system at equilibrium is one which exists under such conditions that there is no tendency for a change of state to occur.   Since any tendency toward change is caused by a driving force of one kind or another, the absence of such a tendency indicates also the absence of any driving force.   Hence a system at equilibrium may be described as one in which all forces are in exact balance.   Whether or not a change will actually occur in a given instance depends not only on driving force but on resistance as well.   Many systems undergo no measurable change even under the influence of large driving forces because the resistance to change is very great.

There are several kinds of driving forces or potentials which tend to cause changes to occur: mechanical forces such as pressure on a piston, temperature differences tending to cause flow of heat, and chemical potentials which tend to cause substances to react chemically or to be transferred from one phase to another.   At equilibrium all such forces are in balance.   Often we are content to deal with systems at partial equilibrium.   In many applications of thermodynamics, chemical reactions are of no concern.   For example, a mixture of hydrogen and oxygen at ordinary conditions is by no means in chemical equilibrium.   However, this system may well be in thermal and mechanical equilibrium with its surroundings.   In analyzing thermal and mechanical processes in such a system, it does not matter whether the system _tends_ to undergo a change by chemical reaction or not.   Just so long as chemical reactions do not occur, purely physical processes may be considered without regard to theoretically possible chemical reactions.

2-8. The Phase Rule.   It was stated earlier that all the properties of a homogeneous substance are automatically fixed if only two of them are set at definite values.   However, systems of greater complexity may behave quite differently, and the number of properties which must be specified in order to fix the state of the system is not always the same. It is important to be able to determine for any system the number of properties that can be independently varied or controlled.   For a homogeneous substance this number is two, and we say that the number of *variants* or *degrees of freedom* of the system is two.   Once these two variables have been fixed, the state of the system is determined, and all other properties have specific values that cannot be altered so long as the temperature and pressure remain constant.   On the other hand, a mixture of steam and water at 1 atm can exist only at 212°F.   It is impossible to change the temperature without also changing the pressure if a mixture of steam and water is to continue to exist.   Thus we say that this system has but one degree of freedom, that it is univariant.   Fortunately, there is a general rule for determining the number of degrees of freedom of any system at equilibrium.   It is the celebrated phase rule of J. Willard Gibbs, who deduced it by theoretical reasoning in 1875.   It will be accepted here in the following form without proof:

$$P + V = C + 2 \qquad (2\text{-}12)$$

where P = number of phases
$\qquad C$ = number of components
$\qquad V$ = number of variants or degrees of freedom of system
Each of these terms has a particular meaning and requires explanation.

A *phase* is a homogeneous region of matter.   A gas or a mixture of gases, a liquid or a liquid solution, and a solid are examples of phases.   It is not necessary for a phase to be continuous, though it may be.   Examples of discontinuous phases are a gas dispersed as small bubbles in a liquid, a liquid dispersed as droplets in another liquid with which it is immiscible, and a crystalline solid with the spaces between the crystals filled with either gas or liquid.   In each of these instances two phases are present, the dispersed phase and the continuous phase.   An abrupt change in properties always occurs at the boundary between phases. Large numbers of phases can coexist, but it is important to note that they *must be in equilibrium* for the phase rule to apply.   An example of a system at equilibrium which is made up of three phases is a boiling saturated solution of a salt in water with excess salt crystals present.   The three phases are solid crystalline salt, the saturated aqueous solution, and the vapor generated by boiling.

The term *component* has a special meaning as used in connection with the phase rule. The components of a thermodynamic system refer to the *minimum* number of chemical species required to prepare the system. The determination of the number of components is a simple problem when no chemical reactions are involved. In this case each chemically distinguishable constituent must be used to prepare the system, and the number of components is equal to the number of chemical compounds or elements present. However, when reactions do occur within the system, the number of components must be decided upon with care.

Consider the decomposition of calcium carbonate. The system consists of three substances, solid calcium carbonate, solid lime, and gaseous carbon dioxide. Although three different chemical species are present, the system in any composition can be prepared from any two of these. For example, if calcium carbonate and carbon dioxide are chosen, a mixture containing any desired fraction of lime may be produced by decomposing the required amount of calcium carbonate and adding or removing carbon dioxide.[1] The system can, of course, be prepared from the three substances, but this is not the minimum number required. On the other hand, the system in any composition could not be prepared from calcium carbonate (or either of the other substances) alone, for the carbon dioxide and lime would always be present in equivalent molal quantities.

For complex reacting systems, the number of components is difficult to determine without some systematic approach. It may be shown that the number of components is equal to the number of chemical species or constituents present in the system minus the number of *independent* chemical reactions at equilibrium. This statement may be expressed mathematically as

$$C = N - r$$

where N is the number of chemical species and r is the number of independent chemical reactions. Thus an alternative form of the phase rule is

$$P + V = N - r + 2 \qquad (2\text{-}12a)$$

The problem of determining the number of components has now been reduced to that of determining the number of independent chemical reactions. The advantage is that a simple rule exists for this purpose.[2] Chemical equations are written for the formation, from the constituent

---

[1] Note that the removal of a constituent makes it a component just as does its addition.

[2] See Kenneth Denbigh, "The Principles of Chemical Equilibrium," Cambridge University Press, New York, 1955.

elements, of each chemical compound present. The elements not actually present in the system are then eliminated from these equations by combination. The set may be reduced by no more than one equation for each element eliminated. The result is a complete set of independent equations, and their number is r.

As a simple example, consider the pyrolysis of methane to produce only ethylene, acetylene, and hydrogen. The chemical constituents of the system are CH_4, C_2H_4, C_2H_2, and H_2. The formation reactions are

$$C + 2H_2 \rightarrow CH_4 \qquad (A)$$
$$2C + 2H_2 \rightarrow C_2H_4 \qquad (B)$$
$$2C + H_2 \rightarrow C_2H_2 \qquad (C)$$

Since carbon is not present in the system, it will be eliminated by combining Eq. (A) with Eqs. (B) and (C). The two resulting equations are

$$2CH_4 \rightarrow C_2H_4 + 2H_2$$
$$2CH_4 \rightarrow C_2H_2 + 3H_2$$

Thus two independent equations result, and $r = 2$. These are by no means the only equations that may be written for these constituents. The point is that of all the equations that may be written, only two are independent.

If carbon had been present in the system, it could not have been eliminated, and the three original equations would constitute an independent set. In this case r would be 3.

For the purpose of determining merely the number of independent reactions, it is not always necessary that the equations be written down. The number of equations in the set is usually (but not always) equal to the number of formation reactions minus the number of elements to be eliminated from them.[1] However, there are many problems involving chemical reactions for which it is necessary to have a set of independent equations. The particular set used is immaterial, for any complete one is sufficient for the determination of the stoichiometry of the process. Applications are found in problems concerning heat effects of chemical reactions (Chap. 5) and chemical equilibrium (Chap. 13).

It has already been indicated that the number of *variants* or *degrees* of *freedom* of a system at equilibrium represents the number of variables which can be independently controlled without altering the nature of the system, *i.e.*, without changing the number of phases or components in the system. It is also the number of variables which must be specified in order to fix completely the properties of the various phases making up the system. It should be emphasized that the variables referred to in

[1] Occasionally, two or more elements may be eliminated in a single combination of equations.

this connection are the intensive properties of the individual phases, properties which are independent of the amount of material present. The variables usually employed are temperature, pressure, and the compositions of the various phases. It would also be possible to use specific volume, internal energy per unit mass, etc., but this is neither desirable nor practical since the pertinent variables are those which may be directly controlled. These are clearly temperature, pressure, and composition. Particular note should be taken of the fact that the compositions referred to are those of the individual phases, and not those of the total system. Over-all or total compositions are not phase-rule variables when more than one phase is present. The reason for this is that the application of the phase rule is not dependent on the size of the system or upon the relative sizes of the various phases present. It gives the same information for a large system as for a small one, and for a system made up predominantly of one phase or for one made up predominantly of another.

The minimum number of degrees of freedom for any system is zero. If $V = 0$, Eq. (2-12) becomes $P = C + 2$. This value of P must be the maximum number of phases which can coexist at equilibrium for C components. For a single-component system this number is three. The system will be invariant since $V = 0$. An example is the triple point of water, where liquid water, water vapor, and the common form of ice exist together in equilibrium. This occurs at 0.01°C and 0.00602 atm. Any change from these conditions will cause at least one phase to disappear.

Example 2-7. How many degrees of freedom has each of the following systems?

(a) Liquid water in equilibrium with its vapor

(b) Liquid water in equilibrium with a mixture of water vapor and nitrogen

(c) A liquid solution of alcohol in water in equilibrium with its vapor

(d) A system consisting of O_2, CO, CO_2, and solid carbon in chemical equilibrium at elevated temperature

(e) A system made by partially decomposing solid $MgCO_3$

(f) A system made by partially decomposing solid NH_4Cl

Solution. (a) This system has but one component. There are two phases (one liquid and one vapor), and no chemical reaction is involved. Thus,

$$V = C + 2 - P = 1 + 2 - 2 = 1$$

This result is in agreement with the well-known fact that for a given pressure water has but one boiling point. Temperature or pressure, but not both, may be specified for a system consisting of water in equilibrium with its vapor.

(b) In this case two components are present. Again there are two phases, and no chemical reaction is involved. Thus

$$V = C + 2 - P = 2 + 2 - 2 = 2$$

It is seen from this example that the addition of an inert gas to a system of water in equilibrium with its vapor changes the characteristics of the system. Now temperature and pressure may be independently varied.   However, once T and p are fixed, the system described can exist only at a particular composition of the vapor phase. (Since nitrogen is negligibly soluble in water, we need not consider the composition of the liquid phase.)

(c) Here $C = 2$, and $P = 2$.   Thus,

$$V = C + 2 - P = 2 + 2 - 2 = 2$$

The phase-rule variables here are temperature, pressure, and the phase compositions. If any two of these variables are specified, *provided they are independent*, the others must have unique values in order for the system as described to exist.   The composition variables always considered in connection with the phase rule are either weight or mole fractions.   It should be noted that for each phase the sum of the weight or mole fractions must be unity.   Thus fixing the mole fraction of water in the liquid phase of the system under consideration automatically fixes the mole fraction of the alcohol in the liquid phase.   These two compositions are therefore not independent, and specifying them will not completely determine the state of the system.

(d) In this example $C = 2$ and $P = 2$.   The number of components is $N - r$. Only two formation reactions can be written:

$$C(s) + O_2(g) \rightarrow CO_2(g)$$
$$C(s) + \tfrac{1}{2}O_2(g) \rightarrow CO(g)$$

Since both oxygen and carbon are present in the system, neither can be eliminated, and these two equations form an independent set.   Hence

$$C = N - r = 4 - 2 = 2$$

and

$$V = C + 2 - P = 2 + 2 - 2 = 2$$

(e) The chemical reaction involved here is

$$MgCO_3(s) \rightleftharpoons MgO(s) + CO_2(g)$$

Two solid phases and one gas phase are present.   Hence $P = 3$.   The general system consisting of these three phases in any proportions may be prepared from any two of the chemical species present.   Therefore $C = 2$, and

$$V = C + 2 - P = 2 + 2 - 3 = 1$$

indicating that the system has but one degree of freedom.

(f) The chemical reaction under consideration is

$$NH_4Cl(s) \rightleftharpoons NH_3(g) + HCl(g)$$

Only two phases are present in this case: solid NH_4Cl and a gaseous mixture of NH_3 and HCl.   The minimum number of constituents required to prepare the general system is two.   Thus $C = 2$, and

$$V = C + 2 - P = 2 + 2 - 2 = 2$$

The general system is seen to have two degrees of freedom.   However, in the special case considered here the system is prepared entirely from NH_4Cl, and the gas phase formed must always have the same composition, *i.e.*, 50 mole per cent NH_3 and 50 mole per cent HCl.   In this case the imposition of a special condition has resulted in the arbitrary fixing of a phase-rule variable, the composition of the gas phase.   Hence this special system has one less degree of freedom than the general system, and $V = 1$

2-9. The Reversible Process.   Important thermodynamic features of a process are revealed by considering how the process can be carried out to yield the maximum work.   This problem will be studied in terms of a gas expanding against a piston.   Suppose a pair of simplifying assumptions are made in order to focus attention on the problem at hand:

1. The cylinder and piston will neither absorb nor transmit heat, so that the effects of heat transfer need not be considered.

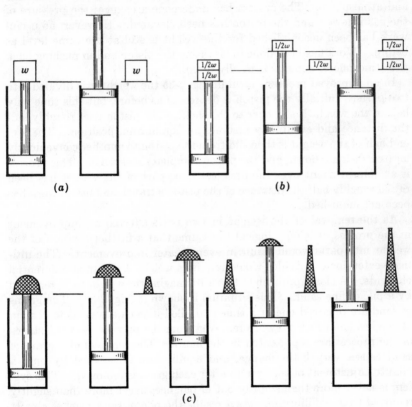

FIG. 2-3. Irreversible and reversible expansion processes.

2. The piston moves within the cylinder without friction, so that the possibility of mechanical inefficiencies is removed.

The apparatus is shown in Fig. 2-3.   The system will be chosen so as to include only the gas.   All else constitutes the surroundings.   The object is to allow the process to take place in such a way as to raise a weight, thereby accomplishing useful work in the surroundings.

Consider first Fig. 2-3a.   The piston is shown inserted far into the cylinder where it confines a gas at a pressure just sufficient to balance the weight of the piston, the atmosphere, and the weight w. This is a condition of equilibrium, for the system has no tendency to change. The weight must be removed if the piston is to rise. Imagine in this first alternative that the weight is suddenly slid from the piston to a shelf that is placed close by and at the same level. The piston rises and eventually reaches a new condition of equilibrium such that the pressure exerted by the gas is just sufficient to balance the weight of the piston and atmosphere. The system has undergone a change; the pressure of the gas is lower, and the piston has been elevated. However, no useful work has been accomplished for the weight is still at the same level as before. Work has been done in elevating the piston and in pushing back the atmosphere, but this is hardly useful.

In an improved process shown in Fig. 2-3b the weight w is divided into two parts. Initially the piston is depressed as before, but this time only half of the weight is slid over to the shelf. The piston rises roughly half the distance and eventually assumes an equilibrium position. The second half of the weight is then slid from the piston to another conveniently located shelf as shown, and the piston completes its stroke. This process is an improvement over the first one since part of the weight has been raised roughly half the distance of the piston's travel, and useful work has been accomplished.

As the removal of the weight in two parts effected an improvement in the process, it is only logical to assume that a further division of the weight into parts would result in even greater improvement. The ultimate extension of this idea would require a weight made up of differential elements. A close approach to this is to imagine the weight to be replaced by a pile of fine sand. This situation is shown in Fig. 2-3c. The grains of sand are removed one at a time and piled in such a way as to remain at the level at which they are removed from the piston. Various stages of the process are represented in the figure. The removal of a grain of sand causes very little change, and equilibrium is restored by only a minute adjustment of the system after each grain is removed. This system is never more than slightly out of balance, never more than slightly removed from equilibrium. As a result, the pile of sand reaches almost the full height of the piston's travel. On the average, all the weight has been raised slightly less than half the distance of the piston's stroke. The only further improvement possible would be obtained if the grains of sand were made infinitesimal in size. It is worthwhile to study the implications of this optimum process, accomplished in differential steps.

The process carried out in this manner yields the maximum possible work that can be obtained under the conditions imposed on the system. In no other way can the process be used to full advantage. This system is always at equilibrium, or at least no more than differentially removed from equilibrium. If the removal of sand from the piston is stopped at any point in the process and sand transferred from the pile to the piston instead, the process would reverse itself and retrace the exact path it had followed up to that point. The piston would be returned to its original position by replacing the sand, grain by grain, taking it always from the pile at the level of the piston. In other words, the system could be restored to its original condition merely by making use of the work it had already accomplished in raising the sand. Not only would the system be restored to its original condition, but so would the surroundings. This kind of process is termed *reversible*.

The two procedures described in Fig. 2-3a and b are *irreversible*. The first one produced no work; therefore none was available for returning the piston to its original position. This could be accomplished only through the use of *extra* work which would come from the surroundings and which would therefore produce some change in the surroundings. The same thing can be said about the second process, though it was more efficient than the first since it produced some useful work. However, some *extra* work would be required to return the piston to the level of the raised weight where it could be used to force the piston back to its initial position.

The reversible process is an ideal one in that it can be approached but never actually realized. It is of practical importance, nevertheless, for it represents the limit of what may be accomplished by actual processes. In thermodynamics, the calculation of work is usually made for ideal systems, because such systems lend themselves completely to mathematical analysis. Often, the choice is between calculations for an ideal system and no calculations at all. Moreover, the results of calculations obtained for ideal systems may be easily combined with various efficiencies to give good approximations of the work for actual processes. The selection of these efficiencies requires knowledge of a practical nature acquired through experience.

It was shown in Sec. 1-11 that the work of compression or expansion of a gas caused by the movement of a piston in a cylinder can be calculated by the equation

$$W = \int_{V_1}^{V_2} p \, dV \qquad (1\text{-}5)$$

Even if the integral in this equation could be evaluated for each of the processes described and shown in Fig. 2-3, it would not equal the work appearing in the surroundings except for the case of the reversible expansion. This can be made clear by the following analysis. The work done on the surroundings in each case appears as an increase in the potential energy of the material supported by the gas. By definition, this equals $\int F \, ds$, where F is the force of gravity on all the material supported by the gas. This includes the piston, the material on it, and the atmosphere. In the case of the reversible process, this force is never more than differentially out of balance with the pressure of the gas. Therefore, it may be described in terms of the internal pressure acting on the piston, that is, $F = pA$, and Eq. (1-5) is then obtained. The situation is different in the case of the irreversible processes. The moment a finite weight is removed from the piston, the force of gravity acting downward is overbalanced by the pressure of the gas by a finite amount, and F does not again equal pA until a new equilibrium position is reached. Thus pA cannot be substituted for F, and Eq. (1-5) does not hold. The conclusion is that W is identical with $\int p\,dV$ only for a reversible process. In other words, the work appearing in the surroundings can be evaluated from the properties of the *system* only for reversible processes. Of course, it may be possible to determine the work from the effects in the *surroundings*.

Attention should be called to other aspects of reversible processes. The removal of sand from the piston in the last process described was accomplished grain by grain, thus requiring a very long time. For the truly reversible process where the weight is removed in differential increments, an infinite time is required. Indeed, this is the case for all reversible processes; they proceed infinitely slowly. That this must be the case should be evident from the fact that only differential driving forces are involved.

It will be recalled that the processes considered were assumed to take place without friction. Without this assumption, it would not have been possible to devise a reversible process. Assume for a moment that the piston is not frictionless. The removal of a finite amount of sand would be required before the piston could move, for friction would cause the piston to stick. Thus the equilibrium condition necessary for a reversible process could not be maintained.

An irreversible process does not produce the maximum work. One may well ask what happens to the potentially available but unobtained work and how it is "lost." A complete answer must await the development of the second law of thermodynamics, but some indication of the answer can be given here. The common phenomenon of friction, which accompanies an irreversible process, is a mechanism for transforming mechanical energy into internal energy. Some of this energy must eventually be transferred, as heat, to the surroundings. It is in this sense that work is lost. Energy is not lost, but simply appears in a form other than mechanical energy in the system and surroundings. In the case of irreversible expansions with frictionless pistons, work is lost, not by mechanical rubbing, but by the stirring of the gas. This stirring or mixing is caused by the rapid expansion of the gas after the sudden removal of a weight and by the oscillations of the free piston as it settles down to its new equilibrium position. This effect, called *turbulence*, decreases the work produced, for stirring always requires work just as it did in Joule's experiments.

The discussion of reversible processes has centered around a single type of process: the expansion of a gas in a cylinder, where the potentials or driving forces involved are fluid pressures and mechanical forces. The reverse process, compression of a gas in a cylinder, is much the same. However, in this case work is done *on* the system rather than *by* the system, and the ideal or reversible process is the one that requires a *minimum* expenditure of work rather than the one that yields a *maximum*. In both cases, it is the reversible work that is given by the integral $\int_{V_1}^{V_2} p \, dV$.

There are many processes which occur under the impulse of potentials other than pressure or mechanical forces. For example, heat flow occurs when a temperature difference exists; electricity flows under the influence of electromotive force; and chemical reactions occur because a chemical potential exists. In general, a process is reversible when the net force driving it is only differential in size. Thus heat is transferred reversibly when it flows from an object at temperature T to another object at temperature $T - dT$.

The concept of a reversible chemical reaction may be illustrated by the decomposition of calcium carbonate. If this substance is heated, it decomposes to form calcium oxide and carbon dioxide gas. At equilibrium, this system consists of three phases, two solid and one gas phase, and two components. Application of the phase rule shows that there is but one degree of freedom. Thus fixing the temperature fixes the pressure also, just so long as all three phases remain. This means that for every temperature calcium carbonate exerts a definite decomposition pressure of CO_2 and that, when the pressure tends to fall below this value, $CaCO_3$ will decom-

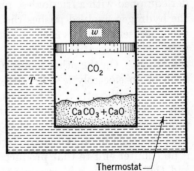

FIG. 2-4. Reversibility of a chemical reaction.

pose. Assume now that a cylinder is fitted with a frictionless piston and contains an equilibrium mixture of $CaCO_3$, CaO, and CO_2. It is immersed in a constant-temperature bath as shown in Fig. 2-4, with the temperature adjusted to a value such that the dissociation pressure of $CaCO_3$ is just sufficient to balance the weight on the piston. The piston is in balance, the temperature of the reaction mixture is equal to that of the bath, and the chemical reaction is held in balance by the pressure of the CO_2. Any alteration of conditions, however slight, will upset the equilibrium and cause the reaction to proceed in one direction or the other. If the weight is differentially increased, the CO_2 pressure will be raised differentially, and CO_2 will combine with CaO to form $CaCO_3$, allowing the weight to fall slowly. The heat given off by this reaction will tend to raise the temperature in the cylinder, and heat will flow to the bath. Decreasing the weight differentially sets off the opposite chain of events. The same results are obtained by raising or lowering the temperature of the bath. If the temperature of the bath is raised differentially, heat flows into the cylinder, where it decomposes calcium carbonate. The CO_2 generated causes the pressure to rise differentially, which in turn raises the piston and weight. This will continue until the $CaCO_3$ has been completely decomposed. The process is reversible, for the system is never more than differentially displaced from equilibrium, and only a differential lowering of the temperature of the bath will cause the system to return to its initial state. Since p is constant, the work done equals $p \, \Delta V$.

The observable results of the chemical potential in the previous example were temperature and pressure driving forces. Consider another reaction system in which the chemical potential is manifested as an electromotive force. Suppose metallic zinc is brought into contact with an aqueous solution of hydrochloric acid at atmospheric pressure in a cylinder equipped with a frictionless piston. As the chemical reaction occurs, the hydrogen evolved pushes the piston against the atmosphere. However, no useful work is accomplished, and the process cannot be reversed with only differential changes in the conditions of the system and surroundings. On the other hand, suppose the apparatus is arranged in the form of an electrolytic cell, with the metallic zinc as one electrode and platinum as the other. The electrodes are connected to an external circuit. When the electrodes are dipped in the acid solution, an emf is produced which can be utilized to accomplish work. The amount of this work depends upon the characteristics of the external circuit. If there is no counter emf to that produced by the cell, no useful work will result and the process is still irreversible. On the other hand, if the counter voltage is only differentially less than that of the cell, a maximum amount of work is produced. The chemical potential of the reaction is balanced by the electrical potential of the external circuit, and the process occurs reversibly. By increasing the counter emf differentially, the reaction will proceed in the reverse direction, taking electrical energy from the surroundings and plating out zinc on the electrode.

In summary, a reversible process is frictionless; it is never more than differentially removed from equilibrium; the driving forces are differential in magnitude; and the process can be reversed, leaving no change in the system or surroundings.

Example 2-8. A horizontal piston-and-cylinder arrangement is placed in contact with a constant-temperature bath. The piston slides in the cylinder with negligible friction, and an external force holds it in place against an initial gas pressure of 200 psia. The initial gas volume is 1 ft^3. The external force on the piston is to be reduced gradually, allowing the gas to expand, until its volume doubles. Under these conditions it has been determined that the volume of the gas is related to its pressure in such a way that the product pV is constant. Calculate the work done by the gas in moving the external force.

How much work would be done if the external force were suddenly reduced to half its initial value instead of being gradually reduced?

Solution. The process, carried out as first described, is a reversible one, and

$$W = \int_{V_1}^{V_2} p \, dV$$

Since

$$pV = k \text{ (a constant)} \qquad p = \frac{k}{V}$$

and

$$W = k \int_{V_1}^{V_2} \frac{dV}{V} = k \ln \frac{V_2}{V_1}$$

But

$$k = pV = p_1 V_1 = (200)(144)(1) = 28{,}800 \text{ ft-lb}_f$$
$$V_1 = 1 \text{ ft}^3 \qquad \text{and} \qquad V_2 = 2 \text{ ft}^3$$

Therefore

$$W = 28{,}800 \ln 2 = 19{,}930 \text{ ft-lb}_f$$

The final pressure will be

$$p_2 = \frac{k}{V_2} = \frac{28{,}800}{2} = 14{,}400 \text{ lb}_f/\text{sq ft or } 100 \text{ psia}$$

In the second case the force exerted is constant and equivalent to a pressure of 100 psia. After half the initial force has been removed, the gas will undergo a sudden expansion. Eventually the system will return to an equilibrium condition identical with the final state attained in the reversible process. Thus ΔV will be the same as before, and the net work accomplished will equal the equivalent external pressure times the volume change, or

$$W = (100)(144)(2 - 1) = 14{,}400 \text{ ft-lb}_f$$

This process is clearly irreversible, and it demonstrates the fact that an irreversible process accomplishes less work than a reversible process for the same change in state. Compared with the reversible process, the irreversible expansion is said to have an efficiency of

$$\frac{14{,}400}{19{,}930} = 0.723, \text{ or } 72.3 \text{ per cent}$$

Example 2-9. The piston-and-cylinder arrangement shown in the accompanying figure contains nitrogen gas trapped below the piston at a pressure of 100 psia. The piston is held in place by latches as shown. The space behind the piston is evacuated.

A pan is attached to the piston rod, and a "weight" w is fastened to the pan. The piston, piston rod, and pan together weigh 50 lb$_f$, and w weighs 100 lb$_f$. The latches holding the piston are released, allowing the piston to rise rapidly until it strikes the top of the cylinder. The distance moved by the piston is 15 in. Friction may *not* be neglected. Discuss the energy changes which occur because of this process.

Solution. This problem will be analyzed to point out some of the difficulties encountered when irreversible nonflow processes are considered. Suppose first the

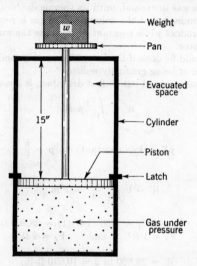

system is taken to consist of the nitrogen gas, the cylinder, and the piston, rod, and pan. The work done by this system is equal to the change in potential energy of the weight w:

$$W = (100)(^{15}\!/_{12}) = 125 \text{ ft-lb}_f$$

(Work done in displacing the atmosphere by the small volume of the rod has been neglected.) This value is consistent with the basic definition of work, for it is the value which would be obtained by integration of Eq. (1-3), where the force is that exerted by the system on the weight. During most of the length of travel the weight is being accelerated so that this force is greater than the force of gravity on the weight. For a short distance at the end of the stroke where the piston strikes the upper end of the cylinder the weight is decelerated, and the force reverses, attaining large negative values. During this short distance, work is done on the system. The value calculated is the *net* work done by the system on the weight (surroundings).

If heat transfer between the atmosphere and the apparatus is slow, the *immediate* result of the sudden change in the system will be to reduce its energy by just 125 ft-lb$_f$ to compensate for the 125 ft-lb$_f$ increase in the surroundings. Energy changes in the system are of two kinds, potential and internal. The potential energy of the piston, rod, and pan assembly has increased by $(50)(^{15}\!/_{12}) = 62.5$ ft-lb$_f$. The internal-energy change of the entire system immediately after the piston has come to rest is given by Eq. (2-3), with Q and $\Delta(KE)$ taken as zero.

$$\Delta E = -W - \Delta(PE) = -125 - 62.5 = -187.5 \text{ ft-lb}_f$$

Without a detailed knowledge of the temperatures of the different parts of the system, we cannot determine the individual internal-energy changes which occur in the gas and in the piston, rod, and cylinder.

An analysis of the process is also possible with the gas alone taken as the system. This introduces a practical difficulty in the calculation of the individual terms Q and W. According to the basic definition, the work done by the gas on the surroundings is equal to $\int p_f \, dV$, where p_f is the pressure exerted on the face of the piston by the gas. Because the expansion is very rapid, pressure gradients will exist in the gas, and p_f will not be equivalent to p in Eq. (1-5). Since p_f is not known, there is no way to calculate the work by considering the changes which occur in the system. However, the problem can be worked by avoiding the calculation of Q and W and returning to the fundamental equation [Eq. (2-1)]. The total energy change of the system (the gas) is its internal-energy change. The energy changes of the surroundings consist of potential-energy changes of the piston, rod, pan, and weight and of internal-energy changes of the piston, rod, and cylinder. Therefore, Eq. (2-1) may be written

$$\Delta E_{sys} + \Delta E_{surr} + \Delta(PE)_{surr} = 0$$

The potential-energy term is

$$\Delta(PE)_{surr} = (150)(15\!\!\!\;\tfrac{1}{2}) = 187.5 \text{ ft-lb}_f$$

Hence

$$\Delta E_{sys} + \Delta E_{surr} = -187.5 \text{ ft-lb}_f$$

This result is the same as that for the case where the system included the piston, cylinder, rod, and pan as well as the gas. Again, it is not possible to determine the individual internal-energy changes which occur in the gas and in the piston-and-cylinder assembly.

2-10. Heat Capacity and Specific Heat. In Sec. 1-13, it was pointed out that heat flow is commonly thought of in terms of the effects it has on the substances which receive the energy. Conversely, it is clear that a certain quantity of heat is required to raise the temperature of a given mass of any material by 1°. This quantity is called the heat capacity of the substance. Although the term may be applied to any amount of material, it is commonly based upon 1 mole or a unit mass of material, and it will be used in this sense throughout this book. The relationship between the heat transferred to a substance and its temperature may be written $dQ = nC \, dT$, where n is the number of moles, C is the molal heat capacity, and dT is the temperature rise caused by the quantity of heat dQ. If a unit mass is taken as the basis for heat capacity, the equation becomes $dQ = mc \, dT$, where m represents mass and c, heat capacity per unit mass. The term *specific heat* is frequently used as being synonymous with heat capacity. This is not strictly correct, because traditionally specific heat has been defined as the ratio of the heat capacity of a substance to the heat capacity of an equal quantity of water. However, the terminology for these quantities is used very loosely, and the term specific heat has come to imply heat capacity per unit mass. It will be given this meaning throughout this book. The specific heat of water is approximately 1 cal/(g)(°C) or 1 Btu/(lb$_m$)(°F). The molal heat capacity of

water is approximately 18 cal/(g mole)(°C) or 18 Btu/(lb mole)(°F).
This illustrates the fact that the common units of heat capacity, as just
indicated, are interchangeable, *i.e.*, the heat capacity of a substance is
the same in both sets of units.

It has been emphasized that heat is not a property. Like work, the
amount required to produce a given change of state depends on the particular process or path taken. It follows that the heat capacity of a
substance also depends on the path followed. Any number of paths are
possible, but heat capacities are usually defined for only two, constant-
pressure and constant-volume processes. Thus, there are in common
use two heat capacities, C_p at constant pressure and C_v at constant
volume. These quantities *are* properties because there is no uncertainty
about the paths to which they apply. For a homogeneous material they
depend on temperature and pressure just as specific volume and density
do. For the present, however, only systems for which C_p and C_v are
constant will be discussed.

Consider a constant-volume process involving 1 mole of a gas confined
in a vessel having rigid walls. The gas will constitute the system. If
heat is added, the temperature of the gas will rise. According to the
definition of heat capacity,

$$dQ = C_v \, dT \tag{2-13}$$

or if C_v is constant

$$Q = C_v \, \Delta T \tag{2-14}$$

Since this process is carried out at constant volume, no work is done, and
the first-law expressions [Eqs. (2-4) and (2-5)] reduce to $\Delta E = Q$ and
$dE = dQ$. Therefore for a constant-volume process

$$dE = dQ = C_v \, dT \tag{2-15}$$

and

$$\Delta E = Q = C_v \, \Delta T \quad \text{(const } C_v) \tag{2-16}$$

showing that the change in internal energy is equal to the heat added.

So far, this discussion has been concerned with processes which actually
occur at constant volume. Consider now the case where the volume
varies during the process, but is the same at the end as at the beginning.
Such a process cannot rightly be called one of constant volume, even
though $V_2 = V_1$ and $\Delta V = 0$. However, changes in state functions or
properties are independent of path and are, therefore, the same for all
processes which occur in such a way that they lead from the same initial
to the same final conditions. Hence, property changes for this case
may be calculated from the equations for a truly constant-volume process
leading from the same initial to the same final conditions. For such
processes, therefore, Eq. (2-16) gives $\Delta E = C_v \, \Delta T$, because E, C_v, and T
are all state functions or properties. On the other hand, it is *not* correct

to write that $Q = \Delta E$ or that $Q = C_v \Delta T$, because the value of Q depends on the path. For the same reason, W will not in general be zero for such processes. This discussion illustrates the reason for the careful distinction that has been made between state functions and heat and work. The principle that state functions are independent of path is an important and useful concept for calculating property changes. For this purpose, an actual process may be replaced by any other process which accomplishes the same change in state. Such an alternative process may be selected; for example, for its simplicity.

For the study of a constant-pressure process suppose the system consists of 1 mole of gas, confined in a cylinder by a frictionless piston at a pressure p. The system is initially at equilibrium. Heat is slowly added, causing the gas to expand reversibly. If the force on the piston is held constant, the process will occur at constant pressure. According to the definition of heat capacity

$$dQ = C_p \, dT \qquad (2\text{-}17)$$

or if C_p is constant.

$$Q = C_p \, \Delta T \qquad (2\text{-}18)$$

Work is accomplished since a force is being moved through a distance. Since the process is carried out reversibly, this work is given by the expression $dW = p \, dV$. Substitution for both dQ and dW in the first-law expression, $i.e.$, Eq. (2-4), gives

$$dE = C_p \, dT - p \, dV$$

or

$$dE + p \, dV = C_p \, dT = dQ \qquad (2\text{-}19)$$

By Eq. (2-3),

$$dH = dE + d(pV)$$

Since p is constant

$$dH = dE + p \, dV$$

A comparison of this equation with Eq. (2-19) shows that

$$dH = C_p \, dT = dQ \qquad (2\text{-}20)$$

and

$$\Delta H = C_p \, \Delta T = Q \qquad (\text{const } C_p) \qquad (2\text{-}21)$$

Thus for a constant-pressure process carried out reversibly, the enthalpy change of the system is equal to the heat added. It will be noted that a reversible process was assumed in the development of this relationship, and it might be supposed that Eqs. (2-20) and (2-21) are therefore applicable only to such processes. This is only partly true. dQ and Q are indeed given by these expressions for reversible processes only. However, H, C_p, and T are properties of the system, and changes in them do not depend upon the path. Although the relations $dH = C_p \, dT$ and

$\Delta H = C_p \, \Delta T$ were derived for a reversible process at constant pressure, they must also give the change in the enthalpy of the system for any process, reversible or not. This is the same point discussed in connection with Eq. (2-16), only in that case the question of reversibility did not arise. In this case it is important, for a constant-pressure process can be carried out irreversibly as well as reversibly. It is only for the reversible constant-pressure path that $Q = \Delta H$, $Q = C_p \, \Delta T$, and $W = p \, \Delta V$. However, $\Delta H = C_p \, \Delta T$ for any process for which $p_2 = p_1$, whether reversible or irreversible, or whether actually carried out at constant pressure or not. Thus for purposes of calculating *changes in properties*, the equations applying to the reversible constant-pressure process may be applied to actual or irreversible processes which accomplish the same change in state.

While the heat capacities at constant volume and constant pressure differ significantly for gases, the distinction is not so important where solids and liquids are involved. This is because solids and liquids expand only slightly when heated. Heating at constant pressure is accomplished at nearly constant volume also, and one commonly refers merely to the heat capacity or specific heat of a solid or liquid without restricting it to any particular process.

Example 2-10. An ideal gas is one for which pV/T is a constant, regardless of the changes which it undergoes. Such a gas has a volume of 359 ft³/lb mole at 32°F and 1 atm. In the following problem, air may be considered an ideal gas having the constant heat capacities

$$C_v = 5 \quad \text{and} \quad C_p = 7 \text{ Btu/(lb mole)(°F)}$$

The initial condition of the air is 1 atm abs and 60°F. It is to be compressed reversibly to 5 atm abs and 60°F by two different *reversible* processes. Calculate the heat and work requirements and ΔE and ΔH of the air for each path:

(a) Cooling at constant pressure followed by heating at constant volume
(b) Heating at constant volume followed by cooling at constant pressure

Solution. In each case the system will be taken as 1 lb mole of air, contained in an imaginary piston-and-cylinder arrangement. Since the processes considered are reversible, the piston must be imagined to move in the cylinder without friction. The initial volume of 1 mole of air is

$$v_1 = (359) \left(\frac{520}{492} \right) = 379 \text{ ft}^3$$

The final volume is

$$v_2 = v_1 \frac{p_1}{p_2} = (379) \left(\frac{1}{5} \right) = 75.8 \text{ ft}^3$$

(a) In this case the final conditions are reached in two steps. The first step consists in cooling the air at the constant pressure of 1 atm until the final volume of 75.8 ft³ is reached. During the second step the volume is held constant at this value while the air is heated to its final state. The temperature of the air at the end of the cooling step is

$$T = (520) \left(\frac{75.8}{379}\right) = 104°R$$

For this step the pressure is constant.   By Eq. (2-21)

$$Q = \Delta H = C_p \, \Delta T = (7)(104 - 520) = -2910 \text{ Btu}$$

Since

$$\Delta E = \Delta H - \Delta(pv)$$

$$\Delta E = \Delta H - p \, \Delta v = -2910 - \frac{(14.7)(144)(75.8 - 379)}{778}$$

$$\Delta E = -2080 \text{ Btu}$$

The second step is accomplished by heating the air at constant volume.   By Eq. (2-16)

$$\Delta E = Q = C_v \, \Delta T = (5)(520 - 104) = 2080 \text{ Btu}$$

The complete process represents the sum of its steps.   Hence

$$Q = -2910 + 2080 = -830 \text{ Btu}$$
$$\Delta E = -2080 + 2080 = 0$$

Since the first law applies to the entire process,

$$\Delta E = Q - W$$
$$0 = -830 - W$$
$$W = -830 \text{ Btu}$$

Equation (2-8) also applies to the entire process.

$$\Delta H = \Delta E + \Delta(pv)$$

But $T_1 = T_2$, and therefore $p_1 v_1 = p_2 v_2$.   Hence $\Delta(pv) = 0$ and

$$\Delta H = \Delta E = 0$$

(b) Two different steps are used in this case to reach the same final state of the air. In the first step the air is heated at a constant volume equal to its initial value until the final pressure of 5 atm is reached.   During the second step the air is cooled at the constant pressure of 5 atm to its final state.   The air temperature at the end of the first step is

$$T = (520)(\tfrac{5}{1}) = 2600°R$$

For this step the volume is constant and

$$Q = \Delta E = C_v \, \Delta T = (5)(2600 - 520) = 10,400 \text{ Btu}$$

For the second step pressure is constant and

$$Q = \Delta H = C_p \, \Delta T = (7)(520 - 2600) = -14,500 \text{ Btu}$$

Also

$$\Delta E = \Delta H - \Delta(pv) = \Delta H - p \, \Delta v$$

$$\Delta E = -14,500 - \frac{(5)(14.7)(144)(75.8 - 379)}{778}$$

$$\Delta E = -10,400 \text{ Btu}$$

For the two steps considered together

$$Q = 10,400 - 14,500 = -4100 \text{ Btu}$$
$$\Delta E = 10,400 - 10,400 = 0$$
$$W = Q - \Delta E = -4100 - 0 = -4100 \text{ Btu}$$

and as before

$$\Delta H = \Delta E = 0$$

Note that the property changes, that is, ΔE and ΔH, calculated for the same change in state are the same for both paths. On the other hand the answers of parts (a) and (b) show that Q and W depend on the path.

PROBLEMS

1. An insulated and nonconducting container filled with 20 lb_m of water at 68°F is fitted with a stirrer. The stirrer is made to turn by lowering a "weight" having a mass of 50 lb_m. The local acceleration of gravity is 32.00 ft/sec². The weight slowly falls a distance of 30 ft while turning the stirrer. Assuming that all the work done by gravity on the weight is transferred to the water, determine:

(a) The amount of work done on the water in foot-pounds *force*

(b) The internal-energy change of the water in foot-pounds *force* and in Btu

(c) The final temperature of the water in °F

(d) The amount of heat which must be removed from the water to return it to its initial temperature

(e) The total energy change of the universe because of (1) the process of lowering the weight, (2) the process of cooling the water back to its initial temperature, and (3) both of these processes taken together

2. Rework Prob. 1, taking into account that the container changes in temperature along with the water and has a heat capacity equivalent to 5 lb_m of water. Work the problem in two ways: (a) taking the water and container as the system, and (b) taking the water only as the system.

3. It has been suggested that the kitchen in your house could be cooled in the summer by closing the kitchen from the rest of the house and opening the door to the electric refrigerator. Comment on this. State clearly and concisely the basis for your conclusions.

4. (a) Liquid water at 212°F and 1 atm has an internal energy (on an arbitrary basis) of 180.02 Btu/lb_m. What is its enthalpy? The specific volume of liquid water at these conditions is 0.01672 ft³/lb_m.   *Ans.* 180.07 Btu/lb_m.

(b) The water of part (a) is brought to the vapor state at 400°F and 100 psia, where its specific volume is 4.936 ft³/lb_m, and its enthalpy is 1228.4 Btu/lb_m. Calculate ΔE and ΔH for the process.   *Ans.* $\Delta E = 957.0$, $\Delta H = 1048.3$ Btu/lb_m.

5. (a) How much difference in elevation will result in a change of potential energy equivalent to 1 Btu/lb_m of the substance considered?

(b) A fluid has a velocity of 100 ft/sec when entering a piece of apparatus. With what velocity must the fluid leave the apparatus so that the difference in entering and leaving kinetic energies is equivalent to 1 Btu/lb_m of the fluid?

(c) What conclusions are indicated by these examples?

6. A stream of hot water at 150°F, flowing at a rate of 50 gal/min, is needed for a certain process. Water at 60°F and steam at 30 psia and 280°F are available. It is proposed that the steam and cold water be mixed to form the hot water.

(a) At what rates (pounds *mass* per minute) should the cold water and steam be fed to the mixer?

(b) If the velocity of the steam in the steam line is to be no more than 10 ft/sec, what is the minimum pipe diameter (ID) allowable?

Data:

	Water at 60°F	Water at 150°F	Steam at 30 psia and 280°F
v, ft^3/lb$_m$.........	0.01603	0.01634	14.39
H, Btu/lb$_m$......	28.1	117.9	1179.3

7. An open barrel of negligible heat capacity contains 400 lb$_m$ of water at 60°F. A hose is connected to a steam line, and the other end is submerged in the water in the barrel. Live steam is run into the barrel and condensed until the water reaches a temperature of 150°F. The final mass of water in the barrel is found to be 430 lb$_m$. What is the enthalpy of the steam in the line? Assume no heat losses.

Ans. 1315.6 Btu/lb$_m$.

NOTE: This is *not* a steady-flow process. Before making numerical calculations, show that the first law as applied to this nonflow process reduces to

$$m_2H_2 = m_1H_1 + m_sH_s$$

where m_1 and m_2 represent the initial and final masses of water in the barrel and m_s is the mass of steam run into the barrel. H_1, H_2, and H_s represent the enthalpies per unit mass of the water at the beginning and end of the process and of the steam, respectively. Would the result be different if the steam and water were mixed in a flow process? The required data for water are given in Prob. 6.

8. (a) Liquid $C_{10}H_8$ in the amount of 1.28 g is completely burned in an oxygen bomb to CO_2 and $H_2O(l)$. The reactants are initially at 20°C and 1 atm pressure, and the products of combustion are cooled to 20°C. Thus 1234.6 cal is transferred to the surroundings. What are the values of Q, W, ΔE, and ΔH for this process? Assume that CO_2 is an ideal gas and that the volume of the liquid $C_{10}H_8$ is equal to the total volume of the liquid H_2O formed.

(b) What are the values of Q, W, ΔE, and ΔH when 1.28 g of $C_{10}H_8$ is burned at 1 atm constant pressure and the initial and final temperatures are 20°C?

9. A plant hydrogenates cottonseed oil at a pressure of 5 psig with pure hydrogen at 180°C. The gas is heated from 20°C to this temperature by passing through a coil. The coil is small in diameter, and the pressure drop through it is 40 psia. There is essentially no pressure drop between the coil outlet and the hydrogenation reactor. What is the heat transferred through the coil wall per 1000 lb of hydrogen? Assume that hydrogen is an ideal gas and that the molal heat capacity at constant pressure is 7.0. Neglect kinetic-energy effects.

10. Water is flowing in a straight horizontal insulated pipe of 1-in. ID. There is no device present for adding or removing energy as work. The upstream velocity is 20 ft/sec. The water flows into a section where the diameter is suddenly increased. What is the change in enthalpy of the water if the downstream diameter is 2 in.? If it is 4 in.? What is the maximum enthalpy change for a sudden enlargement in the pipe?

11. Steam at 200 psia and 600°F (state 1) enters a turbine through a standard 3-in. pipeline with a velocity of 10 ft/sec. The exhaust from the turbine is carried through a standard 10-in. pipeline and is at 4 psia and 160°F (state 2).

Data: $H_1 = 1321.4$ Btu/lb$_m$ $v_1 = 3.059$ ft^3/lb$_m$
             $H_2 = 1129.3$ Btu/lb$_m$ $v_2 = 92.15$ ft^3/lb$_m$

What is the power output of the turbine in horsepower, assuming no heat losses?

Ans. 45.6 hp.

12. Water flows through a horizontal coil heated by steam condensing on the outside. If the inlet pressure and temperature are 2 atm abs and 160°F and at the exit 1 atm abs and 220°F, calculate the heat added to the coil per pound *mass* of water. The entering velocity is 5 ft/sec, and that leaving, 500 ft/sec.

Data:

	Water at 160°F	Steam at 1 atm, 220°F
H, Btu/lb$_m$...	127.9	1154.4

13. What is the variance or number of degrees of freedom for each of the following systems?

(*a*) Solid iodine in equilibrium with its vapor

(*b*) A mixture of liquid water and liquid toluene (immiscible) in equilibrium with their vapors

(*c*) A binary azeotrope

(*d*) A mixture of N_2, H_2, and NH_3 at room temperature ·

(*e*) A mixture of N_2, H_2, and NH_3 at elevated temperature where chemical equilibrium exists

(*f*) A system prepared by heating NH_3 to a high temperature where it decomposes

(*g*) A system consisting of CO, CO_2, H_2, H_2O, CH_3OH, and CH_4 in chemical equilibrium at elevated temperature

(*h*) Same as (*g*) except that solid carbon is present in addition

        Ans. (*a*) 1; (*b*) 1; (*c*) 1; (*d*) 4; (*e*) 3; (*f*) 2; (*g*) 4; (*h*) 3.

14. In a natural gasoline fractionation system there are usually six components present in appreciable quantities: methane, ethane, propane, isobutane, *n*-butane, and *n*-pentane. If a mixture of these components is placed in a bomb and the temperature and pressure are fixed so that a liquid and gas phase exist at equilibrium, how many additional phase-rule variables must be chosen to fix the composition of both phases?

If the temperature and pressure are to remain the same, is there any way that the composition of the total contents of the bomb can be changed (by adding or removing material) without affecting the composition of the gas and liquid phases?

15. How many degrees of freedom are there in a system composed of solid iron, the solid oxides FeO and Fe_3O_4, and gaseous CO and CO_2 in complete chemical equilibrium?

16. A tank of 100 ft³ capacity contains 3000 lb$_m$ of liquid water in equilibrium with its vapor, which fills the remainder of the tank. The temperature and pressure are 450°F and 422.6 psia, respectively. Two thousand pounds *mass* of water at 150°F is to be pumped into the tank without removing any steam. How much heat must be added during this process if the pressure and temperature in the tank are to remain at their initial values? The following data are available:

	Liquid water at 150°F	Liquid water at 450°F	Steam at 450°F and 422.6 psia
v, ft³/lb$_m$.....	0.01634	0.0194	1.0993
H, Btu/lb$_m$...	117.9	430.1	1204.6

        Ans. 597,000 Btu.

17. A tank contains 1 lb_m of steam at a pressure of 300 psia and a temperature of 700°F. It is connected through a valve to a vertical cylinder which contains a frictionless piston. The piston is loaded with a weight such that a pressure of 100 psia is necessary to support it. Initially the piston is at the bottom of the cylinder. The valve is opened slightly so that steam flows into the cylinder until the pressure is uniform throughout the system. The final temperature of the steam in the tank is found to be 440°F. Calculate the temperature of the steam in the cylinder if no heat is transferred from the steam to the surroundings. Data for steam should be taken from steam tables. *Ans.* 569°F.

18. In the following problems take $C_v = 5$ and $C_p = 7$ for nitrogen gas:

(a) Three pound moles of nitrogen at 70°F is contained in a rigid vessel. How much heat must be added to the system to raise its temperature to 230°F if the vessel has a negligible heat capacity? If the vessel weighs 200 lb_m and has a heat capacity of 0.12 Btu/(lb_m)(°F), how much heat is required?

(b) Two pound moles of nitrogen at 350°F is contained in a piston-and-cylinder arrangement. How much heat must be extracted from this system, which is kept at constant pressure by the piston, to cool it to 60°F if the heat capacity of the piston and cylinder is neglected?

19. You wish to calculate ΔE and ΔH for an ideal gas which is changed in some process from an initial condition of 40°F and 10 atm abs to 140°F and 1 atm abs. Devise a reversible nonflow process (any number of steps) for accomplishing this change, and calculate (in Btu) ΔE and ΔH for the process, taking 1 lb mole of the gas as your basis. $C_p = 7$ and $C_v = 5$ Btu/(lb mole)(°F).

CHAPTER 3

THE IDEAL GAS

3-1. The Ideal-gas Law. For single-component or constant-composition gases, the phase rule requires that only two variables need be specified for the state of the gas to be completely determined. Therefore, a series of unique relationships should exist among the various thermodynamic properties of a gas which will allow the calculation of all other properties once two of them are known. The determination of these relationships is one of the major problems of thermodynamics. For this purpose, it is desirable to have an equation which gives the specific volume of a gas as a function of its pressure and temperature. The simplest such p-v-T relationship is known as the ideal-gas law. This law and some of the thermodynamic equations which result when it is assumed are considered in this chapter. Other relationships which more closely approximate the volumetric behavior of real gases will be taken up in the next chapter.

The ideal gas was mentioned in Chap. 1 in connection with the definition of a temperature scale. It was stated that an ideal gas meets the following conditions:

1. The volume of the molecules themselves is negligible compared with the total volume of the gas.

2. No forces act between the molecules of the gas.

With these assumptions, it may be shown from the kinetic theory that the p-v-T relationship is given by the equation

$$pV = nRT \tag{3-1}$$

where V = volume of n moles of gas
   p = absolute pressure
   T = absolute temperature
   R = a universal constant whose value depends only on the units used

If n is chosen as unity,

$$pv = RT \tag{3-2}$$

where v is the volume per mole.

Equations (3-1) and (3-2) express what is generally known as the ideal-gas law. They represent a combination of Charles' law, that volume is directly proportional to temperature at constant pressure, and Boyle's law, that pressure is inversely proportional to volume at constant temperature. The only state in which actual gases fulfill the conditions for ideal behavior is at zero pressure. Nevertheless, this concept is useful, for it leads to the development of a series of simple equations which are frequently applicable as good approximations for actual gases. For engineering calculations, gases at pressures of a few atmospheres may usually be considered ideal.

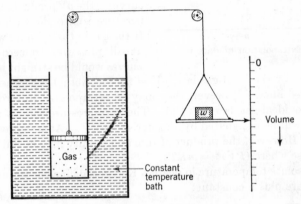

FIG. 3-1. Apparatus for determining R.

The value of R may be determined experimentally from data taken with actual gases. Since real gases are ideal only at pressures approaching zero, it is necessary to take data at finite pressures and extrapolate to the zero-pressure state. In theory this can be accomplished readily, but in practice the required accuracy is difficult to attain. The method used allows not only a determination of R, but at the same time provides a means of locating the absolute zero of temperature.

Figure 3-1 shows a piston-and-cylinder arrangement which could, in principle, be used for this purpose. The piston is loaded in such a way that pressures below atmospheric can be obtained. A sample of n moles of gas is trapped in the cylinder, which is immersed in a constant-temperature bath. The volume of the gas is given by a calibrated scale. For the purpose of this discussion the apparatus will be considered frictionless. Furthermore, the mass of the pan will be made equal to the mass of the piston so that their effects will cancel. Thus the pressure of the gas is equal to the atmospheric pressure pushing down on the piston, minus w/A (w is the force of gravity on the weight, and A is the cross-sectional area of the cylinder). For a given bath temperature, various weights are placed on the pan to give a series of values of p and V, the pressure and volume of the gas in the cylinder. For example, if the constant-temperature bath is filled with an ice-water mixture, measurements of p and V are obtained for a temperature of 0°C. Values of the

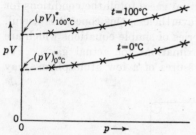

pV product are calculated for this temperature, and are plotted vs. p, as shown in Fig. 3-2. The bath temperature is then raised to 100°C by filling it with boiling water, and the procedure is repeated. The curve for the pV product at this temperature is also shown in Fig. 3-2. If the gas in the cylinder were ideal at all pressures concerned, these curves would be straight horizontal lines, since by the ideal-gas law, $pV = nRT$. Actual experimental data give curved lines. However, they may be extrapolated to zero pressure where the ideal-gas law is valid. The zero-pressure values of pV so obtained will be designated by an asterisk: $(pV)^*$. At zero pressure V is infinite. However, the product of zero and infinity may be finite, as it is in this case where $(PV)^* = nRT$.

FIG. 3-2. Extrapolation of data to zero pressure.

The absolute temperature in degrees Kelvin is defined as the centigrade temperature plus a constant:

$$T°K = t°C + b$$

Thus in the zero-pressure state

$$(pV)^* = nRT = nR(t + b) = nRt + nRb$$

Since nRb is a constant, a plot of $(pV)^*$ vs. t is linear, as shown in Fig. 3-3. The intercept of this line is nRb, and its slope is nR. Measurements of the slope and intercept allow the calculation of both b and R. The results of careful experiments give b as 273.16. Thus,

$$T°K = t°C + 273.16$$

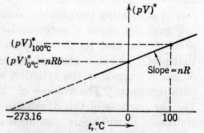

FIG. 3-3. Determination of R.

No temperature below 0°K is thought possible because a negative value of T would require a negative value of $(pV)^*$. Thus the Kelvin temperature scale is called an absolute scale, and 0°K is regarded as the absolute zero of temperature. The other absolute scale, the Rankine scale, is defined by the equation

$$T°R = 1.8(T°K)$$

The value of R depends on the units used for p, V, n, and T in the following way:

$$R = \frac{pV}{nT} = \frac{(\text{absolute pressure})(\text{volume})}{(\text{moles})(\text{absolute temperature})}$$

The product (absolute pressure)(volume) has the units of energy. If pressure is measured in pounds *force* per square foot and volume is given in cubic feet, the product has the units foot-pounds *force*. This may be divided by 778 to yield Btu. A list of the commonly used values of R with their units is given in Table 3-1.

TABLE 3-1. VALUES OF $R = pV/nT$

R	Units
1.987	Btu/(lb mole)(°R) or cal/(g mole)(°K)
0.730	(atm)(ft³)/(lb mole)(°R)
10.73	(psia)(ft³)/(lb mole)(°R)
1545	(lb$_f$/sq ft)(ft³)/(lb mole)(°R) or ft-lb$_f$/(lb mole)(°R)
1.314	(atm)(ft³)/(lb mole)(°K)
82.06	(atm)(cm³)/(g mole)(°K)

As an application of the ideal-gas law, consider the calculation of the volume in cubic feet occupied by 1 lb mole of such a gas at standard conditions, *i.e.*, 1 atm pressure and 32°F or 492°R. The units involved are atmospheres, cubic feet, pound moles, and degrees Rankine. The value of R in these units is 0.730 (atm)(ft³)/(lb mole)(°R). Thus,

$$v = \frac{RT}{p} = \frac{(0.730)(492)}{1} = 359 \text{ ft}^3/\text{lb mole}$$

The value of 359 ft³/lb mole for the molal volume of an ideal gas at standard conditions is a useful one to remember. It gives a base value to work from when the ideal-gas law is used in its alternative form:

$$\frac{p_1 V_1}{n_1 T_1} = \frac{p_2 V_2}{n_2 T_2}$$

With this preliminary treatment completed, the next sections will be devoted to the development of thermodynamic relationships for an ideal gas. In each case the first law will be applied to *reversible nonflow processes involving 1 mole of gas*.

3-2. The Constant-volume (Isometric) Process. The equations which apply to a constant-volume process for an ideal gas are exactly the same as the general expressions developed for this process in the preceding chapter. No further simplification is possible through the use of the ideal-gas law. Since volume is constant, $dv = 0$ and $dW = 0$. Hence

$$dE = dQ = C_v \, dT \qquad (2\text{-}15)$$

In integral form this equation becomes

$$\Delta E = Q = \int C_v \, dT \qquad (3\text{-}3)$$

If C_v is constant, integration gives

$$\Delta E = Q = C_v \, \Delta T \qquad (2\text{-}16)$$

The definition of an ideal gas leads to an important corollary, namely, *that its internal energy is a function of temperature only.* This conclusion

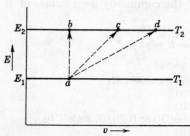

follows from the requirement that no forces exist between the molecules. Because the intermolecular forces are zero, no energy is required to move the molecules further apart. Since this is all that is accomplished when the volume is increased (and pressure decreased) at constant temperature, these changes do not alter the internal energy. Only temperature changes, which affect the kinetic

FIG. 3-4. Internal-energy changes for an ideal gas.

energy of the molecules, can influence the internal energy. As a result the changes in energy of an ideal gas are always given by $\int C_v \, dT$, regardless of the type of process. That this must be the case may be seen by studying Fig. 3-4, which shows a graph of internal energy plotted as a function of molal volume with temperature as parameter.

Since E is independent of v at constant temperature, a plot of E vs. v at constant temperature must give a straight horizontal line. For different temperatures, E has different values; so there will be a separate line for each temperature. Two such lines are shown in Fig. 3-4, one for the temperature T_1 and one for the temperature T_2. The dashed line connecting points a and b represents a constant-volume process involving a temperature increase from T_1 to T_2 and an internal-energy change $\Delta E = E_2 - E_1$. This change in internal energy is given by Eq. (3-3) as $\Delta E = \int C_v \, dT$. The dashed lines connecting points a and c and a and d represent other processes not occurring at constant volume but which also lead from an initial temperature T_1 to a final temperature T_2. It is clear from the graph that the change in E for these processes is the same as for the constant-volume process, and it is therefore given by the same equation, namely, $\Delta E = \int C_v \, dT$. However, ΔE is *not* equal to Q for these processes because Q depends not only on T_1 and T_2 but also on the path followed.

A corollary of this conclusion is that C_v for an ideal gas is also independent of pressure and volume and depends on temperature only. Since $dE = C_v \, dT$ is a general equation for an ideal gas, the only way that E

can be a function solely of temperature is for C_v likewise to be independent of pressure and volume. It should be noted that there is nothing implicit in the concept of an ideal gas to indicate that the heat capacity of such a gas should be independent of *temperature*. This is an additional simplifying assumption, often approximately valid at ordinary temperatures. The relationship between heat capacity and temperature will be discussed in Chap. 5.

3-3. The Constant-pressure (Isobaric) Process. The development of general equations for a reversible constant-pressure process in Chap. 2 leads to Eq. (2-20):

$$dH = dQ = C_p \, dT \qquad (2\text{-}20)$$

In integral form this becomes

$$\Delta H = Q = \int C_p \, dT \qquad (3\text{-}4)$$

or, if C_p is constant,

$$\Delta H = Q = C_p \, \Delta T \qquad (2\text{-}21)$$

Because the energy of an ideal gas depends on the temperature only, its enthalpy also is a function of temperature alone. This is evident from the definition $H = E + pv$, or $H = E + RT$ for an ideal gas. Therefore, just as $\Delta E = \int C_v \, dT$ for any process involving an ideal gas, $\Delta H = \int C_p \, dT$ not only for constant-pressure processes, but also for *all* finite processes.

These expressions for ΔE and ΔH and the definition of enthalpy indicate that a simple relationship exists between C_p and C_v. Thus for an ideal gas

$$dH = dE + R \, dT \qquad (3\text{-}5)$$

or

$$C_p \, dT = C_v \, dT + R \, dT$$

Hence,

$$\boxed{C_p = C_v + R} \qquad (3\text{-}6)$$

Since C_v is a function of temperature only, it follows that C_p also depends on the temperature only. This equation does *not* imply that C_p and C_v are themselves constant for an ideal gas, but only that they vary with temperature in such a way that their difference is equal to R.

3-4. The Constant-temperature (Isothermal) Process. The energy of an ideal gas cannot change for an isothermal process. Therefore,

$$dE = dQ - dW = 0$$

and

$$Q = W$$

Heat and work effects at constant temperature can be evaluated from $p\text{-}v\text{-}T$ information. The results for an ideal gas, where $pv = RT$, are easily obtained. Thus,

$$Q = W = \int p \, dv = \int RT \frac{dv}{v}$$

Integration at constant temperature from the initial volume v_1 to the final value v_2 gives

$$Q = W = RT \ln \frac{v_2}{v_1} \tag{3-7}$$

Since $p_1/p_2 = v_2/v_1$ for the isothermal process, Eq. (3-7) may also be written in terms of pressures:

$$Q = W = RT \ln \frac{p_1}{p_2} \tag{3-8}$$

3-5. The Adiabatic Process. An *adiabatic process* is one in which there is no heat transfer between the system and its surroundings; that is, $dQ = 0$. Therefore, application of the first law to reversible adiabatic processes gives

$$dE = -dW = -p \, dv \tag{3-9}$$

Since the change in energy for any process involving an ideal gas is given by Eq. (2-15),

$$C_v \, dT = -p \, dv \tag{3-10}$$

Substituting RT/v for p and rearranging,

$$\frac{dT}{T} = -\frac{R}{C_v} \frac{dv}{v} \tag{3-11}$$

If the ratio of the specific heats C_p/C_v is designated by γ, Eq. (3-6) may be written

$$\gamma = \frac{C_v + R}{C_v} = 1 + \frac{R}{C_v}$$

or

$$\frac{R}{C_v} = \gamma - 1 \tag{3-12}$$

Substituting $\gamma - 1$ for R/C_v in Eq. (3-11) gives

$$\frac{dT}{T} = -(\gamma - 1) \frac{dv}{v}$$

If γ is constant,[1] integration yields

$$\ln \frac{T_2}{T_1} = -(\gamma - 1) \ln \frac{v_2}{v_1}$$

---

[1] The assumption that γ is constant for an ideal gas is equivalent to the assumption that the heat capacities are themselves constant. This is the only way that the ratio $C_p/C_v = \gamma$ and the difference $C_p - C_v = R$ can *both* be constant.

or

$$\frac{T_2}{T_1} = \left(\frac{v_1}{v_2}\right)^{\gamma-1} \tag{3-13}$$

This equation relates temperature and volume for a reversible adiabatic process involving an ideal gas with constant heat capacities. The analogous relationships between temperature and pressure and between pressure and volume can be obtained from Eq. (3-13) and the ideal-gas law. Thus $p_1 v_1 / T_1 = p_2 v_2 / T_2$, or

$$\frac{v_1}{v_2} = \frac{p_2}{p_1}\frac{T_1}{T_2}$$

If this equation is used to eliminate v_1/v_2 from Eq. (3-13), the result is

$$\frac{T_2}{T_1} = \left(\frac{p_2}{p_1}\right)^{(\gamma-1)/\gamma} \tag{3-14}$$

A comparison of Eqs. (3-13) and (3-14) shows

$$\left(\frac{v_1}{v_2}\right)^{\gamma-1} = \left(\frac{p_2}{p_1}\right)^{(\gamma-1)/\gamma}$$

or

$$p_1 v_1^\gamma = p_2 v_2^\gamma = pv^\gamma = \text{const} \tag{3-15}$$

The work of an adiabatic process may be obtained from the relation

$$-dW = dE = C_v \, dT \tag{3-16}$$

If C_v is constant, integration gives

$$W = -\Delta E = -C_v \, \Delta T \tag{3-17}$$

Equation (3-17) may be converted to a form involving pressure and volume by utilizing Eq. (3-12). Thus

$$C_v = \frac{R}{\gamma - 1}$$

and

$$W = -C_v \, \Delta T = \frac{-R \, \Delta T}{\gamma - 1} = \frac{RT_1 - RT_2}{\gamma - 1}$$

Since $RT_1 = p_1 v_1$ and $RT_2 = p_2 v_2$, the work expression may be written

$$W = \frac{p_1 v_1 - p_2 v_2}{\gamma - 1} \tag{3-18}$$

Frequently in an adiabatic process, the initial state and final pressure, but not the final volume, are known. The volume v_2 can be eliminated from Eq. (3-18) by using Eq. (3-15). This leads to the expression

$$W = \frac{p_1 v_1}{\gamma - 1}\left[1 - \left(\frac{p_2}{p_1}\right)^{(\gamma-1)/\gamma}\right] = \frac{RT_1}{\gamma - 1}\left[1 - \left(\frac{p_2}{p_1}\right)^{(\gamma-1)/\gamma}\right] \tag{3-19}$$

The same result can be obtained by using Eq. (3-15) to integrate

$$W = \int p \, dv$$

Equations (3-18) and (3-19) are strictly correct only for the case of a reversible nonflow adiabatic process involving ideal gases with constant heat capacities. For the common monatomic and diatomic gases at low pressures and at temperatures not too far removed from room temperature, the assumption of constant heat capacities is often justified. Experimental values for γ are given in Table 3-2 for a few gases.

TABLE 3-2. VALUES OF $\gamma = C_p/C_v$†

Gas	γ at 15°C, 1 atm
O_2	1.401
N_2	1.401
H_2	1.410
CH_4	1.31
C_2H_6	1.22
CO_2	1.304
SO_2	1.29
NH_3	1.310
Air	1.403 (17°C)
Air	1.36 (925°C)

† From "International Critical Tables," Vol. V, McGraw-Hill Book Company, Inc., New York.

3-6. The Polytropic Process. This is the general case where no specific conditions other than reversibility are imposed. Thus only the *general* equations for ideal gases which have been developed for nonflow processes apply. These are

$$
\begin{aligned}
dE &= dQ - dW & \Delta E &= Q - W \text{ (first law)} \\
dW &= p \, dv & W &= \int p \, dv \\
dE &= C_v \, dT & \Delta E &= \int C_v \, dT \\
dH &= C_p \, dT & \Delta H &= \int C_p \, dT
\end{aligned}
$$

The heat terms cannot be determined directly; but must be obtained through the first law. Substitution for dE and dW gives

$$dQ = C_v \, dT + p \, dv \qquad (3\text{-}20)$$

and

$$Q = \int C_v \, dT + \int p \, dv \qquad (3\text{-}21)$$

Since the first law has been used for the calculation of Q, the work must be calculated directly from the integral $\int p \, dv$. This may be done graphically provided that data relating p and v are available. If data are not at hand, some relation between p and v must be assumed. The equation most commonly used is

$$pv^\delta = \text{const} \qquad (3\text{-}22)$$

where δ is a constant. If this empirical relationship is valid, Eq. (1-5) may be integrated to give W in exactly the same way as for the adiabatic process where $pv^\gamma =$ constant. The resulting equations are analogous to Eqs. (3-18) and (3-19), with γ replaced by δ. Moreover, equations analogous to Eqs. (3-13) and (3-14) may be derived from Eq. (3-22) by use of the ideal-gas law. In fact, if $\delta = \gamma$, then the process is adiabatic. If $\delta = 1$, $pv^\delta = pv =$ constant $= RT$. In this event, the equations for a polytropic process reduce to those for the isothermal case. Most processes lie between the isothermal and the adiabatic, and values of δ then lie between 1 and γ.

Equation (3-22) is sometimes useful for representing the pressure-volume relationship existing in gas compressors. However, the equation for work required in steady-flow compression is not the same as the equation for nonflow processes. Compressor design is considered in Chap. 8.

It should be emphasized that the equations developed in this chapter have been *derived* for reversible nonflow processes involving ideal gases. However, those equations which relate state functions only are valid for ideal gases regardless of the process and apply equally to reversible and irreversible flow and nonflow processes, because changes in state functions depend only on the initial and final states of the system. On the other hand, an equation for Q or W is specific for the case considered in its derivation.

The work of an *irreversible* process is often approximated by calculating W first as though the process were reversible. This ideal quantity is then multiplied or divided by an efficiency to get the actual work. If the process produces work, the reversible value is too large and must be multiplied by an efficiency. If the process requires work, the reverse is true.

The application of the concepts and equations developed in Secs. 3-1 to 3-6 is illustrated in the examples that follow. In particular, the work of irreversible processes is considered in Example 3-2.

Example 3-1. Air is to be compressed *reversibly* from an initial condition of 1 atm and 60°F to a final state of 5 atm and 60°F by three different processes:

　　(a) Heating at constant volume followed by cooling at constant pressure
　　(b) Isothermal compression
　　(c) Adiabatic compression followed by cooling at constant volume

At these conditions, air may be considered an ideal gas having the constant heat capacities $C_v = 5$ and $C_p = 7$ Btu/(lb mole)(°F).

Calculate the work required, the heat transferred, and the changes in internal energy and enthalpy of the air for each process. Sketch the paths followed in each process on a single p-v diagram.

Solution. In each case the system will be taken as 1 lb mole of air, contained in an imaginary frictionless piston-and-cylinder arrangement. For an ideal gas, $C_p - C_v = R$. For the sake of consistency with the approximate values given for C_p amd C_v, R will be taken as 2 rather than the more exact value of 1.987 Btu/(lb mole)(°R). The initial and final conditions of the air are identical with those of Example 2-10. It was shown there that

$$v_1 = 379 \text{ ft}^3 \quad \text{and} \quad v_2 = 75.8 \text{ ft}^3$$

(a) This part of the problem is identical with part (b) of Example 2-10. However, it may now be solved in a simpler manner. The temperature at the end of the constant-volume heating step was calculated in Example 2-10 to be 2600°R. It was also shown for this step that $W = 0$ and

$$Q = \Delta E = C_v \, \Delta T = 10,400 \text{ Btu}$$

Moreover

$$\Delta H = C_p \, \Delta T = (7)(2600 - 520) = 14,560 \text{ Btu}$$

For the second step

$$Q = \Delta H = C_p \, \Delta T = (7)(520 - 2600) = -14,560 \text{ Btu}$$
$$\Delta E = C_v \, \Delta T = (5)(520 - 2600) = -10,400 \text{ Btu}$$

and

$$W = Q - \Delta E = -14,560 - (-10,400) = -4160 \text{ Btu}$$

For the entire process

$$\Delta E = 10,400 - 10,400 = 0 \text{ Btu}$$
$$\Delta H = 14,560 - 14,560 = 0 \text{ Btu}$$
$$Q = 10,400 - 14,560 = -4160 \text{ Btu}$$
$$W = 0 - 4160 = -4160 \text{ Btu}$$

(b) For an isothermal reversible compression of an ideal gas

$$\Delta E = \Delta H = 0 \text{ Btu}$$

and

$$Q = W = RT \ln \frac{p_1}{p_2} = (2)(520) \ln \frac{1}{5} = -1676 \text{ Btu}$$

(c) The initial adiabatic compression of the air takes it to its final volume of 75.8 ft³. The temperature and pressure at this point are given by Eqs. (3-13) and (3-15):

$$T = T_1 \left(\frac{v_1}{v_2}\right)^{\gamma-1} = (520)\left(\frac{379}{75.8}\right)^{0.4} = 991°\text{R}$$

and

$$p = p_1 \left(\frac{v_1}{v_2}\right)^{\gamma} = (1)\left(\frac{379}{75.8}\right)^{1.4} = 9.5 \text{ atm}$$

For this step $Q = 0$. Hence

$$\Delta E = -W = C_v \, \Delta T = (5)(991 - 520) = 2355 \text{ Btu}$$
$$\Delta H = C_p \, \Delta T = (7)(991 - 520) = 3297 \text{ Btu}$$

For the second step $\Delta v = 0$, $W = 0$. Therefore

$$Q = \Delta E = C_v \, \Delta T = (5)(520 - 991) = -2355 \text{ Btu}$$
$$\Delta H = C_p \, \Delta T = (7)(520 - 991) = -3297 \text{ Btu}$$

For the entire process,

$$\Delta E = 2355 - 2355 = 0 \text{ Btu}$$
$$\Delta H = 3297 - 3297 = 0 \text{ Btu}$$
$$Q = 0 - 2355 = -2355 \text{ Btu}$$
$$W = -2355 + 0 = -2355 \text{ Btu}$$

The accompanying figure shows these processes sketched on a p-v diagram.

A comparison of the answers of the three parts of this problem shows that the property changes ΔE and ΔH are the same regardless of the path for which they were calculated. On the other hand, Q and W depend on the path.

It should be noted that the work for each of these reversible processes could be calculated by

$$W = \int p \, dv$$

In each case the value of this integral is represented by the area below the curve on

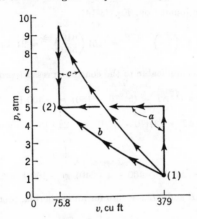

the p-v diagram denoting the path of the process. The relative sizes of these areas correspond to the numerical values of W.

Example 3-2. An ideal gas ($C_v = 3$, $C_p = 5$) undergoes the following reversible processes:

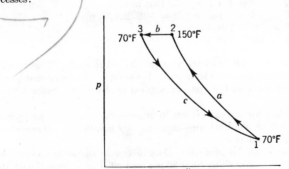

(a) From an initial state of 70°F and 15 psia, it is compressed adiabatically to 150°F.

(b) The gas is cooled from 150 to 70°F at constant pressure.

(c) The gas is expanded isothermally to its original state.

Calculate W, Q, ΔE, and ΔH for each of the three processes and for the entire cycle.

Repeat these calculations for the same *changes in state* accomplished *irreversibly*, provided that the efficiency of each process is 80 per cent compared with the reversible operation.

Solution. The cycle is represented on a p-v diagram in the accompanying figure. Consider first the reversible operation of the cycle.

(*a*) For an ideal gas undergoing adiabatic compression, both the energy change and the work are given by the expression

$$\Delta E = -W = C_v \, \Delta T = (3)(150 - 70) = 240 \text{ Btu/lb mole}$$
$$\Delta H = C_p \, \Delta T = (5)(150 - 70) = 400 \text{ Btu/lb mole}$$
$$Q = 0$$

The pressure p_2 can be found from Eq. (3-14),

$$p_2 = p_1 \left(\frac{T_2}{T_1}\right)^{\gamma/(\gamma-1)} = (15) \left(\frac{610}{530}\right)^{2.5} = 21.3 \text{ psia}$$

(*b*) Equation (2-21) is applicable to the constant-pressure process

$$\Delta H = Q = C_p \, \Delta T = (5)(70 - 150) = -400 \text{ Btu/lb mole}$$

Also

$$\Delta E = C_v \, \Delta T = (3)(70 - 150) = -240 \text{ Btu/lb mole}$$

By the first law

$$W = Q - \Delta E = -400 - (-240) = -160 \text{ Btu/lb mole}$$

(*c*) For ideal gases ΔE and ΔH are zero for an isothermal process. Since $p_3 = p_2$, Eq. (3-8) gives

$$Q = W = RT \ln \frac{p_3}{p_1} = (2)(530) \ln \frac{21.3}{15} = 372 \text{ Btu/lb mole}$$

For the entire process,

$$Q = -400 + 372 = -28 \text{ Btu/lb mole}$$
$$W = -240 - 160 + 372 = -28 \text{ Btu/lb mole}$$
$$\Delta E = 240 - 240 + 0 = 0$$
$$\Delta H = 400 - 400 + 0 = 0$$

It is significant that ΔE and ΔH both are zero for the entire cycle. This must be true since the initial and final states are identical. It should also be noted that $Q = W$ for the cycle. This follows from the first law applied to the cycle. Since $\Delta E = 0$, $Q = W$.

If the same changes in state are carried out by irreversible processes, the property changes for the steps will be identical with those already calculated. However, the values of Q and W will be different.

(*a*) This step can no longer be adiabatic. For reversible adiabatic compression, W was -240 Btu/lb mole. If the process is 80 per cent efficient compared with this,

$$W = \frac{-240}{0.80} = -300 \text{ Btu/lb mole}$$

Since ΔE is still 240 Btu/lb mole, by the first law

$$Q = \Delta E + W = 240 - 300 = -60 \text{ Btu/lb mole}$$

(*b*) The reversible work for this cooling process was -160 Btu/lb mole. For the irreversible process

$$W = \frac{-160}{0.80} = -200 \text{ Btu/lb mole}$$

and

$$Q = \Delta E + W = -240 - 200 = -440 \text{ Btu/lb mole}$$

(c) As work is done *by* the system in this process, the irreversible work is less than the reversible work:

$$W = (0.80)(372) = 298 \text{ Btu/lb mole}$$

and

$$Q = \Delta E + W = 0 + 298 = 298 \text{ Btu/lb mole}$$

For the entire cycle, ΔE and ΔH are again zero, but

$$Q = -60 - 440 + 298 = -202 \text{ Btu/lb mole}$$
$$W = -300 - 200 + 298 = -202 \text{ Btu/lb mole}$$

A summary of these results is given in the accompanying table. All values are in Btu per pound mole of gas.

	Reversible				Irreversible			
	ΔE	ΔH	Q	W	ΔE	ΔH	Q	W
Step a	240	400	0	-240	240	400	-60	-300
Step b	-240	-400	-400	-160	-240	-400	-440	-200
Step c	0	0	372	372	0	0	298	298
Cycle	0	0	-28	-28	0	0	-202	-202

The cycle is one which requires work and produces an equal amount of heat. The most striking feature of the comparison shown in the table is that the work required for the irreversible process is more than seven times that of the reversible process—even though each step of the irreversible process was assumed to be 80 per cent efficient.

Example 3-3. One pound *mass* of nitrogen at 70°F and 19.7 psia is contained in a cylinder by a frictionless piston weighing 5 lb_f per square inch of surface. The apparatus is initially in equilibrium with the surrounding atmosphere at 14.7 psia and 70°F.

(a) The apparatus is immersed in an ice-water bath and allowed to come to equilibrium.

(b) A variable force is slowly applied to the piston so that the nitrogen is compressed reversibly at the constant temperature of 32°F until the gas volume reaches one-half that at the end of step a. At this point the piston is held in place by latches.

(c) The apparatus is removed from the ice bath and comes to thermal equilibrium with the surrounding atmosphere at 70°F.

(d) The latches are removed, and the apparatus is permitted to reach complete equilibrium with the surrounding atmosphere.

Sketch the entire cycle on a p-v diagram, and calculate Q, W, ΔE, and ΔH for the system, *i.e.*, the nitrogen, for each step of the cycle.

Under these conditions nitrogen may be considered an ideal gas with the **constant** heat capacities $C_v = 5$ and $C_p = 7$ Btu/(lb mole)(°R).

Solution. At the end of the cycle the nitrogen will clearly have returned to its original state of 70°F and 19.7 psia. The steps making up this cycle are

$$\text{Step } a: 70°F, 19.7 \text{ psia} \xrightarrow{\text{const } p} 32°F, 19.7 \text{ psia}$$

$$\text{Step } b: 32°F, v_2 \xrightarrow{\text{const } T} 32°F, v_3 = \tfrac{1}{2}v_2$$

$$\text{Step } c: 32°F, v_3 \xrightarrow{\text{const } v} 70°F, v_4 = v_3$$

$$\text{Step } d: 70°F, v_4 \xrightarrow{T_4 = T_1} 70°F, 19.7 \text{ psia}$$

STEP *a.* In this step the nitrogen is cooled at constant pressure. The process is mechanically reversible even though the heat transfer occurs irreversibly under the influence of a finite temperature difference. Thus

$$W_a = \int p\, dv = p\, \Delta v = \frac{R\, \Delta T}{M}$$

If R is taken as 2 Btu/(lb mole)(°R) and the molecular weight M as 28,

$$W_a = \frac{(2)(32 - 70)}{28} = -2.71 \text{ Btu}$$

$$Q_a = \Delta H_a = c_p\, \Delta T = (\tfrac{7}{28})(32 - 70) = -9.50 \text{ Btu}$$

From the first law,

$$\Delta E_a = Q_a - W_a = -9.5 - (-2.71) = -6.79 \text{ Btu}$$

The energy change may also be evaluated from the equation

$$\Delta E_a = c_v\, \Delta T = (\tfrac{5}{28})(32 - 70) = -6.79 \text{ Btu}$$

STEP *b.* The process carried out here is a reversible isothermal compression. Hence

$$\Delta E_b = \Delta H_b = 0$$

and

$$Q_b = W_b = \frac{RT}{M} \ln \frac{v_3}{v_2} = \frac{(2)(492)}{28} \ln \frac{1}{2} = -24.4 \text{ Btu}$$

STEP *c.* For this constant-volume or isometric process, $W_c = 0$, and

$$Q_c = \Delta E_c = c_v\, \Delta T = (\tfrac{5}{28})(70 - 32) = 6.79 \text{ Btu}$$
$$\Delta H_c = c_p\, \Delta T = (\tfrac{7}{28})(70 - 32) = 9.50 \text{ Btu}$$

STEP *d.* The first three steps of the cycle can be sketched on a p-v diagram without difficulty because their paths are known. In the final step this is not possible without more information, because the process is clearly irreversible. When the latches holding the frictionless piston in place are removed, the piston will move rapidly upward, and owing to its inertia it will be carried beyond its equilibrium position. This initial expansion is nearly reversible and adiabatic because relatively little turbulence results from a single stroke of the piston and because heat transfer is relatively slow across gas films. It is the subsequent oscillations of the piston as it gradually reaches its final equilibrium position that cause the process to be highly irreversible. This process goes on for a considerable time during which heat transfer occurs in an amount sufficient to return the gas to its initial temperature of 70°F at a pressure of 14.7 psia. Sufficient data are not available to allow the exact path of the process to be specified. However, the dashed line in the sketch indicates in a qualitative way what form it would take.

The work done during this process cannot be obtained from the integral $\int p\,dv$ because the process is irreversible. Indeed, it is not possible to calculate W from the given information. During the initial expansion of the gas, the work is approximately that of a reversible adiabatic process. This work represents the transfer of energy from the gas to the surroundings, where it results in the pushing back of the atmosphere and in an increase in the potential and kinetic energies of the piston. If the piston were held at its position of maximum travel, the major part of the irrevers-

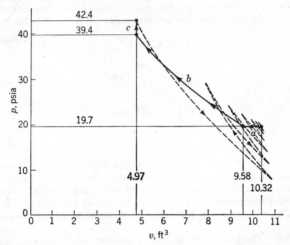

ibility of the process would be avoided, and the work could be calculated to a good approximation by the equations for a reversible adiabatic process. However, as the process actually occurs, some of the energy initially imparted to the piston is subsequently transferred to the gas, and some of it is transferred to the atmosphere, because the oscillating piston causes turbulence or stirring in both places. There is no way to determine how much of this energy is transferred to the gas and how much is transferred to the atmosphere.

The over-all result of step d is to elevate the piston and to push back the atmosphere (the work for which can be calculated) and in addition to increase the internal energy of the surroundings by the work done in stirring it.

Unlike work and heat, the property changes of the system can be computed since they depend only on the initial and final states, and these are known. The internal energy and enthalpy of an ideal gas depend only on temperature. Therefore, ΔE_d and ΔH_d are zero because the initial and final temperatures are both 70°F. The first law may be applied to this process since it is valid for irreversible as well as for reversible processes:

$$\Delta E_d = Q_d - W_d = 0$$

or

$$Q_d = W_d$$

Although neither Q_d nor W_d can be calculated, it is clear that they are equal.

For the entire cycle, the changes in internal energy and enthalpy are also zero because the system has returned to its initial state. Q and W for the entire cycle must be equal, but their values cannot be determined because Q_d and W_d are unknown.

Example 3-4. Air is flowing at a steady rate through a horizontal insulated pipe which contains a partially closed valve. The conditions of the air upstream from the valve are 70°F and 100 psia, and the downstream pressure is 50 psia. The line leaving the valve is enough larger than the entrance line so that the kinetic-energy change of the air in flowing through the valve is negligible. If air is regarded as an ideal gas, what will be the temperature of the air downstream from the valve?

Solution. Flow through a partially closed valve is known as a *throttling process.* Since flow is at a steady rate, Eq. (2-10) applies. Q should be very small, because the line is insulated. Furthermore, the potential-energy and kinetic-energy changes are negligible. No shaft work is accomplished; so $W_s = 0$. Hence, Eq. (2-10) reduces to

$$\Delta H = 0$$

For an ideal gas

$$\Delta H = \int_{T_1}^{T_2} C_p \, dT$$

Thus

$$\int_{T_1}^{T_2} C_p \, dT = 0$$

and

$$T_2 = T_1$$

The result that $\Delta H = 0$ is general for a throttling process because the assumptions of negligible heat transfer and potential-energy and kinetic-energy change are usually valid. If the fluid is an ideal gas, no temperature change occurs. Note that, even though the throttling process is irreversible, the relation $\Delta H = \int C_p \, dT$ is valid for an ideal gas. This is because only properties are involved, and these are independent of path.

Example 3-5. The pressure in an oxygen cylinder, which has been standing for a long time in a room at 70°F, is 1500 psia. A valve on the discharge line from the cylinder is opened wide, until the cylinder pressure is reduced to 1000 psia, and then closed. Estimate the temperature of the oxygen remaining in the cylinder at the instant the valve is closed.

Solution. The initial expansion of gas in the cylinder when the valve is opened will result in a decrease in temperature. Heat will be transferred from the surroundings to the gas at a rate proportional to the temperature drop of the gas. Therefore, the process will not be truly adiabatic. However, if the time the valve is open is short, the quantity of heat transferred will be small. This is especially true in this particular example because of the low coefficients of heat transfer across gas films. As an approximation the temperature will be given by Eq. (3-14), since oxygen will follow ideal-gas behavior quite closely even at these relatively high pressures:

$$T_2 = T_1 \left(\frac{p_2}{p_1}\right)^{(\gamma-1)/\gamma} = (70 + 460) \left(\frac{1000}{1500}\right)^{0.4/1.4}$$

$$= (530)(0.89) = 472°R, \text{ or } 12°F$$

It will be noted that the gas remaining in the cylinder has been assumed to expand reversibly and adiabatically even though the flow through the valve is decidedly irreversible. This may be visualized by imagining a thin diaphragm in the cylinder, placed to separate the gas that remains in the cylinder from that which ultimately is removed. The gas below the diaphragm is not affected by the nature of the flow of gas out through the valve but behaves as though the diaphragm were a piston moving upward within the cylinder. If no heat is transferred from the surroundings, the gas below the diaphragm expands adiabatically and reversibly since there are negligible pressure and temperature differentials across the diaphragm.

To gain an idea of the extent of deviation from adiabatic operation, suppose the over-all rate of heat transfer is 1.0 Btu/(hr)(sq ft)(°F), the surface area of the cylinder is 10 sq ft, and the average temperature difference between surroundings and gas is 20°F. The rate of heat transfer per minute is $(1)(10)(20)/60 = 3.3$ Btu/min. If the cylinder contains 8 lb_m of oxygen, this corresponds to an increase in temperature of the gas of about 2°F/min. Therefore (according to this very approximate calculation) if the decrease from 1500 to 1000 psia occurs within 1 min, the adiabatic-temperature calculation should be not more than 2°F below the actual temperature.

PROBLEMS

1. One pound mole of an ideal gas ($C_p = 7$, $C_v = 5$) undergoes reversible changes from $p_1 = 10$ atm abs and $v_1 = 60$ ft³ to $p_2 = 1$ atm abs according to the following paths:

    (a) Constant volume
    (b) Constant temperature
    (c) Adiabatically
    (d) Polytropically, $\delta = 1.2$

Calculate W, Q, ΔE, and ΔH for the gas for each process. Show each path on a single p-v diagram.

2. An ideal gas ($C_p = 5$, $C_v = 3$) is changed from $p_1 = 1$ atm abs and $v_1 = 359$ ft³ to $p_2 = 10$ atm abs and $v_2 = 35.9$ ft³ by the following reversible processes:

    (a) Isothermal compression
    (b) Adiabatic compression followed by cooling at constant pressure
    (c) Adiabatic compression followed by cooling at constant volume
    (d) Heating at constant volume followed by cooling at constant pressure
    (e) Cooling at constant pressure followed by heating at constant volume

Calculate the work required, the heat transferred, and the changes in internal energy and enthalpy for each of these over-all processes. Sketch the paths followed in each process on a single p-v diagram.

3. A rigid nonconducting tank with a volume of 120 ft³ is divided in two equal parts by a thin membrane. On one side of the membrane the tank contains H_2 gas at 50 psia and 100°F, and on the other side is a perfect vacuum. The membrane is suddenly ruptured, and the gas fills the tank. Calculate the final temperature of the gas. How much work is done? Is the process reversible? Hydrogen may be considered an ideal gas, with constant heat capacities $C_p = 7$, $C_v = 5$.

4. With reference to the preceding problem, describe a reversible process by which the gas in its final state could be returned to the initial condition. How much work is required and how much heat is added or removed during this return to the initial state?

5. A rigid nonconducting tank with a volume of 120 ft³ is divided into two equal parts by a thin membrane. Hydrogen gas is contained on both sides of the membrane. On one side its temperature and pressure are 300°F and 5 psia and on the other side, 100°F and 20 psia. The membrane is suddenly ruptured, and complete mixing results. What are the final temperature and pressure? Considering the system as all the gas in the tank on both sides of the membrane, calculate the work done by the system. Hydrogen may be assumed to behave as an ideal gas, with $C_p = 7$, $C_v = 5$.

                                    Ans. $T = 131$°F, $p = 12.5$ psia.

6. One pound of nitrogen, originally at 70°F and 20 psia in a horizontal piston-cylinder assembly, is compressed to one-half its original volume. The compression step is carried out by applying a constant pressure of 100 psia to the piston, latches being used to hold the piston in its final position.   Assume nitrogen to be an ideal gas. The apparatus is well insulated.

(a) Neglecting the heat capacity of the piston and cylinder, calculate the final temperature of the nitrogen.   Take $C_p = 7$ and $C_v = 5$.

(b) If the piston and cylinder have a mass of 20 lb_m and a specific heat of 0.32 Btu/ $(lb_m)(°F)$, what is the final temperature?

7. An ideal gas $(C_p = 7, C_v = 5)$ undergoes the following reversible changes in a series of nonflow processes:

(a) From an initial state of 70°F and 15 psia, it is compressed adiabatically to 75 psia.

(b) It is then cooled to 70°F at a constant pressure of 75 psia.

(c) Finally, the gas is expanded isothermally to its original state.

Calculate Q, W, ΔE, and ΔH for each of the three processes and for the entire cycle.

Repeat these calculations for exactly the same changes in state accomplished irreversibly, the efficiency of each process being 75 per cent compared with reversible operation.

8. Under certain conditions, the differential equation for the molal volume of a gas is given by the following expression:

$$dV = R\frac{dT}{p} - \frac{RT}{p^2}\,dp$$

(a) From this equation show that volume is a state function.

(b) Having proved that volume does not depend upon the path, determine $V(p,T)$, that is, the integrated equation relating the volume to the temperature and pressure.

9. A well-insulated (no heat loss to the surroundings) vertical cylinder of negligible heat capacity, fitted with a piston weighing 1000 lb_f and having an area of 100 sq in., contains an ideal gas at 200°F and a pressure of 50 psia.   The piston is held in position by a latch, and its upper surface is exposed to the atmosphere.   The latch is released and the piston moves in the cylinder, eventually coming to rest (because of friction) at a point where the gas pressure is 26 psia.   If the gas has a constant-volume molal heat capacity of 5.0 Btu/(lb mole)(°F), what will be its final temperature?

10. A lagged tank of 100 ft³ capacity fitted with a valve contains air at 70°F and 10 atm pressure.   The valve is opened and the pressure allowed to drop quickly to 50 psia.   Estimate the final temperature of the air left in the tank.

11. The following questions refer to an ideal gas in nonflow processes $(C_p = 7$ and $C_v = 5)$.   The initial state in all cases is 1 atm and 70°F.

(a) One pound mole of gas is heated at constant volume to 170°F.   Calculate ΔE, ΔH, Q, and W.

(b) One pound mole of gas is heated at constant pressure to 170°F.   Calculate ΔE, ΔH, Q, and W if the process is reversible.   Which answers would be different if the process were irreversible?

(c) One pound mole of gas is changed from its initial state to a final state of 10 atm and 170°F by several different reversible processes.   Will the following quantities be the same for all these processes: ΔE, ΔH, Q, and W?   If the different processes were irreversible, would any of the answers be changed?   If so, which?

12. Methane gas is stored in a tank at a pressure of 200 psia and 70°F.   The tank has a capacity of 2 ft³.   Gas is allowed to flow from the tank through a partially opened valve to a gas holder where the pressure is constant at 2 psig.   When the pressure in the tank has dropped to 100 psia, calculate the mass of methane removed under the following conditions:

(a) If the process took place slowly enough so that the temperature was constant.

Ans. 0.563 lb_m.

(b) If the process occurred rapidly enough so that heat transfer was negligible.

Ans. 0.464 lb_m.

Assume CH_4 to be an ideal gas for which $\gamma = 1.31$.

13. Air, initially at 240°F and 8 atm, undergoes the following change: It is expanded reversibly and isothermally to a pressure such that when it is cooled at constant volume to 40°F its final pressure is 2 atm.

Assuming air to be an ideal gas ($C_p = 7$, $C_v = 5$), calculate the work, heat transferred, and changes in internal energy and enthalpy of the air during this process.

Ans. $Q = 470$, $W = 1470$, $\Delta E = -1000$, $\Delta H = -1400$ Btu/lb mole.

14. An ideal gas is flowing in steady state through a horizontal tube which has nonconducting walls. No heat is added, nor is any shaft work done. The cross-sectional area of the tube changes with length, and this causes the velocity to change. Derive an expression relating the temperature and velocity of the gas.

If nitrogen at 270°F flows past one section of the tube at a velocity of 50 ft/sec, what will be its temperature at another section where the velocity is 1200 ft/sec? $C_p = 7$ Btu/(lb mole)(°F).

Ans. 155°F.

15. One pound mole of an ideal gas, initially at 80°F and 1 atm pressure, is changed to 220°F and 12 atm pressure by three different processes:

(a) The gas is first heated at constant volume until the temperature is 220°F; then it is compressed isothermally until its pressure is 12 atm.

(b) The gas is first heated at constant pressure until its temperature is 220°F; then it is compressed isothermally to 12 atm pressure.

(c) The gas is first compressed isothermally to 12 atm pressure and is then heated at constant pressure to 220°F.

Calculate Q, W, ΔE, and ΔH in each case. Take $C_p = 7$, $C_v = 5$. Repeat, using $C_p = 5$, $C_v = 3$.

16. One pound mole of an ideal gas, initially at 70°F and 1 atm pressure, undergoes the following changes: It is first compressed isothermally to a point such that when it is heated at constant volume to 200°F its final pressure will be 10 atm abs. $\gamma = 1.40$ and $C_v = 5$. Calculate Q, W, ΔE, and ΔH for the process.

17. Derive an expression for the slope of an adiabatic line on a p-v diagram in terms of constants and the volume. The case considered is for an ideal gas in an adiabatic nonflow process. The heat capacities are constant.

What conclusions can be drawn from this equation about the shape of an adiabatic line on the p-v diagram?

18. Air at 70°F and 10 atm pressure is enclosed by a frictionless piston in a steel cylinder 4 in. in diameter. The face of the piston is 12 in. from the closed end of the cylinder. The cylinder is in the atmosphere, and a weight is placed on the piston.

(a) The gas is heated and allowed to expand at constant pressure; *i.e.*, the force of gravity on the piston and weight is equivalent to 9 atm pressure. The final volume is twice the initial volume. Considering the gas as the system, what is the work done by the system?

(b) In this case the force of gravity on the piston and weight is equivalent to 1 atm. No heat is applied. The piston is held in place with latches; the latches are suddenly removed, and the piston is stopped when the volume has reached twice the original value. Choose a system, and discuss the work done by that system.

19. One pound of steam is subjected to the following reversible processes: steam at 400 psia and 800°F (state 1) is expanded isothermally to 80 psia (state 2), cooled at constant volume to 50 psia and 341.0°F (state 3), cooled at constant pressure to a volume of 8.646 ft³ and a temperature of 290°F (state 4), compressed adiabatically to 400 psia and 767°F (state 5), and finally heated at constant pressure to state 1.

Sketch the path of the cycle on a p-v diagram.

Compute Q, W, ΔE, and ΔH for each step and also for the entire process. The following data for steam are available:

H, Btu/lb$_m$	p, psia	v, ft^3/lb$_m$	T, °F
1415.5	400	1.8179	800
1428.2	80	9.313	800
1205.7	50	9.313	341.0
1179.5	50	8.646	290
1397.9	400	1.7632	767

20. One pound mole of air is subjected to the following series of processes:

(a) An expansion from an initial temperature of 140 to 240°F.

(b) A constant-pressure cooling process from 240 to 100°F.

(c) A constant-volume heating process from 100 to 300°F.

(d) A constant-pressure cooling process from 300 to 140°F. The state of the air at the end of this process is the same as that at the beginning of step a.

The total heat absorbed by the air during the cycle is 750 Btu. Calculate Q, W, ΔE, and ΔH for each of the processes and for the cycle as a whole. Assume that air behaves as an ideal gas. The molal heat capacity at constant pressure may be assumed constant and equal to 7.0 Btu/(lb mole)(°F).

21. Show that on a p-v diagram the negative slope of an adiabatic line through a given point is always greater than the negative slope of an isothermal line through the same point. Show also that the slope of a polytropic line for which $pv^\delta = $ constant is intermediate between the isothermal and the adiabatic provided that $1 < \delta < \gamma$.

22. Carbon dioxide gas is being compressed from an initial pressure of 15 psia in a steady-flow process to a final pressure of 520 psia. The shaft work supplied to the compressor is 5360 Btu per pound mole of CO_2 compressed. The initial temperature of the CO_2 is 50°F, and it is required that the final temperature after compression be 200°F. The CO_2 flows to the compressor through a pipe, having an inside diameter of 6 in., with a velocity of 10 ft/sec. At the initial conditions, $H_1 = 307$ Btu/lb$_m$ and $v_1 = 9.25$ ft^3/lb$_m$. At the desired final state, $H_2 = 330$ Btu/lb$_m$ and $v_2 = 0.280$ ft^3/lb$_m$. In order to obtain these final conditions, will heat have to be added to the CO_2 or transferred from it? Calculate the rate of heat transfer in Btu per hour. The kinetic-energy and potential-energy changes of the CO_2 in this process may be neglected.   *Ans.* $Q = -75,640$ Btu/hr.

23. Show that integration of the equation $W = \int p\, dv$ for a reversible adiabatic process involving 1 mole of an ideal gas with constant heat capacities leads to Eq. (3-19).

CHAPTER 4

PRESSURE-VOLUME-TEMPERATURE RELATIONS
OF FLUIDS

The properties of matter most useful in the study of thermodynamics can be divided into two classes:

I. The directly measurable properties: pressure, specific volume, temperature, composition, and heat capacity.

II. The so-called "thermodynamic" properties, such as internal energy and enthalpy, which in general are not capable of direct measurement.

One of the chief justifications for the existence of this second group is that they can be simply related to the heat and work effects which accompany actual processes in nature and industry. Since they are properties of matter, they are not influenced by the process itself and, indeed, may be evaluated once and for all as a function of the measurable properties (group I) of the material. For example, the enthalpy of a gas (above an arbitrary datum plane) may be tabulated as a function of its temperature and pressure. The development of the relationships between these two groups of properties is an important part of thermodynamics. It has already been accomplished in Chap. 3 for the special case of an ideal gas; the general treatment will be given in Chap. 7. However, before that can be done it is necessary to inquire into the interrelationships among the variables of the first group, pressure, specific volume, temperature, and composition when the ideal-gas law does not apply. This is the objective of the present chapter.

Besides providing the background for calculating thermodynamic properties, the p-v-T relations of fluids, especially gases, are of importance in themselves in many industrial problems. These include the large-scale metering of fluids (such as manufactured and natural gas), calculation of the size of vessels and tanks used in the chemical and petroleum industries, compression of gases, and flow of fluids in pipes.

Homogeneous substances may be divided into three classes, gases, liquids, and solids, according to their degree of compressibility. The volume of a gas can be changed enormously by the application of pressure, while the degree of compressibility of a liquid or solid is usually

85

small.   For this reason the p-v-T relations of liquids and solids are not so important as those of gases and will not be considered at length.

4-1. The p-v-T Behavior of Pure Substances.   If two properties of a single-phase system of a pure substance are specified, its state is completely determined.   It follows that the specific volume of any pure gas or liquid phase must be uniquely related to its temperature and pressure. It would be possible, of course, to measure the pressure, temperature, and specific volumes of common substances in a large number of states and to tabulate or plot the results.   Although a number of such measurements have been made,[1] they are difficult and time-consuming, and complete data are available for few substances.   Therefore, relations connecting these variables are especially important to engineers for the prediction of the volumetric behavior of a wide variety of materials.

The simplest relationship, the ideal-gas law, has already been discussed. For many engineering applications involving gases at pressures of no more than a few atmospheres, this equation is sufficiently accurate.   However, as a gas approaches the region of liquefaction, either by increase in pressure or by decrease in temperature, the ideal-gas law does not suffice. More accurate equations will be considered in the next section.   First it is worthwhile to examine in a general way the observed volumetric behavior of pure fluids.

The clearest presentation is probably a plot of pressure vs. molal volume, with temperature as parameter.   The graph shown in Fig. 4-1 is typical.   The line labeled T_1 represents an isotherm (constant-temperature line) at high temperature where the relationship between molal volume and pressure is closely represented by a rectangular hyperbola, pv = constant.   Along this curve, the gas is far removed from the condensation boundary ACB, and the ideal-gas law approximates actual behavior.   As the temperature is decreased, the isotherms become distorted near the region of condensation.   This is illustrated by the curves for temperatures T_2, T_c, T_3, and T_4.   Here the ideal-gas law, indicated by dashed lines, would not be even approximately correct for the isotherms near the two-phase boundary ACB.

The lines labeled T_3 and T_4, which represent isotherms for lower temperatures, consist of three distinct sections corresponding to the gas region, the two-phase region, and the liquid region.   The area under the dome ACB is the two-phase region, while the areas to the right and left are the gas and liquid regions.

The isotherms for the liquid phase are nearly vertical because liquid volumes change little with large changes in pressure.   In the two-phase region, the isotherms are horizontal because the phase change from liquid

[1] See, for example, the bibliography given by E. W. Comings, "High Pressure Technology," p. 490, McGraw-Hill Book Company, Inc., New York, 1956.

to vapor occurs at constant temperature and pressure for a pure substance. This flat portion becomes shorter as the temperature is raised, and the isotherm labeled T_c has only a differential horizontal length at the top of the dome. This horizontal inflection point at C is known as the *critical point* and may be defined, for a pure material, as the point of highest temperature and pressure at which liquid and vapor phases

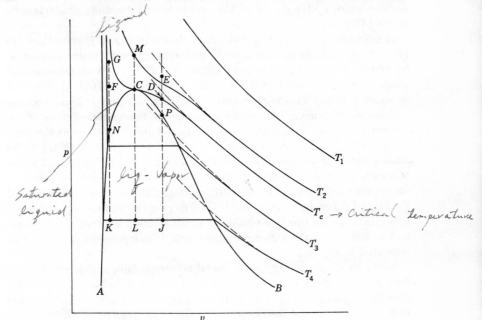

Fig. 4.1. *p-v* diagram for a pure substance.

can exist in equilibrium. A more general definition, also applicable to mixtures, is that the critical point represents the condition at which the specific properties of the gas and liquid phases in equilibrium become identical. Here the phases cannot be distinguished from one another, because their properties, *i.e.*, densities, indices of refraction, etc., are the same. A pure gas at temperatures above its critical temperature cannot be liquefied, regardless of the degree of compression.

The horizontal inflection at the critical point C must meet the following mathematical requirements:

$$\left(\frac{\partial p}{\partial v}\right)_{T_c} = 0 \tag{4-1}$$

$$\left(\frac{\partial^2 p}{\partial v^2}\right)_{T_c} = 0 \tag{4-2}$$

The isotherms for temperatures between T_1 and T_c change gradually in shape from a rectangular hyperbola at the elevated temperature T_1 to the inflected curve characteristic of the critical isotherm. In the liquid state the attractive forces between molecules are very large. As the dome ACB of Fig. 4-1 is approached, these forces become appreciable and cause the isotherms in the neighborhood of the critical point to deviate more and more from the rectangular hyperbola characteristic of the ideal gas.

It is instructive to consider the data shown in Fig. 4-1 when they are plotted on a graph of pressure vs. temperature, with molal volume as parameter. This type of graph is shown in Fig. 4-2. With pressure and temperature as coordinates, the two-phase region ACB of Fig. 4-1 becomes a line. This is the solid line of Fig. 4-2 and is known as the vapor-pressure curve. It represents a plot of the values of p vs. T for the horizontal lines under the dome of Fig. 4-1 and terminates at the critical point C. Points on the line AC in Fig. 4-1 represent liquid at its boiling point, or *saturated liquid*. Points on the line BC represent vapor at its condensation temperature, or *saturated vapor*. Points on the horizontal lines connecting AC and BC represent the mixtures of saturated liquid and saturated vapor which exist during the process of isothermal vaporization. In this two-phase region the relation between temperature and pressure, *i.e.*, the vapor-pressure curve, is independent of volume, as indicated in Fig. 4-2.

In the single-phase regions the molal volume is uniquely determined by pressure and temperature, and lines of constant volume (isometrics) therefore appear in Fig. 4-2 in these regions. The dashed lines labeled v_1, v_2, and v_3 represent the isometrics in the vapor region, which lies below and to the right of the vapor-pressure curve, and those labeled v_1', v_2', v_3' denote isometrics for the liquid region, which lies on the other side of the vapor-pressure curve. The isometrics are very nearly straight lines.

It is helpful for an understanding of the physical significance of the critical point to consider the phase changes which occur when pure substances are heated in a sealed vertical tube of constant volume. If the tube is filled with either liquid or gas, the heating process is represented by one of the dashed lines of Fig. 4-2, for example, from D to E on v_3 if the tube is filled with gas or from F to G on v_3' if the tube is initially filled with liquid. No phase change is observed in either case. These changes are represented by vertical lines in Fig. 4-1 which lie entirely above the dome ACB.

However, if the tube is only partially filled with liquid (the remainder being vapor in equilibrium with the liquid), heating results in changes which are at first represented by the vapor-pressure curve, *i.e.* the solid line of Fig. 4-2. If the meniscus separating the two phases is initially near the bottom of the tube, liquid vaporizes, and the meniscus recedes to the bottom of the tube and disappears as the last drop of liquid vaporizes. For example, in Figs. 4-1 and 4-2, the path goes from J to P, where all the liquid is vaporized, and then follows the constant-volume line v_3 (Fig. 4-2) in the vapor region from P to D. If the meniscus is

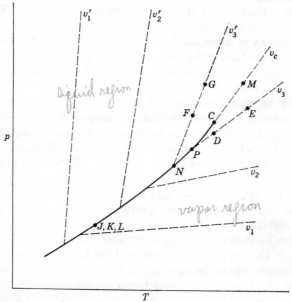

FIG. 4-2. p-T diagram for a pure substance.

originally near the top of the tube, the liquid expands upon heating until it completely fills the tube, *i.e.*, the meniscus rises to the top of the tube. This process is represented, for example, by the vertical line KNF in Fig. 4-1. In Fig. 4-2, point K lies on the vapor-pressure curve and coincides with point J. The path again follows the vapor-pressure curve as long as two phases are present. After the vapor phase has disappeared, the path follows the constant-volume line v_3'.

It is evident that between these extremes there is an amount of liquid that could be added to the tube initially such that the path of the process would be on the vapor-pressure curve all the way to its end, the critical point C. Physically, the meniscus would go neither down to the bottom nor up to the top of the tube but would stay near the center until C was reached. At this point the meniscus would suddenly disappear, since the system would change from two phases (on the vapor-pressure curve) to a single phase, as represented by the region above C. Further heating would be represented in Fig. 4-2 by a path along v_c, corresponding to the critical molal volume of the fluid. In Fig. 4-1 this path is represented by the vertical line LCM. These experiments provide an approximate method for determining the critical point, that is, the critical temperature and volume. (The critical specific volume is equal to the volume of the tube divided by the mass of fluid added to the tube.) It is interesting to note that the meniscus disappears not only when the path leads exactly through the critical point but also for paths passing near it. The reason for this is not well understood.[1]

4-2. Equations of State for Gases.

Many attempts have been made to represent the behavior of pure materials, as shown in Figs. 4-1 and 4-2, by an equation. The difficulty of realizing this is apparent from the complexity of these graphs. For the gas region alone, it is clear that the facts cannot be represented by the ideal-gas law. Many equations of greater complexity have been published, but none has been entirely successful in representing the behavior of actual gases over the entire practical range of conditions, and new equations are still being developed. All these equations relate pressure, volume, and temperature and are known as *equations of state*. The ideal-gas law is the simplest example. In general, the most accurate equations are also the most complex and laborious to use. For engineering purposes high accuracy is usually not necessary, and simplicity is a great recommendation. On the other hand, accuracy greater than that provided by the ideal-gas law is often required.

In 1873, J. D. van der Waals proposed the first practical equation of state to improve upon the ideal-gas law. He attempted to take into account the effect of the attractive forces among the molecules and also the effect of the volume occupied by the molecules themselves. His equation may be written

$$\left(p + \frac{a}{v^2}\right)(v - b) = RT \tag{4-3}$$

where a and b are positive constants, characteristic of the particular gas. The term a/v^2 was proposed as the correction, applied to the pressure, to account for the forces of attraction among the molecules; *i.e.*, the actual gas pressure is less than the ideal pressure by an amount equal to a divided by v^2. Similarly, the actual volume is greater than the ideal volume by an amount equal to the constant b. If the constants a and b are equal to zero, the equation is identical to that for an ideal gas. For best results a and b should be determined by fitting this equation to experimental p-v-T data.[2] Actually, van der Waals' equation is mainly

---

[1] For a discussion of this point, see M. W. Zemansky, "Heat and Thermodynamics," 4th ed., pp. 199, 200, McGraw-Hill Book Company, Inc., New York, 1957.

[2] Most of the published values of the constants a and b for van der Waals' equation have been calculated from critical data. The method makes use of Eqs. (4-1) and

of historical interest, since better methods of representing p-v-T data are now available.   A partial list would include the equations of Berth-

(4-2), which represent conditions which must be satisfied at the critical point.   Solved for pressure, Eq. (4-3) becomes

$$p = \frac{RT}{v - b} - \frac{a}{v^2}$$

Differentiation at constant temperature gives

$$\left(\frac{\partial p}{\partial v}\right)_T = \frac{-RT}{(v - b)^2} + \frac{2a}{v^3}$$

and

$$\left(\frac{\partial^2 p}{\partial v^2}\right)_T = \frac{2RT}{(v - b)^3} - \frac{6a}{v^4}$$

According to Eqs. (4-1) and (4-2), these derivatives should equal zero when $p = p_c$, $v = v_c$, and $T = T_c$.   Thus,

$$\frac{RT_c}{(v_c - b)^2} = \frac{2a}{v_c^3}$$

and

$$\frac{RT_c}{(v_c - b)^2} = \frac{3a(v_c - b)}{v_c^4}$$

Simultaneous solution of these equations yields

$$v_c = 3b \qquad (A)$$

and

$$T_c = \frac{8a}{27Rb} \qquad (B)$$

Equations (A) and (B) may be used to calculate values of a and b from the critical data v_c and T_c.   However, the critical volume is difficult to measure, and relatively few accurate values are available.   On the other hand, accurate values of p_c and T_c are known for many substances.   An equation relating p_c to a and b may be developed by writing van der Waals' equation for the specific conditions of the critical point.   Thus,

$$p_c = \frac{RT_c}{v_c - b} - \frac{a}{v_c^2}$$

Equation (A) is now used to eliminate v_c from this equation, giving

$$p_c = \frac{RT_c}{2b} - \frac{a}{9b^2} \qquad (C)$$

The simultaneous solution of Eqs. (B) and (C) for a and b yields the desired equations in terms of the critical temperature and pressure:

$$a = \frac{27R^2T_c^2}{64p_c} \qquad b = \frac{RT_c}{8p_c}$$

It is not to be inferred that the values of a and b so calculated are necessarily the best possible values, for they are calculated from data for a single point, *i.e.*, the critical point.

elot[1] (1898), Dieterici[2] (1898), A. Wohl[3] (1914), Keyes[4] (1917), K. Wohl[5] (1927), Beattie-Bridgeman[6] (1928), Beattie[7] (1930), Benedict-Webb-Rubin[8] (1940), Redlich and Kwong[9] (1949), and Martin and Hou[10] (1955).

The variation in complexity is well illustrated by comparing the equation of Benedict, Webb, and Rubin, which contains eight constants, with the one developed by Redlich and Kwong, which contains but two:

Benedict-Webb-Rubin (or Kellogg) equation:

$$p = \frac{RT}{v} + \frac{B_0 RT - A_0 - C_0/T^2}{v^2} + \frac{bRT - a}{v^3} + \frac{a\alpha}{v^6}$$
$$+ \frac{c}{v^3 T^2}\left(1 + \frac{\gamma}{v^2}\right)e^{-\gamma/v^2} \quad (4\text{-}4)$$

where A_0, B_0, C_0, a, b, c, α, and γ are constants.

Redlich and Kwong equation:

$$p = \frac{RT}{v - b} - \frac{a}{T^{1/2}v(v + b)} \quad (4\text{-}5)$$

where a and b are constants.[11]

Equations containing two constants, like those of van der Waals and Redlich and Kwong, are relatively easy to use. They apply over wide ranges of conditions, but do not in general give high accuracy. The constants may be calculated from the critical constants T_c and p_c, or they may be determined by fitting the equations to experimental data. The Benedict-Webb-Rubin equation, on the other hand, is very complex. It is highly accurate when applied over a limited range of conditions, provided that enough data are available to evaluate the constants accurately.

---

[1] D. Berthelot, *Compt. rend.*, **126**, 954 (1898).
[2] C. Dieterici, *Ann. Physik*, **66**, 826 (1898).
[3] A. Wohl, *Z. physik. Chem.*, **87**, 1 (1914).
[4] F. G. Keyes, *Proc. Natl. Acad. Sci. U.S.*, **3**, 323 (1917).
[5] K. Wohl, *Z. physik. Chem.*, **133**, 305 (1927).
[6] J. A. Beattie and O. C. Bridgeman, *Proc. Am. Acad. Arts Sci.*, **63**, 229 (1928).
[7] J. A. Beattie, *Proc. Natl. Acad. Sci. U.S.*, **16**, 14 (1930).
[8] M. Benedict, G. B. Webb, and L. C. Rubin, *J. Chem. Phys.*, **8**, 334 (1940).
[9] O. Redlich and J. N. S. Kwong, *Chem. Rev.*, **44**, 233 (1949).
[10] J. J. Martin and Y. C. Hou, *AIChE J.*, **1**, 142 (1955).
[11] The "virial" form of the equation of state is often employed in scientific work:

$$\frac{pv}{RT} = 1 + \frac{B}{v} + \frac{C}{v^2} + \frac{D}{v^3} + \cdots$$

The quantities B, C, and D are known as the second, third, and fourth "virial" coefficients and are functions of temperature only. If they are all zero, the virial equation reduces to the ideal-gas law. For minor deviations from ideality, C and D are often taken as zero.

For the most precise work, its use may be justified. In the past, calculations with such complex equations were almost prohibitively time-consuming. However, with the advent of automatic computing machines, this difficulty has been overcome. Nevertheless, simpler methods are used for most engineering calculations. As a matter of fact, for general engineering work the graphic method described on the following pages is commonly employed because it is simpler to use than equations of state and requires a minimum of experimental data.

4-3. The Principle of Corresponding States. The deviation of the volume of real gases from that predicted by the ideal-gas law can be simply represented by plotting the ratio of the actual volume to that predicted by the ideal-gas law vs. pressure—in other words by plotting

$$\frac{v}{RT/p} = \frac{pv}{RT} = Z = \text{compressibility factor} \qquad (4\text{-}6)$$

as the ordinate vs. pressure as the abscissa—for lines of constant temperature. The shapes of these compressibility-factor curves are illustrated in Fig. 4-3, which has been prepared from experimental data for methane, propane, and isobutane. Methane, which has the lowest boiling point of the three substances, shows the least deviation from ideal-gas behavior. Propane, with a boiling point between methane and isobutane, deviates more than the former but less than the latter. This relative position is the same for the entire range of pressure shown on the chart, though the magnitudes of the deviations vary greatly with pressure. As the pressure approaches zero, the compressibility factor approaches unity. This would be expected, since the postulates of ideal-gas behavior (no attractive forces among the molecules and negligible volume of the molecules themselves) are essentially true at this condition.

The relative positions of the three curves illustrate the point made earlier in the chapter that departure from ideal behavior increases as the region of condensation is approached. Thus isobutane is closer to the point of liquefaction at 250°F than propane and methane. In fact, the curve for isobutane ends at a pressure of about 400 psia, for that pressure corresponds to its vapor pressure at 250°F. This correspondence between the deviation from ideality and proximity to the region of liquefaction suggests the possibility of correlating the behavior of all gases by considering not the actual temperature and pressure, but ratios of those values to the temperature and pressure at the point of condensation. In other words, the deviations of methane, propane, and isobutane, while very different at the same temperature and pressure (Fig. 4-3), might be the same if considered at equal temperatures and pressures relative to values representing the region of condensation. If the critical temperature and pressure are used as characteristics of the region of condensation, this hypothesis may be tested by evaluating the compressibility factors for a series of gases at the same ratios of T/T_c and p/p_c. The ratio T/T_c is commonly called *reduced temperature*, and similarly p/p_c is the *reduced pressure.* From Fig. 4-3, at 200 psia and 250°F, the compressibility factor for isobutane is 0.83. At these conditions,

$$T_r = \frac{460 + 250}{(408)(1.8)} = 0.97$$

$$p_r = \frac{200}{(36)(14.7)} = 0.38$$

(For isobutane $T_c = 408°K$ and $p_c = 36.0$ atm.)

At the same reduced conditions the actual temperature and pressure of methane are

$$T = (191 \times 1.8)(0.97) = 334°R, \text{ or } -126°F$$
$$p = (45.8 \times 14.7)(0.38) = 256 \text{ psia}$$

From experimental data the compressibility factor of methane at these different conditions is 0.83, the same as for isobutane. Hence, the

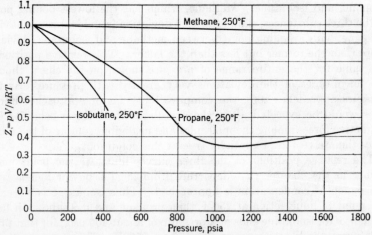

FIG. 4-3. Compressibility factors for methane, propane, and isobutane at 250°C.

method has worked out very well for these two chemically similar materials. A more severe test would be to apply it to other types of compounds, such as water and ammonia. The results of many such calculations are conclusive in showing reasonably good agreement when compressibility factors are compared at the same reduced temperature and pressure.

The practical result of this observation is that a single chart may be drawn which correlates experimental p-v-T data for all gases. Figure 4-4

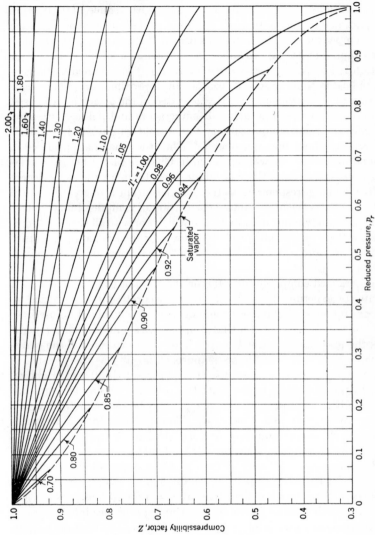

FIG. 4-4a. Generalized compressibility-factor diagram. Low-pressure range. (*Based on data compiled by A. L. Lydersen, R. A. Greenkorn, and O. A. Hougen, Generalized Thermodynamic Properties of Pure Fluids, Univ. Wisconsin, Eng. Expt. Sta., Rept. 4, 1955. By permission.*)

shows such a chart. It was prepared by plotting the compressibility factors Z for various gases vs. reduced pressure with reduced temperature as the parameter. Data plotted in this way fall in a band for each reduced temperature. The best lines drawn through the data are then taken to represent the approximate p-v-T behavior of all gases. This correlation is known as a *generalized* chart, for it is assumed to be generally applicable to all gases, at least as an approximation. This leads to the concept of corresponding states as stated in the principle: All gases, when compared at the same reduced temperature and reduced pressure, have nearly the same compressibility factor, and all deviate from ideal-gas behavior to about the same degree. Thus they may be considered in corresponding states. It will be shown in Chap. 7 that other properties of gases also deviate from those of an ideal gas to about the same degree when they are in corresponding states. This concept is of great practical value, for it allows the approximate correlation of compressibility factors and other thermodynamic data by charts which apply to all gases. Moreover, to use these charts, one needs to know only the critical temperature and critical pressure. A list of these data for a number of gases is given in Table 4-1.

The generalized compressibility-factor chart is not to be regarded as a substitute for experimental p-v-T data. If accurate data are available, as they are for some of the more common gases, they should be used.

It will be noted from Fig. 4-4 that Z approaches unity for all temperatures as the pressure approaches zero. This serves to confirm the statement made previously that all gases approach ideality as the pressure is reduced to zero. For most gases the critical pressure is 30 atm or above. Thus at 1 atm, p_r is 0.033 or less. At this pressure, for any temperature above the critical temperature ($T_r = 1$), it will be seen that Z deviates from unity by no more than 1 per cent. Thus at 1 atm for temperatures greater than T_c, the assumption that the ideal-gas law is valid usually leads to errors of less than 1 per cent. It should also be noted that for reduced temperatures between 3 and 10 the compressibility factor is nearly unity for reduced pressures up to 6. For very high temperatures the isotherms approach a horizontal line at $Z = 1$ for all pressures. Thus all gases approach ideality as the temperature approaches infinity.

The approximate nature of the generalized p-v-T correlation as presented in Fig. 4-4 has prompted efforts by a number of investigators[1-3] to improve it by introducing other parameters in addition to p_c and T_c. After a careful consideration of the various possibilities, Lydersen, Green-

---

[1] A. L. Lydersen, R. A. Greenkorn, and O. A. Hougen, Generalized Thermodynamic Properties of Pure Fluids, *Univ. Wisconsin, Eng. Expt. Sta., Rept.* 4, 1955.

[2] K. S. Pitzer, *J. Am. Chem. Soc.*, **77**, 3427 (1955).

[3] L. Reidel, *Chem.-Ing.-Tech.*, **26**, 679 (1954), and **27**, 209 (1955).

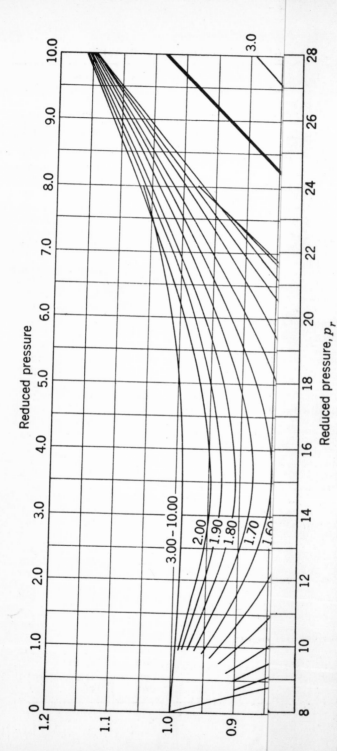

Reduced pressure

3.00 – 10.00
2.00
1.90
1.80
1.70
1.60

3.0

Reduced pressure, p_r

FIG. 4-4b. Generalized compressibility-factor diagram. Medium- and high-pressure range. (Based on data compiled by A. L. Lydersen, R. A. Greenkorn, and O. A. Hougen, Generalized Thermodynamic Properties of Pure Fluids, Univ. Wisconsin, Eng. Expt. Sta., Rept. 4, 1955. By permission.)

TABLE 4-1. CRITICAL CONSTANTS OF GASES†

	T_c, °K	p_c, atm	Z_c
Paraffins:			
Methane.........................	191	45.8	0.290
Ethane..........................	306	48.2	0.284
Propane.........................	370	42.0	0.276
n-Butane........................	425	37.5	0.274
Isobutane.......................	408	36.0	0.282
n-Pentane.......................	470	33.3	0.268
Isopentane......................	461	32.9	0.268
Neopentane......................	434	31.6	0.268
n-Hexane........................	508	29.9	0.264
n-Heptane.......................	540	27.0	0.260
n-Octane........................	569	24.6	0.258
Monoolefins:			
Ethylene........................	282	50.0	0.268
Propylene.......................	365	45.6	0.276
1-Butene........................	420	39.7	0.276
1-Pentene.......................	474	40	?
Miscellaneous organic compounds:			
Acetic acid......................	595	57.1	0.200
Acetone.........................	509	46.6	0.237
Acetylene.......................	309	61.6	0.274
Benzene.........................	562	48.6	0.274
1,3-Butadiene...................	425	42.7	0.270
Cyclohexane.....................	553	40.0	0.271
Dichlorodifluoromethane (Freon-12)..........	385	39.6	0.273
Diethyl ether....................	467	35.6	0.261
Ethyl alcohol....................	516	63.0	0.249
Ethylene oxide...................	468	71.0	0.25
Methyl alcohol...................	513	78.5	0.220
Methyl chloride..................	416	65.9	0.276
Methyl ethyl ketone..............	533	39.5	0.26
Toluene.........................	594	41.6	0.27
Trichlorofluoromethane (Freon-11)............	471	43.2	0.277
Trichlorotrifluoroethane (Freon-113)..........	487	33.7	0.274
Elementary gases:			
Bromine.........................	584	102	0.307
Chlorine........................	417	76.1	0.276
Helium..........................	5.3	2.26	0.300
Hydrogen........................	33.3	12.8	0.304
Neon...........................	44.5	26.9	0.307
Nitrogen........................	126	33.5	0.291
Oxygen.........................	155	50.1	0.29
Miscellaneous inorganic compounds:			
Ammonia........................	406	111	0.242
Carbon dioxide...................	304	72.9	0.276
Carbon monoxide.................	133	34.5	0.294
Hydrazine.......................	653	145	?

TABLE 4-1. CRITICAL CONSTANTS OF GASES† *(Continued)*

	T_c, °K	p_c, atm	Z_c
Hydrogen chloride	325	81.5	0.266
Hydrogen sulfide	374	88.9	0.284
Nitric oxide (NO)	180	64	0.25
Nitrous oxide (N_2O)	310	71.7	0.271
Sulfur	1313	116	?
Sulfur dioxide	431	77.8	0.268
Sulfur trioxide	491	83.8	0.262
Water	647	218	0.23

† Selected values from K. A. Kobe and R. E. Lynn, Jr., *Chem. Rev.*, **52**, 117 (1953). By permission.

korn, and Hougen selected the critical compressibility factor, defined as

$$Z_c = \frac{p_c v_c}{R T_c}$$

as the most suitable. The introduction of this additional parameter naturally makes the representation of the generalized p-v-T behavior of gases more complicated. Ideally, a separate chart would be required for each value of Z_c. Since this is impractical, Lydersen, Greenkorn, and Hougen presented average data for four groups of materials:

Group I: Z_c from 0.24 to 0.26, average value, 0.25
Group II: Z_c from 0.26 to 0.28, average value, 0.27
Group III: Z_c from 0.28 to 0.30, average value, 0.29
Group IV: $Z_c = 0.23$, the value for water

These four groups include almost all materials for which data are available. Group II, with an average value of $Z_c = 0.27$, represents more than 60 per cent of the substances investigated. Hence, the data for this group are represented in Fig. 4-4. For most engineering purposes the data of this figure are adequate for any gas when experimental data are not available.

4-4. Note on Experimental Compressibility Data. Experimental p-v-T data for gases are sometimes reported in the literature as Amagat compressibility factors, defined as the ratio of the pv product at a given temperature and pressure to the pv product at the standard conditions of 0°C and 1 atm. These ratios will be represented by the symbol A. Thus

$$A = \frac{pv}{(pv)_0} \tag{4-7}$$

For example, Perry[1] lists such information for 12 gases. These data may be used directly in calculations, or they may be converted to compressibility factors Z. If used directly, the molal volume of the gas at standard conditions v_0 is usually required and is generally listed along with the pv data.

The relationship between A and Z may be developed in the following way. Let $(pv)_T^*$ designate the limit of the pv product as p approaches zero at a given temperature T. The limiting value of A for this temperature as p approaches zero is then given by

$$A_T^* = \frac{(pv)_T^*}{(pv)_0} = \frac{RT}{(pv)_0}$$

At the same temperature, but at any pressure,

$$A_T = \frac{(pv)_T}{(pv)_0} = \frac{ZRT}{(pv)_0}$$

Therefore

$$\frac{A_T}{A_T^*} = \frac{ZRT/(pv)_0}{RT/(pv)_0} = Z \tag{4-8}$$

Thus if the value of A_T^*, the Amagat compressibility factor at zero pressure, is known at temperature T, it is a simple matter to calculate values of Z for this temperature. However, values of A_T^* are frequently given only for the standard temperature of $0°C$, and values at other temperatures must be calculated. If A_T^* represents the value of A at zero pressure and the temperature T, and A_0^* represents the value of A at zero pressure and the standard temperature of $0°C$,

$$\frac{A_T^*}{A_0^*} = \frac{RT/(pv)_0}{RT_0/(pv)_0} = \frac{T}{T_0}$$

Thus

$$A_T^* = A_0^* \frac{T}{T_0} \tag{4-9}$$

Values of A_0^* are usually included with experimental values of A.[†]

Example 4-1. One pound *mass* of gaseous ammonia is contained in a 1.091-ft³ steel bomb immersed in a constant-temperature bath at 150°F. Calculate the pres-

---

[1] J. H. Perry (ed.), "Chemical Engineers' Handbook," 3d ed., pp. 205–209, McGraw-Hill Book Company, Inc., New York, 1950.

[†] For example, in J. H. Perry (ed.), "Chemical Engineers' Handbook," 3d ed., p. 205, Table 151, McGraw-Hill Book Company, Inc., New York, 1950, values of A_0^* are listed under the heading $1 + \lambda$. In addition values of v_0 are given under the heading $22{,}414.1/(1 + \lambda)$.

ure within the bomb by the following methods:

(a) The ideal-gas law
(b) The van der Waals equation of state, evaluating the constants a and b from the critical data of Table 4-1
(c) The generalized compressibility-factor method $\left[\frac{ft^3 \cdot psia}{lbmole \cdot {}^{\circ}R}\right]$

Solution. (a) IDEAL-GAS LAW

$$p = \frac{nRT}{V} = \frac{(1/17.02)(10.73)(460 + 150)}{1.091} = 352 \text{ psia}$$

(b) VAN DER WAALS' EQUATION. The constants a and b are calculated from the data of Table 4-1:

$$a = \frac{27R^2T_c^2}{64p_c} = \frac{(27)(10.73)^2(406 \times 1.8)^2}{(64)(111 \times 14.7)} = 15,800 \text{ (psia)(ft}^3)^2/(\text{lb mole})^2$$

$$b = \frac{RT_c}{8p_c} = \frac{(10.73)(406 \times 1.8)}{(8)(111 \times 14.7)} = 0.598 \text{ ft}^3/\text{lb mole}$$

Note that, in order to obtain a and b in English units, pounds per square inch, cubic feet, degrees Rankine, and pound moles, it was necessary to employ the value of R in these units and convert the critical temperature and pressure read from Table 4-1 to degrees Rankine and pounds per square inch.

The molal volume to substitute in Eq. (4-3) is

$$v = (1.091)(17.02) = 18.58 \text{ ft}^3/\text{lb mole}$$

Then

$$p = \frac{(10.73)(460 + 150)}{18.58 - 0.598} - \frac{15,800}{(18.58)^2}$$

$$p = 364 - 46 = 318 \text{ psia}$$

(c) GENERALIZED COMPRESSIBILITY-FACTOR CHART. The reduced conditions may be calculated from the data of Table 4-1:

$$T_r = \frac{150 + 460}{(406)(1.8)} = 0.836$$

$$p_r = \frac{p}{(111)(14.7)} \tag{A}$$

where p is the pressure in pounds per square inch absolute. Since the molal volume is 18.58 ft^3/lb mole, Eq. (4-6) becomes

$$p(18.58) = Z(10.73)(610)$$

or

$$p = 352Z \tag{B}$$

It is not possible to find Z from Fig. 4-4 without first knowing p_r and hence p. Thus the solution must involve a trial calculation. Equations (A) and (B) and the $T_r = 0.836$ isotherm of Fig. 4-4 constitute three relationships among p, p_r, and Z, and may therefore be used to solve the problem. As an initial step Eqs. (A) and (B) may be combined to give

$$Z = \frac{(111)(14.7)p_r}{352} = 4.68p_r \tag{C}$$

Values of p_r may now be assumed until the same value of Z is given by both Eq. (C) and Fig. 4-4 for the assumed value of p_r.

A simpler method is to carry out the trial procedure graphically. Equation (C) shows that Z is directly proportional to p_r. Thus, the correct value of Z must lie on a line drawn on the compressibility-factor plot with a slope of 4.68 and passing through the origin. The correct value of Z must also lie on the line representing the $T_r = 0.836$ isotherm. Therefore, the value of Z and the value of p_r are found on the compressibility-factor chart at the intersection of these two lines. Then p may be calculated either from Z by Eq. (B) or from p_r by Eq. (A).

In this example either procedure leads to the results $Z = 0.87$, $p_r = 0.186$, and $p = 303$ psia.

Experimental data indicate that the pressure would be 300 psia at the conditions of this problem. The percentage deviations of the three calculated values from this actual pressure are

(a) Ideal-gas law.. +17.3 per cent
(b) van der Waals' equation............................. +6.0 per cent
(c) Generalized compressibility-factor chart................ +1.0 per cent

Example 4-2. It is necessary to store 1 lb mole of methane at a temperature of 122°F and a pressure of 600 atm. What is the volume of the vessel that must be provided? Use the following methods:

(a) Ideal-gas law
(b) van der Waals' equation
(c) Generalized compressibility-factor chart
(d) Experimental Amagat compressibilities from Perry[1]

Solution. (a) IDEAL-GAS LAW

$$v = \frac{RT}{p} = \frac{(0.73)(122 + 460)}{600} = 0.709 \text{ ft}^3$$

(b) VAN DER WAALS' EQUATION

$$a = \frac{27R^2T_c^2}{64p_c} = \frac{(27)(0.73)^2(191 \times 1.8)^2}{(64)(45.8)} = 580 \text{ (atm)(ft}^3)^2/(\text{lb mole})^2$$

$$b = \frac{RT_c}{8p_c} = \frac{(0.73)(191 \times 1.8)}{(8)(45.8)} = 0.685 \text{ ft}^3/\text{lb mole}$$

Thus

$$600 = \frac{(0.73)(122 + 460)}{v - 0.685} - \frac{580}{v^2}$$

or

$$600v^3 - 836v^2 + 580v - 397 = 0$$

This is a cubic equation in v, and it is probably most easily solved by trial. The result is

$$v = 1.07 \text{ ft}^3/\text{lb mole}$$

(c) GENERALIZED COMPRESSIBILITY-FACTOR CHART

$$T_r = \frac{582}{(191)(1.8)} = 1.7 \qquad p_r = \frac{600}{45.8} = 13.1$$

[1] J. H. Perry (ed.), "Chemical Engineers' Handbook," 3d ed., p. 207, Table 158, McGraw-Hill Book Company, Inc., New York, 1950.

From Fig. 4-4

$$Z = 1.34$$

Thus

$$v = \frac{ZRT}{p} = \frac{(1.34)(0.73)(582)}{600} = 0.95 \text{ ft}^3/\text{lb mole}$$

(d) EXPERIMENTAL DATA. Values of A are given by Perry for methane at a temperature of 50°C, or 122°F. At this temperature and a pressure of 600 atm,

$$A = 1.5653 = \frac{pv}{(pv)_0}$$

$$(pv)_0 = (1)(22,360) \text{ (atm)(cm}^3/\text{g mole)}†$$

or

$$(pv)_0 = \left(\frac{22,360}{28,320}\right)(454) = 358.5 \text{ (atm)(ft}^3)/\text{lb mole}$$

Thus

$$v = \frac{(1.5653)(pv)_0}{p} = \frac{(1.5653)(358.5)}{600}$$

$$v = 0.936 \text{ ft}^3/\text{lb mole}$$

Compared with the experimental value, the other values are in error as follows:

      (a) Ideal-gas law...................... −24.3 per cent
      (b) van der Waals' equation........... +14.3 per cent
      (c) Generalized chart................. +1.5 per cent

Example 4-3. A meter in a high-pressure natural-gas line indicates a flow rate of 10,000 ft³/day at the conditions 500 psig and 85°F. This gas is sold to a utility company on the basis of its volume at 60°F and 1 atm. Assuming natural gas to be pure methane and using Fig. 4-4, calculate the volumetric rate of flow at these conditions.

Solution. At 500 psig and 85°F for methane,

$$p_r = \frac{514.7}{(45.8)(14.7)} = 0.76$$

$$T_r = \frac{85 + 460}{(191)(1.8)} = 1.59$$

From Fig. 4-4, $Z = 0.96$.

The number of pound moles flowing per day is given by the expression

$$n = \frac{p_1 V_1}{Z_1 R T_1} = \frac{(514.7)(10,000)}{(0.96)(10.73)(545)}$$

The volume corresponding to this number of moles at 60°F and 1 atm is

$$V_2 = \frac{nZ_2 R T_2}{p_2} = \frac{(514.7)(10,000)(10.73)(520)}{(0.96)(10.73)(545)(14.7)} Z_2$$

where Z_2 is the compressibility factor at 1 atm pressure and 60°F. At this pressure, $p_r = 0.022$; at 60°F, $T_r = 1.51$. From Fig. 4-4, Z_2 is essentially unity. Therefore,

$$V_2 = 348,000 \text{ ft}^3/\text{day}$$

---

† J. H. Perry (ed.), "Chemical Engineers' Handbook," p. 205, Table 151, under heading 22,414.1/(1 + λ), McGraw-Hill Book Company, Inc., New York, 1950.

4-5. Gas Mixtures. The p-v-T relations which have just been discussed were developed specifically for pure gases. In addition, it is necessary to have methods of dealing with constant-composition gas mixtures, since they are frequently encountered in practice. In contrast to the limited significance of pure gases, there are an indefinite number of industrially important gas mixtures. Experimental data might eventually become available for nearly every common pure gas, but the data for mixtures are likely to remain incomplete. It is therefore necessary to develop methods for calculating p-v-T data for mixtures from data for the pure components. This problem has not been completely solved, but a number of methods have been proposed. Several will be discussed in the following paragraphs.

Mixtures of Ideal Gases. If a gas mixture behaves according to the ideal-gas law, then all the molecules making up the gas are equivalent, since no forces exist between molecules and the molecules themselves occupy no volume. Thus the part of the total pressure exerted by an ideal-gas mixture due to a given constituent is independent of the nature of the other gases present. It is given by the expression

$$p_i = \frac{n_i R T}{V} \qquad (4\text{-}10)$$

where n_i is the number of moles of component i in the mixture and V is the total volume of the vessel. It is apparent that this pressure is the same as that which would be obtained if the n_i moles of component i occupied the vessel alone. Hence it is termed the *pure-component pressure*.

The total pressure is the sum of the pure-component pressures of all components present, so that

$$p = \sum p_i = \frac{RT}{V} \sum n_i = \frac{nRT}{V} \qquad (4\text{-}11)$$

Dividing Eq. (4-10) by Eq. (4-11),

$$p_i = p \frac{n_i}{n} = p y_i \qquad (4\text{-}12)$$

where y_i is the mole fraction of i in the mixture.

Equation (4-12) shows that the pure-component pressure[1] for any

---

[1] These pressures have often been called *partial pressures*, and for an ideal gas this term is entirely satisfactory. However, for an actual gas the pressure given by Eq. (4-12) is *not* the same as the pressure exerted by component i if it alone occupies the total volume. It therefore seems logical to use two different terms for these two pressures. Accordingly, partial pressure will *always* be defined as the pressure given by Eq. (4-12) and will hereafter be designated by the symbol p_i. Thus partial pressure is *defined* by the equation

$$p_i = y_i p \qquad (4\text{-}12a)$$

The pure-component pressure, assigned the symbol p_i, will be defined as the pressure

component in a mixture of ideal gases is proportional to the total pressure. In a similar fashion it can be shown that for ideal gases the *pure-component volume* for any component is equal to its mole fraction times the total volume of the mixture, that is,

$$V_i = y_i V \tag{4-13}$$

The volume V_i is the volume which would be occupied by component i if it existed alone at the temperature and total pressure of the mixture. The sum of the pure-component volumes equals the total volume, that is,

$$V = \sum V_i$$

Dalton's Law of Additive Pressures. It has been shown that for ideal gases the total pressure is equal to the sum of the pure-component pressures. For actual gases this may still be true, and indeed this is the condition postulated by Dalton's law of additive pressures, that is,

$$p_A + p_B + p_C + \cdots + p_N = p$$

For actual gases this is an assumption, but it appears to be approximately true at relatively low pressures. For each pure component when it occupies the total volume alone at the temperature of the mixture,

$$p_i = \frac{Z_i n_i R T}{V} \tag{4-14}$$

where Z_i is the compressibility factor for component i at the pressure p_i and the temperature of the mixture T. If Dalton's law is valid, the sum of the pure-component pressures gives the total pressure:

$$p = \sum p_i = \sum \frac{Z_i n_i R T}{V} = \frac{RT}{V} \sum Z_i n_i$$

But

$$p = \frac{Z_m n R T}{V} \tag{4-15}$$

where Z_m is the compressibility factor for the mixture. Since values of p by these two equations must be the same,

$$\frac{Z_m n R T}{V} = \frac{RT}{V} \sum Z_i n_i$$

or

$$Z_m = \frac{\sum Z_i n_i}{n} = \frac{Z_A n_A}{n} + \frac{Z_B n_B}{n} + \frac{Z_C n_C}{n} + \cdots + \frac{Z_N n_N}{n}$$

exerted by pure i when it occupies the total volume alone. For ideal gases these two terms are equivalent, but for actual gases they are different and must be distinguished.

or

$$Z_m = y_A Z_A + y_B Z_B + y_C Z_C + \cdots + y_N Z_N = \sum y_i Z_i \quad (4\text{-}16)$$

Thus the compressibility factor of a mixture which obeys Dalton's law is equal to the molal average of the compressibility factors of the pure components, each taken at the temperature of the mixture and *at its pure-component pressure.* Values of Z_i should be obtained from experimental data if available; otherwise they may be determined through the use of the compressibility-factor chart (Fig. 4-4). Once Z_m has been determined, it can be used in Eq. (4-15) to calculate p or V. Dalton's law is most accurate if the pressure is low, and should probably not be used for pressures much above 50 atm.

It is to be noted that this method involves a trial-and-error procedure when either the volume or the pressure of a gas mixture is to be calculated, but fortunately the calculations are not difficult. The method is illustrated in the examples given at the end of this section.

Amagat's Law of Additive Volumes. For ideal gases, the pure-component volumes must add to give the total volume. Amagat's law postulates that this is true for actual gases as well. Thus,

$$V_A + V_B + V_C + \cdots + V_N = V$$

This is an alternative to the use of Dalton's law where real gases are involved, for Amagat's law and Dalton's law cannot both be valid except for ideal gases. For each pure component at the temperature and total pressure of the mixture, its pure-component volume is given by

$$V_i = \frac{Z_i n_i R T}{p} \quad (4\text{-}17)$$

where Z_i is the compressibility factor for component i at the temperature and pressure *of the mixture.* If Amagat's law is valid, the total volume is given by the sum of the pure-component volumes:

$$V = \sum V_i = \sum \frac{Z_i n_i R T}{p} = \frac{R T}{p} \sum Z_i n_i$$

but

$$V = \frac{Z_m n R T}{p} \quad (4\text{-}15)$$

where Z_m is the compressibility factor of the mixture. Since V by these two equations must be the same,

$$\frac{Z_m n R T}{p} = \frac{R T}{p} \sum Z_i n_i$$

or

$$Z_m = \frac{\sum Z_i n_i}{n} = \frac{Z_A n_A}{n} + \frac{Z_B n_B}{n} + \frac{Z_C n_C}{n} + \cdots + \frac{Z_N n_N}{n}$$

or

$$Z_m = y_A Z_A + y_B Z_B + y_C Z_C + \cdots + y_N Z_N = \sum y_i Z_i \quad (4\text{-}18)$$

This equation appears to be identical with Eq. (4-16). However, the values of Z_A, Z_B, etc., are here determined at the temperature of the mixture and at the total pressure of the mixture. Again experimental data should be used for the values of Z_i if available; otherwise the generalized compressibility-factor chart may be used. Once Z_m has been determined, p or V can be calculated by Eq. (4-15). Amagat's law is generally valid at high pressures, *i.e.*, above about 300 atm.

If volume is the quantity sought, the application of Amagat's law is straightforward. However, if pressure is unknown, the solution must be by trial.

 The Pseudocritical-point Method. The fact that the principle of corresponding states brings the individual compressibility-factor curves for gases into approximate agreement with each other suggests the possibility that such a compressibility-factor chart should be applicable to gas mixtures, provided that a suitable critical temperature and critical pressure are used in evaluating the reduced properties of the mixture. The problem then is reduced to calculating the correct critical temperature and pressure of the mixture in terms of those quantities for the individual components. It might be expected that the actual critical temperature and pressure of the mixture would be the proper values to use. However, this is not the case, especially in regard to pressure, since the critical pressure of a mixture bears no simple relationship to the critical pressures of the individual components and, indeed, may have a value much higher than the critical pressures of any of the components involved. The next logical step is to try to find some method for combining the critical constants of the pure components making up the gas mixture to give fictitious or "pseudo" values for the critical properties of the mixture. These pseudocritical temperatures and pressures could then be used for the calculation of T_r and p_r, and values of Z for mixtures would be obtained from the generalized compressibility-factor chart. Various methods for combining the critical constants of the pure components were investigated by Kay,[1] and he found that one of the simpler methods of combination gave rather satisfactory results, particularly for hydrocarbons.

Kay suggested that molal average values be used, that is,

$$T_{pc} = y_A T_{c_A} + y_B T_{c_B} + \cdots + y_N T_{c_N} = \sum y_i T_{c_i} \quad (4\text{-}19)$$

[1] W. B. Kay, *Ind. Eng. Chem.*, **28**, 1014 (1936).

and

$$p_{pc} = y_A p_{c_A} + y_B p_{c_B} + \cdots + y_N p_{c_N} = \sum y_i p_{c_i} \qquad (4\text{-}20)$$

where T_{pc} and p_{pc} are defined as the pseudocritical temperature and pressure, respectively. These values can be used to evaluate the pseudo-reduced quantities T_{pr} and p_{pr}. Then the compressibility factor of the mixture is estimated from Fig. 4-4, just as for pure gases. This method has the advantage of simplicity and is accurate enough for much engineering work. In the intermediate-pressure range, 50 to 300 atm, where neither Dalton's law nor Amagat's law is likely to apply, it represents the only convenient method of determining the compressibility factors of mixtures.

The methods described for dealing with gas mixtures are illustrated in the following examples.

Example 4-4. Calculate the molal volume of a mixture containing 40.1 mole per cent N_2 and 59.9 mole per cent C_2H_4 at 600 atm and 50°C by each of the following methods:

(a) Ideal-gas law
(b) Amagat's law and the generalized Z chart
(c) Dalton's law and the generalized Z chart
(d) Pseudocritical method
(e) Using the experimental value of $Z_m = 1.40$

Solution. (a) IDEAL-GAS LAW

$$v = \frac{RT}{p} = \frac{(1.314)(50 + 273)}{600} = 0.708 \text{ ft}^3/\text{lb mole}$$

(b) AMAGAT'S LAW. By Eq. (4-18),

$$Z_m = \sum y_i Z_i$$

where the values of Z_i are evaluated at the temperature and pressure of the mixture. Thus, for N_2,

$$T_r = \frac{323}{126} = 2.56 \qquad p_r = \frac{600}{33.5} = 17.9$$

and

$$Z_{N_2} = 1.50$$

For C_2H_4,

$$T_r = \frac{323}{282} = 1.14 \qquad p_r = \frac{600}{50.0} = 12.0$$

and

$$Z_{C_2H_4} = 1.33$$
$$Z_m = \sum y_i Z_i = (0.401)(1.50) + (0.599)(1.33) = 1.40$$

Therefore,

$$v = \frac{Z_m RT}{p} = \frac{(1.40)(1.314)(323)}{600} = 0.990 \text{ ft}^3/\text{lb mole}$$

(c) DALTON'S LAW. By Eq. (4-16),

$$Z_m = \sum y_i Z_i$$

where the values of Z_i are evaluated at the temperature of the mixture, but at their pure-component pressures. Since the pure-component pressures are not known, values must be assumed, and the answer can be reached only by a series of successive approximations. As a starting assumption, the pure-component pressures will be taken equal to the partial pressures of the components in the mixture, that is,

$$p_i = \bar{p}_i = y_i p$$

Thus assume

$$p_{N_2} = (0.401)(600) = 240.6 \text{ atm}$$
$$p_{C_2H_4} = (0.599)(600) = 359.4 \text{ atm}$$

On this basis, for N_2

$$p_r = \frac{240.6}{33.5} = 7.19 \quad \text{and} \quad Z_{N_2} = 1.03$$

and for C_2H_4

$$p_r = \frac{359.4}{50.0} = 7.12 \quad \text{and} \quad Z_{C_2H_4} = 0.87$$

As a first approximation

$$Z_m = (0.401)(1.03) + (0.599)(0.87) = 0.93$$

This value of Z_m may now be used to estimate new values of the pure-component pressures. Since $p = Z_m RT/v$ and $p_i = y_i Z_i RT/v$,

$$\frac{p_i}{p} = \frac{y_i Z_i RT/v}{Z_m RT/v}$$

or

$$p_i = \frac{y_i Z_i p}{Z_m}$$

Then as a second approximation

$$p_{N_2} = \frac{(0.401)(1.03)(600)}{0.93} = 266$$

and

$$p_{C_2H_4} = \frac{(0.599)(0.87)(600)}{0.93} = 336$$

This procedure is repeated until the calculated values of p_i check the assumed ones. Two or three trials are usually sufficient. In this case the result is $Z_m = 0.925$. Hence

$$v = \frac{Z_m RT}{p} = \frac{(0.925)(1.314)(323)}{600} = 0.655 \text{ ft}^3/\text{lb mole}$$

(d) PSEUDOCRITICAL METHOD. By Eqs. (4-19) and (4-20),

$$T_{pc} = (0.401)(126) + (0.599)(282) = 220°K$$
$$p_{pc} = (0.401)(33.5) + (0.599)(50.0) = 43.4 \text{ atm}$$

Thus

$$T_{pr} = \frac{323}{220} = 1.47 \quad p_{pr} = \frac{600}{43.4} = 13.8$$

and
$$Z_m = 1.41$$
Hence
$$v = \frac{Z_m RT}{p} = \frac{(1.41)(1.314)(323)}{600} = 0.997 \text{ ft}^3/\text{lb mole}$$

(e) EXPERIMENTAL DATA. The experimental value of Z_m is 1.40, identical with that calculated by Amagat's law. The experimental value of v is therefore the same as that of part (b):

$$v = 0.990 \text{ ft}^3/\text{lb mole}$$

In the example considered here the various methods give results which deviate from the measured value by

    (a) Ideal-gas law..................... −28.3 per cent
    (b) Amagat's law.....................   0.0 per cent
    (c) Dalton's law..................... −33.8 per cent
    (d) Pseudocritical method............ +0.7 per cent

At the very high pressure of 600 atm, Amagat's law gives the best results, as would be expected. The pseudocritical method also gives an excellent approximation to the true value. Dalton's law, on the other hand, is more in error than the ideal-gas law, illustrating that it is not satisfactory at high pressures.

Example 4-5. A natural gas (see analysis) is being metered at 1330 psig and 100°F. The average daily rate at line conditions is 20,000 ft³/day. Calculate the gas rate at standard conditions (60°F and 1 atm pressure) by the following methods:

(a) Ideal-gas law
(b) Dalton's law and the compressibility-factor chart
(c) Amagat's law and the compressibility-factor chart
(d) Pseudocritical-point method

Gas analysis	Mole per cent
Methane...................	86.02
Ethane....................	7.70
Propane...................	4.26
Isobutane.................	0.57
n-Butane..................	0.87
Pentane...................	0.25
Hexane....................	0.33
Total....................	100.00

Solution. (a) IDEAL-GAS LAW

$$V (60°F, 1 \text{ atm}) = (20,000) \left(\frac{1344.7}{14.7}\right) \left(\frac{460 + 60}{460 + 100}\right) = 1,700,000 \text{ ft}^3/\text{day}$$

(b) DALTON'S LAW. The compressibility factor for the mixture at 1330 psig and 100°F is given by Eq. (4-16):

$$Z_m = \sum y_i Z_i$$

The Z_i values are evaluated at the pure-component pressures and the temperature of the mixture. As an approximation, the pure-component pressures will be assumed equal to the partial pressures; that is, $p_i = y_i p$.

The determination of the individual compressibility factors and the summation of $y_i Z_i$ are carried out in the accompanying table:

Component	$T_r = \dfrac{560}{T_c}$	$p_i = y_i p$	$p_r = \dfrac{p_i}{p_c}$	Z_i	$y_i Z_i$	Revised p_i
Methane..........	1.63	1155.7	1.72	0.89	0.765	1147
Ethane............	1.02	104.5	0.15	0.94	0.0723	108
Propane...........	0.84	57.3	0.093	0.94	0.0401	60
Isobutane.........	0.77	7.7	0.01	0.99	0.0056	8
n-Butane..........	0.73	11.7	0.02	0.99	0.0086	13
Pentane†..........	0.66	3.4	0.01	(0.99)	0.0025	4
Hexane‡..........	0.61	4.4	0.01	(0.99)	0.0033	5
Total............	....	1344.7	.....	......	0.8974	

† Assumed to be n-pentane.
‡ The critical temperature and pressure of the hexane fraction were taken as 508°K and 29.5 atm.

If Eq. (4-15) is applied to the mixture,

$$p = 1344.7 = \frac{Z_m n R T}{V}$$

Solving for the total number of moles of gas,

$$n = \frac{(1344.7)(20,000)}{(10.73)(100 + 460)(0.897)} = 4990 \text{ moles/day}$$

The volume at 60°F and 1 atm pressure may be evaluated from n and the ideal-gas law, since at this low pressure the average compressibility factor would be nearly unity.

$$V = \frac{(4990)(10.73)(520)}{14.7} = 1,900,000 \text{ ft}^3/\text{day}$$

The assumed values of p_i now can be checked using Eq. (4-14). For example, for methane,

$$p_i = Z_i y_i \frac{n R T}{V} = Z_i y_i \frac{p}{Z_m} = (0.89)(0.8602)\left(\frac{1344.7}{0.897}\right) = 1147 \text{ psia}$$

The revised values are sufficiently close to the assumed set that the compressibility factors would not be affected significantly.

(c) AMAGAT'S LAW. The pure-component volumes are given by Eq. (4-17), in which the Z_i values are computed at the total pressure of the mixture instead of at the pure-component pressures as in the preceding method. The calculations are summarized in the accompanying table.   The Z_i values in parentheses are hypothetical,

Component	T_r	$p_r = \dfrac{1344.7}{p_c}$	Z_i	$Z_i y_i$
Methane............	1.63	2.00	0.88	0.757
Ethane..............	1.02	1.88	0.32	0.025
Propane.............	0.84	2.17	(0.25)	0.011
Isobutane...........	0.77	2.47	(0.30)	0.002
n-Butane............	0.73	2.54	(0.30)	0.003
Pentane.............	0.66	2.77	(0.30)	
Hexane.............	0.61	3.10	(0.35)	
Total.............	....	....	......	0.798

since these pure components would be liquids at the total pressure.   For example, the vapor pressure of isobutane at 100°F is 73.5 psia.   Hence, at $p_i = 1345$ psia, isobutane would be liquid.   The effect of the assumed values of Z_i for the last five components is not serious since they are present only in small quantities.

$$V = \sum V_i = \frac{nRT}{1344.7} \sum Z_i y_i = \frac{nRT}{1344.7}\,(0.798) = 20,000$$

$$n = \frac{(1344.7)(20,000)}{(10.73)(560)(0.80)} = 5620 \text{ moles/day}$$

$$V \,(60°F, 1 \text{ atm pressure}) = \frac{(5620)(10.73)(520)}{14.7} = 2,150,000 \text{ ft}^3/\text{day}$$

(*d*) PSEUDOCRITICAL-POINT METHOD.   The pseudocritical-point calculation is summarized in tabular form:

Component	Mole fraction	T_c, °K	p_c, atm	yT_c, °K	yp_c, atm
Methane............	0.8602	191	45.8	164.3	39.4
Ethane.............	0.0770	306	48.2	23.5	3.8
Propane............	0.0426	370	42.0	15.8	1.8
Isobutane...........	0.0057	408	36.0	2.3	0.2
n-Butane...........	0.0087	425	37.5	3.7	0.3
Pentane............	0.0025	470	33.3	1.2	0.1
Hexane............	0.0033	508	29.9	1.7	0.1
Total............	1.0000	...	....	212.5	45.7

The pseudocritical temperature and pressure are 212.5°K and 45.7 atm.   The average compressibility factor for the mixture as a whole can be evaluated from Fig. 4-4 and the following reduced temperature and pressure:

$$T_{pr} = \frac{560}{(212.5)(1.8)} = 1.46$$

$$p_{pr} = \frac{1344.7}{(45.7)(14.7)} = 2.15$$

From Fig. 4-4, $Z_m = 0.80$.

This factor may be applied in the equation $pV = Z_m nRT$ to calculate n.

$$n = \frac{(1344.7)(20,000)}{(0.80)(10.73)(560)} = 5620 \text{ moles/day}$$

and

$$V \ (60°F, 1 \text{ atm pressure}) = 2,150,000 \text{ ft}^3/\text{day}$$

The results of the four methods of calculation compared with the experimental value are as follows:

Method	Effective compressi-bility factor
Ideal-gas law	1
Dalton's law	$\sum Z_i y_i = 0.90$
Amagat's law	$\sum Z_i y_i = 0.80$
Pseudocritical	0.80
Observed compressibility factor for this gas	0.80

In this particular example, the ideal-gas law is in error about 25 per cent, and Dalton's law by 12 per cent, and Amagat's law and the pseudocritical method both give results which are in good agreement with the observed value.

4-6. The Behavior of Liquids. The problem of predicting the p-v-T behavior of liquids is different from that encountered with gases in several respects. In the first place, liquid volumes can usually be easily measured experimentally under the more common conditions of temperature and pressure. Furthermore, pressure and temperature, particularly the former, have relatively small influence on the liquid volume under most conditions. Thus there has been less incentive for the development of a general equation relating pressure, volume, and temperature of liquids than there has been for gases, and much less effort has been expended in this direction. On the other hand, the structure of liquids is more complex and less well described than that of gases, and consequently the development of a general equation of state is a more difficult problem. Recent developments in the theory of the liquid state and progress in predicting the p-v-T behavior of liquids are summarized by Hirschfelder, Curtiss, and Bird.[1] It should be mentioned that the Benedict-Webb-Rubin equation of state [Eq. (4-4)] may be used to calculate liquid volumes, provided that the specific volume of the liquid is not much less than two-thirds the critical volume. This equation is too complex, however, for most engineering calculations, and a simpler empirical method has been developed by Lydersen, Greenkorn, and Hougen.[2]

This method is based on the principle of corresponding states, and applies to all liquids in much the same way as the generalized compressi-

[1] J. O. Hirschfelder, C. F. Curtiss, and R. B. Bird, "Molecular Theory of Gases and Liquids," Chap. 4, John Wiley & Sons, Inc., New York, 1954.

[2] A. L. Lydersen, R. A. Greenkorn, and O. A. Hougen, Generalized Thermodynamic Properties of Pure Fluids, *Univ. Wisconsin, Eng. Expt. Sta., Rept.* 4, 1955.

bility-factor correlation applies to gases.   In the case of liquids, a more suitable correlation is obtained if reduced density is plotted as a function of reduced temperature and pressure.   Reduced density is defined as

$$\rho_r = \frac{\rho}{\rho_c}$$

where ρ_c is the density at the critical point.   The generalized correlation is shown in Fig. 4-5.   This figure may be used directly for the determination of liquid densities if an accurate value of the critical density is known. However, this value is frequently not available because the critical density, or specific volume, is difficult to determine.   A better procedure is to make use of a single known liquid density at any conditions by the relationship

$$\rho_2 = \rho_1 \frac{\rho_{r_2}}{\rho_{r_1}} \tag{4-21}$$

where ρ_2 = required density
ρ_1 = known density
ρ_{r_1}, ρ_{r_2} = reduced densities read from Fig. 4-5 for conditions 1 and 2
This method gives good results and requires only experimental data that are usually available.   It should be noted that as the critical point is approached both temperature and pressure have increasingly greater effects on the densities of liquids.

Example 4-6.   Estimate the density of liquid ammonia at 211.9 psia and 100°F (saturation conditions).   At 16 psia and −25°F, the density is 42.2 lb$_m$/ft³.

Solution

$$\rho_1 = 42.2 \text{ lb}_m/\text{ft}^3$$
$$T_{r_1} = \frac{460 - 25}{(406)(1.8)} = 0.60$$
$$p_{r_1} = \frac{16}{(14.7)(111)} = 0.01$$

From Fig. 4-5,
$$\rho_{r_1} = 2.74$$

At 100°F and 211.9 psia,
$$T_{r_2} = \frac{560}{(406)(1.8)} = 0.77$$
$$p_{r_2} = \frac{211.9}{(14.7)(111)} = 0.130$$

From Fig. 4-5,
$$\rho_{r_2} = 2.35$$

Then the required density can be evaluated from Eq. (4-21):

$$\rho_2 = (42.2)\left(\frac{2.35}{2.74}\right) = 36.2 \text{ lb}_m/\text{ft}^3$$

The experimental value at these conditions is 36.4 lb$_m$/ft³.

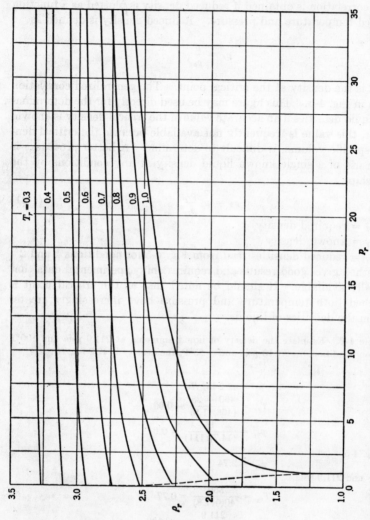

Fig. 4-5. Generalized density correlation for liquids. (Based on data compiled by A. L. Lydersen, R. A. Greenkorn, and O. A. Hougen, Generalized Thermodynamic Properties of Pure Fluids, Univ. Wisconsin, Eng. Expt. Sta., Rept. 4, 1955. By permission.)

114

PROBLEMS

1. Estimate the density (in pounds *mass* per cubic foot) of chlorine gas at 230°C and 2500 psia.   *Ans.* 32.6 lb_m/ft^3.

2. Calculate the specific volume of steam at 1500 psia and 700°F, using the following methods:

(a) The ideal-gas law
(b) The van der Waals equation
(c) The compressibility chart

Compare the results with the value given in the steam tables.

3. Compare the specific volume of steam at 2000 psia and 1400°F obtained using the compressibility-factor chart with the value obtained by the ideal-gas law and with the value given in the steam tables.

4. (a) Calculate the volume (in cubic feet) occupied by 1.5 lb moles of ethane at 125°F and 500 psia.

(b) Calculate the number of pounds *mass* of ethane contained in a cylinder of 0.8 ft^3 capacity if its temperature is 110°F and the pressure is 2000 psia.

5. If the maximum allowable pressure for a cylinder is 3000 psia, what is the maximum quantity of nitrogen which can safely be stored in the cylinder?

6. Methyl chloride for use in domestic refrigerators is sold in small cylinders having a volume of 0.15 ft^3.   Calculate the weight of methyl chloride gas contained in a cylinder if the pressure is 68 psia at 68°F.

7. Consider ammonia at 250 psig and 50°C.   Calculate the molal volume in cubic feet per pound mole by each of the following methods:

(a) Ideal-gas law   *Ans.* 23.6.
(b) van der Waals' equation   *Ans.* 21.4.
(c) Generalized compressibility-factor chart   *Ans.* 20.3.
(d) Compressibility-factor data for NH_3 *Ans.* 20.0.

8. For the production of liquid oxygen it is desired that the gas be compressed to a pressure of 100 atm at a temperature of −90°C.   Oxygen at a pressure of 14.5 psia and a temperature of 22°C is compressed and cooled to these conditions.   Calculate the volume of compressed gas resulting from 100 ft^3 of the original gas.

9. One hundred forty cubic feet of methane at 60°F and 1 atm is equivalent to 1 gal of gasoline in an automotive engine of ordinary design.   If methane were compressed to 3000 psia and 60°F, what would be the required volume of a vessel to hold the equivalent of 10 gal of gasoline?   *Ans.* 5.6 ft^3.

10. (a) What pressure in atmospheres would be developed by storing 10 lb moles of nitrogen in a volume of 15 ft^3 at 200°C?   *Ans.* 560 atm.

(b) What temperature in degrees Fahrenheit would be developed if 150 ft^3 of nitrogen as measured at standard conditions were compressed into a volume of 2 ft^3, the final pressure being 50 atm?   *Ans.* −96°F.

11. (a) Calculate the volume occupied by 1 lb_m of ethane at 144°F and 2000 psig.

(b) Calculate the mass of ethane contained in a cylinder of 0.5 ft^3 capacity if the temperature is 144°F and the pressure is 2000 psig.

(c) If the volume occupied by 10 lb_m of ethane at 3000 psig is 0.5 ft^3, calculate the temperature of the ethane.

12. What pressure would be developed if 100 ft^3 of NH_3, measured at 20 atm at 400°F, were compressed into a volume of 5 ft^3, the temperature being 350°F?   Solve by two methods:

116   CHEMICAL ENGINEERING THERMODYNAMICS   [CHAP. 4

(a) The van der Waals equation of state, evaluating a and b from the critical temperature and pressure

(b) The generalized compressibility chart

13. To what pressure would a 3-ft³ cylinder have to be filled at 70°F if one wished to store 50 lb$_m$ of ethylene in it?

14. One pound of water in a 1-ft³ container is heated to 900°F. What pressure does it develop?

15. A closed tank having a volume of 10 ft³ holds ethane vapor at 62°F and 360 psia. The ethane is heated until it reaches a temperature of 400°F. What is the final pressure in pounds per square inch absolute? *Ans.* 770 psia.

16. What pressure (in atmospheres) would be developed by storing 15 lb$_m$ of CO_2 in a 1.5-ft³ cylinder at 100°F?

17. A rigid vessel is filled to one-half its volume with liquid nitrogen at its normal boiling point. The vessel is then closed and allowed to warm to 70°F. Calculate the pressure developed. The specific volume of liquid nitrogen at its normal boiling point is 34.7 cm³/g mole. *Ans.* 500 atm.

18. Estimate the work required for the isothermal compression of 1 lb mole of propane in a reversible nonflow process from 1 atm abs to 84 atm abs at 190°C. Use:

(a) The generalized compressibility-factor chart. (Note that the isotherm on the chart representing this process is essentially straight.)

(b) The van der Waals equation of state. Evaluate the constants from critical data.

19. Calculate the work required to compress 1 lb mole of carbon dioxide from 1 atm to 200 atm in a reversible nonflow process at a constant temperature of 70°C, using

(a) The ideal-gas law   *Ans.* −5,050,000 ft-lb$_f$.
(b) Data from Fig. 4-4   *Ans.* −4,840,000 ft-lb$_f$.
(c) Data given by J. H. Perry (ed.), "Chemical Engineers' Handbook," 3d ed., p. 206, McGraw-Hill Book Company, Inc., New York, 1950.

Ans. −4,840,000 ft-lb$_f$.

20. One pound *mass* of *n*-heptane (C_7H_{16}) at 70°F and 1 atm (liquid, density = 0.68 g/cm³) is brought to the condition 700°F and 40 atm. The change in enthalpy accompanying this change of state is 2510 Btu. What is the change in internal energy? *Ans.* 2495 Btu.

21. A compressor handles 1000 lb$_m$/hr of an equimolal mixture of methane and ethane. The gas leaves the compressor at 50 atm abs and 300°F. What is the volumetric flow rate of the gas leaving the compressor in cubic feet per hour? *Ans.* 450 ft³/hr.

22. Three hundred pounds *mass* of a mixture containing 10 mole per cent propane, 20 mole per cent *n*-butane, and 70 mole per cent *n*-pentane is completely vaporized per hour in a pipestill. At the outlet the temperature and pressure are 515°F and 600 psia. What is the velocity of the vapor in feet per second at the outlet from the still under these conditions? The inside diameter of the pipe is 2.00 in.

23. An equimolal mixture of nitrogen and methane is compressed isothermally from 1 atm and 0°F to 50 atm. What volume will 10 lb$_m$ of this mixture occupy at the tw o conditions?

24. What is the density in grams per cubic centimeter of an equimolal mixture of hydrogen and carbon monoxide at 100 atm and 100°F?

25. A mixture of hydrogen and nitrogen is fed to a reactor in the stoichiometric proportion for the formation of ammonia. The mixture enters at 600 atm and 77°F at a rate of 200 ft³/hr, and the conversion to ammonia is 15 per cent. The gases leaving the reactor are refrigerated to condense out the ammonia formed, and the unreacted gases are recycled.

(a) Calculate the pounds of ammonia formed per hour. *Ans.* 270 lb_m/hr.

(b) If the products from the reactor (before condensation of the ammonia) are at 550 atm and 350°F, calculate the velocity they would have in a 2-in. pipe.
Ans. 4.7 ft/sec.

26. A compressor handles 1000 lb_m/hr of a mixture of ethane and propane containing 67 per cent ethane by weight. The gas leaves the compressor at 50 atm abs and 100°C. Calculate the volume of gas leaving the compressor per hour.

27. A natural gas has the following composition by weight:

Methane (CH_4).......... 85 per cent
Ethane (C_2H_6).......... 5 per cent
Nitrogen (N_2)............ 10 per cent

It is compressed to 600 psia for transport through a pipeline at 60°F. One million cubic feet (as measured at 1 atm and 60°F) is compressed per hour and sent through the pipeline, which has an inside diameter of 1 ft. Calculate the velocity of the gas in the pipeline in feet per second. *Ans.* 8 ft/sec.

28. Cracked gas from a petroleum refinery is metered at 300 psia and 150°F. The average chart reading is 2000 ft³/day, and the average analysis is as follows:

Gas	Mole per cent
Methane...........	45
Ethane............	10
Ethylene..........	25
Propane...........	7
Propylene.........	8
Butane............	5

Calculate the gas rate at standard conditions (60°F, 1 atm pressure) by the following methods:

(a) Ideal-gas law
(b) Dalton's law
(c) Amagat's law
(d) Pseudocritical method

29. It is necessary to prepare a mixture of carbon dioxide and nitrogen having a molal volume of 1.00 ft³/lb mole at a temperature of 50°C and a pressure of 400 atm. What should be the composition of the mixture? Use the data given by J. H. Perry (ed.), "Chemical Engineers' Handbook," 3d ed., McGraw-Hill Book Company, Inc., New York, 1950. *Ans.* 58.1 mole per cent CO_2.

30. A natural gas, having a molal composition 84 per cent CH_4, 9 per cent N_2, and 7 per cent C_2H_6, is compressed and cooled to 100°F. If the molal volume of the compressed-gas mixture is to be 2.3 ft³/lb mole, to what pressure must the gas be compressed? Solve by Dalton's law, Amagat's law, and the pseudocritical method. Which method would you expect to give the most reliable result?

31. The specific volume of isobutane liquid at 70°F and 45 psia is 0.0286 ft³/lb_m. Estimate the specific volume at 250°F and 750 psia. (The experimental value at these conditions is 0.0387 ft³/lb_m.)

32. The density of liquid nitrogen is 37.5 lb_m/ft³ at −153°C under a pressure of 25.04 atm abs. Estimate the density at −168°C and 10.7 atm.

CHAPTER 5

HEAT EFFECTS

In nearly every industry of importance to chemical engineers there are operations accompanied by heat effects. These operations may be purely physical or may include chemical reactions. As an illustration, consider the process for the manufacture of ethylene glycol (widely used as an antifreeze agent) by the oxidation of ethylene to ethylene oxide and subsequent hydration of the oxide to glycol. The catalytic oxidation process has been found to be most effective when carried out at temperatures in the neighborhood of 250°C. Therefore, it is necessary to preheat the reactants ethylene and air to this temperature before they enter the reactor. In order to design a satisfactory preheater, the chemical engineer must be able to compute accurately the heat requirement, which in this case is a sensible heat effect accompanying a purely physical change. Sensible heat effects are so named because they always result in temperature changes in the system.

The oxidation reaction between ethylene and the oxygen in air evolves energy as heat. Since temperatures much above 250°C reduce the conversion to ethylene oxide, it is necessary to remove heat from the reactor to control the temperature. To design a suitable reactor, the chemical engineer must be able to evaluate such reaction heat effects. Following the reaction, the ethylene oxide formed must be separated from the remainder of the gas stream and hydrated to glycol. Frequently this is accomplished by absorbing the oxide in water. The absorption is accompanied by an evolution of heat due to a combination of processes involving a phase change, the formation of a solution, and the hydration reaction between the dissolved ethylene oxide and water. Finally, the glycol must be separated from the water by distillation, giving rise to yet other heat requirements, the purely physical ones involved in separating a solution and vaporizing a liquid.

In this relatively simple chemical-manufacturing process, all the important types of heat effects were noted. In addition to sensible heat quantities, there were those accompanying phase changes, chemical reactions, and the formation and separation of solutions. These latter effects may all occur in the absence of any temperature change in the system. It is the purpose of this chapter to apply the concepts of thermodynamics to

118

the problem of evaluating heat requirements for both physical and chemical operations.

5-1. Heat Capacities of Gases as a Function of Temperature. In Chaps. 2 and 3 a number of equations involving heat capacities were developed. When written for finite changes, these equations include the integrals

$$\int C_v \, dT \quad \text{and} \quad \int C_p \, dT$$

If heat capacity is independent of temperature, these integrals are readily evaluated. However, such an assumption is not even approximately valid when large temperature changes are considered, and in general these expressions can be integrated only when the heat capacity is known as a function of temperature.

Of the two heat capacities in common use, the one at constant pressure C_p is the more important from a practical standpoint, and this discussion will be limited for the most part to a consideration of this quantity. In thermodynamic calculations involving gases, it is possible to evaluate the effect of pressure on heat effects without using heat capacities at high pressures. Thus, it is rarely necessary to consider the effect of pressure on heat capacity. Listed values are usually those for low pressure, and frequently for a pressure approaching zero. In this book an asterisk (*) will be used to denote zero-pressure quantities.[1] At zero pressure the ideal-gas law is exact, and C_p^* and C_v^* are related by

$$C_p^* - C_v^* = R \tag{3-6}$$

The values of C_p^* discussed in this section are exactly correct only at zero pressure. However, they are approximately valid for pressures up to several atmospheres and are sufficiently accurate for almost all calculations involving gases at atmospheric pressure.

The effect of temperature on C_p^* and C_v^* can be determined only experimentally. The most direct method is to observe the change in temperature when a measured quantity of heat is added to a measured quantity of material. Results are presented graphically, or in tabular form, or most concisely as equations relating heat capacity and temperature.

A method of determining heat capacities from spectroscopic data has been widely used for gases and is based on the principles of statistical mechanics. The general approach depends on the concept that the total internal energy E of a material is equal to the sum of the energies due to translational and rotational motion of the molecules and to the vibrational motion of the atoms making up the molecules.

[1] Since C_p for an ideal gas is independent of pressure, the zero-pressure values are valid for an ideal gas at any pressure. Listed values of heat capacity are often tabulated for a *standard state* of an ideal gas at 1 atm and are given the symbol C_p°. These are identical with C_p^*.

The equipartition-of-energy theory provides a means of estimating in a very approximate way the molal heat capacity of any gas at low pressures (where the gas behavior approaches that of an ideal gas). This theory states that each translational and rotational degree of freedom[1] contributes $R/2$ cal/(g mole)(°C) to C_v^*, while the maximum vibrational contribution is R cal/(g mole)(°C). The translational and rotational contributions are fully effective at all except very low temperatures, while the extent of the vibrational contribution depends upon the temperature even to rather high temperatures. Since there is a total of $3N$ (N = number of atoms in the molecule) degrees of freedom, the molal heat capacity is given by the expressions:

For a nonlinear molecule (three rotational degrees of freedom),

$$C_p^* = R + C_v^* = R + \frac{3R}{2} + \frac{3R}{2} + (3N - 6)RF = 4R + (3N - 6)RF$$

For a linear molecule (two rotational degrees of freedom),

$$C_p^* = \frac{7R}{2} + (3N - 5)RF$$

In these expressions, F, the fraction of the maximum vibrational contribution, depends upon the temperature. For a linear molecule, such as O_2, the second equation would apply. There is one degree of vibrational freedom ($N = 2$); hence

$$C_p^* = 6.95 + RF$$

At room temperatures F is small and C_p^* is about 7 for most diatomic molecules. As the temperature increases, F and C_p^* increase. Therefore, the maximum value for diatomic molecules is about 9 (corresponding to $F = 1$). The heat capacities of water vapor and carbon dioxide increase more rapidly with temperature, for there are a larger number of vibrational degrees of freedom.

Excellent results are obtained by this method when satisfactory experimental data concerning the vibration spectra are available. For a description of the general method, reference should be made to articles by Giauque[2] and Glasstone.[3] Illustrative calculations are carried out by Wenner for certain simple types of molecules.[4]

---

[1] The term *degree of freedom* as used here has no relation to the same term as used in connection with the phase rule, but refers to the directions of motion of the atoms and molecules.

[2] W. F. Giauque, *J. Am. Chem. Soc.*, **52**, 4808 (1930).

[3] S. Glasstone, "Thermodynamics for Chemists," Chap. VI, D. Van Nostrand Company, Inc., Princeton, N.J., 1944.

[4] R. R. Wenner, "Thermochemical Calculations," Chap. VII, McGraw-Hill Book Company, Inc., New York, 1941.

The heat capacities of gases in the zero-pressure state increase smoothly as temperature increases.[1]   The analytical relationship most frequently used to relate point values of C_p^* with temperature has the form

$$C_p^* = \alpha + \beta T + \gamma T^2 + \cdots \tag{5-1}$$

where α, β, and γ are constants, characteristic of the gas considered.   More than three terms are seldom used, and sometimes two are sufficient. Values of α, β, and γ for a number of common gases are given in Table 5-1.

The use of Eq. (5-1) for C_p^* allows the following integration to be performed:

$$\int_{T_1}^{T_2} C_p^* \, dT = \alpha(T_2 - T_1) + \frac{\beta}{2}(T_2^2 - T_1^2) + \frac{\gamma}{3}(T_2^3 - T_1^3) \tag{5-2}$$

If C_p^* is represented by a different function of temperature than that given by Eq. (5-1), the integrated result given in Eq. (5-2) is, of course, not valid, and the integration must be performed for the particular function used.[2]

The constants for use with Eq. (5-1) are given in Table 5-1 for temperatures in degrees Kelvin, and only temperatures on the Kelvin scale may be used with these constants.   The units of C_p^* are either cal/ (g mole)(°C) or Btu/(lb mole)(°F), since numerical values of C_p^* are the same for either set of units.   Equation (5-1) may also be used for temperatures expressed in degrees centigrade, degrees Rankine, or degrees Fahrenheit, but in this event some of the constants have different numerical values.   Thus when constants from different sources are used, one must take care to use temperatures in the units specified for the particular constants given.   In the solution of problems, it is sometimes convenient to switch temperature units.   Because this frequently causes confusion, the method for doing it is illustrated in the following examples.

[1] Apparent heat capacities at finite pressures are occasionally observed to decrease with increasing temperature.   This is the result of a chemical reaction.   For example, acetaldehyde and acetic acid vapor associate, mainly to form the dimer, at temperatures near saturation.   Thus the heat of dissociation of the dimer becomes indistinguishable from the sensible heat, and the apparent heat capacity decreases in this region as the temperature is raised.

[2] The extensive compilation of thermal data prepared by K. K. Kelley, *U.S. Bur. Mines, Bull.* 476, 1949, presents heat-capacity equations in the form

$$C_p = a + bT + \frac{c}{T^2}$$

This reference is a valuable source of heat-capacity data, not only for gases, but for liquids and solids as well.

TABLE 5-1. MOLAL HEAT CAPACITIES OF GASES IN THE IDEAL GASEOUS STATE†
Constants for the equation $C_p^* = \alpha + \beta T + \gamma T^2$, where T is in degrees Kelvin and C_p^* is in Btu/(lb mole)(°F) or cal/(g mole)(°C).

298 to 1500°K

Compound	Formula	α	$\beta \times 10^3$	$\gamma \times 10^6$
Normal paraffins:				
Methane..........................	CH₄	3.381	18.044	−4.300
Ethane............................	C₂H₆	2.247	38.201	−11.049
Propane...........................	C₃H₈	2.410	57.195	−17.533
n-Butane..........................	C₄H₁₀	3.844	73.350	−22.655
n-Pentane.........................	C₅H₁₂	4.895	90.113	−28.039
n-Hexane..........................	C₆H₁₄	6.011	106.746	−33.363
n-Heptane.........................	C₇H₁₆	7.094	123.447	−38.719
n-Octane..........................	C₈H₁₈	8.163	140.217	−44.127
Increment per C atom above 8........	......	1.097	16.667	−5.338
Normal monoolefins (1-alkenes):				
Ethylene..........................	C₂H₄	2.830	28.601	−8.726
Propylene.........................	C₃H₆	3.253	45.116	−13.740
1-Butene..........................	C₄H₈	3.909	62.848	−19.617
1-Pentene.........................	C₅H₁₀	5.347	78.990	−24.733
1-Hexene..........................	C₆H₁₂	6.399	95.752	−30.116
1-Heptene.........................	C₇H₁₄	7.488	112.440	−35.462
1-Octene..........................	C₈H₁₆	8.592	129.076	−40.775
Increment per C atom above 8........	......	1.097	16.667	−5.338
Miscellaneous materials:				
Acetaldehyde‡.....................	C₂H₄O	3.364	35.722	−12.236
Acetylene.........................	C₂H₂	7.331	12.622	−3.889
Ammonia..........................	NH₃	6.086	8.812	−1.506
Benzene...........................	C₆H₆	−0.409	77.621	−26.429
1,3-Butadiene.....................	C₄H₆	5.432	53.224	−17.649
Carbon dioxide.....................	CO₂	6.214	10.396	−3.545
Carbon monoxide...................	CO	6.420	1.665	−0.196
Chlorine...........................	Cl₂	7.576	2.424	−0.965
Cyclohexane.......................	C₆H₁₂	−7.701	125.675	−41.584
Ethyl alcohol......................	C₂H₆O	6.990	39.741	−11.926
Hydrogen..........................	H₂	6.947	−0.200	0.481
Hydrogen chloride..................	HCl	6.732	0.433	0.370
Hydrogen sulfide...................	H₂S	6.662	5.134	−0.854
Methyl alcohol.....................	CH₄O	4.394	24.274	−6.855
Nitric oxide........................	NO	7.020	−0.370	2.546
Nitrogen...........................	N₂	6.524	1.250	−0.001
Oxygen............................	O₂	6.148	3.102	−0.923
Sulfur dioxide......................	SO₂	7.116	9.512	3.511
Sulfur trioxide.....................	SO₃	6.077	23.537	−0.687
Toluene...........................	C₇H₈	0.576	93.493	−31.227
Water.............................	H₂O	7.256	2.298	0.283

† Selected mainly from values given by H. M. Spencer and coworkers, *J. Am. Chem. Soc.*, **56**, 2311 (1934); **64**, 2511 (1942); **67**, 1859 (1945); and *Ind. Eng. Chem.*, **40**, 2152 (1948). Also personal communication.

‡ 298 to 1000°K.

Example 5-1. The molal heat capacity of methane in the zero-pressure state is given by the equation

$$C_p^* = 3.381 + 18.044 \times 10^{-3}T - 4.300 \times 10^{-6}T^2$$

where C_p^* is in Btu/(lb mole)(°F) or cal/(g mole)(°C) and T is in degrees Kelvin. Develop equations for C_p^* in terms of the temperature in
(a) Degrees Rankine
(b) Degrees Fahrenheit
(c) Degrees centigrade
The units of C_p^* are to remain unchanged.

Solution. (a) T in the given equation stands for degrees Kelvin:

$$T°K = \frac{T°R}{1.8}$$

Thus,

$$C_p^* = 3.381 + 18.044 \times 10^{-3}\left(\frac{T}{1.8}\right) - 4.300 \times 10^{-6}\left(\frac{T}{1.8}\right)^2$$

or

$$C_p^* = 3.381 + 10.03 \times 10^{-3}T - 1.327 \times 10^{-6}T^2$$

where T is in degrees Rankine.

(b)
$$T°K = \frac{t°F + 460}{1.8}$$

Thus,

$$C_p^* = 3.381 + 18.044 \times 10^{-3}\left(\frac{t + 460}{1.8}\right) - 4.300 \times 10^{-6}\left(\frac{t + 460}{1.8}\right)^2$$

or

$$C_p^* = 7.79 + 8.81 \times 10^{-3}t - 1.327 \times 10^{-6}t^2$$

where t is in degrees Fahrenheit.

(c)
$$T°K = t°C + 273$$

Therefore,

$$C_p^* = 3.381 + 18.044 \times 10^{-3}(t + 273) - 4.300 \times 10^{-6}(t + 273)^2$$

or

$$C_p^* = 7.99 + 15.70 \times 10^{-3}t - 4.300 \times 10^{-6}t^2$$

where t is in degrees centigrade.

Example 5-2. (a) Using the equation given in Example 5-1, calculate the heat required in Btu to raise the temperature of 1 lb mole of methane from 500 to 1000°F in a flow process at a pressure of approximately 1 atm.

(b) How much heat in calories is required to raise the temperature of 1 g mole of methane from 500 to 1000°F?

Solution. The general energy balance for a steady-flow process reduces to $Q = \Delta H$ if kinetic- and potential-energy changes are neglected. At a pressure of 1 atm, methane will behave essentially as an ideal gas. Hence $\Delta H = \int C_p^* \, dT$, and

$$Q = \int_{T_1}^{T_2} C_p^* \, dT$$

$$T_1 = 500°F = 960°R = 533°K = 260°C$$
$$T_2 = 1000°F = 1460°R = 811°K = 538°C$$

(a) The units of T used in evaluating Q must be consistent. Several courses are open. If the equation used for C_p^* is

$$C_p^* = 3.381 + 18.044 \times 10^{-3}T - 4.300 \times 10^{-6}T^2$$

where T is in degrees Kelvin, then the limits on the integral must also be in degrees Kelvin. Thus

$$Q = \int_{533}^{811} (3.381 + 18.044 \times 10^{-3}T - 4.300 \times 10^{-6}T^2)\, dT$$

In this case C_p^* is multiplied by dT in units of degrees Kelvin and the units of the integral and hence of Q are either

$$[\text{Btu}/(\text{lb mole})(°F)](°K) \quad \text{or} \quad [\text{cal}/(\text{g mole})(°C)](°K)$$

In either case this result must be multiplied by 1.8 to obtain the units of Btu per pound mole. Thus

$$(1.8)[\text{Btu}/(\text{lb mole})(°F)](°K) = (\text{Btu}/\text{lb mole}) \left(\frac{1.8°K}{°F} \right)$$

$$= (\text{Btu}/\text{lb mole}) \left(\frac{°R}{°F} \right) = \text{Btu}/\text{lb mole}$$

or

$$(1.8)[\text{cal}/(\text{g mole})(°C)](°K) = (1.8)(\text{cal}/\text{g mole}) \left(\frac{°K}{°C} \right)$$

$$= (1.8)(\text{cal}/\text{g mole}) = \text{Btu}/\text{lb mole}$$

It should be noted here that degrees Rankine have been canceled against degrees Fahrenheit and degrees Kelvin against degrees centigrade. This is possible because these symbols in each case stand for a *change* in temperature. The size of a Fahrenheit degree is the same as that of a Rankine degree, and that of a centigrade degree is the same as that of a Kelvin degree. Thus

$$Q = (1.8) \int_{533}^{811} (3.381 + 18.044 \times 10^{-3}T - 4.300 \times 10^{-6}T^2)\, dT$$

Integration gives

$$Q = 6750 \text{ Btu}/\text{lb mole}$$

The same result is obtained directly by integration of the equations for C_p^* developed in parts (a) and (b) of Example 5-1 when all temperatures are expressed in degrees Rankine or degrees Fahrenheit, respectively.

(b) In this case the direct integration of the equation for C_p^* with all temperatures in degrees Kelvin gives the desired result. The most convenient units in the integral

$$Q = \int_{T_1}^{T_2} C_p^*\, dT$$

are

$$[\text{cal}/(\text{g mole})(°C)](°K) = \text{cal}/\text{g mole}$$

Hence

$$Q = \int_{533}^{811} (3.381 + 18.044 \times 10^{-3}T - 4.300 \times 10^{-6}T^2)\, dT$$

and

$$Q = 3750 \text{ cal}/\text{g mole}$$

The same result is obtained if the equation for C_p^* developed in part (c) of Example 5-1 is used, provided that all temperatures are expressed in degrees centigrade.

Since $\int C_p^* \, dT$ must be evaluated frequently, a short-cut method for doing so has been developed and is often used for the more common gases. The definite integral may always be written $C_{p_{\text{mean}}}^* \, \Delta T$, provided that the proper mean value of C_p^* is used. If integration is between the limits of T_0 and T, and if Eq. (5-1) is used to express C_p^* as a function of T,

$$\int_{T_0}^{T} C_p^* \, dT = C_{p_{\text{mean}}}^*(T - T_0) = \alpha(T - T_0) + \frac{\beta}{2}(T^2 - T_0^2) + \frac{\gamma}{3}(T^3 - T_0^3)$$

or

$$C_{p_{\text{mean}}}^* = \alpha + \frac{\beta}{2}(T + T_0) + \frac{\gamma}{3}(T^2 + TT_0 + T_0^2) \qquad (5\text{-}3)$$

If T_0 is taken to be constant at some base temperature such as 298°K (25°C or 77°F) and T is allowed to vary, values of $C_{p_{\text{mean}}}^*$ may be calculated for the temperature interval from T_0 to the variable temperature T. For a given gas, Eq. (5-3) relates $C_{p_{\text{mean}}}^*$ to the single variable T, and a table or graph of the values of $C_{p_{\text{mean}}}^*$ for various gases as a function of T may be prepared. Then in subsequent work the integration can be carried out by the simple expression

$$\int_{T_0}^{T} C_p^* \, dT = C_{p_{\text{mean}}}^*(T - T_0) \qquad (5\text{-}4)$$

Such a graph for a number of common gases is shown in Fig. 5-1. These results were calculated from experimental data, with t_0 taken as 77°F ($T_0 = 460 + 77$). The values of $C_{p_{\text{mean}}}^*$ read from this graph are mean values between the base temperature T_0 and the upper temperature limit T and are plotted against this upper temperature limit. The temperatures shown on the graph are in degrees Fahrenheit as a matter of convenience. Thus for CO_2 the value of 12.1 Btu/(lb mole)(°F) or cal/(g mole)(°C) read for $C_{p_{\text{mean}}}^*$ at 2000°F is the mean value between 77 and 2000°F.

It might appear that this method is of restricted utility because the lower temperature limit T_0 is always the same. However, the method may be used for changes between any two temperatures by dividing the integral $\int_{T_1}^{T_2} C_p^* \, dT$ into two parts as follows:

$$Q = \Delta H = \int_{T_1}^{T_2} C_p^* \, dT = \int_{T_0}^{T_2} C_p^* \, dT - \int_{T_0}^{T_1} C_p^* \, dT = C_{p_{\text{mean}}}^*(T_2 - T_0) - C_{p_{\text{mean}}}^*(T_1 - T_0)$$

The two integrals on the right can then be evaluated from Fig. 5-1.

Gas mixtures of constant composition may be treated in exactly the same way as pure gases. The additional problem involved, as is always the case when mixtures are considered, is that of calculating mixture properties from the properties of the pure components. In this instance, the problem is easy since the heat capacities discussed here apply to

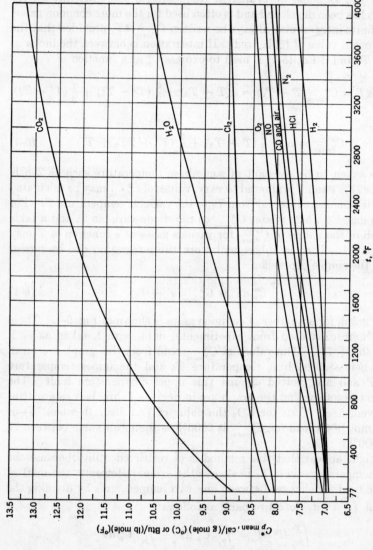

FIG. 5-1a. Mean molal heat capacities of gases in the ideal-gas state. Base temperature, 77°F. [Based mainly on data from D. D. Wagman (ed.), Selected Values of Chemical Thermodynamic Properties, National Bureau of Standards.]

126

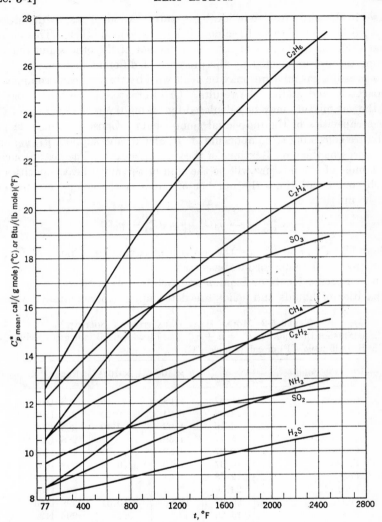

FIG. 5-1b. Mean molal heat capacities of gases in the ideal-gas state.　Base temperature, 77°F.　[*Based mainly on data from D. D. Wagman* (ed.), *Selected Values of Chemical Thermodynamic Properties, National Bureau of Standards.*]

gases in the zero-pressure or ideal-gas state. An ideal gas, by definition, is a gas whose molecules have no influence on one another. This means that each gas exists in a mixture independent of the others and that its properties are unaffected by the presence of different molecules. Thus low-pressure gas mixtures may be dealt with by treating each component separately and adding the results. Or alternatively the heat capacity of the gas mixture may be calculated by taking the molal average of the heat capacities of the individual components. Consider 1 mole of gas mixture consisting of components A, B, and C, and suppose y_A, y_B, and y_C represent the mole fractions of these components. The heat capacity of 1 mole of the mixture will be the sum of the molal heat capacities of each component times the number of moles of the component present in the mixture, or

$$C^*_{p_{\text{mixture}}} = y_A C^*_{p_A} + y_B C^*_{p_B} + y_C C^*_{p_C} \tag{5-5}$$

where $C^*_{p_A}$, $C^*_{p_B}$, and $C^*_{p_C}$ are the molal heat capacities of pure A, B, and C in the zero-pressure or ideal-gas state.

5-2. Specific Heats of Liquids and Solids. As with gases, the heat capacities of liquids and solids are determined experimentally. Again

TABLE 5-2. MOLAL HEAT CAPACITIES OF SOLIDS†

Constants for the equation $C_p = a + bT + c/T^2$, where T is in degrees Kelvin and C_p is Btu/(lb mole)(°F) or cal/(g mole)(°C).

Solid	a	$b \times 10^3$	$c \times 10^{-5}$	Range, °K
CaO...............	11.67	1.08	−1.56	298–1800
CaCO₃.............	24.98	5.24	−6.20	298–1200
C (graphite).........	4.10	1.02	−2.10	298–2300
Cu.................	5.41	1.59	....	298–1357
CuO...............	9.27	4.80	....	298–1250
Fe (α).............	3.37	7.10	0.43	298–1033
FeO...............	12.38	1.62	−0.38	298–1200
Fe₂O₃.............	23.36	17.24	−3.08	298–1100
Fe₃O₄.............	39.92	18.86	−10.01	298–1100
FeS...............	15.20	.....	....	298–412
NH₄Cl.............	11.80	32.00	....	298–458
Na.................	5.00	5.36	....	298–371
NaCl...............	10.98	3.90	....	298–1073
NaOH.............	19.2	.....	....	298–595
S (rhombic).........	3.58	6.24	....	298–369

† Selected from K. K. Kelley, *U.S. Bur. Mines, Bull.* 476, 1949.

Eq. (5-1) is the type of function most commonly used. For liquids and solids the heat capacities are usually given on a unit-mass basis and are called specific heats. Under common conditions, pressure has little influ-

Specific heat: B.t.u./(lb)(deg. F.) or colories/(gm.)(deg.C.)

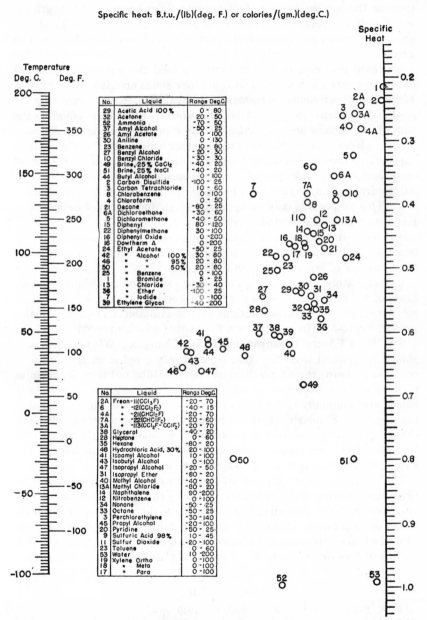

No.	Liquid	Range Deg.C.
29	Acetic Acid 100%	0 - 80
32	Acetone	20 - 50
52	Ammonia	-70 - 50
37	Amyl Alcohol	-50 - 25
26	Amyl Acetate	0 -100
30	Aniline	0 -130
23	Benzene	10 - 80
27	Benzyl Alcohol	-20 - 30
10	Benzyl Chloride	-30 - 30
49	Brine, 25% CaCl₂	-40 - 20
51	Brine, 25% NaCl	-40 - 20
44	Butyl Alcohol	0 -100
2	Carbon Disulfide	-100 - 25
3	Carbon Tetrachloride	10 - 60
8	Chlorobenzene	0 -100
4	Chloroform	0 - 50
21	Decane	-80 - 25
6A	Dichloroethane	-30 - 60
5	Dichloromethane	-40 - 50
15	Diphenyl	80 -120
22	Diphenylmethane	30 -100
16	Diphenyl Oxide	0 -200
16	Dowtherm A	0 -200
24	Ethyl Acetate	-50 - 25
42	" Alcohol 100%	30 - 80
46	" " 95%	20 - 80
50	" " 50%	20 - 80
25	" Benzene	0 -100
1	" Bromide	5 - 25
13	" Chloride	-30 - 40
36	" Ether	-100 - 25
7	" Iodide	0 -100
39	Ethylene Glycol	-40 -200

No.	Liquid	Range Deg.C.
2A	Freon-11(CCl₃F)	-20 - 70
6	" -12(CCl₂F₂)	-40 - 15
4A	" -21(CHCl₂F)	-20 - 70
7A	" -22(CHClF₂)	-20 - 60
3A	" -113(CCl₂F-CClF₂)	-20 - 70
38	Glycerol	-40 - 20
28	Heptane	0 - 60
35	Hexane	-80 - 20
48	Hydrochloric Acid, 30%	20 -100
41	Isoamyl Alcohol	10 -100
43	Isobutyl Alcohol	0 -100
47	Isopropyl Alcohol	-20 - 50
31	Isopropyl Ether	-80 - 20
40	Methyl Alcohol	-40 - 20
13A	Methyl Chloride	-80 - 20
14	Naphthalene	90 -200
12	Nitrobenzene	0 -100
34	Nonane	-50 - 25
33	Octane	-50 - 25
3	Perchlorethylene	-30 -140
45	Propyl Alcohol	-20 -100
20	Pyridine	-50 - 25
9	Sulfuric Acid 98%	10 - 45
11	Sulfur Dioxide	-20 -100
23	Toluene	0 - 60
53	Water	10 -200
19	Xylene Ortho	0 -100
18	" Meta	0 -100
17	" Para	0 -100

FIG. 5-2. Specific heats of liquids. (*Chilton, Colburn, and Vernon, personal communication. Based mainly on data from "International Critical Tables," McGraw-Hill Book Company, Inc., New York. Reproduced by permission.*)

ence on the specific heats of liquids and solids; hence c_p and c_v are not usually distinguished. Although the effect of temperature must frequently be taken into account, it is not so pronounced as is the case with gases.

The available data for heat capacities of solid elements and compounds are summarized by Kelly.[1] Data for a few solids are given in Table 5-2. Where no experimental information is available, Kopp's rule may be used. This states that the *molal heat capacity* at 20°C is equal to the sum of the atomic heat capacities of the elements making up the compound. Kopp suggested that the following values for the atomic heat capacity be used in obtaining heat capacities for compounds: 6.4 for all the elements with high molecular weight; boron, 2.7; carbon, 1.8; fluorine, 5.0; hydrogen, 2.3; oxygen, 4.0; phosphorus, 5.4; silicon, 3.5; and sulfur, 5.4. This proposal is only an approximation, and errors of considerable magnitude may be expected in certain cases.

Tables of specific heats of liquids are available in the literature, and much of this information has been summarized by Perry.[2] Specific heats for a number of liquids are given in Fig. 5-2.

Unfortunately, no simple general rule exists for combining specific heats of the pure components to give the specific heats of liquid or solid solutions. Where data for solutions are not available, an equation analogous to Eq. (5-5) is frequently used for want of a better procedure.

5-3. Heat Effects Accompanying Phase Changes. When a pure substance is liquefied from the solid state or vaporized from the liquid at constant pressure, there is no change in temperature, but there is a definite transfer of heat from the surroundings to the substance. These heat effects are commonly called the *latent heat of fusion* and the *latent heat of vaporization.* Similarly, there are heats of transition accompanying the change of a substance from one solid state to another; for example, the heat absorbed when rhombic crystalline sulfur changes to the monoclinic structure at 95°C and 1 atm pressure is 86 cal/g atom.

The characteristic feature of all such processes is the coexistence of two phases, so that the state is determined by the specification of but one intensive property (according to the phase rule the system is univariant). Under such conditions there is a fundamental relationship between the latent heat accompanying the transfer of material between the two phases and p-v-T data for the system. This is the *Clausius-Clapeyron equation:*

$$\frac{dp'}{dT} = \frac{\Delta H}{T \, \Delta v} \tag{5-6}$$

[1] K. K. Kelley, *U.S. Bur. Mines, Bull.* 476, 1949.
[2] J. H. Perry (ed.), "Chemical Engineers' Handbook," 3d ed., pp. 225–228, McGraw-Hill Book Company, Inc., New York, 1950. (Extensive data for gases and solids are also given in this reference.)

where dp'/dT = rate of change of phase-equilibrium pressure (or vapor
　　　　　　 pressure) with temperature
　　　ΔH = latent heat
　　　Δv = volume change accompanying the phase change at spe-
　　　　　　 cific temperature T

The derivation of this equation is simple once the second law has been
introduced. Therefore, its development will be delayed until Chap. 7.
If experimental p-v-T data are available, latent heats are readily calculated by Eq. (5-6).

If Eq. (5-6) is applied to the vaporization of a pure liquid, dp'/dT
becomes the slope of the vapor-pressure vs. temperature curve at the
temperature in question, Δv is the difference between the volume of the
saturated vapor and the saturated liquid, and ΔH is the latent heat of
vaporization.

Equation (5-6) can be converted to a simpler integrated form provided
that certain assumptions are made regarding the behavior of the substance during vaporization. At low pressures the volume of the saturated
gas is large with respect to that of the liquid so that $\Delta v = v_g$ is a good
approximation. Also at low pressures the volume of the saturated vapor
can in many cases be calculated from the ideal-gas law with little error.
With these two assumptions Eq. (5-6) can be written

$$\frac{dp'}{dT} = \frac{\Delta H}{Tv_g} = \frac{(\Delta H)p'}{RT^2}$$

or

$$\frac{d(\ln p')}{dT} = \frac{\Delta H}{RT^2} \tag{5-7}$$

Over a small temperature range, Eq. (5-7) may be integrated without
serious error by assuming ΔH to be constant:

$$\int_{p'_1}^{p'_2} d(\ln p') = \frac{\Delta H}{R} \int_{T_1}^{T_2} \frac{dT}{T^2}$$

$$\ln \frac{p'_2}{p'_1} = \frac{-\Delta H}{R}\left(\frac{1}{T_2} - \frac{1}{T_1}\right) \tag{5-8}$$

This expression (the Clapeyron equation) can be used to calculate the
average ΔH over the range T_1 to T_2 when the corresponding vapor pressures p'_1 and p'_2 are known. It must be remembered that the accuracy
of the result is dependent upon the validity of the three assumptions used
to develop Eq. (5-8). For example, near the critical point the saturated-
liquid volume is of the same order of magnitude as v_g; hence, the first
assumption is not true. Likewise, the saturated-gas volume could not
be accurately determined by the ideal-gas law near the critical point.
Hence, the accuracy of Eq. (5-8) increases as the pressure decreases.

The advantage of Eq. (5-8) over (5-6) lies in the fact that no volumetric data are necessary for its application.

Example 5-3. The vapor pressures of water at 212 and 222°F are 14.7 and 17.9 psia, respectively. Estimate the average heat of vaporization of water between 212 and 222°F.

Solution. Equation (5-8) may be used directly.

$$\Delta H = \frac{RT_1 T_2}{T_2 - T_1} \ln \frac{p_2'}{p_1'} = \frac{(1.987)(672)(682)}{682 - 672} \ln \frac{17.9}{14.7}$$

$$= 17,800 \text{ Btu/lb mole or } 990 \text{ Btu/lb}_m$$

The actual average value of ΔH between 212 and 222°F is 967 Btu/lb$_m$. An error of 2.4 per cent is introduced by use of the approximate equation. If the rigorous equation (5-6) were used with experimental values of Δv and dp'/dT, the exact value of ΔH could be computed. However, it should be noted that accurate values of dp'/dT can be determined only from accurate vapor-pressure data by precise differentiation techniques.

Latent heats may also be measured calorimetrically. Experimental values are available at selected temperatures for many substances. For example, extensive lists are given by Perry.[1] However, such data are frequently unavailable at the desired temperature, and in many cases the p-v-T data necessary for the use of Eq. (5-6) are also not known. In this event approximate methods must be used to estimate the heat effect accompanying a phase change. Since the vaporization of a liquid is by far the most important from a practical standpoint, most of the investigations have been for this case. The methods developed are of two types: (1) means of predicting the heat of vaporization at the normal (atmospheric-pressure) boiling point and (2) means of estimating the heat of vaporization at any temperature from the known value at a single temperature.

The simplest method for predicting ΔH at the normal boiling point is by the use of Trouton's rule, which states that the ratio of the molal heat of vaporization to the absolute boiling point is a constant for all liquids. Actually, this ratio varies over a considerable range. It is about 26 for water and 17 for nitrogen but is close to 21 for a number of substances. A more accurate method is based upon the equation developed by Kistiakowsky:[2]

$$\frac{\Delta H_n}{T_n} = 8.75 + 1.987 \ln T_n \tag{5-9}$$

where T_n = normal boiling point, °K

     ΔH_n = molal latent heat of vaporization at normal boiling point, cal/g mole

[1] *Ibid.*, pp. 210–216.

[2] W. Kistiakowsky, *Z. physik. Chem.*, **107**, 65 (1923).

Equation (5-9) is reasonably accurate for nonpolar substances but may be in error for polar materials such as water and aldehydes.   For example, for water Eq. (5-9) gives

$$\Delta H_n = [8.75 + 1.987 \ln (273 + 100)](373)$$
$$= (8.75 + 11.75)(373) = 7640 \text{ cal/g mole}$$

This corresponds to 764 Btu/lb$_m$ while the experimental value is 970 Btu/lb$_m$.   Trouton's rule and Kistiakowsky's equation predict the heat of vaporization at T_n from but one item of experimental data, *viz.*, the normal boiling point.

A number of methods have been developed for estimating the latent heat of vaporization of pure liquids at any temperature from the knowledge of its value at a single temperature.   This value may be experimental, or it may be estimated by Eq. (5-9) for nonpolar substances or by Eq. (5-8) if two values of the vapor pressure are known.   Of the many methods proposed, that of Su[1] best combines accuracy and simplicity.

The basic assumption of this method is that the ratio of the latent heat ΔH of a pure substance at any reduced temperature T_r to the latent heat ΔH_0 of the substance at a base reduced temperature of T_{r_0} is nearly the same for all substances.   Thus a plot of the ratio $\Delta H/\Delta H_0$ vs. T_r for one substance should give a curve approximately valid for all pure materials, provided that ΔH_0 is taken at the same reduced temperature for all materials.   Such a plot, based on the data for water, is shown in Fig. 5-3.   The reference temperature for water was taken as 32°F or $T_{r_0} = 0.424$.   If the latent heat of any other pure material is known or can be approximated for a single temperature, values at other temperatures may be estimated by means of this graph.   The known value may be for any temperature, but in most cases it will be for the normal boiling point.

For a particular substance, assume that the latent heat ΔH_1 is known at the reduced temperature T_{r_1}.   It is required to estimate the latent heat ΔH_2 at the reduced temperature T_{r_2}.   The values $\Delta H_1/\Delta H_0$ and $\Delta H_2/\Delta H_0$ are read from Fig. 5-3 for the reduced temperatures T_{r_1} and T_{r_2}.   Since ΔH_0 is constant for a given material,

$$\frac{\text{Ordinate on chart at } T_{r_2}}{\text{Ordinate on chart at } T_{r_1}} = \frac{\Delta H_2/\Delta H_0}{\Delta H_1/\Delta H_0} = \frac{\Delta H_2}{\Delta H_1} \tag{5-10}$$

The only unknown in this equation is ΔH_2.   The data required are a single value of the latent heat and the critical temperature of the substance.

Example 5-4.   Given that the normal boiling point of methane is 111.5°K and that its critical temperature is 191.1°K, estimate the latent heat at a temperature of 165°K.

[1] G. J. Su, *Ind. Eng. Chem.*, **38**, 923 (1946).

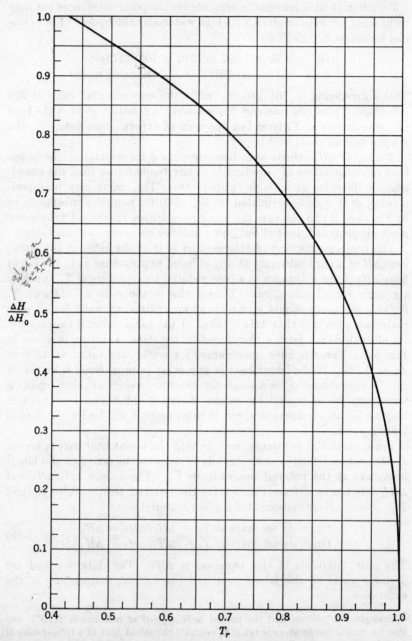

Fig. 5-3. Latent heats of vaporization as a function of reduced temperature. [*Based on an article by G. J. Su, Ind. Eng. Chem.*, **38**, 923 (1946). *By permission.*]

Solution. By Eq. (5-9),

$$\Delta H_n = (8.75 + 1.987 \ln T_n)T_n = (8.75 + 1.987 \ln 111.5)(111.5)$$
$$\Delta H_n = 2020 \text{ cal/g mole}$$

At the normal boiling point,

$$T_r = \frac{111.5}{191.1} = 0.584$$

and from Fig. 5-3, $\Delta H_n/\Delta H_0 = 0.895$.

At 165°K,

$$T_r = \frac{165}{191.1} = 0.865$$

Then from Fig. 5-3, $\Delta H_{165}/\Delta H_0 = 0.595$.

Substituting these figures in Eq. (5-10) gives

$$\frac{0.595}{0.895} = \frac{\Delta H_{165}}{2020}$$

Thus

$$\Delta H_{165} = \left(\frac{0.595}{0.895}\right)(2020) = 1344 \text{ cal/g mole, or } 84 \text{ cal/g}$$

The accepted value is also 84.0 cal/g.

5-4. The Standard Heat of Reaction. The heat quantities considered up to this point have been for physical processes. Chemical reactions as well are generally accompanied by the evolution or absorption of heat, because of the differences in molecular structure, and therefore in energy, of the products and reactants. For example, if the products of a reaction possess greater energy as a result of their structure than the reactants, it will be necessary to supply energy to accomplish the reaction.

There are a vast number of possible chemical reactions, and each may be carried out in many ways. For each reaction carried out in a particular way, there is a particular heat effect. It would be an impossible task to tabulate all possible heat effects resulting from chemical reactions. Therefore, methods are necessary for *calculating* the heat effect for any reaction from data for certain specific types of reactions carried out in some standard way. Such methods reduce the required data to a minimum.

The exact amount of heat required for a definite reaction depends upon the temperatures of the reactants and the products. If the reactants enter the reaction zone at a high temperature, their sensible heat will supply part of the heat of reaction. If the products leave the reaction zone at a low temperature, the heat requirement will be further decreased. In order to have a consistent basis for treating reaction heat effects, the heat of reaction is defined for the particular process where the products are restored to the same temperature as the reactants.

Consider the flow-calorimeter method of evaluating heats of combustion of gases. The fuel is mixed with air at room temperature and ignited, and the products of combustion are cooled to the temperature of the reactants by contact with a cooling jacket through which water is flowing. The actual process is complicated. The rate of burning of the fuel is rapid with respect to the rate of heat transfer to the cooling jacket. Hence, the actual operation could be approximated by a two-step process, the adiabatic reaction followed by cooling of the gases to room temperature. This is not exactly true, for there is some heat transfer to the jacket during the reaction. However, these difficulties regarding the actual mechanism of the process need not complicate the calculation of the heat effect of this reaction, because the over-all energy balance for this steady-flow process [Eq. (2-10)] reduces to

$$Q = \Delta H$$

No shaft work is produced by the process, and the calorimeter is built so that changes in potential and kinetic energy are negligible. Thus it is clear that the heat Q absorbed by the water is identical with the enthalpy change caused by the combustion reaction, and universal practice is to designate ΔH as the *heat of reaction*. The fact that the heat of reaction is a property change is of great importance, for it becomes independent of the path followed in going from an initial to a final state. Thus the heat of reaction may be calculated by any convenient path, just as long as the over-all change is from the desired initial to final states.

For purposes of tabulating data, it is necessary to define a *standard heat of reaction*. Since ΔH is a property change, a standard value of the heat of reaction depends only on the definition of *standard states* for the reactants and products. The only fixed convention is that the standard states of the products and reactants must be at the same temperature. Thus the standard heat of reaction is defined as the difference between the enthalpies of the products in their standard states and the enthalpies of the reactants in their standard states *all at the same temperature T*. Within this limitation, the choice of a standard state for a particular reactant or product is a matter of convenience. Fortunately, only a few standard states have been found convenient enough to come into general use. For gases, the standard state is taken as the pure gas in the ideal-gas state at 1 atm. For liquids and solids the standard state is usually taken as the pure liquid or solid at 1 atm. Although other states are possible as standard states, these are by far the most useful, and no others will be considered in this book. Property values in the standard state will be designated by the superscript °.

It will be noted that the standard state chosen for gases is a hypothetical one, for at 1 atm actual gases are not ideal. However, they seldom deviate much from ideality, and in most instances the ideal-gas state at 1 atm may be regarded for practical purposes as the actual state of the gas at atmospheric pressure. Since pressure does not affect the enthalpy of an ideal gas, the enthalpy in the ideal-gas state at 1 atm is identical with that in the zero-pressure state.

When a heat of reaction is given for a particular reaction, it applies for the stoichiometric numbers as written. If each stoichiometric number is doubled, the heat of reaction is doubled. For example, the ammonia-synthesis reaction may be written

$$\tfrac{1}{2}N_2 + \tfrac{3}{2}H_2 \rightarrow NH_3 \qquad \Delta H^\circ_{298} = -11,040 \text{ cal}$$

or

$$N_2 + 3H_2 \rightarrow 2NH_3 \qquad \Delta H^\circ_{298} = -22,080 \text{ cal}$$

The symbol ΔH°_{298} indicates that the heat of reaction is the *standard* value for a temperature of 298°K.

5-5. The Standard Heat of Formation. Even limited to standard heats of reaction, it would not be possible to tabulate data for the vast number of possible reactions. However, the standard heat of reaction for any reaction can be calculated if the *heats of formation* of the compounds taking part in the reaction are known. A *formation reaction* is defined as a reaction which forms a single compound *from the elements which make it up.* For example, the reaction $C + \tfrac{1}{2}O_2 + 2H_2 \rightarrow CH_3OH$ is the formation reaction for methyl alcohol. The reaction $H_2O + SO_3 \rightarrow H_2SO_4$ is not a formation reaction since it represents the synthesis of sulfuric acid not from the elements, but from other compounds. Formation reactions are always understood to result in the formation of 1 mole of the compound, *and the heat of formation is therefore based on 1 mole of the compound formed.*

Since heats of reaction at any temperature can be calculated if the value for one temperature is known, the tabulation of data reduces to the compilation of *standard heats of formation* at a single temperature. The modern choice for this temperature is 25°C (298°K), though some older data are given for 18°C. The standard heat of formation of a compound at 25°C is represented by the symbol $\Delta H^\circ_{f_{298}}$. The superscript ° indicates that it is the standard value, the subscript f shows that it is a heat of formation, and the 298 is the absolute temperature in °K. Tables of these values for common substances may be found in the standard handbooks, but the most extensive compilations available will be found in the publications of Rossini and coworkers.[1] Values for heats of formation are usually reported in the units of calories per gram mole. An abridged list of values is given in Table 5-3.

[1] F. D. Rossini et al., "Selected Values of Physical and Thermodynamic Properties of Hydrocarbons and Related Compounds," American Petroleum Institute Research Project 44, Carnegie Institute of Technology, Pittsburgh, 1953. Also loose-leaf supplements.

F. D. Rossini et al., Selected Values of Chemical Thermodynamic Properties, *Natl. Bur. Standards U.S., Circ.* 500, 1952. Also loose-leaf supplements, edited by D. D. Wagman.

F. D. Rossini et al., "Selected Values of Properties of Chemical Compounds," Research Project of the Manufacturing Chemists' Association, Inc., Carnegie Institute of Technology, Pittsburgh. Issued periodically in loose-leaf form.

TABLE 5-3. STANDARD HEATS OF FORMATION AND COMBUSTION AT 25°C IN
CALORIES PER GRAM MOLE†
For combustion reactions the products are $H_2O(l)$ and $CO_2(g)$

Substance	Formula	State	ΔH°_{f298}	$-\Delta H^\circ_{c298}$
Normal paraffins:				
Methane...................	CH_4	g	$-17,889$	$212,800$
Ethane.....................	C_2H_6	g	$-20,236$	$372,820$
Propane....................	C_3H_8	g	$-24,820$	$530,600$
n-Butane...................	C_4H_{10}	g	$-30,150$	$687,640$
n-Pentane..................	C_5H_{12}	g	$-35,000$	$845,160$
n-Hexane...................	C_6H_{14}	g	$-39,960$	$1,002,570$
Increment per C atom above C_6	....	g	$-4,925$	$157,440$
Normal monoolefins (1-alkenes):				
Ethylene...................	C_2H_4	g	$12,496$	$337,230$
Propylene..................	C_3H_6	g	$4,879$	$491,990$
1-Butene...................	C_4H_8	g	-30	$649,450$
1-Pentene..................	C_5H_{10}	g	$-5,000$	$806,850$
1-Hexene...................	C_6H_{12}	g	$-9,960$	$964,260$
Increment per C atom above C_6	....	g	$-4,925$	$157,440$
Miscellaneous organic compounds:				
Acetaldehyde..............	C_2H_4O	g	$-39,760$	
Acetic acid................	$C_2H_4O_2$	l	$-116,400$	
Acetylene..................	C_2H_2	g	$54,194$	$310,620$
Benzene...................	C_6H_6	g	$19,820$	$789,080$
Benzene...................	C_6H_6	l	$11,720$	$780,980$
1,3-Butadiene.............	C_4H_6	g	$26,330$	$607,490$
Cyclohexane...............	C_6H_{12}	g	$-29,430$	$944,790$
Cyclohexane...............	C_6H_{12}	l	$-37,340$	$936,880$
Ethanol....................	C_2H_6O	g	$-56,240$	
Ethanol....................	C_2H_6O	l	$-66,356$	
Ethylbenzene..............	C_8H_{10}	g	$7,120$	$1,101,120$
Ethylene glycol............	$C_2H_6O_2$	l	$-108,580$	
Ethylene oxide.............	C_2H_4O	g	$-12,190$	
Methanol..................	CH_4O	g	$-48,100$	
Methanol..................	CH_4O	l	$-57,036$	
Methylcyclohexane..........	C_7H_{14}	g	$-36,990$	$1,099,590$
Methylcyclohexane..........	C_7H_{14}	l	$-45,450$	$1,091,130$
Styrene....................	C_8H_8	g	$35,220$	$1,060,900$
Toluene....................	C_7H_8	g	$11,950$	$943,580$
Toluene....................	C_7H_8	l	$2,870$	$934,500$
Miscellaneous inorganic compounds:				
Ammonia..................	NH_3	g	$-11,040$	
Calcium carbide............	CaC_2	s	$-15,000$	
Calcium carbonate.........	$CaCO_3$	s	$-288,450$	
Calcium chloride...........	$CaCl_2$	s	$-190,000$	
Calcium chloride...........	$CaCl_2 \cdot 6H_2O$	s	$-623,150$	
Calcium hydroxide..........	$Ca(OH)_2$	s	$-235,800$	
Calcium oxide..............	CaO	s	$-151,900$	

TABLE 5-3. STANDARD HEATS OF FORMATION AND COMBUSTION AT 25°C IN
CALORIES PER GRAM MOLE (*Continued*)
For combustion reactions the products are $H_2O(l)$ and $CO_2(g)$

Substance	Formula	State	ΔH°_{f298}	$-\Delta H^\circ_{c298}$
Carbon....................	C	Graphite	....	94,052
Carbon dioxide...............	CO_2	g	−94,052	
Carbon monoxide.............	CO	g	−26,416	67,636
Hydrochloric acid............	HCl	g	−22,063	
Hydrogen..................	H_2	g	....	68,317
Hydrogen sulfide.............	H_2S	g	−4,815	
Iron oxide..................	FeO	s	−64,300	
Iron oxide..................	Fe_3O_4	s	−267,000	
Iron oxide..................	Fe_2O_3	s	−196,500	
Iron sulfide.................	FeS_2	s	−42,520	
Lithium chloride.............	LiCl	s	−97,700	
Lithium chloride.............	$LiCl \cdot H_2O$	s	−170,310	
Lithium chloride.............	$LiCl \cdot 2H_2O$	s	−242,100	
Lithium chloride.............	$LiCl \cdot 3H_2O$	s	−313,500	
Nitric acid.................	HNO_3	l	−41,404	
Nitrogen oxides.............	NO	g	21,600	
	NO_2	g	8,041	
	N_2O	g	19,490	
	N_2O_4	g	2,309	
Sodium carbonate............	Na_2CO_3	s	−270,300	
Sodium carbonate............	$Na_2CO_3 \cdot 10H_2O$	s	−975,600	
Sodium chloride..............	NaCl	s	−98,232	
Sodium hydroxide............	NaOH	s	−101,990	
Sulfur dioxide...............	SO_2	g	−70,960	
Sulfur trioxide..............	SO_3	g	−94,450	
Sulfur trioxide..............	SO_3	l	−104,800	
Sulfuric acid................	H_2SO_4	l	−193,910	
Water.....................	H_2O	g	−57,798	
Water.....................	H_2O	l	−68,317	

† Most values have been selected from the publications of F. D. Rossini et al.,
"Selected Values of Physical and Thermodynamic Properties of Hydrocarbons and
Related Compounds," American Petroleum Institute Research Project 44, Carnegie
Institute of Technology, Pittsburgh, 1953; Selected Values of Chemical Thermo-
dynamic Properties, *Natl. Bur. Standards U.S.*, *Circ.* 500, 1952.

It was mentioned that the standard heat of any reaction may be calculated from the standard heats of formation of the compounds taking
part in the reaction. Chemical equations may be combined by addition
and subtraction, and the standard heats of reaction associated with each
equation may likewise be combined to give the standard heat of reaction
associated with the resulting equation. This is possible because enthalpy
is a property, and changes in it are independent of path. In particular,
formation equations and standard heats of formation may always be

combined to produce any desired equation (not itself a formation equation) and its accompanying standard heat of reaction. Equations written for this purpose should include an indication of the physical state of each reactant and product, *i.e.*, the letter *g*, *l*, or *s* should be placed in parentheses after the chemical symbol to show whether it is a gas, a liquid, or a solid. This might seem unnecessary since a pure material at 25°C and 1 atm can usually exist only in one physical state. However, it is often convenient to make use of fictitious states for which substances are assumed to exist in unstable form.

Consider the reaction $CO_2(g) + H_2(g) \rightarrow CO(g) + H_2O(g)$ at 25°C. This is a reaction commonly encountered in industry (the water-gas-shift reaction), though it takes place only at temperatures well above 25°C. However, the data to be used are for 25°C, and the initial step in making any calculations of thermal effects concerned with this reaction is to evaluate the standard heat of reaction at 25°C. Since the reaction is actually carried out entirely in the gas phase at high temperature, it is convenient even at 25°C to consider all reactants and products as gases in their standard states of 1 atm even though water cannot actually exist as a gas under these conditions. The formation reactions involved are

$CO_2(g)$: $C(s) + O_2(g) \rightarrow CO_2(g)$ $\Delta H^{\circ}_{f298} = -94{,}052$ cal

$H_2(g)$: Since hydrogen is an element, its heat of formation is zero

$CO(g)$: $C(s) + \frac{1}{2}O_2(g) \rightarrow CO(g)$ $\Delta H^{\circ}_{f298} = -26{,}416$ cal
$H_2O(g)$: $H_2(g) + \frac{1}{2}O_2(g) \rightarrow H_2O(g)$ $\Delta H^{\circ}_{f298} = -57{,}798$ cal

These equations can be written so that their sum gives the desired reaction:

$$
\begin{array}{ll}
CO_2(g) \rightarrow C(s) + O_2(g) & \Delta H^{\circ}_{f298} = 94{,}052\dagger \\
C(s) + \frac{1}{2}O_2(g) \rightarrow CO(g) & \Delta H^{\circ}_{f298} = -26{,}416 \\
H_2(g) + \frac{1}{2}O_2(g) \rightarrow H_2O(g) & \Delta H^{\circ}_{f298} = -57{,}798 \\
\hline
CO_2(g) + H_2(g) \rightarrow CO(g) + H_2O(g) & \Delta H^{\circ}_{298} = 9{,}838 \text{ cal}
\end{array}
$$

The meaning of this result is that the enthalpy of 1 g mole of CO plus 1 g mole of H_2O is greater than the enthalpy of 1 g mole of CO_2 plus 1 g mole of H_2 by 9838 cal when each component of the reaction is taken as the pure gas at 25°C in the ideal-gas state at 1 atm.

In this example the standard heat of formation of water was available for its hypothetical standard state as a gas at 25°C. One might expect the value of the heat of formation of water to be given for its actual state

---

† Note that the reaction as written is the reverse of the formation reaction of CO_2. The numerical value of ΔH°_{f298} is therefore the same as that given in Table 5-3, but the sign has been reversed.

as a liquid at 1 atm and 25°C.   As a matter of fact values for both states are available because they are both so frequently used.   This is true for many compounds which normally exist as liquids at 25°C and atmospheric pressure.   Cases do arise, however, where values are given for the standard state as a liquid when what is needed is the value for the gas state.   Suppose that this were the case for the preceding example and that the only value available is for the standard heat of formation of liquid water.   It now becomes necessary to include an equation for the physical change of vaporizing water.   The enthalpy change for this physical process is the latent heat of vaporization of water at 25°C:

$$CO_2(g) \rightarrow C(s) + O_2(g) \qquad \Delta H^{\circ}_{f298} = \qquad 94{,}052 \text{ cal}$$
$$C(s) + \tfrac{1}{2}O_2(g) \rightarrow CO(g) \qquad \Delta H^{\circ}_{f298} = -26{,}416$$
$$H_2(g) + \tfrac{1}{2}O_2(g) \rightarrow H_2O(l) \qquad \Delta H^{\circ}_{f298} = -68{,}317$$
$$H_2O(l) \rightarrow H_2O(g) \qquad \Delta H^{\circ}_{298} = \quad 10{,}520$$

$$\overline{CO_2(g) + H_2(g) \rightarrow CO(g) + H_2O(g) \qquad \Delta H^{\circ}_{298} = \qquad 9{,}839 \text{ cal}}$$

This result is in agreement with the original answer.

Example 5-5.   Calculate the standard heat of reaction at 25°C for the following reaction:

$$4HCl(g) + O_2(g) \rightarrow 2H_2O(g) + 2Cl_2(g)$$

Solution.   Standard heats of formation from Table 5-3 are

HCl: −22,063 cal/g mole
H₂O: −57,798 cal/g mole

The following combination gives the desired result:

$$4HCl(g) \rightarrow 2H_2(g) + 2Cl_2(g) \qquad \Delta H^{\circ}_{298} = (4)(22{,}063)$$
$$2H_2(g) + O_2(g) \rightarrow 2H_2O(g) \qquad \Delta H^{\circ}_{298} = (2)(-57{,}798)$$

$$\overline{4HCl(g) + O_2(g) \rightarrow 2H_2O(g) + 2Cl_2(g) \qquad \Delta H^{\circ}_{298} = -27{,}344 \text{ cal}}$$

5-6. The Standard Heat of Combustion.   Only a few formation reactions can actually be carried out, and therefore the data for these reactions must usually be determined indirectly.   One type of reaction which readily lends itself to experimental investigation is the combustion reaction, and many standard heats of formation have been calculated from standard heats of combustion, measured calorimetrically.   As a matter of fact, standard heats of combustion are often tabulated along with standard heats of formation.   In cases where the necessary heats of formation are not available, heats of combustion can sometimes be used directly for the calculation of standard heats of reaction.   A combustion reaction is defined as a reaction between an element or compound and oxygen to form specified combustion products.   For organic compounds made up of carbon, hydrogen, and oxygen only, the products are carbon dioxide and water, but the state of the water may be vapor or liquid. Any table of *standard heats of combustion* must be accompanied by a complete description of the combustion products and the standard states. Data are always based on 1 mole of the material burned. Values for a number of substances are given in Table 5-3.

A reaction such as the formation of *n*-butane:

$$4C(s) + 5H_2(g) \rightarrow C_4H_{10}(g)$$

cannot be carried out in practice. However, this equation can be obtained by combining the combustion reactions of its components:

$$4C(s) + 4O_2(g) \rightarrow 4CO_2(g) \qquad \Delta H^\circ_{298} = (4)(-94,052)$$
$$5H_2(g) + 2\tfrac{1}{2}O_2(g) \rightarrow 5H_2O(g) \qquad \Delta H^\circ_{298} = (5)(-57,798)$$
$$4CO_2(g) + 5H_2O(g) \rightarrow C_4H_{10}(g) + 6\tfrac{1}{2}O_2(g) \qquad \Delta H^\circ_{298} = 635,045$$

$$\overline{4C(s) + 5H_2(g) \rightarrow C_4H_{10}(g) \qquad \Delta H^\circ_{298} = -30,153 \text{ cal}}$$

This value is the same as the standard heat of formation listed for normal butane in Table 5-3.

The heat of reaction of the water-gas-shift reaction may also be calculated by combining heats of combustion. CO_2 and H_2O are already final products of combustion, and thus have no heats of combustion. Hence,

$$H_2(g) + \tfrac{1}{2}O_2(g) \rightarrow H_2O(g) \qquad \Delta H^\circ_{298} = -57,798 \text{ cal}$$
$$CO_2(g) \rightarrow CO(g) + \tfrac{1}{2}O_2(g) \qquad \Delta H^\circ_{298} = 67,636 \text{ cal}$$

$$\overline{CO_2(g) + H_2(g) \rightarrow CO(g) + H_2O(g) \qquad \Delta H^\circ_{298} = 9,838 \text{ cal}}$$

The experimental measurements of standard heats of combustion may be made in flow systems under conditions such that the over-all energy balance reduces to $Q = \Delta H$. More often, heats of combustion are determined by burning a small sample of the material in a constant-volume bomb in an atmosphere of oxygen. The technique employed is highly developed but rather specialized, and for very accurate work, the calculations are involved. For a complete description, the reader is referred to the work of Bichowsky and Rossini.[1] It should be pointed out, however, that the heat effect measured with a bomb calorimeter is not ΔH but ΔE. Since the process is nonflow, the first law is written $\Delta E = Q - W$. Combustion occurs at constant volume so that $W = 0$ and $Q = \Delta E$. From the definition of enthalpy

$$\Delta H = \Delta E + \Delta(pV)$$

[1] F. R. Bichowsky and F. D. Rossini, "Thermochemistry of the Chemical Substances," Reinhold Publishing Corporation, New York, 1936.

If the gases in the bomb are assumed ideal and if the volume of any liquid or solid present is neglected,

$$\Delta(pV) = \Delta(n_{gas}RT)$$

Thus

$$\Delta H = \Delta E + \Delta(n_{gas}RT)$$

If the reaction is carried out so that the initial and final temperatures are the same, then this equation becomes

$$\Delta H = \Delta E + (\Delta n_{gas})RT \qquad (5\text{-}11)$$

where Δn_{gas} is the difference between the number of moles of gaseous products and the number of moles of gaseous reactants. The value of ΔH calculated by Eq. (5-11) represents the change in enthalpy for the reaction as carried out *at constant volume*, whereas the value usually reported is that for a constant-pressure reaction, *i.e.*, with all reactants and products in their standard states at 1 atm. However, the ideal-gas law was assumed in deriving Eq. (5-11), and for ideal gases, enthalpy is independent of volume and pressure. In this special case, ΔH for a constant-volume process is the same as for a constant-pressure process, and Eq. (5-11) may be used to give the desired result, that is, $\Delta H°$.

Example 5-6. The experimental value for the heat evolved when liquid benzene is burned to carbon dioxide and liquid water in a constant-volume bomb calorimeter at 25°C is 780,090 cal per gram mole of benzene. Calculate the standard heat of combustion of benzene at 25°C.

Solution. The reaction considered is

$$C_6H_6(l) + 7\tfrac{1}{2}O_2(g) \rightarrow 3H_2O(l) + 6CO_2(g)$$

The experimental value given for the heat evolved at constant volume represents $-\Delta E$ for this reaction. If the gaseous components in the reaction are considered ideal, the standard heat of reaction may be calculated by Eq. (5-11):

$$\Delta H°_{298} = \Delta H = \Delta E + (\Delta n_{gas})RT$$

where $\Delta E = -780,090$ cal
$\Delta n_{gas} = 6 - 7\tfrac{1}{2} = -1\tfrac{1}{2}$
$R = 1.987$ cal/(g mole)(°K)
$T = 298°K$

Thus

$$\Delta H°_{298} = -780,090 + (-1\tfrac{1}{2})(1.987)(298)$$
$$= -780,090 - 890$$
$$= -780,980 \text{ cal}$$

The heat of combustion for this reaction is often called the *gross*, or *higher*, value because the water produced is in the liquid phase. The corresponding value when the water is in the vapor phase is designated the *net*, or *lower*, heat of combustion. The difference between the two corresponds to the heat of vaporization of the water formed.

5-7. Effect of Temperature on the Standard Heat of Reaction. In the foregoing sections, standard heats of reaction have been discussed for the base temperature of 25°C only. In this section the calculation of standard heats of reaction at other temperatures from a knowledge of the value at 25°C will be considered.

Since heats of reaction are enthalpy changes between given initial and final states, they may be calculated for any convenient path connecting these two states. Suppose that it is necessary to evaluate the standard heat of reaction at a temperature T which is above 25°C. The change accomplished by the reaction at T can also be brought about by the following three-step process:

1. Cool the reactants in their standard states from the temperature T to 298°K. For the common standard states, this process involves the cooling of the pure reactants at a constant pressure of 1 atm from T to 298°K. The total enthalpy change for this step is readily calculated if the heat capacities of the reactants are known:

$$\Delta H_R^\circ = \sum_{\text{reactants}} \left(n \int_T^{298} C_p^\circ \, dT \right) \tag{5-12}$$

where ΔH_R° represents the enthalpy change of all the reactants in their standard states during the cooling process.

2. Allow the reaction to proceed isothermally at 298°K to yield the reaction products in their standard states. The enthalpy change for this step is the known standard heat of reaction at 298°K, that is, ΔH_{298}°.

3. Heat the products in their standard states from 298°K to the temperature T. The total enthalpy change for this step is given by an equation analogous to Eq. (5-12):

$$\Delta H_P^\circ = \sum_{\text{products}} \left(n \int_{298}^T C_p^\circ \, dT \right) \tag{5-13}$$

The enthalpy change for the three-step process must be the standard heat of reaction at temperature T. Thus ΔH_T° is the sum of the enthalpy changes for the preceding steps:

$$\Delta H_T^\circ = \Delta H_R^\circ + \Delta H_{298}^\circ + \Delta H_P^\circ \tag{5-14}$$

The method of calculation is illustrated by Example 5-7.

✶Example 5-7. Calculate the standard heat of combustion of methane at 500°F (533°K). The products of combustion are $CO_2(g)$ and $H_2O(g)$.

Solution

$$CH_4(g) + 2O_2(g) \rightarrow CO_2(g) + 2H_2O(g)$$

The desired result may be obtained by the direct application of Eqs. (5-12) to (5-14). It is helpful to represent the method of calculation schematically as follows:

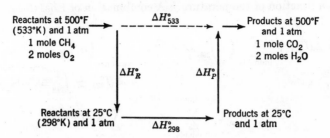

According to Eq. (5-14),

$$\Delta H^{\circ}_{533} = \Delta H^{\circ}_R + \Delta H^{\circ}_{298} + \Delta H^{\circ}_P$$

If Eqs. (5-12) and (5-13) are employed, this expression becomes

$$\Delta H^{\circ}_{533} = \Delta H^{\circ}_{298} + \sum_{\text{products}} \left(n \int_{298}^{533} C^{\circ}_p \, dT \right) - \sum_{\text{reactants}} \left(n \int_{298}^{533} C^{\circ}_p \, dT \right)$$

The integral terms of this equation may, of course, be evaluated by use of heat-capacity equations. A simpler procedure is to use mean heat capacities when they are available. In terms of mean heat capacities, the equation becomes

$$\Delta H^{\circ}_{533} = \Delta H^{\circ}_{298} + \left[\sum_{\text{products}} (nC^{\circ}_{p,\text{mean}}) - \sum_{\text{reactants}} (nC^{\circ}_{p,\text{mean}}) \right] (533 - 298)$$

The average molal heat capacities from 298 to 533°K (77 to 500°F) taken from Fig. 5-1 are as follows:

CH₄	10.0
O₂	7.3
CO₂	9.9
H₂O	8.2

From Table 5-3 the heat of combustion of methane at 25°C with liquid water as a product is −212,800 cal/g mole. Since the reaction as considered yields gaseous water as a product, the latent heat of 2 moles of water at 25°C must be added to this figure:

$$\Delta H^{\circ}_{298} = -212,800 + (2)(10,520) = -191,760 \text{ cal/g mole}$$

Substitution of these values in this equation gives

$$\Delta H^{\circ}_{533} = -191,760 + [(1)(9.9) + (2)(8.2) - (1)(10.0) - (2)(7.3)](533 - 298)$$
$$= -191,360 \text{ cal/g mole}$$

or

$$(-191,360)(1.8) = -344,450 \text{ Btu/lb mole}$$

If the heat capacities of the products and reactants are expressed as a function of temperature by equations of the form

$$C^{\circ}_p = \alpha + \beta T + \gamma T^2 \qquad (5-1)$$

an analytical expression may be developed for the standard heat of reaction as a function of temperature. A combination of Eqs. (5-12), (5-13), and (5-14) gives

$$\Delta H_T^\circ = \Delta H_{298}^\circ + \sum_{\text{products}} \left(n \int_{298}^T C_p^\circ \, dT \right) - \sum_{\text{reactants}} \left(n \int_{298}^T C_p^\circ \, dT \right)$$

$$= \Delta H_{298}^\circ + \int_{298}^T \Delta C_p^\circ \, dT \quad (5\text{-}15)$$

where

$$\Delta C_p^\circ = \sum_{\text{products}} n C_p^\circ - \sum_{\text{reactants}} n C_p^\circ$$

Suppose that the heat capacity for each product and reactant is expressed by Eq. (5-1):

$$\Delta C_p^\circ = \Delta\alpha + (\Delta\beta)T + (\Delta\gamma)T^2$$

where

$$\Delta\alpha = \sum_{\text{products}} n\alpha - \sum_{\text{reactants}} n\alpha$$

with similar definitions for $\Delta\beta$ and $\Delta\gamma$. Then Eq. (5-15) becomes

$$\Delta H_T^\circ = \Delta H_{298}^\circ + \int_{298}^T [\Delta\alpha + (\Delta\beta)T + (\Delta\gamma)T^2] \, dT$$

or

$$\Delta H_T^\circ = \Delta H_{298}^\circ + \Delta\alpha(T - 298) + \frac{\Delta\beta}{2}(T^2 - 298^2) + \frac{\Delta\gamma}{3}(T^3 - 298^3)$$

If all the constant terms in this equation are collected and lumped together in a constant designated as ΔH_0, the result is

$$\Delta H_T^\circ = \Delta H_0 + \Delta\alpha T + \frac{\Delta\beta}{2} T^2 + \frac{\Delta\gamma}{3} T^3 \quad (5\text{-}16)$$

where ΔH_T° is the standard heat of reaction at temperature T and ΔH_0 is a constant. ΔH_0 may be calculated if the standard heat of reaction is known at a single temperature, *e.g.*, 25°C.

Example 5-8. Using the data of Tables 5-1 and 5-3, develop an equation for the standard heat of the following reaction as a function of temperature between the limits 298 and 1500°K:

$$\tfrac{3}{2}H_2 + \tfrac{1}{2}N_2 \rightarrow NH_3$$

Solution. The following data are available from Table 5-1:

	α	β	γ
H_2	6.947	-0.200×10^{-3}	0.481×10^{-6}
N_2	6.524	1.250×10^{-3}	-0.001×10^{-6}
NH_3	6.086	8.812×10^{-3}	-1.506×10^{-6}

Thus

$$\Delta\alpha = 6.086 - (\tfrac{3}{2})(6.947) - (\tfrac{1}{2})(6.524) = -7.596$$
$$\Delta\beta = 8.812 \times 10^{-3} - (\tfrac{3}{2})(-0.200 \times 10^{-3}) - (\tfrac{1}{2})(1.250 \times 10^{-3})$$
$$= 8.487 \times 10^{-3}$$
$$\Delta\gamma = -1.506 \times 10^{-6} - (\tfrac{3}{2})(0.481 \times 10^{-6}) - (\tfrac{1}{2})(-0.001 \times 10^{-6})$$
$$= -2.227 \times 10^{-6}$$

For this case Eq. (5-16) becomes

$$\Delta H_T^\circ = \Delta H_0 - 7.596T + \frac{8.487 \times 10^{-3}}{2} T^2 - \frac{2.227 \times 10^{-6}}{3} T^3$$
$$= \Delta H_0 - 7.596T + 4.243 \times 10^{-3}T^2 - 0.742 \times 10^{-6}T^3$$

From Table 5-3 it is found that $\Delta H_{f\,298}^\circ = -11{,}040$ cal. This allows the calculation of the constant ΔH_0:

$$-11{,}040 = \Delta H_0 - (7.596)(298) + (4.243 \times 10^{-3})(298)^2 - (0.742 \times 10^{-6})(298)^3$$
$$\Delta H_0 = -9140$$

Therefore, the standard heat of formation of $NH_3(g)$ is given as a function of temperature by the equation

$$\Delta H_{f\,T}^\circ = -9140 - 7.596T + 4.243 \times 10^{-3}T^2 - 0.742 \times 10^{-6}T^3$$

5-8. Heat Effects of Industrial Reactions. The preceding sections have dealt with the *standard* heat of reaction. Industrial reactions are rarely carried out under standard-state conditions. Furthermore, in actual reactions the reactants may not be present in stoichiometric proportions, the reaction may not go to completion, and the final temperature may differ from the initial temperature. Moreover, inert constituents may be present, and several reactions may occur simultaneously. However, the general methods of calculating the heat effects of actual reactions are based on the principles already considered and are probably best illustrated by examples.

★ **Example 5-9.** What is the maximum temperature that can be reached by the combustion of methane with 20 per cent excess air? Both the methane and the air enter the burner at 25°C. Assume complete combustion.

Solution. The reaction is

$$CH_4 + 2O_2 \rightarrow CO_2 + 2H_2O(g) \qquad \Delta H_{298}^\circ = -191{,}760 \text{ cal}$$

Since the maximum attainable temperature is to be calculated, the process will be assumed adiabatic, that is, $Q = 0$. With the usual assumptions that the kinetic- and potential-energy terms are negligible and that there is no shaft work, the over-all energy balance for this process reduces to

$$\Delta H = 0$$

The final temperature of the products t°C is unknown and must be calculated.[1] For

---

[1] This temperature is often called the theoretical flame temperature, because it is the maximum temperature attainable in a flame resulting from the burning of the gas with the stated amount of air.

purposes of calculation, any convenient path between the initial and final states may be used.   The path chosen is indicated in the diagram.   One gram mole of methane burned will be taken as a basis.

$$\text{Moles } O_2 \text{ required} = 2.0$$
$$\text{Moles excess } O_2 = (0.2)(2.0) = 0.4$$
$$\text{Moles } N_2 \text{ entering} = (2.4)\left(\frac{79}{21}\right) = 9.03$$

The gases leaving the burner will contain 1 mole CO_2, 2 moles $H_2O(g)$, 0.4 mole O_2, and 9.03 moles N_2.

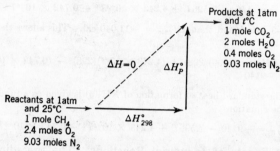

Since the enthalpy change must be the same regardless of the path considered,

$$\Delta H^\circ_{298} + \Delta H^\circ_P = \Delta H = 0$$

But

$$\Delta H^\circ_{298} = -191,760 \text{ cal}$$

and

$$\Delta H^\circ_P = \sum_{\text{products}} (nC^\circ_{pmean})(t - 25)$$

Thus

$$\sum_{\text{products}} (nC^\circ_{pmean})(t - 25) = 191,760$$

Because the mean heat capacities of the products depend on the final temperature, this equation is most conveniently solved for t by trial.   A value is assumed for the final temperature t for the purpose of determining the mean heat capacities from Fig. 5-1.   The previous equation is then solved for t.   If the result agrees with the assumed value, the equation is satisfied.   If it does not, new values of t are proposed until the assumed and calculated values agree.

As a first trial assume that $t = 2000°C$, or 3630°F.   Then

$$\left[\begin{array}{c}(1)(13.1) + (2)(10.4) + (0.4)(8.4) + (9.03)(8.0)\\ CO_2 \qquad\quad H_2O \qquad\quad O_2 \qquad\quad N_2\end{array}\right](t-25) = 191,760$$

and

$$t = 1775°C$$

It is evident that t will be less than 2000°C.   Assume that $t = 1800°C$, or 3270°F. Then

$$\left[\begin{array}{c}(1)(12.95) + (2)(10.25) + (0.4)(8.3) + (9.30)(7.9)\\ CO_2 \qquad\quad H_2O \qquad\quad O_2 \qquad\quad N_2\end{array}\right](t-25) = 191,760$$

and $$t = 1765°C$$

This result would not be appreciably changed by another trial.

Example 5-10. One method for the manufacture of "synthesis gas" (primarily a mixture of CO and H_2) is the catalytic re-forming of methane with steam at high temperature and atmospheric pressure:

$$CH_4(g) + H_2O(g) \rightarrow CO(g) + 3H_2(g)$$

The only other reaction which occurs to an appreciable extent is the water-gas-shift reaction:

$$CO(g) + H_2O(g) \rightarrow CO_2(g) + H_2(g)$$

If the reactants are supplied in the ratio of 2 moles of steam to 1 mole of methane and if heat is supplied to the reactor so that the products reach a temperature of 1300°K, the methane will be completely converted, and the product stream will contain 17.4 mole per cent CO. Assuming the reactants to be preheated to 600°K, calculate the heat requirement for the reactor.

Solution. The standard heats of reaction at 25°C for the two reactions involved are readily calculated from the data of Table 5-3:

$$CH_4(g) + H_2O(g) \rightarrow CO(g) + 3H_2(g) \qquad \Delta H°_{298} = 49,270 \text{ cal}$$
$$CO(g) + H_2O(g) \rightarrow CO_2(g) + H_2(g) \qquad \Delta H°_{298} = -9840 \text{ cal}$$

These two reactions may be added to give a third reaction:

$$CH_4(g) + 2H_2O(g) \rightarrow CO_2(g) + 4H_2(g) \qquad \Delta H°_{298} = 39,430 \text{ cal}$$

Any two of these three reactions constitute an independent set. The odd reaction is not independent since it may be obtained by a combination of the other two. The two most convenient to work with here are

$$CH_4(g) + H_2O(g) \rightarrow CO(g) + 3H_2(g) \qquad \Delta H°_{298} = 49,270 \text{ cal} \qquad (A)$$
$$CH_4(g) + 2H_2O(g) \rightarrow CO_2(g) + 4H_2(g) \qquad \Delta H°_{298} = 39,430 \text{ cal} \qquad (B)$$

It is first necessary to determine the fraction of methane converted by each of these reactions. As a basis for calculations, let 1 mole of methane together with 2 moles of steam be fed to the reactor. If x moles of methane reacts by Eq. (A), then $1 - x$ moles reacts by Eq. (B). On this basis the products of the reaction are

$$CO: x$$
$$H_2: 3x + 4(1 - x) = 4 - x$$
$$CO_2: 1 - x$$
$$\underline{H_2O: 2 - x - 2(1 - x) = x}$$
Total: 5 moles of products

The composition of carbon monoxide in the product stream is $x/5 = 0.174$ and $x = 0.870$. Thus, on the basis chosen, 0.870 mole of methane reacts by Eq. (A) and 0.130 mole reacts by Eq. (B). Furthermore, the amount of each constituent in the product stream is

Moles CO $= x = 0.87$
Moles $H_2 = 4 - x = 3.13$
Moles $CO_2 = 1 - x = 0.13$
Moles $H_2O = x = 0.87$

It is now necessary to devise a path, for purposes of calculation, to proceed from the reactants at 600°K to the products at 1300°K. Since data are available for the standard heats of reaction at 25°C, the most convenient path is the one which includes the reactions at 25°C (298°K). This is shown schematically in the accompanying diagram.

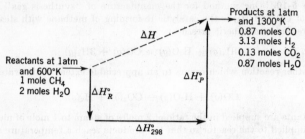

The dashed line represents the actual path for which the enthalpy change is ΔH. But

$$\Delta H = \Delta H_R^\circ + \Delta H_{298}^\circ + \Delta H_P^\circ$$

For the calculation of ΔH_{298}°, reactions (A) and (B) must both be considered. Since 0.87 mole of CH_4 reacts by reaction (A) and 0.13 mole reacts by reaction (B)

$$\Delta H_{298}^\circ = (0.87)(49,270) + (0.13)(39,430) = 47,990 \text{ cal}$$

The enthalpy change of the reactants as they are cooled from 600°K (620°F) to 298°K is most easily calculated with mean heat capacities taken from Fig. 5-1.

$$\Delta H_R^\circ = \sum_{\text{reactants}} (nC_{p_{\text{mean}}}^\circ)(298 - 600)$$

$$= \left[\begin{array}{cc} (1)(10.46) & + (2)(8.32) \\ CH_4 & H_2O \end{array} \right] (-302) = -8180 \text{ cal}$$

The enthalpy change of the products as they are heated from 298 to 1300°K (1880°F) is calculated similarly:

$$\Delta H_P^\circ = \sum_{\text{products}} (nC_{p_{\text{mean}}}^\circ)(1300 - 298)$$

$$= \left[\begin{array}{cccc} (0.87)(7.60) & + (3.13)(7.12) & + (0.13)(11.97) & + (0.87)(9.28) \\ CO & H_2 & CO_2 & H_2O \end{array} \right] (1002)$$

$$= 38,620 \text{ cal}$$

Therefore $\Delta H = -8180 + 47,990 + 38,620 = 78,430$ cal.

The process is one of steady flow for which W_s, $\Delta z(g/g_c)$, and $\Delta u^2/2g_c$ are presumed negligible. Thus

$$Q = \Delta H = 78,430 \text{ cal}$$
$$Q = (78,430)(1.8)$$
$$= 141,200 \text{ Btu/lb mole } CH_4 \text{ fed to the reactor}$$

Example 5-11. A boiler is fired with a high-grade fuel oil (consisting only of hydrocarbons) having a higher heating value of 18,700 Btu/lb$_m$. This is the negative of the standard heat of combustion on a unit-mass basis at 25°C (77°F) with $CO_2(g)$ and $H_2O(l)$ as products. The temperature of the fuel and air entering the combustion chamber is 77°F. The air may be assumed dry. The flue gases leave at 560°F, and their average Orsat analysis is 11.2 per cent CO_2, 0.4 per cent CO, 6.2 per cent O_2, 82.2 per cent N_2. Calculate the fraction of the heating value of the oil that is available for transfer as heat to the boiler.

Solution. Take as a basis 100 lb moles of dry flue gas, made up as follows:

CO_2................	11.2 moles
CO................	0.4 mole
O_2.................	6.2 moles
N_2.................	82.2 moles
Total............	100.0 moles

This analysis is on a dry basis, and does not take into account the water vapor present in the flue gases. The amount of water formed by the combustion reaction may be found from an oxygen balance. The oxygen supplied in the air represents 21 mole per cent of the air stream. The remaining 79 per cent is nitrogen, which goes through the combustion process unchanged. Thus the 82.2 moles of N_2 appearing in 100 moles of dry flue gas was supplied with the air, and the oxygen accompanying this nitrogen is

$$(82.2)\left(\frac{21}{79}\right) = 21.85 \text{ moles } O_2 \text{ supplied}$$

$$\text{Moles of } O_2 \text{ accounted for in the dry flue gas} = 11.2 + \frac{0.4}{2} + 6.2 = 17.60$$

The difference between these figures represents the moles of O_2 which reacts to form H_2O. Therefore the amount of water formed per 100 moles of dry flue gases is

$$(21.85 - 17.60)(2) = 8.50 \text{ moles } H_2O$$
$$\text{Moles of } H_2 \text{ in the fuel} = \text{moles of } H_2O \text{ formed} = 8.50$$

The amount of C in the fuel is determined by a carbon balance:

$$\text{Moles C in flue gases} = 11.2 + 0.4 = 11.60 \text{ moles C in fuel}$$

The weight of fuel burned to produce 100 lb moles of dry flue gases is therefore

$$(8.50)(2) + (11.6)(12) = 156.2 \text{ lb}_m$$

If this amount of fuel is burned completely to $CO_2(g)$ and $H_2O(l)$ at 25°C, the heat of combustion is

$$\Delta H^\circ_{298} = (-18,700)(156.2) = -2,921,000 \text{ Btu}$$

However, the reaction actually occurring does not represent complete combustion, and the water is formed as vapor rather than as liquid. The 156.2 lb_m of fuel may be represented by the empirical formula $C_{11.6}H_{17}$, and the reaction may be written

$$C_{11.6}H_{17}(l) + 21.85O_2(g) + 82.2N_2(g) \rightarrow 11.2CO_2(g) + 0.4CO(g)$$
$$+ 8.5H_2O(g) + 6.2O_2(g) + 82.2N_2(g)$$

This equation can be obtained by addition of the following reactions, for each of which the standard heat of reaction at 25°C is available:

$$C_{11.6}H_{17}(l) + 15.85O_2(g) \rightarrow 11.6CO_2(g) + 8.5H_2O(l) \quad \Delta H^\circ_{298} = -2,921,000 \text{ Btu}$$
$$8.5H_2O(l) \rightarrow 8.5H_2O(g) \quad \Delta H^\circ_{298} = (10,520)(8.5)(1.8) = 161,000 \text{ Btu}$$
$$0.4CO_2(g) \rightarrow 0.4CO(g) + 0.2O_2(g) \quad \Delta H^\circ_{298} = (67,636)(0.4)(1.8) = 49,000 \text{ Btu}$$
$$6.2O_2(g) + 82.2N_2(g) \rightarrow 6.2O_2(g) + 82.2N_2(g) \quad \Delta H^\circ_{298} = 0 \text{ Btu}$$

The sum of these yields the actual reaction, and the sum of the ΔH_{298}° values gives the standard heat of reaction at 25°C for the reaction occurring, that is,

$$\Delta H_{298}^{\circ} = -2,711,000 \text{ Btu}$$

This value will be used in calculating the heat effect of the process considered. The method is represented by the accompanying diagram.

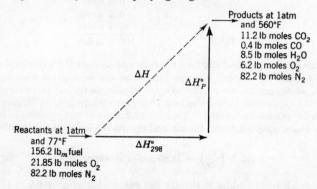

The actual process leading from reactants at 77°F to products at 560°F is represented by the dashed line in the diagram. For purposes of calculating ΔH for this process, any convenient path may be used. The one drawn with solid lines is a logical one because the enthalpy changes for these steps are easily calculated. ΔH_{298}° has already been evaluated. The enthalpy change caused by heating the products of the reaction from 77 to 560°F is most readily calculated by the use of mean heat capacities read from Fig. 5-1.

$$\Delta H_P^{\circ} = \sum_{\text{products}} (nC_{p_{\text{mean}}}^{\circ})(560 - 77)$$
$$= [(11.2)(10.1) + (0.4)(7.1) + (8.5)(8.2) + (6.2)(7.3)$$
$$+ (82.2)(7.05)](560 - 77) = 391,000 \text{ Btu}$$
$$\Delta H = \Delta H_{298}^{\circ} + \Delta H_P^{\circ} = -2,711,000 + 391,000 = -2,320,000 \text{ Btu}$$

Since the process is one of steady flow for which the shaft work and potential-energy and kinetic-energy terms in the energy balance are zero or negligible, $\Delta H = Q$. Thus $Q = -2,320,000$ Btu. In other words, 2,320,000 Btu of heat is available for transfer to the boiler for every 100 lb moles of dry flue gases formed. This represents

$$\left(\frac{2,320,000}{2,921,000}\right) (100) \text{ or } 79.5 \text{ per cent}$$

of the higher heating value of the fuel.

In the foregoing examples the pressures of the products and reactants have been low, approximately 1 atm. Some reactions are carried out at elevated pressures, and in this case the products and reactants cannot be considered to be in their standard states of ideal gases at 1 atm, and additional calculations must be made to take into account the effect of pressure on the heat of reaction. The method of doing this will be considered in Chap. 7. Suffice it to say at this point that the effect of pressure on the heat of reaction is usually small compared with the effect of temperature.

5-9. Heat Effects of Mixing Processes. When two or more pure substances are mixed to form a solution, a heat effect usually results. *Heats of mixing* are defined as the enthalpy changes which occur when two or more pure substances are mixed to form a solution at constant temperature and at a pressure of 1 atm. If the treatment is restricted to binary systems, the definition is given by the equation

$$\underline{H}_s = \underline{H}_A + \underline{H}_B + \Delta\underline{H} \qquad (5\text{-}17)$$

where $\underline{H}_s$ is the total (as distinguished from the molal or specific) enthalpy of the solution, $\underline{H}_A$ and $\underline{H}_B$ are the total enthalpies of the pure components which are mixed to form the solution, and $\Delta\underline{H}$ is the total heat of mixing.

Equation (5-17) is general for the calculation of the enthalpies of solutions. It applies alike for solutions of gases, liquids, and solids and also for solutions of solids or gases in liquids. Values of the heat of mixing must be determined experimentally. For a given system, the values of $\Delta\underline{H}$ depend on the amounts of components A and B which are mixed to form the solution. Several bases are used for reporting these values.

Heats of Solution. When the solution of solids in a liquid solvent is considered, the heat effect is called a heat of solution, and Eq. (5-17) is usually written for the solution of 1 *mole of solute* in n moles of solvent. On this basis, Eq. (5-17) becomes

$$\underline{H}_s = H_A + nH_B + \Delta H \qquad (5\text{-}18)$$

where H_A and H_B are the molal enthalpies of pure A and B and ΔH becomes the heat of solution per mole of the solute A. Heats of solution for liquid and gaseous solutes are also sometimes reported on this basis.

Data for heats of solution may be given for a range of temperatures, but more often values are available only for a temperature of 25°C. If the heat capacities of the pure components and the solution are known, heats of solution may be calculated for other temperatures by a method entirely analogous to the calculation of standard heats of reaction at elevated temperatures from the value at 25°C.

Heats of solution are similar in many respects to heats of reaction. When a chemical reaction occurs, the energy of the products may be different from the energy of the reactants at the same temperature and pressure because of the chemical rearrangement of the constituent atoms. When solutions are formed, a similar energy change frequently occurs because of the difference between the forces of attraction of unlike and like molecules. These forces are generally much smaller than those associated with chemical bonds; thus heats of solution are generally much smaller than heats of reaction.

A solution process may be conveniently represented by a *physical* equation analogous to chemical equations. Thus if 1 mole of LiCl is dissolved in 12 moles of water, the process may be represented as

$$LiCl(s) + 12H_2O(l) \rightarrow LiCl(12H_2O)$$

The designation $LiCl(12H_2O)$ means that the product is a solution of 1 mole of LiCl in 12 moles of water. The enthalpy change accompanying this process at 25°C and atmospheric pressure is -8011 cal per mole of LiCl, that is, a solution of 1 g mole of LiCl in 12 g moles of water has an enthalpy 8011 cal less than that of 1 g mole of pure $LiCl(s)$ and 12 g moles of pure $H_2O(l)$. It is possible to combine the equations for physical reactions such as this with equations for chemical reactions. This is illustrated in the following example.

Example 5-12. Calculate the heat of formation of LiCl in 12 moles of water.

Solution. The process to be considered results in the formation from its constituent elements of 1 mole of LiCl *in solution* in 12 moles of water. The equation representing this process is obtained as follows:

$$
\begin{array}{lll}
Li + \frac{1}{2}Cl_2 \rightarrow LiCl(s) & \Delta H^\circ_{298} = & -97,700 \text{ cal} \\
LiCl(s) + 12H_2O(l) \rightarrow LiCl(12H_2O) & \Delta H_{298} = & -8,011 \text{ cal} \\
\hline
Li + \frac{1}{2}Cl_2 + 12H_2O(l) \rightarrow LiCl(12H_2O) & \Delta H_{298} = & -105,711 \text{ cal}
\end{array}
$$

The first reaction designates a chemical change resulting in the formation of $LiCl(s)$ from its elements, and the enthalpy change accompanying this reaction at 25°C is the standard heat of formation of $LiCl(s)$ at 25°C. The second reaction represents the physical change resulting in the solution of 1 g mole of $LiCl(s)$ in 12 moles of $H_2O(l)$. The enthalpy change accompanying this reaction is a heat of solution. The enthalpy change of $-105,711$ cal per gram mole of LiCl for the over-all process is known as the heat of formation of LiCl *in* 12 moles of water. It is especially to be noted that this figure does not include the heat of formation of the water.

Often heats of solution are not reported directly and must be calculated from heats of formation by the reverse of the calculation just illustrated. The data given by the Bureau of Standards[1] for the heats of formation of 1 g mole of lithium chloride are:

$LiCl(s)$	$-97,700$ cal
$LiCl \cdot H_2O(s)$	$-170,310$ cal
$LiCl \cdot 2H_2O(s)$	$-242,100$ cal
$LiCl \cdot 3H_2O(s)$	$-313,500$ cal
LiCl in 3 moles H_2O	$-102,620$ cal
LiCl in 4 moles H_2O	$-103,730$ cal
LiCl in 5 moles H_2O	$-104,431$ cal
LiCl in 8 moles H_2O	$-105,310$ cal
LiCl in 10 moles H_2O	$-105,554$ cal
LiCl in 12 moles H_2O	$-105,711$ cal
LiCl in 15 moles H_2O	$-105,848$ cal

[1] F. D. Rossini, D. D. Wagman, et al., "Selected Values of Chemical Thermodynamic Properties," *Natl. Bur. Standards U.S., Circ.* 500, 1952.

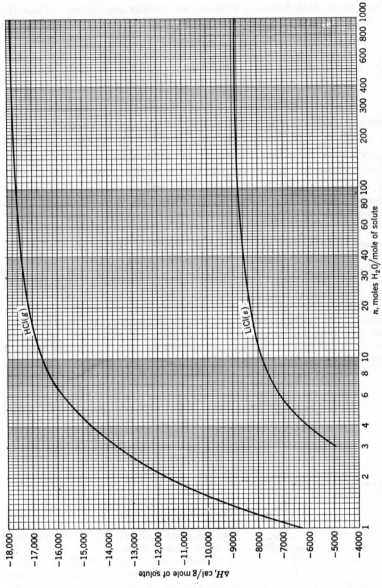

FIG. 5-4. Integral heats of solution.   [Based on data from D. D. Wagman (ed.), *Selected Values of Chemical Thermodynamic Properties, National Bureau of Standards*.]

From these data heats of solution are readily calculated. Take the case of the solution of 1 mole of LiCl in 4 moles of H_2O. The reaction representing this process may be obtained as follows:

$$\begin{array}{lll}
\text{Li} + \tfrac{1}{2}\text{Cl}_2 + 4\text{H}_2\text{O}(l) \rightarrow \text{LiCl}(4\text{H}_2\text{O}) & \Delta H_{298} = & -103{,}730 \text{ cal} \\
\underline{\text{LiCl}(s) \rightarrow \text{Li} + \tfrac{1}{2}\text{Cl}_2} & \underline{\Delta H^\circ_{298} =} & \underline{97{,}700 \text{ cal}} \\
\text{LiCl}(s) + 4\text{H}_2\text{O}(l) \rightarrow \text{LiCl}(4\text{H}_2\text{O}) & \Delta H_{298} = & -6{,}030 \text{ cal}
\end{array}$$

This calculation can be carried out for each quantity of water for which data are given. The results are then conveniently represented graphically by a plot of the heat of solution per mole of solute vs. the moles of solvent. Figure 5-4 shows examples for the cases of solid lithium chloride and for hydrogen chloride gas dissolved in water at 25°C. It is convenient to have data in this form for a number of practical problems. Consider the following example.

Example 5-13. A single-effect evaporator operating at atmospheric pressure is to be used to concentrate a 15 per cent aqueous LiCl solution to 40 per cent. The feed enters the evaporator at the rate of 14,000 lb_m/hr at 77°F. The normal boiling point of a 40 per cent LiCl solution is about 270°F, and its specific heat is estimated as 0.65 Btu/(lb_m)(°F). For what heat-transfer rate in Btu per hour should the evaporator be designed?

Solution. Take as a basis 100 lb_m of 15 per cent LiCl solution fed to the evaporator. On this basis 15 lb_m LiCl enters the evaporator along with 85 lb_m H_2O. A material balance shows that 62.5 lb_m H_2O is evaporated and that 37.5 lb_m of 40 per cent LiCl solution is produced. The process is indicated schematically as follows:

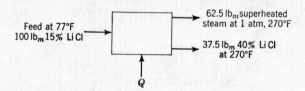

The energy balance for this flow process gives

$$\Delta H = Q$$

where ΔH is the total enthalpy of the product streams minus the total enthalpy of the feed stream. Thus the problem reduces to finding ΔH from the available data. Since enthalpy is a state function, the path used for the calculation of ΔH is immaterial and may be selected as convenience dictates and without reference to the actual path followed in the evaporator. Since the data available are the heats of solution of LiCl in water at 77°F (see Fig. 5-4), the calculational path should be such that these data may be used directly. A suitable path is illustrated in the accompanying diagram.

With reference to the diagram, it is evident that

$$\Delta H = \Delta H_1 + \Delta H_2 + \Delta H_3 + \Delta H_4$$

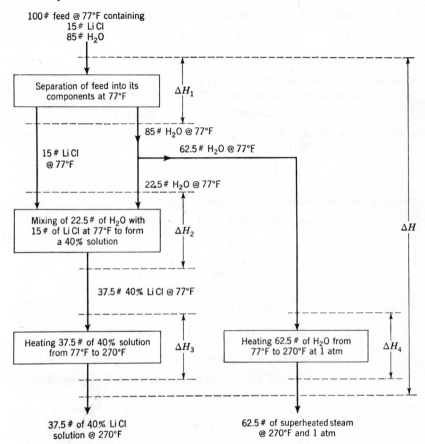

100# feed @ 77°F containing
15# Li Cl
85# H$_2$O

ΔH_1

Separation of feed into its
components at 77°F

85# H$_2$O @ 77°F

15# Li Cl
@ 77°F

62.5# H$_2$O @ 77°F

22.5# H$_2$O @ 77°F

Mixing of 22.5# of H$_2$O with
15# of Li Cl at 77°F to form
a 40% solution

ΔH_2

ΔH

37.5# 40% Li Cl @ 77°F

Heating 37.5# of 40% solution
from 77°F to 270°F

ΔH_3

Heating 62.5# of H$_2$O from
77°F to 270°F at 1 atm

ΔH_4

37.5# of 40% Li Cl
solution @ 270°F

62.5# of superheated steam
@ 270°F and 1 atm

The individual ΔH's are determined as follows:

ΔH_1: This step involves the separation of 100 lb$_m$ of a 15 per cent LiCl solution into its pure components at 77°F. This is an "unmixing" process, and the heat effect has the same value but the opposite sign as the corresponding mixing process. On the basis of 100 lb$_m$ of the 15 per cent LiCl solution, the amounts of material entering are

$$15 \text{ lb}_m \text{ or } 0.354 \text{ lb mole of LiCl}$$

and

$$85 \text{ lb}_m \text{ or } 4.72 \text{ lb moles of } H_2O$$

Thus the solution contains 13.34 moles H$_2$O per mole LiCl. From Fig. 5-4 the heat of mixing to form a solution of this composition is −8080 cal per gram mole LiCl. For the "unmixing" process on the basis of 100 lb$_m$ of solution,

$$\Delta H_1 = (+8080)(1.8)(0.354) = 5140 \text{ Btu}$$

ΔH_2: This step results in the mixing of 22.5 lb$_m$ of water with 15 lb$_m$ of LiCl to form a 40 per cent solution at 77°F.   This solution is made up of

$$15 \text{ lb}_m \text{ or } 0.354 \text{ lb mole of LiCl}$$

and

$$22.5 \text{ lb}_m \text{ or } 1.25 \text{ lb moles of } H_2O$$

Thus this solution contains 3.53 moles H_2O per mole LiCl.   From Fig. 5-4 the heat of mixing is -5560 cal per gram mole LiCl.   Therefore

$$\Delta H_2 = (-5560)(1.8)(0.354) = -3540 \text{ Btu}$$

ΔH_3: For this step 37.5 lb_m of 40 per cent LiCl is heated from 77 to 270°F, and $\Delta H = (m)(c_p)(\Delta T)$.   Thus

$$\Delta H_3 = (37.5)(0.65)(270 - 77) = 4700 \text{ Btu}$$

ΔH_4: In this step liquid water is vaporized and heated to 270°F.   The enthalpy change is most easily obtained from the steam tables:

$$\Delta H_4 = (62.5)(1178.6 - 45.0) = 70,850 \text{ Btu}$$

Adding the individual enthalpy changes,

$$\begin{aligned} \Delta H &= \Delta H_1 + \Delta H_2 + \Delta H_3 + \Delta H_4 \\ &= 5140 - 3540 + 4700 + 70,850 \\ &= 77,150 \text{ Btu per 100 lb}_m \text{ of feed} \end{aligned}$$

On the basis of 14,000 lb_m of feed per hour

$$Q = \Delta H = (77,150)\left(\frac{14,000}{100}\right) = 10,800,000 \text{ Btu}$$

The required heat-transfer rate to the evaporator is 10,800,000 Btu/hr.

The values of $-\Delta H_1$ and ΔH_2 in the preceding example represent heats of mixing as determined by reference to Fig. 5-4.   For many salt-water systems the heat-of-mixing curve is virtually a straight horizontal line over a wide concentration range.   In this event, the values of ΔH_1 and ΔH_2 are the same but of opposite sign.   Hence they cancel and could very well be omitted from the calculation.   This is the basis of the "heat-balance" method of solving evaporation problems.   In many cases it leads to correct results, but in others, *e.g.*, the present problem, it would be in error.

Enthalpy-Concentration Diagrams.   The most convenient method for representing enthalpy data for solutions is by enthalpy-concentration (H-x) diagrams.   These diagrams are graphs of the enthalpy of a binary solution plotted as a function of composition (mole fraction or weight fraction of one component) with the temperature as parameter.   The pressure is constant and is usually 1 atm.   Figure 5-5 shows a partial diagram for the H_2SO_4-H_2O system.

The enthalpy values are based on a unit mass or a mole of *solution*. If 1 mole of solution containing x_A moles of component A and x_B moles of component B is taken as the basis, Eq. (5-17) becomes

$$H_s = x_A H_A + x_B H_B + \Delta H \qquad (5\text{-}19)$$

where H_s, H_A, and H_B are the molal enthalpies of the solution, pure A, and pure B, respectively, all at the same temperature and pressure, and ΔH is the heat of mixing per mole of solution formed.

It is seen from Eq. (5-19) that the values of H_s depend not only on the heats of solution but also on the enthalpies of the pure components A and B. Thus its use presupposes a knowledge of the enthalpies H_A and H_B of the pure components. Once H_A and H_B are known, H_s is fixed for all mixtures of A and B because ΔH has unique and measurable values. Since absolute enthalpies are unknown, arbitrary zero points must be chosen for the enthalpies of the pure components. It is clear from Eq. (5-19) that the enthalpies of solutions are given relative to the bases selected for the pure components, rather than with respect to some other independent datum. The *basis* of an enthalpy-concentration diagram is then said to be $H_A = 0$ for some specified state of component A and $H_B = 0$ for some specified state of component B. It is by no means necessary that the same temperature be selected for both components. In the case of the H_2SO_4-H_2O diagram shown in Fig. 5-5, it was found convenient to define $H_{H_2O} = 0$ for pure liquid H_2O at 32°F and $H_{H_2SO_4} = 0$ for pure liquid H_2SO_4 at 77°F. In this case the 32°F isotherm terminates at $H = 0$ only at that end of the chart representing pure liquid H_2O, and the 77°F isotherm terminates at $H = 0$ at the other end of the chart representing pure liquid H_2SO_4.

For systems having water as one component, it is desirable to take the enthalpy of pure liquid water as zero at 32°F because this is the base used for the steam tables. It is then possible to use enthalpy values directly from the steam tables in conjunction with values taken from the enthalpy-concentration chart. Were some other base used for the chart, one would have to apply a correction to the steam-table values to put them on the same basis as the chart.

If ΔH is zero, Eq. (5-19) shows that the enthalpy of a solution is simply the sum of the enthalpies of the pure components making up the solution:

$$H_s = x_A H_A + x_B H_B \qquad (5\text{-}20)$$

This is a special case of Eq. (5-19), and it is valid only for what is known as an *ideal solution*. An ideal solution is like an ideal gas in that it is an idealization and does not actually exist. Nevertheless, it is a useful concept, for a number of solutions approach ideal behavior, and the simplified equations which apply are often used as approximations. This will be considered in more detail in Chap. 7.

For an ideal solution, isotherms on an enthalpy-concentration diagram would be straight lines connecting the enthalpy of pure B at $x_A = 0$ with

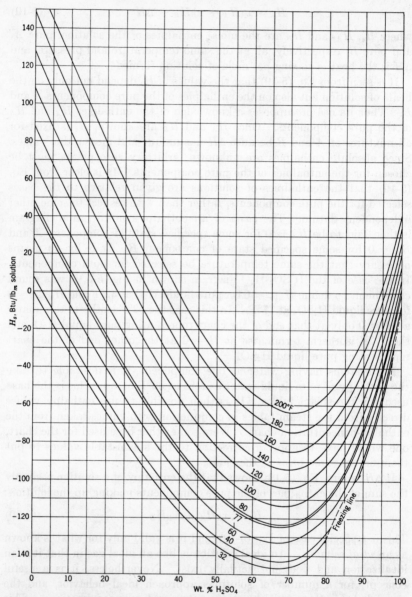

FIG. 5-5. Enthalpy-concentration diagram for H_2SO_4-H_2O. [*Redrawn from the data of W. D. Ross, Chem. Eng. Progr.,* **48,** 314 (1952). *By permission.*]

the enthalpy of pure A at $x_A = 1$.† This is illustrated for a single iso-therm in Fig. 5-6 by the dashed line. The heavy solid curve shows how the isotherm might appear for a real solution. Since Eq. (5-19) represents the solid line and Eq. (5-20) the dashed line, ΔH is the vertical distance between the two curves. Thus the actual isotherm is displaced vertically from the ideal-solution isotherm at a given point by the value of ΔH at that point. In the case illustrated ΔH is negative over the entire com-position range. This means that heat must be evolved whenever the

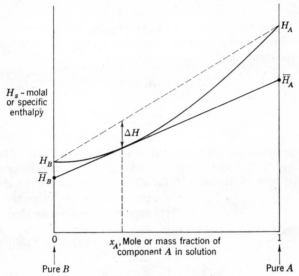

FIG. 5-6. Basic relations on an enthalpy-concentration diagram.

pure components at the given temperature are mixed to form a solution at the same temperature. Such a system is said to be exothermic. The H_2SO_4-H_2O system is an example. An endothermic system is one for which the heats of solution are positive, $i.e.$, solution at constant tempera-ture is accompanied by the absorption of heat. An example is the methanol-benzene system.

† This is easily shown by utilizing the relationship between x_A and x_B:

$$x_A + x_B = 1 \quad \text{or} \quad x_B = 1 - x_A$$

Equation (5-20) then becomes

$$H_s = x_A H_A + (1 - x_A)H_B$$

or

$$H_s = (H_A - H_B)x_A + H_B$$

Since H_A and H_B are constants for a given isotherm, this is the equation of a straight line on a graph of H_s vs. x_A with a slope of $(H_A - H_B)$ and an intercept of H_B.

One feature of an enthalpy-concentration diagram which makes it particularly useful is the ease with which problems involving adiabatic mixing may be solved. This results from the fact that adiabatic mixing may be represented by a straight line on an H-x diagram. More precisely, the point on an H-x diagram which represents a solution formed by adiabatic mixing of two other solutions must lie on the straight line connecting the points representing the two initial solutions. This may be shown as follows:

Let the subscripts 1 and 2 denote the two initial binary solutions, and let the subscript 3 denote the final solution obtained by mixing solutions 1 and 2. Three equations can be written for the mixing process, two material balances and an energy balance. A total material balance and a balance for component A give

$$n_1 + n_2 = n_3 \tag{5-21}$$

and

$$x_{A_1} n_1 + x_{A_2} n_2 = x_{A_3} n_3 \tag{5-22}$$

where the n's represent moles (or masses) of the respective solutions and the x_A's represent mole (or mass) fractions of component A in the respective solutions. Since the process is adiabatic and does not involve work, the first law reduces to $\Delta H = 0$ for either a flow process or a constant-pressure nonflow process. The energy balance therefore expresses the fact that for adiabatic mixing the enthalpy of the final solution is the sum of the enthalpies of the initial solutions:

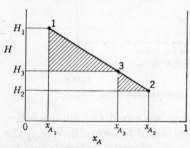

FIG. 5-7. Adiabatic mixing represented on an enthalpy-concentration diagram.

$$n_1 H_1 + n_2 H_2 = n_3 H_3 \tag{5-23}$$

where the H's represent the molal (or specific) enthalpies of the respective solutions.

Equation (5-21) may be combined first with Eq. (5-22), and second with Eq. (5-23), to eliminate n_3. The two resulting equations may be written as

$$n_1(x_{A_1} - x_{A_3}) = n_2(x_{A_3} - x_{A_2}) \tag{5-24}$$

and

$$n_1(H_1 - H_3) = n_2(H_3 - H_2) \tag{5-25}$$

Division of Eq. (5-24) by Eq. (5-25) yields

$$\frac{x_{A_1} - x_{A_3}}{H_1 - H_3} = \frac{x_{A_3} - x_{A_2}}{H_3 - H_2} \tag{5-26}$$

Equation (5-26) represents a relationship between x_{A_3}, the composition of the final solution, and H_3, its enthalpy. The other terms in the equation are constant for a given pair of initial solutions. It will be noted that the amounts of the various solutions canceled in the derivation of Eq. (5-26), and therefore this equation is a general relation independent of the amounts of solution involved in the mixing process. An examination of the similar triangles shown in Fig. 5-7 will show that Eq. (5-26) can be correct only if solutions 1, 2, and 3 lie along a straight line drawn on an H-x chart.

The use of enthalpy-concentration diagrams is illustrated in the following problems for the NaOH-H$_2$O system, for which an H-x diagram is shown in Fig. 5-8.

Example 5-14. A single-effect evaporator is to concentrate 10,000 lb$_m$/hr of a 10 per cent NaOH solution to 50 per cent. The feed is to enter at 70°F. The evaporator is to operate at an absolute pressure of 3 in. Hg, and under these conditions the boiling point of a 50 per cent solution of NaOH is 190°F. For what heat-transfer rate in Btu per hour should the evaporator be designed?

Solution. On the basis of 10,000 lb$_m$ of 10 per cent NaOH fed to the evaporator, a material balance shows that the product streams consist of 8000 lb$_m$ of superheated steam at 3 in. Hg abs and 190°F and 2000 lb$_m$ of 50 per cent NaOH at 190°F. The process is indicated schematically as follows:

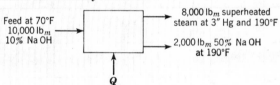

The energy balance for this flow process is

$$\Delta H = Q$$

ΔH is easily determined in this case from the H-x diagram of Fig. 5-8 used in conjunction with the steam tables:

Enthalpy of superheated steam at 3 in. Hg and 190°F = 1146 Btu/lb$_m$
Enthalpy of 10 per cent NaOH solution at 70°F = 34 Btu/lb$_m$
Enthalpy of 50 per cent NaOH solution at 190°F = 215 Btu/lb$_m$

$$Q = \Delta H = (8000)(1146) + (2000)(215) - (10,000)(34)$$
$$= 9,260,000 \text{ Btu/hr}$$

A comparison of this problem with Example 5-13 shows the simplification introduced by the use of an enthalpy-concentration diagram.

Example 5-15. A 10 per cent NaOH solution at 70°F is mixed with a 70 per cent NaOH solution at 200°F to form a solution containing 40 per cent NaOH.

(a) If the mixing is done adiabatically, what will be the final temperature of the solution?

(b) If the final temperature is to be brought to 70°F, how much heat must be removed during the process?

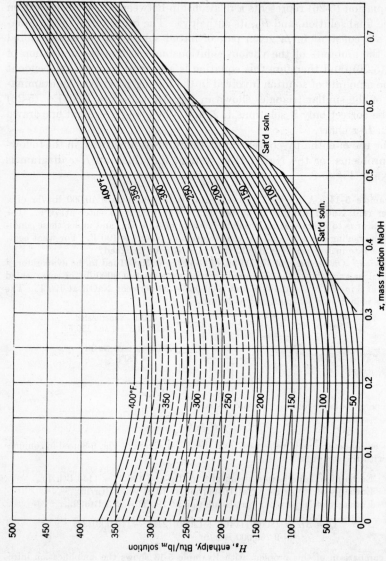

FIG. 5–8. Enthalpy-concentration diagram for NaOH-H₂O. [Reproduced by permission. W. L. McCabe, Trans. AIChE, **31**, 129 (1935); R. H. Wilson and W. L. McCabe, Ind. Eng. Chem., **34**, 558 (1942).]

Solution. (*a*) A straight line drawn on Fig. 5-8 connecting the points representing the two initial solutions must include all possible solutions obtained by adiabatic mixing of the two initial solutions. The particular solution represented by a point on this line at a concentration of 40 per cent NaOH has an enthalpy of 192 Btu/lb$_m$, and the isotherm passing through the point is that for 220°F. Thus the final temperature, obtained graphically, is 220°F.

(*b*) This process cannot be represented by a straight line on Fig. 5-8. However, any convenient path may be selected for calculating ΔH of the process and hence Q, since the energy balance gives $Q = \Delta H$. Thus the process may be considered as occurring in two steps: adiabatic mixing followed by simple cooling of the resulting solution to the required temperature. The first step is one of constant enthalpy and has been considered in part (*a*). It results in a solution at 220°F with an enthalpy of 192 Btu/lb$_m$. If this solution is cooled to 70°F, the resulting enthalpy from Fig. 5-8 is 70 Btu/lb$_m$ and

$$Q = \Delta H = 70 - 192 = -122 \text{ Btu/lb}_m$$

Thus 122 Btu is *evolved* per pound *mass* of solution formed.

Partial Enthalpies. Although the enthalpy of a solution is in general not merely the sum of the enthalpies of its *pure* components at the same temperature and pressure, it does represent the sum of the enthalpies of the components *as they exist in solution.* To understand this one must realize that a given material may be regarded as having discrete properties associated with it in whatever state it exists. For example, H_2O has distinct properties as a solid, as a liquid, as a vapor, and also when it exists in solution. Data are given for pure H_2O as liquid and vapor in the steam tables. These values are arbitrarily based on $H = 0$ for saturated liquid water at 32°F. On this same basis water also has definite enthalpies whenever it exists in solution. As would be expected, the values depend on composition and on the nature of the other components, as well as on the temperature and pressure. The main point is that, whenever a base is selected for the enthalpy of a pure substance, its values are fixed and measurable for all states of the substance: solid, liquid, gas, and in solution.

In order to distinguish the property of a component in solution from that of the pure material, a bar is placed over the symbol; thus $\bar{H}_A$ represents the enthalpy of A in solution and is called a *partial enthalpy.* The word *partial* indicates that the enthalpy of the component in solution represents only *part* of the total enthalpy of the solution. The total value is the sum of the partial enthalpies of the components which make up the solution, according to the expression

$$H_s = x_A\bar{H}_A + x_B\bar{H}_B \tag{5-27}$$

where H_s is the molal enthalpy of the solution and $\bar{H}_A$ and $\bar{H}_B$ are the partial molal enthalpies of components A and B in solution. For 1 mole of solution, x_A and x_B represent the number of moles of A and B present and also their mole fractions. Equation (5-27) may also be written for a unit mass. In that event H_s is the specific enthalpy of the solution, e.g., Btu per pound *mass*, and $\bar{H}_A$ and $\bar{H}_B$ are partial specific enthalpies. The quantities x_A and x_B represent the masses of A and B in a unit mass of solution and also their mass fractions.

The calculation of $\bar{H}_A$ and $\bar{H}_B$ for a binary solution of A and B is easily accomplished with the aid of an enthalpy-concentration diagram by a simple graphic construction. If $\bar{H}_A$ and $\bar{H}_B$ are required for a solution of composition x_A, a tangent is drawn to the appropriate isotherm on the H-x diagram at the composition x_A. This construction is illustrated in Fig. 5-6. The intersection of the tangent with the ordinate at $x_A = 0$ (representing pure B) gives the partial enthalpy of component B in the solution, and the intersection of the tangent with the ordinate at $x_A = 1$ (representing pure A) gives the partial enthalpy of component A.†

This discussion has been concerned with enthalpy. However, an entirely analogous treatment holds for the other thermodynamic properties. From a practical standpoint the partial properties of solutions are not yet of great value. The reason for this in the case of enthalpy is that their main practical use would be for the calculation of the total enthalpy of the solution by Eq. (5-27). But the only general methods so far developed for the calculation of the partial properties depend on knowing the total enthalpy to start with. The same comment applies more or less to all the partial properties. Nevertheless, the concept is frequently encountered in engineering and scientific literature, and it is an aid in reasoning about the properties of solutions.

† This may be shown as follows: Suppose that 1 mole of a particular solution has a composition x_A and that its components have the partial molal enthalpies $\bar{H}_A$ and $\bar{H}_B$. Suppose further that a differential amount of component A, dx_A, is added to this solution and that at the same time a differential amount of component B, dx_B, is removed so that the amount of solution remains exactly 1 mole. During this process the temperature is held constant by the addition or extraction of heat as needed. The enthalpy change of the solution dH_s must be equal to the sum of the enthalpy changes caused by adding dx_A moles of A with a partial molal enthalpy of $\bar{H}_A$ and extracting dx_B moles of B with a partial molal enthalpy of $\bar{H}_B$. Thus

$$dH_s = \bar{H}_A \, dx_A + \bar{H}_B \, dx_B$$

Since $dx_B = -dx_A$, the equation can be written in terms of x_A alone:

$$dH_s = \bar{H}_A \, dx_A - \bar{H}_B \, dx_A$$

or

$$\frac{dH_s}{dx_A} = \bar{H}_A - \bar{H}_B$$

The quantity dH_s/dx_A is the slope of the isotherm on an H-x diagram at the appropriate composition. Thus $\bar{H}_A - \bar{H}_B$ must also represent this slope. For this to be true $\bar{H}_A$ and $\bar{H}_B$ must be the intersections of the tangent to the isotherm with the boundaries of the diagram, as shown in Fig. 5-6.

Example 5-16. Determine the enthalpy of solid NaOH at 68°F on the basis used for the NaOH-H$_2$O enthalpy-concentration diagram shown in Fig. 5-8.

Solution. In the case of aqueous salt solutions a concentration representing the limit of solubility of the salt is reached for each isotherm on an *H-x* diagram. Hence, the isotherm terminates at that point, as illustrated for the NaOH-H$_2$O system shown in Fig. 5-8. Since the isotherms do not extend to an NaOH concentration representing pure sodium hydroxide, a problem arises as to how the basis of the diagram with respect to NaOH is to be selected. In this case $H_{H_2O} = 0$ for liquid water at 32°F in conformity with the base for the steam tables, and $\bar{H}_{NaOH} = 0$ for sodium hydroxide in an infinitely dilute solution at 68°F.

This reference state means that the enthalpy of NaOH as it exists in a solution of infinite dilution (*i.e.*, at a concentration of x_{NaOH} approaching zero) at 68°F has been arbitrarily taken as zero. The graphic interpretation is that the chart is constructed in such a way that a tangent drawn to the 68°F isotherm at $x_{NaOH} = 0$ intersects the $x_{NaOH} = 1$ ordinate (not shown) at an enthalpy of zero. The selection of $\bar{H}_{NaOH}^{\infty}$ to be zero at 68°F automatically fixes the values of the enthalpy of sodium hydroxide in all other states. In particular, the enthalpy of solid NaOH at 68°F may be calculated for the basis selected.

The procedure for calculating H_{NaOH} at 68°F is as follows. If 1 lb$_m$ of solid NaOH at 68°F is dissolved in an infinite amount of water at 68°F and if the temperature is held constant by extracting the heat of solution, the resulting solution will be one of infinite dilution at 68°F. The enthalpy change for this process is equal to the enthalpy change of the water plus the enthalpy change of the NaOH. However, the water does not change in enthalpy because it is essentially pure in both its initial and final states. Thus the total ΔH results from the change in state of the NaOH, *i.e.*, the change from a solid at 68°F to a solute at infinite dilution at 68°F. Therefore,

$$\Delta H_{68°F}^{\infty} = \bar{H}_{NaOH}^{\infty} - H_{NaOH}$$

Since

$$\bar{H}_{NaOH}^{\infty} = 0 \text{ at } 68°F$$
$$\Delta H_{68°F}^{\infty} = -H_{NaOH}$$

The enthalpy of solid NaOH at 68°F, H_{NaOH}, may therefore be calculated from a measurement of the heat of solution of 1 lb$_m$ of NaOH in an infinite amount of water at 68°F. Lists of values of the heat of solution at infinite dilution are available from several sources. For example, Perry[1] gives the value of the *heat evolved* when 1 g mole of NaOH is dissolved in water to form an infinitely dilute solution at 18°C as 10,180 cal per gram mole NaOH. Since *heat evolved* is defined as negative,

$$\Delta H_{18°C}^{\infty} = -10,180 \text{ cal per gram mole NaOH}$$

If the difference in temperature between 18°C (64°F) and 68°F is neglected, the enthalpy of solid NaOH at 68°F is

$$H_{NaOH} = -\Delta H_{68°F}^{\infty} = \frac{-(-10,180)(1.8)}{40}$$
$$= 458 \text{ Btu per pound } mass \text{ NaOH}$$

This figure represents the enthalpy of solid NaOH at 68°F on the same basis as was selected for the NaOH-H$_2$O enthalpy-concentration diagram shown in Fig. 5-8.

Example 5-17. Solid NaOH at 70°F is mixed with water at 70°F to give a solution

---

[1] J. H. Perry (ed.), "Chemical Engineers' Handbook," 3d ed., p. 248, McGraw-Hill Book Company, Inc., New York, 1950.

containing 45 per cent NaOH at 70°F.   How much heat must be transferred per pound of solution formed?

Solution.   On a basis of 1 lb_m of 45 per cent NaOH solution, 0.45 lb_m of solid NaOH must be dissolved in 0.55 lb_m of water.   The energy balance gives $\Delta H = Q$.

The enthalpy of water at 70°F may be taken from the steam tables, or it may be read from Fig. 5-8 at $x = 0$.   In either case, $H_{H_2O} = 38$ Btu/lb_m.

The enthalpy of solid NaOH at 68°F was calculated in the preceding example to be 458 Btu/lb_m.   The value at 70°F will be virtually the same so that $H_{NaOH} = 458$ Btu/lb_m.   The enthalpy of 45 per cent NaOH at 70°F is read from Fig. 5-8 as $H = 93$ Btu/lb_m.   Therefore

$$Q = \Delta H = (1)(93) - (0.55)(38) - (0.45)(458) = -134 \text{ Btu}$$

or 134 Btu is *evolved* per pound *mass* of solution formed.

PROBLEMS

1. From the data of Table 5-1, write equations for C_p^* of ethane in terms of temperatures in (a) degrees centigrade, (b) degrees Fahrenheit, and (c) degrees Rankine.

2. Calculate ΔH (in Btu) for the following processes:

(a) Heating 7 lb moles of CO_2 from 77 to 1000°F at 1 atm.   Use (1) the mean molal heat capacity from Fig. 5-1, (2) the data of Table 5-1.

(b) Cooling 22 lb_m of benzene from its boiling point to 77°F at 1 atm.

(c) Heating 10 tons of calcium carbonate from 70 to 1200°F.

(d) Cooling a solution of 50 weight per cent H_2SO_4 in H_2O from 250 to 75°F.

3. If 150,000 Btu as heat is added to 13.8 lb moles of SO_2, originally at 77°F, what will be the final temperature?   Pressure is constant at 1 atm.   *Ans.* 1050°F.

4. (a) In the equation

$$\int_{T_1}^{T_2} C_p \, dT = C_{p_m}(T_2 - T_1)$$

show that when C_p is linear with temperature, *i.e.*, when $C_p = \alpha + \beta T$, C_{p_m} is the heat capacity evaluated at the arithmetic average of T_1 and T_2.

(b) In the equation

$$\int_{T_1}^{T_2} C_p \frac{dT}{T} = C_{p_m} \ln \frac{T_2}{T_1}$$

show that, when C_p is linear with temperature, C_{p_m} is the heat capacity evaluated at the logarithmic mean of T_1 and T_2.

5. Calculate the mean molal heat capacity of methane gas at low pressure (C_p^*) between 600 and 1200°F using

(a) The data from Fig. 5-1

(b) The equation $C_p^* = 5.34 + 0.0115T$, where T is in degrees Kelvin

6. Ten pounds *mass* of CO_2 is heated at constant pressure from 200 to 3200°F. Calculate the quantity of heat required using

(a) Equation (5-2) with data from Table 5-1

(b) The mean molal heat capacity

(c) The heat capacity at the average temperature

Is any of these methods not strictly correct?   Explain. CO_2 may be assumed to be an ideal gas.

7. SO_2 gas at approximately atmospheric pressure is to be heated from 400 to

$1600°F$ in a flow process. If the flow rate of SO_2 is 400 lb_m/min, what rate of heat transfer in Btu per minute is required?

8. In a chemical process water vapor is cooled at a constant pressure of 20 psia from 1600 to 228°F. Calculate the heat given off per 100 lb_m of water vapor by three methods:

(a) Equation (5-2) with data from Table 5-1
(b) Using the mean molal heat capacities of Fig. 5-1
(c) Data from the steam tables

9. Calculate the heat required to raise the temperature of 1 lb mole of methane from 500 to 1000°F at 1 atm. *Ans.* 6900 Btu.

10. Calculate the heat required to raise the temperature of 1 mole of a mixture containing 70 mole per cent CO_2 and 30 per cent CO from 500 to 1500°F at constant volume. *Ans.* 8870 Btu.

11. Ammonia is cooled at constant pressure from 245 to 95°F in a parallel-flow heat exchanger by cooling water; 53,000 ft^3/hr of ammonia gas (nonideal) enters the exchanger at 160 psia. If the water enters at 75°F and the minimum temperature difference between the streams is 5°F, calculate the water rate in pounds per hour. (Assume no heat losses.)

The heat capacity of ammonia at 160 psia may be taken as

$$C_p = 19.53 - 0.0238T$$

where T is in degrees Kelvin and C_p is in cal/(g mole)(°C). *Ans.* 131,500 lb_m/hr.

12. The normal boiling point of ethylene oxide is 10.5°C, and its critical temperature 192°C. Estimate from these data the vapor pressure of ethylene oxide at 20°C and its heat of vaporization at 100°C.

13. (a) Using the Kistiakowsky equation, estimate the latent heat of vaporization of n-butane at its normal boiling point of 31.1°F.

(b) Using the result obtained in (a), estimate the latent heat of vaporization of n-butane at 280°F.

(c) Calculate the latent heat of vaporization of n-butane at 280°F from the accompanying experimental data.

Temp, °F	p, atm	v_l, ft^3/lb_m	v_g, ft^3/lb_m
260......................	24.662	0.0393	0.222
270......................	27.134	0.0408	0.192
280......................	29.785	0.0429	0.165
290......................	32.624	0.0458	0.138
305.56 (critical point)........	37.47	0.0712	0.0712

From Prengle, Greenhaus, and York, *Chem. Eng. Progr.*, **44**, 863 (1948).
NOTE: The reported value is 67.3 Btu/lb_m.

14. (a) Using the Kistiakowsky equation, estimate the latent heat of vaporization of benzene at its normal boiling point of 176.2°F.

(b) Using the result obtained in (a), estimate the latent heat of vaporization of benzene at 450°F.

(c) Calculate the latent heat of vaporization of benzene at 450°F from the following experimental data:

Temp, °F	p, psia	v_l, ft³/lb$_m$	v_g, ft³/lb$_m$
430........................	286.3	0.0258	0.3102
440........................	310.5	0.0262	0.2818
450........................	336.7	0.0268	0.2565
460........................	364.2	0.0273	0.2328
470........................	393.4	0.0279	0.2112
553.1 (critical point)..........	715.7	0.0538	0.0538

From Organick and Studhalter, *Chem. Eng. Progr.*, **44**, 847 (1948).
NOTE: The reported value is 103.1 Btu/lb$_m$.

15. Calculate the standard heat of reaction at 25°C for the following chemical reaction:

$$CH_4(g) + H_2O(g) \rightarrow CO(g) + 3H_2(g)$$

(a) Using heat-of-formation data
(b) Using heat-of-combustion data

16. Calculate the standard heat of reaction at 25°C for each of the following reactions:

(a) $N_2(g) + 3H_2(g) \rightarrow 2NH_3(g)$
(b) $4NH_3(g) + 5O_2(g) \rightarrow 4NO(g) + 6H_2O(g)$
(c) $3NO_2(g) + H_2O(l) \rightarrow 2HNO_3(l) + NO(g)$
(d) $CaC_2(s) + H_2O(l) \rightarrow C_2H_2(g) + CaO(s)$
(e) $2Na(s) + 2H_2O(g) \rightarrow 2NaOH(s) + H_2(g)$
(f) $C_3H_8(g) \rightarrow C_2H_4(g) + CH_4(g)$
(g) $\quad C_2H_4O(g) \quad + H_2O(l) \rightarrow \quad C_2H_6O_2(l)$
$\quad$ (Ethylene oxide) $\qquad\qquad$ (Ethylene glycol)
(h) $\quad C_2H_4O(g) \quad \rightarrow \quad C_2H_4O(g)$
$\quad$ (Ethylene oxide) $\quad$ (Acetaldehyde)
(i) $H_2S(g) + \tfrac{3}{2}O_2(g) \rightarrow H_2O(g) + SO_2(g)$
(j) $2H_2S(g) + O_2(g) \rightarrow 2H_2O(g) + 2S(s)$
(k) $N_2(g) + O_2(g) \rightarrow 2NO(g)$
(l) $CaCO_3(s) \rightarrow CaO(s) + CO_2(g)$
(m) $SO_3(g) + H_2O(l) \rightarrow H_2SO_4(l)$
(n) $C_2H_4(g) + H_2O(g) \rightarrow C_2H_5OH(l)$
(o) $C_2H_5OH(l) + O_2(g) \rightarrow CH_3COOH(l) + H_2O(l)$
(p) $3C_2H_2(g) \rightarrow C_6H_6(l)$
(q) $\quad C_7H_{14}(g) \qquad \rightarrow \quad C_7H_8(g) + 3H_2(g)$
$\quad$ (Methyl cyclohexane) $\quad$ (Toluene)
(r) $CH_4(g) + 2H_2O(g) \rightarrow CO_2(g) + 4H_2(g)$
(s) $4HCl(g) + O_2(g) \rightarrow 2Cl_2(g) + 2H_2O(g)$
(t) $4CO(g) + 8H_2(g) \rightarrow 3CH_4(g) + CO_2(g) + 2H_2O(g)$

17. Calculate the heat effect for each of the following reactions carried out at 25°C under conditions of

(a) Constant pressure
(b) Constant volume

$$C_7H_8(g) + 9O_2(g) \rightarrow 4H_2O(l) + 7CO_2(g)$$
$$\mathbf{C_7H_8}(l) + 9O_2(g) \rightarrow 4H_2O(g) + 7CO_2(g)$$

18. A fuel oil with an average chemical composition of $C_{10}H_{20}$ is burned with oxygen in a bomb calorimeter. The heat evolved was measured as 12,380 cal/g for the reaction at 25°C. Calculate the standard heat of combustion of the fuel oil at 25°C with the water formed as vapor, *i.e.*, the net heating value.

$$Ans. \ \Delta H^\circ_{298} = -1,633,000 \ \text{cal/g mole.}$$

19. For the reaction given in Prob. 15, calculate the standard heat of reaction at 1000°C. *Ans.* $\Delta H^\circ = 54,270$ cal.

20. Calculate the standard heat of combustion of carbon monoxide at 500, 1000, and 2000°F.

21. Calculate the standard heat of combustion of sulfur dioxide to sulfur trioxide at 500, 1000, and 2000°F.

22. Develop a general equation for the standard heat of reaction as a function of temperature for one of the reactions given in parts (b), (f), (i), (k), (r), (s), and (t) of Prob. 16.

23. Calculate the theoretical flame temperature when carbon monoxide at 77°F is burned with

(a) The theoretical amount of air at 77°F

(b) 20 per cent excess air at 77°F

(c) 50 per cent excess air at 77°F

(d) 100 per cent excess air at 77°F

(e) 50 per cent excess air preheated to 1000°F

24. Dry methane gas at 77°F is burned completely at 1 atm with 20 per cent excess air saturated with water vapor at 77°F. The flue gases leave the furnace at 3000°F and pass through a cooler. How much heat is lost from the furnace, and how much heat must be removed in the cooler if the flue gases emerge at 100°F? Take 1 lb mole CH_4 burned as a basis.

$$Ans. \ Q_{\text{furnace}} = -21,000 \ \text{Btu}; \ Q_{\text{cooler}} = -352,600 \ \text{Btu.}$$

25. The heat of combustion of a light liquid hydrocarbon in a constant-volume bomb calorimeter at 25°C is 19,000 Btu/lb$_m$. The composition of the hydrocarbon may be represented by the formula $(CH_2)_n$. Suppose this fuel could be completely burned in an internal-combustion engine with 100 per cent excess air, the air-fuel mixture entering at 77°F and atmospheric pressure and the exhaust gases leaving at 600°F. If the engine develops 1.4 hp-hr of work per pound of fuel burned, how much heat would have to be removed by the cooling jacket per pound of fuel?

26. Ammonia gas enters the catalyst chambers of a synthetic nitric acid plant mixed with the required amount of air to convert the nitrogen in NH_3 completely to NO and the hydrogen to H_2O. The gases enter at 150°F. If the conversion is 90 per cent, if no side reactions occur, and if the reactor operates adiabatically, what will be the temperature of the gases leaving the catalyst? For purposes of calculation assume the reaction to occur at atmospheric pressure. *Ans.* 925°C.

27. A process for the manufacture of ethylene oxide by the air oxidation of ethylene is based upon passing the reactants over a silver catalyst at temperatures from 200 to 260°C. Suppose that a 5 volume per cent ethylene–95 per cent air mixture enters the reactor at 200°C, and 50 per cent of the ethylene is converted to ethylene oxide and 40 per cent completely burned to carbon dioxide. How much heat must be removed from the reactor per mole of ethylene if the exit temperature of the gases is not to exceed 260°C? The average molal heat capacity of ethylene may be taken as 18 Btu/(lb mole)(°R) between 25 and 200°C and as 19 Btu/(lb mole)(°R) between 25 and 260°C. Similar values for ethylene oxide are 20 and 21 Btu/(lb mole)(°R).

28. A hydrogen plant using the Bosch process produces 10 tons of hydrogen per day according to the reaction

$$CO(g) + H_2O(g) \rightarrow CO_2(g) + H_2(g)$$

The carbon monoxide and steam enter the reactor at 300°F and atmospheric pressure, and the products leave the catalyst bed at 900°F. The entire reactor assembly is surrounded by a water jacket.

An amount of steam 50 per cent in excess of stoichiometric requirements is used to improve the kinetics of the reaction so that the product stream contains very little carbon monoxide. If the temperature rise of the cooling water is not to exceed 20°F, calculate the amount of cooling water required in pounds *mass* per hour.

29. A direct-fired dryer operates on a fuel oil having a net heating value of 19,000 Btu/lb$_m$. The composition of the oil is 85 per cent carbon, 12 per cent hydrogen, 2 per cent nitrogen, and 1 per cent water by weight. The flue gases leave the dryer at 400°F containing 3 per cent CO_2 and 11.8 per cent CO, by an Orsat analysis. The fuel, air, and material to be dried may be assumed to enter the dryer at 77°F. If the entering air is saturated with water vapor, and if 30 per cent of the net heating value of the oil is allowed for heat losses (including losses from the dried product), how much water is evaporated in the dryer per pound *mass* of oil burned?

30. In order to increase its supply of ethylene for the manufacture of synthetic organic chemicals, a chemical company has contracted with a petroleum manufacturer to crack propane thermally to ethylene and methane. The extent of the side reactions under carefully controlled operating conditions is small and may be neglected.

You have been asked to check the design of the equipment proposed by the petroleum organization. It plans to crack the propane by passing it through a pipestill furnace (consisting of 100 ft of 3½-in.-ID alloy steel pipe) at high temperature and pressure. The process is entirely vapor phase, and the propane enters the pipestill at 400°F and 250 psia. On the basis of pilot-plant data a conversion to ethylene of about 50 per cent may be expected as long as the exit temperature of the gases from the pipestill does not exceed 1000°F. The propane feed rate is 10,000 lb/hr, and the furnace design is such that the rate of heat transfer to the material in the pipestill is 10,000,000 Btu/hr. Calculate the temperature of the gas mixture leaving the furnace.

NOTES

1. The heats of formation at 400°F and 1 atm pressure are

Propane:
$$\Delta H = -27,600 \text{ cal/g mole}$$
Ethylene:
$$\Delta H = 11,800 \text{ cal/g mole}$$
Methane:
$$\Delta H = -19,300 \text{ cal/g mole}$$

2. The average molal heat capacities between 400°F and the exit temperature are

Propane:
$$56.4 \text{ Btu/(lb mole)(°F)}$$
Ethylene:
$$24.0 \text{ Btu/(lb mole)(°F)}$$
Methane:
$$10.5 \text{ Btu/(lb mole)(°F)}$$

3. Neglect the effect of pressure on ΔH and on the heat capacities.

31. It is proposed to make solid NaOH by introducing metallic sodium at 77°F and saturated steam at 150 psia into a reactor, the solid NaOH and the hydrogen formed being removed from the reactor at 358.4°F:

$$2\text{Na}(s) + 2\text{H}_2\text{O}(g) \rightarrow 2\text{NaOH}(s) + \text{H}_2(g)$$

For every ton of NaOH formed, how much heat must be added to or withdrawn from the reactor?

32. The synthetic process for the production of hydrochloric acid is based on the direct combination of gaseous hydrogen and chlorine. If 618 lb_m/hr of chlorine and 22.1 lb_m/hr of hydrogen are fed to a reactor, and if the reactants enter at 25°C and the products leave at 500°C, calculate the heat evolved in Btu per hour. The reaction may be assumed to go to completion.

33. Hydrogen and oxygen are being produced by the continuous electrolysis of a dilute caustic solution at atmospheric pressure. Liquid water is supplied to the cell at 25°C and gaseous hydrogen and oxygen are removed at the same temperature. A current of 3000 amp at 2.00 volts is passed through the cell at a current efficiency of 90 per cent. At what rate (Btu per hour) must heat be supplied or removed from the cell so that its temperature will be constant at 25°C? Current efficiency is defined as the ratio of actual product to that formed according to Faraday's law of electrolysis.

34. $\text{CaCl}_2\cdot6\text{H}_2\text{O}$ is mixed with water in a continuous process to form a solution containing 25 per cent CaCl_2 by weight. How much heat must be added to or extracted from the system in order to keep the temperature constant at 25°C? Express the result as Btu per pound *mass* of solution formed.

35. One thousand pounds *mass* of a 50 per cent caustic soda (NaOH) solution at 100°F is mixed with 400 lb_m of a 10 per cent solution at 180°F.

(a) How much heat must be given off if the final mixture is to be at 70°F?

(b) What would be the temperature of the final mixture if the mixing were done adiabatically?

36. A single-effect evaporator is to concentrate a 10 per cent solution of sulfuric acid in water to 65 per cent. The feed rate is 60,000 lb_m/hr, and the feed temperature is 70°F. The evaporator is maintained at an absolute pressure of 4 in. Hg. Under these conditions the boiling point of 65 per cent H_2SO_4 is 205°F. Calculate the required heat-transfer rate in the evaporator.

37. Two hundred and ten pounds *mass* per hour of $\text{Cu(NO}_3)_2\cdot6\text{H}_2\text{O}$ at 25°C and 189 lb_m/hr of water at 25°C are fed to a tank in which solution takes place. The resulting solution is passed through a heat exchanger which adjusts its temperature to 25°C. Calculate the required rate of heat transfer in the exchanger. The following data are available:

For $\text{Cu(NO}_3)_2$: $\Delta H^{\circ}_{f\,298} = -73,400$ cal/g mole

For $\text{Cu(NO}_3)_2\cdot6\text{H}_2\text{O}$: $\Delta H^{\circ}_{f\,298} = -504,300$ cal/g mole

The heat of solution of $\text{Cu(NO}_3)_2$ in water at 25°C is nearly independent of concentration and has the value $-10,400$ cal/g mole of $\text{Cu(NO}_3)_2$.

38. Calculate the heat of formation of 1 lb mole of hydrochloric acid *in* 15 lb moles of water at 25°C.

39. Calculate the heat of hydration at 25°C of sodium carbonate as represented by the equation

$$\text{Na}_2\text{CO}_3 + 10\text{H}_2\text{O} \rightarrow \text{Na}_2\text{CO}_3\cdot10\text{H}_2\text{O}$$

40. Calculate the temperature which results when sufficient solid NaOH at 70°F is dissolved adiabatically in a 20 per cent NaOH solution, originally at 70°F, to bring the concentration up to 40 per cent.

41. Calculate the heat effect for a process in which sufficient liquid SO_3 at 25°C is reacted with water at 25°C to give a 65 per cent H_2SO_4 solution at 100°C.

★42. In the Daniels process for the fixation of nitrogen, nitric oxide (NO) is formed by the direct combination of the nitrogen and oxygen in air at atmospheric pressure and at temperatures above 2000°C. These temperatures are attained by burning natural gas in preheated air. The preheating is accomplished by heat exchange between the reaction products and the entering air stream. Although the actual process is more complicated, the accompanying diagram shows its essential features.

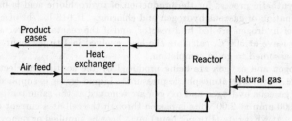

If natural gas is assumed to be essentially methane, the only reactions which occur to an appreciable extent are

$$CH_4 + 2O_2 \rightarrow CO_2 + 2H_2O$$
$$\tfrac{1}{2}N_2 + \tfrac{1}{2}O_2 \rightarrow NO$$

The combustion of methane may be considered to be complete. Equilibrium considerations indicate that 1.5 per cent of the entering nitrogen in the air stream can be converted to NO. If the air and natural gas enter the process at 25°C and if the product gases leave at 225°C, calculate the minimum amount of natural gas (CH_4) which must be burned per mole of air fed to the process.

43. A steam plant operates with a gas-fired boiler. During a test of the plant the following information was collected. The natural gas used as fuel had the following analysis on a dry basis: 89.1 mole per cent CH_4, 4.2 mole per cent C_2H_6, 3.9 mole per cent N_2, and 2.8 mole per cent CO_2. It entered the furnace at 70°F saturated with water vapor at a rate of 20,000 ft³/hr as measured at 70°F and 1.8 in. Hg gauge. Barometric pressure was 29.86 in. Hg.

The air entered the furnace at 78°F with a humidity of 37 per cent. The stack-gas temperature was 653°F, and its Orsat analysis was 7.9 per cent CO_2, 3.2 per cent CO, 3.4 per cent O_2, and 85.5 per cent N_2. The feedwater to the boiler entered at 127°F at a rate of 11,150 lb$_m$/hr. Steam was generated at 235 psig and superheated to 500°F.

Calculate the material and energy balances for the plant.

44. Pure H_2SO_4 at 100°F and pure H_2O at 70°F are mixed to form a 30 per cent solution. If the mixing is done adiabatically, what will be the final temperature of the solution? How much heat must be removed per pound *mass* of solution formed if the mixing is accompanied by cooling so that the final temperature is 70°F?

45. A 90 per cent sulfuric acid solution is to be added continuously over a period of 5 hr to a tank containing 8000 lb$_m$ of pure water. The final concentration of acid in the tank is to be 50 per cent. It is required that the contents of the tank be continuously cooled so that the temperature remains constant at 70°F. Furthermore, the cooling system is designed so that the rate of heat transfer must be constant. In order to meet these conditions, the 90 per cent acid must be added to the tank at a variable rate. If the water is initially at 70°F and if the 90 per cent acid is also at 70°F, determine the instantaneous acid rate as a function of time, and prepare a graph showing this rate in pounds *mass* of 90 per cent acid per hour vs. time in hours.

CHAPTER 6

THE SECOND LAW OF THERMODYNAMICS

Thermodynamics is concerned with the transformations of energy, and the laws of thermodynamics describe the bounds within which these transformations are observed to occur. The first law, stating that energy must be conserved in all ordinary processes, has been the underlying principle of the preceding chapters. The first law imposes no restriction on the *direction* of energy transformations. Yet, all human experience indicates the existence of such a restriction. To complete the foundation for the science of thermodynamics, it is necessary to formulate this second limitation. Its concise statement constitutes the second law.

One of the clearest interpretations of the second-law principle may be achieved by considering the differences between the two forms of energy, heat and work. In the first law no distinction is made between these two quantities; in the expression for the increase in energy of a system both work and heat are included as simple additive terms, implying that one unit of heat, such as a calorie or Btu, is equivalent to the same unit of work. Although this is true with respect to a total energy balance, experience teaches that there is a difference in *quality* between heat and work. This experience can be summarized by the following facts.

First, the efficiency of the transformation from one form of work to another, such as electrical to mechanical as accomplished in an electric motor, can be made to approach 100 per cent as closely as is desired by exerting more and more care in eliminating irreversibilities in the apparatus. On the other hand, the efforts during the last century to convert energy transferred to a system as heat into any of the forms of work show that, regardless of improvements in the machines employed, the conversion is limited to low values (40 per cent is an approximate maximum). These efficiencies are so low, in comparison with those obtained for the transformation of work from one form to another, that there can be no escape from the conclusion that there is an intrinsic difference between heat and work. Proceeding in the other direction, the problem of converting work into heat with 100 per cent efficiency is a very simple one. Indeed, efforts are made in nearly every machine to eliminate this conversion, which usually results in a decreased efficiency of operation. These facts lead to the conclusion that heat is a less versatile or more

175

degraded form of energy than work. Work might be termed energy of a higher quality than heat.

To draw further upon our experience of natural phenomena, it is known that heat is always transferred from a higher temperature level to a lower one and never in the reverse direction. This suggests that heat itself may be assigned a characteristic quality as well as quantity and that this quality depends upon the temperature.

Finally, this use of temperature to measure the quality of heat may be related to the efficiency of conversion of heat into work. Experience shows that, the higher the temperature of the heat used for partial conversion to work, the greater the efficiency of conversion. For example, the efficiency, or work output per unit of fuel burned, of a stationary power plant increases as the temperature of the steam in the boiler and superheater rises.

6-1. Statements of the Second Law. The observations just described are results of the restriction imposed by the second law on the direction of actual processes. Many general statements may be made which define this restriction and, hence, serve as statements of the second law. Two of the most useful are:

1. No apparatus can operate in such a way that its only effect (in system *and* surroundings) is to convert the heat taken in completely into work.

2. Any process which consists *solely* in the transfer of heat from one temperature to a higher one is impossible.

Statement 1 does not imply that heat cannot be converted into work, but does mean that changes other than those resulting directly from the conversion of heat into work must occur in either the system or surroundings. Consider the case of an ideal gas in a vertical cylinder-and-piston assembly, expanding reversibly at constant temperature. Work is produced in the surroundings (consider the gas as the system) equal to the integral of the pressure times the change in volume. Since the gas is ideal, $\Delta E = 0$. Then, according to the first law, the heat absorbed by the gas from the surroundings is equal to the work produced in the surroundings because of the reversible expansion in the gas. At first this might seem to be a contradiction of statement 1, since in the surroundings the only result has been the complete conversion of heat into work. However, the second-law statement requires that there also be no change in the system, a requirement which has not been met in this example. Since the pressure of the gas has decreased, this process could not be continued indefinitely. The pressure of the gas would soon reach that of the surroundings, and further expansion would be impossible. Therefore, a method of continuously producing work from heat by this method would fail. If the original state of the system were restored in order to

3. Carnot reversible heat engine of efficiency η 3/20/4

comply with the requirements of statement 1, it would be necessary to take energy from the surroundings in the form of work in order to compress the gas back to its original pressure. At the same time energy as heat would be transferred to the surroundings in order to maintain constant temperature. This reverse process would require just the amount of work gained from the expansion; hence the net work produced would be zero. From this discussion it is evident that statement 1 might be expressed in an alternative way, *viz.:*

1*a*. It is impossible to convert the heat taken in completely into work in a cyclical process.

The term *cyclical* requires that the system be restored periodically to its original state. In the previous example the expansion and compression back to the original state constituted a complete cycle. If the process is repeated, it becomes a cyclical process. The restriction of a cyclical process in statement 1*a* amounts to the same limitation as that introduced by the words *only effect* in statement 1.

The second law does not prohibit the production of work from heat, but it does place a limitation upon the efficiency of any cyclic process. The partial conversion of heat into work forms the basis for nearly all commercial plants for the production of power (water power is an exception). The consideration of a quantitative expression for the efficiency of this process is the next objective in the treatment of the second law.

6-2. The Heat Engine. In order to develop a quantitative interpretation of the second law, the mechanism for partially converting heat into work will be considered in detail.

A machine for producing work from heat in a cyclic process is termed a *heat engine.* An example is the steam power plant in which the medium (steam) periodically returns to its original state. In such a power plant the cycle (in simple form) is as follows:

(*a*) Part of the heat from the fuel (heat of combustion of coal, oil, or gas or heat from a nuclear reaction) is transferred to liquid water, converting it into steam at a high pressure and temperature.

(*b*) Energy is transferred from this steam as shaft work by a device such as a turbine.

(*c*) The exhaust steam from the turbine is condensed at a low temperature by transferring heat to cooling water.

(*d*) The liquid water is pumped back to the boiler, thus completing the cycle.

In process (*a*) heat is absorbed by the steam; let the amount be Q_1. In process (*b*), which is adiabatic, energy as shaft work is extracted from the steam; and in (*c*) an amount of heat Q_2 is transferred to the cooling water. The final step (*d*) is also adiabatic and requires the addition of a relatively small amount of work to the water.

Since the energy change of the system must be zero for the complete cycle,

$$\Delta E_{\text{cycle}} = 0 = Q_1 - Q_2 - W$$

or

$$Q_1 - Q_2 = W \tag{6-1}^1$$

where W is the net work taken from the steam and represents the difference between the work produced in process (b) and that required in process (d). Of the heat Q_1 absorbed at the high temperature, part is converted into work and part, Q_2, is rejected at the low (condenser) temperature. Although in a power plant the temperatures during processes (a) and (c) normally vary, assume for the present that all the heat Q_1 is absorbed at a constant temperature θ_1 and that all the heat Q_2 is rejected at the constant temperature θ_2. The symbol θ is used for temperature rather than the temperature T employed in the ideal-gas equation, for thus far in the development of the temperature concept there is no justification that the thermodynamic temperature θ, based upon the second law, is the same as T.

The ratio of W to Q_1, the efficiency of the engine for converting heat into work, would be expected to depend upon the degree of reversibility of processes (a), (b), (c), and (d). In particular, it may be shown that an irreversible heat engine cannot have an efficiency greater than a reversible one. To do this consider two heat engines, one reversible and one irreversible, operating in reverse directions between the same temperatures θ_1 and θ_2. The irreversible engine will be operated in the conventional manner, absorbing an amount of heat Q_1 at the high temperature θ_1, converting part of it into work W, and discarding the remainder Q_2 at the lower temperature θ_2. The reversible heat engine runs in the opposite direction and is directly connected to the irreversible one. It uses the work W produced by the irreversible engine to absorb the heat Q_2' at the low temperature θ_2 and discards the heat Q_1' (equal to $Q_2' + W$) at θ_1. The scheme of operations is depicted in Fig. 6-1. If it were possible for the irreversible engine to have the greater efficiency, W/Q_1 would be greater than W/Q_1' for the reversible engine. Since W is the same in both cases, the heat Q_1'

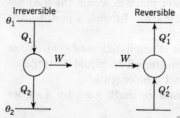

FIG. 6-1. Efficiency of reversible and irreversible heat engines.

---

[1] In this equation both Q_1 and Q_2 are taken as positive quantities. This means that the usual sign convention (taking heat to be positive when it is absorbed by the system) has been discarded. This procedure of considering all heat quantities as positive simplifies the development of the second law and will be adopted in Secs. 6-2 to 6-4.

for the reversible engine would be greater than Q_1 for the irreversible. From Eq. (6-1),

$$Q_2 = Q_1 - W \qquad \text{irreversible}$$

and

$$Q_2' = Q_1' - W \qquad \text{reversible}$$

If Q_1' is greater than Q_1, then Q_2' must also be greater than Q_2 by the same magnitude. Therefore, the net result of this operation is that an amount of heat $Q_2' - Q_2$ has been transferred from the low temperature θ_2 to the high temperature θ_1. This is impossible according to statement 2 of the second law, and the original premise that the irreversible engine has a higher efficiency than that of the reversible is false.

No violation of the second law is encountered if the irreversible engine has a lower efficiency than the reversible one. In this case W/Q_1' for the reversible engine is greater than W/Q_1 for the irreversible, and Q_1' is less than Q_1 for the same W. This means that not so much heat is discarded at θ_1 by the reversible engine as is absorbed at θ_1 by the irreversible. By an energy balance, Q_2 is greater than Q_2' by the same amount. Therefore, the net result is the transfer of an amount of heat $Q_1 - Q_1'$ from θ_1 to θ_2, which is, of course, entirely possible. Hence, an irreversible heat engine must have an efficiency less than that of a reversible engine operating between the same two temperatures.

By a similar method it can be shown that all reversible engines operating between the same temperature limits must have identical efficiencies. If this were not so, the more efficient engine could be used to run the less efficient in the reverse direction and the net result would be the transfer of heat from a low to a high temperature. This is impossible according to the second law.

These corollaries of the second law point to the important conclusion (first conceived by Sadi Carnot in 1824) that the efficiency of converting heat into work in a reversible heat engine must depend, not upon the medium employed to run the engine, but only upon the temperature levels θ_1 and θ_2. Or from another point of view (originally advanced by Lord Kelvin), the reversible heat engine defines a thermodynamic scale of temperature which is the same for all materials. It can be used as a basis of comparison for the various temperature scales based upon physical properties, such as the mercury-in-glass and the ideal-gas thermometers. The thermodynamic temperature θ and its relationship to the ideal-gas temperature T are considered in Secs. 6-3 and 6-4.

6-3. The Absolute Temperature Scale. Carnot's principle, that the efficiency of converting heat into work in a reversible engine depends only upon the temperature levels involved, can be stated mathematically as follows:

$$\frac{W}{Q_1} = \phi(\theta_1, \theta_2) \qquad (6\text{-}2)$$

From an over-all energy balance on the heat engine, $W = Q_1 - Q_2$ [Eq. (6-1)] so that (6-2) may be written

$$\frac{Q_1 - Q_2}{Q_1} = \phi(\theta_1, \theta_2) \quad = \frac{T_1 - T_2}{T_1}$$

or

$$\frac{Q_2}{Q_1} = 1 - \phi(\theta_1, \theta_2) = f(\theta_1, \theta_2) = \frac{T_2}{T_1} \qquad (6\text{-}3)$$

Equation (6-3) means that the ratio of heat rejected at the low temperature θ_2 to that absorbed by the heat engine at the high temperature θ_1 is a function of these two temperatures only. More about the nature of the unknown function $f(\theta_1, \theta_2)$ can be determined by considering two

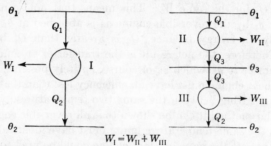

$$W_I = W_{II} + W_{III}$$

FIG. 6-2. Thermodynamic temperature and reversible heat engines.

reversible heat engines (II and III) operating between temperatures θ_1 and θ_3, and θ_3 and θ_2, respectively. The situation is illustrated in Fig. 6-2. The original engine I, for which Eq. (6-3) is applicable, absorbs an amount of heat Q_1 at θ_1 and discards Q_2 at θ_2. Engine II absorbs this same amount of heat Q_1 at θ_1 but rejects a different amount Q_3 at the intermediate temperature θ_3. The third engine absorbs this same amount of heat Q_3 and discards heat at θ_2. Equations similar to (6-3) may be written for engines II and III:

$$\frac{Q_3}{Q_1} = f(\theta_1, \theta_3) \qquad (6\text{-}4)$$

$$\frac{Q_2}{Q_3} = f(\theta_3, \theta_2) \qquad (6\text{-}5)$$

The function of the temperatures must be of the same form in all three equations, for all three represent reversible heat engines operating in the same way. The quantity of heat Q_2 in Eq. (6-5) for engine III must be exactly the same as the heat discarded at θ_2 by engine I. If this were not so, engines II and III could be operated in the reverse direction, using the work W_1 and transferring a net amount of heat from the lower temperature θ_2 to the higher one θ_1. This would be a violation of the second law. Stated in a slightly different way, this means that the combined efficiencies of engines II and III in converting heat into work must be the same as that of engine I.

Since the values of Q_2 in Eqs. (6-5) and (6-3) are the same, Eqs. (6-4) and (6-5) can be multiplied and equated to (6-3), resulting in the expression

$$\frac{Q_2}{Q_1} = f(\theta_1,\theta_3)f(\theta_3,\theta_2) = f(\theta_1,\theta_2) \tag{6-6}$$

It is apparent that the effect of θ_3 in the product of the two functions in the middle member of Eq. (6-6) must disappear, for otherwise the product could not be equal to the last member, $f(\theta_1,\theta_2)$, which does not involve θ_3. This results in the important simplification that $f(\theta_1,\theta_2)$ can be separated into the product of two functions, each of which involves only one temperature. Hence Eq. (6-6) may be written

$$\frac{Q_2}{Q_1} = f'(\theta_1)f''(\theta_3)f'(\theta_3)f''(\theta_2) \tag{6-7}$$

where the primes denote two different functions. If the effect of θ_3 is to drop out of Eq. (6-7), f' and f'' must be reciprocal functions, or

$$f'(\theta) = \frac{1}{f''(\theta)}$$

Applying this restriction to (6-7) yields

$$\frac{Q_2}{Q_1} = f'(\theta_1)f''(\theta_2) = \frac{f''(\theta_2)}{f''(\theta_1)} \tag{6-8}$$

which states that the ratio of the heat rejected at θ_2 to that absorbed at θ_1 must be equal to a ratio of the same function of the two temperatures θ_2 and θ_1.

This is as far as the second law goes in the definition of the absolute temperature scale. It requires that the ratio of the heat rejected to that absorbed in a reversible heat engine be equal to the ratio of some function of the true temperatures, provided that the same function is used for each temperature. The simplest kind of function would be one equal to the temperature, or

$$f''(\theta) = \theta \tag{6-9}[1]$$

With this choice, Eq. (6-8) becomes

$$\frac{Q_2}{Q_1} = \frac{\theta_2}{\theta_1} \tag{6-10}$$

[1] The original choice of Kelvin was $f''(\theta) = e^\theta$.

In terms of the efficiency of the heat engine, Eq. (6-10) becomes

$$\frac{W}{Q_1} = 1 - \frac{Q_2}{Q_1} = \frac{\theta_1 - \theta_2}{\theta_1} \tag{6-11}$$

Equation (6-10) defines the absolute thermodynamic temperature scale. If a truly reversible heat engine could be constructed and Q_2 and Q_1 measured, their ratio would be equal to the ratio of the thermodynamic temperatures of the heat sink and source. Since such a heat engine cannot be constructed, it is important to relate the temperature θ to the ideal-gas temperature T, a more readily determined quantity. This problem is considered in the next section.

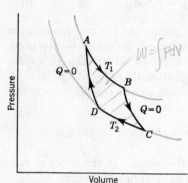

FIG. 6-3. Carnot heat-engine cycle with an ideal gas as the working fluid.

6-4. The Ideal-gas Temperature Scale. Suppose an ideal gas is employed as the working fluid in a reversible cyclical heat engine, e.g., a Carnot engine. The cycle consists of an isothermal expansion from A to B (see Fig. 6-3) during which process an amount of heat Q_1 is absorbed at T_1. The next step is the adiabatic expansion BC to a lower temperature T_2. An amount of heat Q_2 is discarded at the constant temperature T_2 during the third process, an isothermal compression from C to D. Finally, the gas is returned to its original state by the adiabatic compression DA.

The net work done by the gas is the algebraic sum of the work effects for each of the four steps:

$$W_{net} = W_{AB} + W_{BC} + W_{CD} + W_{DA} \tag{6-12}$$

Processes BC and DA are adiabatic and reversible; hence the work for each step, according to the first law, is equal to $-\Delta E$:

$$W_{BC} = -\Delta E_{BC} = -\int_{T_1}^{T_2} C_v\, dT \quad \text{(for 1 mole)} \tag{6-13}$$

$$W_{DA} = -\Delta E_{DA} = -\int_{T_2}^{T_1} C_v\, dT \tag{6-14}$$

The last equality follows from the fact that for an ideal gas $dE = C_v\, dT$. It is evident from Eqs. (6-13) and (6-14) that W_{BC} and W_{DA} are numerically equal and opposite in sign. Hence Eq. (6-12) may be written

$$W_{net} = W_{AB} + W_{CD} \tag{6-15}$$

Since AB and CD are isothermal processes

$$W_{net} = RT_1 \ln \frac{p_A}{p_B} + RT_2 \ln \frac{p_C}{p_D} \tag{6-16}$$

For the isothermal processes $\Delta E = 0$.   Therefore,

$$Q_1 = W_{AB} = RT_1 \ln \frac{p_A}{p_B} \tag{6-17}$$

The ratio of the work obtained to the heat absorbed, the efficiency,[1] is obtained by dividing Eq. (6-16) by (6-17):

$$\frac{W_{net}}{Q_1} = \frac{1}{T_1}\left[T_1 + T_2 \frac{\ln(p_C/p_D)}{\ln(p_A/p_B)}\right] \tag{6-18}$$

From the fact that $pV = RT$ for all the processes in the cycle and $pV^\gamma = $ a constant for the adiabatic reversible processes, it can be shown (see Example 6-1) that

$$r = C_p/C_v \qquad \frac{p_B}{p_A} = \frac{p_C}{p_D} \tag{6-19}$$

Substituting this relationship in Eq. (6-18),

$$\frac{W_{net}}{Q_1} = \frac{T_1 - T_2}{T_1} \tag{6-20}$$

Since $Q_2 = Q_1 - W_{net}$,

$$\frac{Q_1 - Q_2}{Q_1} = \frac{T_1 - T_2}{T_1}$$

$$\frac{Q_2}{Q_1} = \frac{T_2}{T_1} \tag{6-21}$$

Comparison of this last equation with Eq. (6-10) shows the arbitrary choice of $f''(\theta) = \theta$ to be such that the ratio of the ideal-gas temperatures is the same as the ratio of the thermodynamic temperatures.   Since the ideal-gas temperature scale has been determined, the thermodynamic scale is also fixed.   In Chap. 3, it was shown that absolute zero was 273.16°C below the ice point on the ideal-gas scale.   Hence, the thermodynamic absolute zero is also -273.16°C $(-459.69$°F).

Since θ is equivalent to T, two designations for temperature are no longer necessary.   Subsequently, the single symbol T will be used to denote absolute temperature.

Equation (6-20) shows that the only conditions under which the efficiency of a heat engine can approach unity are those for which T_1 approaches infinity or T_2 approaches zero.   Since neither of these con-

---

[1] As used here, the term *efficiency* refers to the ratio of work obtained to the heat absorbed, sometimes called thermal efficiency.   The term efficiency is also used in connection with engines to define the fraction of the maximum possible work that is actually realized.   The word is used in many contexts in engineering, and its various meanings have to be carefully distinguished.

184 CHEMICAL ENGINEERING THERMODYNAMICS [CHAP. 6

ditions is attainable in practice, all heat engines operate at efficiencies of considerably less than 100 per cent. The practical value of T_2 is about 300°K, the approximate temperature of our environment. The vital point is that all heat engines must discard a certain amount of heat to the surroundings (usually to cooling water or to the atmosphere), and this discarded heat cannot be converted into work by the engine. However, a significant increase in the efficiencies of actual heat engines has been made during the present century by increasing the temperature T_1 at which heat is absorbed by the engine. This improvement is predicted by the second law, as shown by Eq. (6-20). Modern steam power plants operate at efficiencies of about 30 per cent.

Example 6-1. Verify Eq. (6-19) for an ideal gas with constant heat capacities.

Solution. For the adiabatic reversible process DA, the temperatures and pressures are related by Eq. (3-14):

$$\frac{T_1}{T_2} = \left(\frac{p_A}{p_D}\right)^{(\gamma-1)/\gamma}$$

Similarly, for the process BC

$$\frac{T_1}{T_2} = \left(\frac{p_B}{p_C}\right)^{(\gamma-1)/\gamma}$$

By equating these two expressions there is obtained

$$\frac{p_A}{p_D} = \frac{p_B}{p_C}$$

or

$$\frac{p_B}{p_A} = \frac{p_C}{p_D}$$

which is Eq. (6-19).

6-5. The Concept of Entropy. If we now return to the usual sign convention that heat is positive when absorbed by the system and negative when rejected by the system, Eq. (6-21) becomes

$$\frac{Q_1}{T_1} = -\frac{Q_2}{T_2} \tag{6-22}$$

or

$$\frac{Q_1}{T_1} + \frac{Q_2}{T_2} = 0 \tag{6-23}$$

This equation shows that the sum of the quantities Q_1/T_1 and Q_2/T_2, associated with the absorption and rejection of heat by the fluid of a reversible heat engine, is zero for the entire cycle. Since the fluid of the engine returns to its initial state at the end of the cycle, it undergoes no net change in properties. This fact suggests that the quantities Q_1/T_1 and Q_2/T_2 represent property changes of the working fluid, because their sum is zero for the cycle, and this is the characteristic of a property or state function. The amount of heat transfer is known to depend on the

path of the process.   However, if the heat is divided by the temperature
at which the transfer takes place, the result is independent of the path.
It is important to remember that this conclusion is valid for reversible
processes only.

Up to this point only a special type of reversible process has been
considered, *viz.*, one in which heat transfer has occurred at constant temperature.   This restriction can be removed by considering a cyclical
reversible process (represented in
Fig. 6-4) which does not consist of the
simple isothermals and adiabatics
which characterized the processes in
Fig. 6-3.   First divide the enclosed
cycle by a series of adiabatic curves
(shown dashed) sufficiently close together so that each element, such as
1 to 2 or 7 to 8, can be considered
as isothermal.   Then the cyclical
process $ADBCA$ is equivalent to the
summation of the elemental cycles.
For example, start with the element

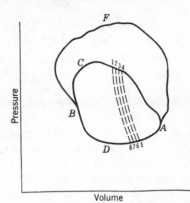

Fig. 6-4. Generalized heat-engine cycle.

1-2-7-8 and proceed from 1 to 2, then
from 2 to 7, 7 to 8, and 8 to 1.   On
the next element proceed from 2 to 3, 3 to 6, 6 to 7, and 7 to 2.   The
adiabatic 2-7 has been traversed twice, once in each direction, so that its
net effect is zero.   By continuing this process, the whole cycle can be
traversed.   For any differential element such as 1-2-7-8, Eq. (6-23)
becomes

$$\frac{dQ_1}{T_1} + \frac{dQ_2}{T_2} = 0 \qquad (6\text{-}24)$$

Subscript 1 refers to heat effects on the part of the cycle BCA and subscript 2 to ADB.   This equation is general in that it may be applied to
any differential reversible cycle regardless of the path of the process.   In
integrated form it is

$$\oint \frac{dQ_R}{T} = 0 \qquad (6\text{-}25)$$

where the subscript R emphasizes the necessity of reversibility and the
circle in the integral sign denotes a cyclical process.

It should be emphasized again that all the processes considered have
been reversible.   The concept that the efficiency of a heat engine is
independent of the medium and depends only upon the temperature limits
goes back to the stipulation of reversibility.   Actually, processes are
never truly reversible and seldom approach reversibility.   Therefore, if

the second-law principle is to be of importance, it must be extended to apply to irreversible processes. The method of doing this is very simple but worthy of considerable thought.

With reference to Fig. 6-4, suppose that BFA represents an irreversible path proceeding from B to A in contrast with BCA and BDA, which are reversible processes for accomplishing this same change in state. Equation (6-24) may be rewritten in integrated form as follows:

$$\int_{BCA} \frac{dQ_R}{T} + \int_{ADB} \frac{dQ_R}{T} = 0$$

or

$$\int_{BCA} \frac{dQ_R}{T} = \int_{BDA} \frac{dQ_R}{T} \tag{6-26}$$

Equation (6-26) states mathematically the conclusion already advanced in words, that the integral of dQ_R/T is the same for any reversible path and, therefore, depends only upon the initial and final states. This quantity has been given the name *change in entropy* (en'-tro-py) ΔS. Since ΔS is a function of the initial and final states only, its value from B to A by the irreversible process BFA must be the same as that for process BCA or BDA or any other process between B and A. However, the integral of dQ/T for the irreversible path would not have given ΔS from B to A. The calculation of entropy changes must always be for reversible conditions. The integral of dQ/T is equal to the change in entropy for a reversible process only.

So far only the entropy changes of the working substance of heat engines have been considered. Since no limitations have been placed on such substances, the property of entropy must be ascribed to all matter. Furthermore, if heat transfer to the working substance of a reversible heat engine causes its entropy to change in the amount $\Delta S = \int dQ_R/T$, then heat transfer in any reversible process should cause entropy changes given by the same equation.

This discussion may be summarized as follows:

1. The change in entropy for a reversible process is equal to dQ/T. That is,

$$dS = \frac{dQ_R}{T} \tag{6-27}$$

or

$$\Delta S = \int \frac{dQ_R}{T} \tag{6-28}$$

2. To evaluate ΔS for an irreversible change in state, devise a reversible process for accomplishing the same change, and then evaluate dQ/T over this reversible process. This quantity will be equal to the change in entropy for the irreversible process, since entropy is a state function.

The reason for devising reversible processes for evaluating entropy changes is difficult to understand because, in certain cases, the correct result can be calculated using the actual irreversible process. In particular, when there is a transfer of energy as heat to a system, it is immaterial, as far as the system is concerned, whether the temperature difference causing the heat transfer is differential (making the process reversible) or finite. Thus the entropy change of a system resulting from the transfer of heat can always be calculated by $\int dQ/T$ whether the heat transfer is accomplished reversibly or irreversibly. However, when a process is irreversible because of finite differences in other potentials, such as partial pressures and chemical potentials, it is impossible to calculate entropy changes without devising a reversible means of accomplishing the same change in state.

It would be helpful here if some simple, concise word definition of entropy could be given. Unfortunately, none is available. Many properties of matter are readily detectable, at least qualitatively, to the senses, but this is not the case with the thermodynamic properties such as enthalpy and entropy. Their existence is recognized only indirectly. This introduction to entropy through a consideration of heat engines is the classical approach, and it closely follows the actual historical development of this concept. A more recent and perhaps more fundamental approach to entropy is based on the probability concepts of statistical mechanics. This will be considered briefly at the end of the chapter.

6-6. Mathematical Statement of the Second Law. An analysis of the relationship between entropy and reversibility leads to a concise mathematical equation describing the limitation on the direction of actual processes. To develop this equation, consider the following example. Suppose there are two heat reservoirs, one at a temperature T_1 and a second at a lower temperature T_2. Let a quantity of energy Q be transferred as heat from the high-temperature reservoir to the low-temperature reservoir by bringing the two into intimate contact. Also suppose that the two reservoirs are sufficiently large so that this transfer of energy does not change the temperature of either appreciably. The process is irreversible since the difference in potential (temperature) between the two reservoirs is not differential in amount. The entropy change for the high-temperature reservoir is $-Q/T_1$. Similarly the change in entropy of the low-temperature reservoir is Q/T_2. Thus, the high-temperature reservoir suffered a decrease in entropy (because Q is negative with respect to this reservoir) and the low-temperature reservoir an increase in entropy. Adding these two contributions results in a positive *total* change in entropy since T_2 is less than T_1. Now suppose that the process of heat transfer is made nearly reversible by changing the temperature T_1 to a value only slightly greater than T_2. When this is done, the total

change in entropy for the process of transferring Q units of energy as·
heat approaches zero. Therefore, as the process is made more and more
nearly reversible, the total change in entropy becomes less positive, with
the ultimate value of zero obtainable for a reversible process. This statement applies just to the *total* change in entropy; a decrease in entropy
either in the system or in the surroundings frequently accompanies an
irreversible process. Thus, in the example, the entropy of the high-temperature reservoir decreased.

Although only the transfer of energy as heat has been considered, the
same conclusion applies to any process. This may be shown by examining
another irreversible process, the free fall of a weight. The original potential energy is transferred as heat to the surroundings when the weight
strikes the ground. The total change in entropy is positive and equal to
the heat transferred divided by the temperature at which the transfer
occurs. If the operation of lowering the weight were made more nearly
reversible by attaching, through a pulley, another slightly smaller weight,
most of the potential energy transferred by the first weight would be
received by the second. In this case the total change in entropy would
be much less than in the free fall of the weight. If the pulley assembly
could be made reversible, the second weight would be only differentially
smaller than the first and the total change in entropy would be only
differentially greater than zero.

These results show that all processes proceed in such a direction that
the total entropy change is positive, approaching zero as a limit as the
process approaches reversibility. This conclusion can be stated mathematically by the equation

$$\Delta S_{\text{total}} \geqq 0 \tag{6-29}$$

As a corollary to Eq. (6-29), it may be added that no process is possible
for which the *total* entropy decreases.

Example 6-2. A reversible heat engine absorbs 1000 Btu at 500°F, produces work,
and discards heat at 100°F. What is the change
in entropy of the heat source, the heat sink, and
what is the total entropy change resulting from
the process?

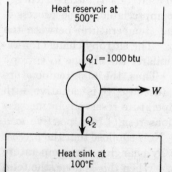

The work done by the heat engine is

$$W = Q_1 \frac{T_1 - T_2}{T_1} = (1000) \left(\frac{960 - 560}{960} \right)$$

$$= 417 \text{ Btu}$$

With respect to the heat source, Q_1 is negative.
Thus,

$$\Delta S_1 = - \frac{1000}{960} = -1.04 \text{ Btu/°R}$$

From Eq. (6-22),

$$\frac{Q_1}{T_1} = \frac{1000}{960} = -\frac{Q_2}{T_2} = \frac{-Q_2}{560}$$

$$Q_2 = -583 \text{ Btu}$$

However, with respect to the heat sink, Q_2 is positive. Thus

$$\Delta S_2 = \frac{583}{560} = 1.04 \text{ Btu/°R}$$

The total entropy change is therefore zero. This result would be expected since all processes involved were taken to be reversible. An irreversible case is analyzed in Example 6-3.

6-7. Entropy Changes and Irreversibility.   A simple quantitative relationship between the degree of irreversibility of a process and the *total* entropy increase may be derived by considering the following example: When an amount of heat Q is transferred from a system at a temperature T_1 to surroundings at a lower temperature T_2, the total change in entropy is

$$\Delta S_{\text{surr}} + \Delta S_{\text{sys}} = \Delta S_{\text{total}} = \frac{Q}{T_2} - \frac{Q}{T_1} = \frac{Q(T_1 - T_2)}{T_1 T_2} \qquad (6\text{-}30)$$

Suppose that the process had been carried out *reversibly* in a heat engine, absorbing an amount of heat Q at T_1, converting part of it to work, and rejecting the remainder at T_2. Then the quantity of work that could have been obtained, but which was lost because of the irreversible nature of the process, is given by Eq. (6-20):

$$W = Q \frac{T_1 - T_2}{T_1} = T_2 Q \frac{T_1 - T_2}{T_1 T_2} \qquad (6\text{-}31)$$

Elimination of Q between Eqs. (6-30) and (6-31) shows this lost work to be equal to the total change in entropy times the temperature of the surroundings:

$$W_{\text{lost}} = T_2(\Delta S_{\text{surr}} + \Delta S_{\text{sys}}) = T_2 \Delta S_{\text{total}} \qquad (6\text{-}32)$$

This expression has been developed for a process involving only heat transfer. However, exactly the same result is obtained from a consideration of any irreversible process. Hence Eq. (6-32) is a general one and can be used to calculate the loss in capacity to do work accompanying any irreversible process. This is shown in Chap. 11, where the general expression for lost work is derived in the form

$$W_{\text{lost}} = T_0 \Delta S_{\text{total}} \qquad (6\text{-}33)$$

where T_0 is the absolute temperature of the surroundings.

The temperature T_0, which may seem somewhat arbitrary, can be assigned a definite value in practice. For example, in a steam power plant, the lowest temperature at which heat can be discarded corresponds to the temperature of the cooling water. Similarly, in a domestic electric refrigerator, the temperature T_0 is the temperature of the air used as a cooling medium for the condenser. In general, T_0 is approximately equal to the temperature of the atmosphere.

It is clear from Eq. (6-33) that the total increase in entropy accompanying an actual process is a measure of the loss in capacity of the system and surroundings as a whole to do work. By combining this loss in work with the ideal, or reversible, work that could be obtained, it is possible to assign a thermodynamic efficiency to any processes. This efficiency of the utilization of energy is developed and applied in several examples in Chap. 11.

[Specific heat, 0.12 Btu/(lbm)(°F)].

Example 6-3. A steel casting weighing 75 lb_m and having a temperature of 800°F is quenched in 300 lb_m of oil [specific heat, 0.6 Btu/(lb_m)(°F)]. If there are no heat losses, what is the change in entropy of (a) the casting? (b) The oil? (c) Both considered together?

Solution. The final temperature of the oil and the steel casting are found by an energy balance. Let t be the final temperature in degrees Fahrenheit. The total change in energy of the oil and steel is zero.

Heat lost by steel casting:
$$Q = (75)(0.12)(800 - t)$$
Heat gained by the oil:
$$Q = (300)(0.6)(t - 70)$$

Equating these two expressions leads to a value of $t = 104.8°F$.
(a) Change in entropy of the casting:

$$\Delta S = \int \frac{dQ}{T} = \int \frac{C_p \, dT}{T} = C_p \ln \frac{T_2}{T_1}$$

$$\Delta S = (75)(0.12) \ln \frac{460 + 104.8}{460 + 800} = -7.21 \text{ Btu/°R}$$

(b) Change in entropy of the oil:

$$\Delta S = (300)(0.6) \ln \frac{460 + 104.8}{460 + 70} = 11.8 \text{ Btu/°R}$$

(c) Total entropy change:

$$\Delta S_{total} = 11.8 - 7.21 = 4.59 \text{ Btu/°R}$$

As a matter of interest, the loss of capacity for doing work because of the irreversibility of the process will be calculated by Eq. (6-33). The temperature of the surroundings is not stated and will be assumed to be 70°F. Thus,

$$W_{lost} = (70 + 460)(4.59) = 2430 \text{ Btu}$$

This is the net amount of work which could have been accomplished if all changes resulting from the process had been accomplished reversibly. The opportunity for accomplishing this work is forever lost once the quenching operation has been carried out. This is a characteristic of irreversible processes and is of vital practical concern from the standpoint of efficient use of energy resources.

It should also be noted in this example that, although the total entropy change was positive, the entropy of the casting decreased.

Example 6-4. What is the change in entropy of 1 mole of an ideal gas which is initially at 120°F and 10 atm pressure and is expanded irreversibly to 1 atm and 70°F? The molal heat capacity at constant pressure is 7 Btu/(lb mole)(°F).

Solution. Since this process is not characterized by constant temperature, constant pressure, or constant volume, and since it is not adiabatic, the solution will be a general one for the change in entropy of an ideal gas. Since entropy is a state function, any path that is reversible will be a satisfactory one for determining ΔS. Suppose the gas is first expanded isothermally to 1 atm pressure and then cooled at constant pressure to the final temperature (70°F), both steps being reversible.

For the isothermal step, $Q_R = W$ ($\Delta E = 0$ for a constant-temperature process involving an ideal gas).

$$\Delta S_a \text{ (isothermal step)} = \frac{W}{T_1} = \frac{1}{T_1} \int_{v_1}^{v_3} p \, dv = \frac{RT_1}{T_1} \ln \frac{v_3}{v_1}$$

where v_3 is the volume at the end of the isothermal process. The volume ratio may be replaced by the inverse-pressure ratio so that (since $p_3 = p_2$)

$$\Delta S_a = R \ln \frac{p_1}{p_2}$$

For the constant-pressure process,

$$\Delta S_b = \int \frac{dQ_R}{T} = \int_{T_1}^{T_2} C_p \frac{dT}{T} \tag{6-34}$$

The total change in entropy of 1 mole of gas is

$$\Delta S = \Delta S_a + \Delta S_b = R \ln \frac{p_1}{p_2} + \int_{T_1}^{T_2} C_p \frac{dT}{T} \tag{6-35}$$

where the subscripts 1 and 2 refer to the initial and final states.

Another method of accomplishing the same change in state would be to expand the gas isothermally to the final volume v_2 and then cool it at constant volume to the final temperature T_2. In this case

$$\Delta S = \Delta S_a + \Delta S_b = R \ln \frac{v_2}{v_1} + \int_{T_1}^{T_2} C_v \frac{dT}{T} \tag{6-36}$$

Both Eqs. (6-35) and (6-36) are general expressions for the change in entropy of an ideal gas in terms of the properties of the initial and final states. That the two expressions will give the same result can be shown by use of the ideal-gas law:

$$\frac{v_2}{v_1} = \frac{T_2 p_1}{T_1 p_2}$$

Substituting this equation in (6-36) and noting that $C_p - C_v = R$ for an ideal gas,

$$\Delta S = R \ln \frac{T_2}{T_1} + R \ln \frac{p_1}{p_2} + \int_{T_1}^{T_2} (C_p - R) \frac{dT}{T}$$

or

$$\Delta S = R \ln \frac{p_1}{p_2} + R \ln \frac{T_2}{T_1} - R \ln \frac{T_2}{T_1} + \int_{T_1}^{T_2} C_p \frac{dT}{T}$$

$$= R \ln \frac{p_1}{p_2} + \int_{T_1}^{T_2} C_p \frac{dT}{T}$$

which is the same as Eq. (6-35).

Calculations could be made for other paths as well, but the two illustrated serve to show that all lead to the same result.

The numerical answer for the problem as stated is

$$\Delta S = 1.98 \ln \frac{10}{1} + 7 \ln \frac{70 + 460}{120 + 460}$$
$$= 4.55 - 0.64 = 3.9 \text{ Btu/(lb mole)(°R)}$$

It is observed that entropy has the same units as the molal heat capacity and therefore will have the same numerical value in English or metric units.

Example 6-5. An inventor claims to have devised a process using only saturated steam at 212°F which will, by a complicated series of steps, make heat continuously available at a temperature of 350°F. He claims further that, for every pound of steam taken into the process, 800 Btu of energy as heat is liberated at this higher temperature of 350°F. Show whether or not such a process is possible. In order to give the inventor the benefit of any doubt, assume cooling water to be available in unlimited quantity at a temperature of 32°F.

Solution. For any process to be theoretically possible, it must meet the requirements of the first and second laws of thermodynamics. The detailed mechanism need not be known in order to determine whether this is the case; only the over-all result is required. If the results of the process satisfy the laws of thermodynamics, means for realizing these results are theoretically possible. The determination of a mechanism is then a matter of ingenuity. Otherwise, the process is impossible, and no mechanism for carrying it out can be devised.

In the present instance, saturated steam is to be taken into some sort of apparatus, and heat is to be made continuously available at a temperature of 350°F. Hence, the process is continuous. Since cooling water is available at 32°F, the maximum use can be made of the steam only by discharging it at this temperature. Therefore, it will be assumed that the steam is condensed and cooled to 32°F in the process and is discharged at atmospheric pressure. All the heat liberated in this operation cannot be made available at 350°F, for this would violate the second law (see statement 2 of Sec. 6-1). It must therefore be supposed that some heat is transferred to the cooling water at 32°F, and the amount can be calculated by assuming that the process meets the requirements of the first law. In other words, the first-law equation for a steady-flow process must be satisfied, that is,

$$\Delta H = Q - W_s$$

where ΔH is the enthalpy change per pound *mass* of steam as it flows through the apparatus (this is the basis of calculations) and Q is the sum of all heat-transfer effects between the apparatus and the surroundings. Since no shaft work is accomplished by the process, $W_s = 0$. The surroundings consist of the cooling water, which acts as a heat sink at the constant temperature of 32°F, and a heat reservoir at 350°F to which 800 Btu is transferred as heat for every pound *mass* of steam entering the apparatus. The accompanying diagram pictures the over-all results of the proposed process.

The values of H and S for saturated steam at 212°F and for liquid water at 32°F were taken from the steam tables. The sum of the heat-transfer effects is

$$Q = -800 + Q_0$$

Hence, the first law becomes

$$Q = -800 + Q_0 = \Delta H = 0.0 - 1150.4 = -1150.4$$

and

$$Q_0 = -350.4 \text{ Btu}$$

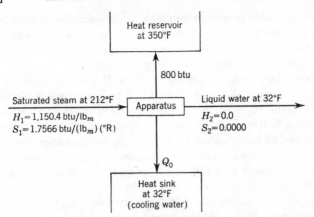

The process must now be examined in the light of the second law. It must be shown whether ΔS_{total} is greater than or less than zero for the proposed process.

For the steam:

$$\Delta S = 0.0000 - 1.7566 = -1.7566 \text{ Btu}/(\text{lb}_m)(°R)$$

For the heat reservoir at 350°F:

$$\Delta S = \frac{800}{350 + 460} = 0.9877 \text{ Btu}/°R$$

For the heat sink at 32°F:

$$\Delta S = \frac{350.4}{32 + 460} = 0.7122 \text{ Btu}/°R$$

Thus

$$\Delta S_{total} = -1.7566 + 0.9877 + 0.7122 = -0.0567 \text{ Btu}/°R$$

Since this result is negative, it must be concluded that the process for the conditions given is impossible, since Eq. (6-29) requires that $\Delta S_{total} \geqq 0$ for all actual processes.

This does not mean that all processes of this general nature are impossible, but only that the inventor has claimed too much. Indeed, one could calculate the maximum amount of heat which could be transferred to the heat reservoir at 350°F, other conditions remaining the same. This calculation is left as an exercise.

6-8. Entropy and Probability. Up to this point entropy has been discussed mainly in terms of its relationship to heat. Perhaps a clearer picture of the entropy concept can be obtained by considering the relationship between entropy and probability. Consider the example of a rock balanced on the edge of a canyon. Suppose the balance is destroyed and the rock falls to the bottom of the canyon. This is an irreversible process; the rock cannot be returned to its original position without taking energy as work from the surroundings. The entropy of the universe has increased, and the rock is now in a more stable state; it cannot undergo further irreversible processes of this nature if it is at the bottom of the canyon.   It is also in a more probable state since the possibility of find-ing rocks at the bottom of a canyon is much greater than finding them balanced at the top.   Therefore an increase in stability, or probability, is accompanied by an increase in entropy.

Suppose a box with a partition dividing it into two sections contains only oxygen molecules in one section and only nitrogen molecules in the other.   Let the partition be withdrawn, allowing the two gases to mix. This process is irreversible (since the system cannot be returned to its original state without taking work from the surroundings) and is accom-panied by an increase in entropy.   The probability has likewise increased, since to find oxygen and nitrogen together as a mixture is more likely than to find each in the pure state.   The mixing process has resulted in a more random arrangement of the system; hence an increase in entropy can be associated with a change from a more ordered to a less ordered, or more random, state.

In connection with this idea of relating entropy and random arrange-ment, consider the process of heating water at constant pressure from a state of solid ice to water vapor.   The ice crystals represent a highly ordered state; except for vibrational motions, each atom is in a definite position with respect to its neighbors.   As heat is absorbed, the ice melts and the entropy of the water increases according to the equation $dS = dQ_R/T$.   Also the state becomes more random, since the atoms are able to move from one position to another as the molecules with which they are associated move.   With the absorption of more heat the liquid will reach its boiling point and vaporize.   Again the arrangement becomes more random, as the motion of the molecules is even less restricted in the vapor state than in the liquid phase.   The increase in entropy for the entire process may be written

$$S - S_1 = \frac{\Delta H_f}{T_f} + \int_{T_f}^{T_v} \frac{C_p \, dT}{T} + \frac{\Delta H_v}{T_v} \qquad (6\text{-}37)$$

where S_1 is the entropy in the original state, ice at its melting point, ΔH_f and T_f are the enthalpy change on melting and the melting tem-perature, and ΔH_v and T_v are similar quantities for the vaporization process.   If the original state were at absolute zero temperature, an equa-tion similar to (6-37) would be applicable but it would have to include the entropy effect accompanying the rise in temperature from $0°K$ to T_f and also the entropy contributions due to transitions from one solid state to another.   If this is done, an expression is obtained for $S - S_0$, where S_0 is the entropy at absolute zero temperature.   It is logical to believe that the atoms making up solid water would have a less random, or more ordered, arrangement at absolute zero temperature than at any other state and, thus have a lower entropy. Planck[1] postulated in addition that the entropy value would be zero at this point. Since the same reasoning would apply to any substance, the entropy of all substances would be zero at absolute zero temperature (in their most stable states). This postulate[2] has been widely accepted and makes it possible to calculate absolute entropies from heat-capacity measurements down to very low temperatures, *i.e.*, by evaluating the expression for $S - S_0$ and postulating that $S_0 = 0$.

The relationship between entropy and probability, in fact the entire concept of the second law, is based upon the fact that the thermodynamic system is macroscopic in size. Returning to the example of nitrogen and oxygen gases in the box, if only one molecule of each species were present, there would be a good opportunity of reversing the mixing process; *i.e.*, the probability is high for the process of replacing the barrier at such a time that the single molecule of oxygen is in one section and the molecule of nitrogen in the other section of the box. This reversal of an irreversible process, with no resultant change in the surroundings, constitutes a violation of the second law. However, the probability of replacing the barrier so as to separate the gases decreases rapidly as the number of molecules increases. For practical engineering applications this possibility of circumventing the second law is negligible.

For an interesting and worthwhile discussion of the physical significance of entropy in terms of probability the reader is referred to the text by Lewis and Randall.[3] The quantitative aspects of this subject are well developed by Glasstone.[4]

PROBLEMS

1. (*a*) Calculate the difference in entropy of 1 lb_m of liquid water at 32°F and 1 atm pressure and 1 lb_m at 212°F and 1 atm pressure. Assume the specific heat of water to be 1.0 over this temperature range.

(*b*) Calculate the difference in entropy of 1 lb_m of liquid water at 32°F and 1 atm pressure and 1 lb_m of water vapor at 212°F and 1 atm pressure. The latent heat of vaporization at 212°F is 970 Btu/lb_m.

2. A lump of copper having a mass of 10 lb_m at a temperature of 1000°F is dropped into a well-insulated bucket containing 100 lb_m of water at a temperature of 70°F. If the specific heats of copper and water are 0.095 and 1.000, respectively, calculate the

[1] M. Planck, *Ber. deut. chem. Ges.*, **45**, 5 (1912).

[2] This idea is the essence of the third law of thermodynamics.

[3] G. N. Lewis and Merle Randall, "Thermodynamics and the Free Energy of Chemical Substances," Chap. XI, McGraw-Hill Book Company, Inc., New York, 1923.

[4] S. Glasstone, "Textbook of Physical Chemistry," Chap. III, p. 222, D. Van Nostrand Company, Inc., Princeton, N.J., 1940.

resulting changes in entropy of the water and copper, and calculate the total entropy change resulting from the process.   *Ans.* $\Delta S_{total} = 0.693$ Btu/°R.

3. A heat exchanger is to be constructed in which air (assume $C_p = 7$) is to be heated from 70 to 200°F by another stream of air, originally at 360°F. Equal amounts of heated air and heating air are to be used. Assume that heat losses from the exchanger are negligible.

(a) Calculate the entropy changes of the heated air and the heating air for both parallel and countercurrent flow in the exchanger.
          Ans. 1.540 and -1.223 Btu/(lb mole)(°R).

(b) What is the total entropy change in each case? *Ans.* $\Delta S_{total} = 0.317$ Btu/°R.

(c) Repeat parts (a) and (b) for countercurrent flow if the heating air enters at 200°F.   *Ans.* $\Delta S_{total} = 0$.

4. Calculate the entropy changes for the heated water and the heating material and the total entropy changes when 10 lb_m of water is heated from 60 to 150°F:

(a) By saturated steam at 100 psia

(b) By saturated steam at 50 psia

(c) By superheated steam at 50 psia and 350°F of superheat

(d) In a perfect countercurrent heat exchanger with 10 lb_m of water at 150°F

(e) In a perfect parallel heat exchanger with the minimum amount of water at 200°F

Arrange the total entropy changes in the order of increasing magnitude. Explain. In parts (a), (b), and (c), the steam condenses completely but does not subcool.

Ans. Values of ΔS_{total} are (d) 0; (e) 0.179; (b) 0.381; (c) 0.417; and (a) 0.453 Btu/°R.

5. Nitrogen gas at 25°C and 2 atm pressure passes through a partly opened valve (Joule-Thomson expansion) in an insulated pipe. The pressure on the downstream side of the valve is 1 atm.

(a) What is the temperature on the downstream side?

(b) What is the change in entropy accompanying the passage of 1 g mole of gas through the valve?

(c) Is the process reversible?

(d) What would have been the downstream temperature if the pipe had not been insulated? The surroundings temperature is 25°C.

6. A reversible engine working on the Carnot cycle has 5000 Btu/min supplied from a source at a temperature of 800°F and rejects heat to a sink at a temperature of 70°F. Calculate the horsepower developed and the heat rejected.

7. In the study of equipment, cycles other than Carnot's are sometimes used. One cycle consists of these steps:

(a) An isothermal expansion from p_1, T_1, v_1 to p_2, T_1, v_2

(b) A constant-volume path from p_2, T_1, v_2 to p_3, T_2, v_2

(c) An isothermal compression from p_3, T_2, v_2 to p_4, T_2, v_1

(d) A constant-volume path from p_4, T_2, v_1 to p_1, T_1, v_1

Sketch this cycle on a p-v diagram, and calculate ΔE, ΔS, Q, and W for each of the steps and for the entire cycle. What is the efficiency of the cycle? Assume reversible operation, and take the working substance to be an ideal gas with constant heat capacities.

8. A heat exchanger for cooling a hot hydrocarbon liquid uses 10,000 lb_m/hr of cooling water, which enters the exchanger at 70°F. The hot oil, 5000 lb_m/hr, enters at 300°F and leaves at 150°F, and has an average specific heat of 0.6. Assuming no heat losses from the exchanger, calculate:

(a) The change in entropy of the oil.

(b) The total change in entropy as a result of the heat-exchange process. Is the process reversible?

(c) How much work could have been obtained had the process of cooling the hot oil been carried out by using the heat to operate a reversible Carnot engine with a sink temperature of 90°F?

9. A body of total heat capacity A is cooled by a Carnot engine, and the heat rejected by the engine is absorbed by another body of total heat capacity B. Starting with the expression

$$dW_{rev} = \frac{T_a - T_b}{T_a} dQ_a$$

(a) Derive an expression relating T_a and T_b at any time.

(b) Derive an expression for the work obtained as a function of A, B, T_a and the initial temperatures T_{a_0} and T_{b_0}.

10. Show whether or not the following process is possible: Air at 100 psig and 70°F enters an apparatus which is well insulated from the surroundings. One-half the air issues from the apparatus at 180°F, and the other half at -40°F, both at 1 atm. No work is done on or by the apparatus, and both exit streams have the same composition as the entering air. Take C_p constant at 7, and assume air to be an ideal gas.

Ans. Process is possible, because $\Delta S_{total} = 7.91$ Btu/°R on the basis of 2 lb moles of air entering the apparatus.

11. A test of a Hilsch vortex tube was reported as follows: Air entered at 75 psia and 19.3°C. The warm air leaving the tube had a temperature of 26.5°C, and the cool air, a temperature of -21.8°C, both at a pressure of 1 atm. The ratio of warm air to cool air was 5.39. Check these results to see whether they are possible. Assume air to be an ideal gas.

12. Diphenyl, triphenyl, and hydrogen are simultaneously produced by the pyrolytic dehydrogenation of benzene. The product from a continuous reactor has the following molal composition: benzene, 62 per cent; diphenyl, 13 per cent; triphenyl, 4 per cent; and hydrogen, 21 per cent. It leaves the reactor at 1325°F and is passed through a countercurrent heat exchanger to heat the benzene feed from 700°F to the reaction temperature of 1250°F. The product and feed (both gaseous) flow rates are each 9000 lb$_m$/hr. Calculate:

(a) The change in entropy of the feed

(b) The change in entropy of the product

(c) The total entropy change as a result of the process

The following molal-heat-capacity equations may be used ($T =$ °K):

Hydrogen:	$C_p = 6.88 + 0.066 \times 10^{-3}T$
Benzene:	$C_p = 0.23 + 77.8 \times 10^{-3}T$
Diphenyl:	$C_p = -0.20 + 149 \times 10^{-3}T$
Triphenyl:	$C_p = 1.74 + 214 \times 10^{-3}T$

13. Silver and iodide ions react in aqueous solution to precipitate silver iodide. The heats of formation of the reactants and product are as follows:

$$\Delta H_f^\circ, \ Ag^+ \ (0.1 \ molal) = 25,200 \ cal/g \ mole \ at \ 25°C$$
$$\Delta H_f^\circ, \ I^- \ (0.1 \ molal) = -13,370 \ cal/g \ mole \ at \ 25°C$$
$$\Delta H_f^\circ, \ AgI(s) = -14,940 \ cal/g \ mole \ at \ 25°C$$

The cell Ag, AgI(s), KI(0.1 molal): AgNO₃(0.1 molal), Ag has a reversible potential of 0.807 volt at 25°C.

(a) Calculate the change in entropy (entropy of the product minus that of the reactants) accompanying the following reaction at 25°C:

$$Ag^+ \text{ (0.1 molal)} + I^- \text{ (0.1 molal)} \rightarrow AgI(s)$$

Note that a simple mixing of the solutions of Ag^+ and I^- would not constitute a satisfactory process for evaluating ΔS, for the path is not reversible.

The electrical energy, in joules, taken from a cell is equal to the potential in volts multiplied by the quantity of electricity produced by the cell in coulombs. There is obtained 96,500 coulombs per gram equivalent of cell reaction.

(b) Also calculate the total entropy change accompanying the irreversible process of simple mixing of 0.1 molal solutions of Ag^+ and I^-. Assume that the temperature of the solutions and surroundings is 25°C.

CHAPTER 7

THERMODYNAMIC PROPERTIES OF FLUIDS

From the phase rule (see Chap. 2) it is possible to determine the number of intensive properties that must be known before the state of a system is completely determined, *i.e.*, before all other intensive properties are fixed. However, the phase rule offers no information as to how these other properties can be evaluated. The purpose of this chapter is to consider the relationships between the enthalpy, energy, and entropy and the more easily measurable quantities, such as pressure, temperature, volume, and heat capacity.

A knowledge of these relationships is of primary importance, since one of the chief objectives of thermodynamics is to develop methods of relating path functions such as work and heat to changes in the volume, enthalpy, and entropy. If these properties are not known, such methods have no practical value. As an example consider the design of a compressor for a refrigeration unit. If the compressor operates adiabatically, the first-law flow equation (neglecting kinetic-energy effects, which would be small) studied in Chap. 2 reduces to

$$-W_s = \Delta H \qquad (7\text{-}1)$$

Note that the work has been related to ΔH, which depends upon only the initial and final states. If the minimum work were required, this would correspond to a completely reversible process. For a reversible adiabatic process it was shown in Chap. 6 that ΔS is zero. Hence W_s can be calculated from a knowledge of the initial state of the ammonia and the final pressure desired, provided that the enthalpy and entropy of ammonia are known as a function of temperature and pressure. To indicate the path of the process, Eq. (7-1) could be modified to read

$$-W_s = (H_2 - H_1)_{\text{const } S} \qquad (7\text{-}2)$$

The numerical calculation of W_s would consist of noting H_1 and S_1 at the initial temperature and pressure and finding the value of H_2 at the final pressure and the same entropy S_1. The difference between these enthalpies would represent the minimum energy that must be supplied as work by the compressor. The problem has become extremely simple through the use of the concepts of enthalpy and entropy and by knowing the numerical values of these quantities for the substance involved. For convenient utilization, such thermodynamic data should be presented in tabular or graphic form. The steam tables are an example of the former, and they will be described later in the chapter. It is sufficient here to note that in these tables the specific volume, the specific entropy, and the specific enthalpy are listed as a function of the temperature and pressure. If the data are reported in terms of graphs, the same information is usually included, although the rectangular coordinates normally are not temperature and pressure and, also, some of the variables may be eliminated if the chart becomes confusing to read.

A number of equations connecting the properties p, v, T, H (or E), and S of a substance can be developed from the first and second laws of thermodynamics. These relationships fix the minimum amount of experimental data necessary for the preparation of tables or graphs of these properties. Therefore, of first importance in this chapter will be the derivation of several of these general relationships and their application to the problem of constructing tables or graphs of properties. Following this, examples of the common types of tables and diagrams will be considered. Finally, the approximate methods of correlating properties on a generalized basis will be reviewed. These methods are valuable when sufficient experimental data are not available for the construction of complete tables or graphs of properties.

7-1. Relationships among the Thermodynamic Properties. Changes in properties of a system depend only on the initial and final states and are independent of the means by which the changes are brought about. Therefore, the system and process used to derive the relationships between properties can be chosen on the basis of convenience. Accordingly, nonflow reversible processes will be employed and the system will be taken as a mole or a unit mass of material. The equations will be restricted to constant-composition or single-component systems.

The first law for a nonflow process is given in differential form by Eq. (2-5):

$$dE = dQ - dW \tag{2-5}$$

For a reversible process, dQ and dW may be eliminated in terms of the properties of the system by the equations

$$dQ = T \, dS \quad \text{(the second law)}$$

and

$$dW = p \, dv$$

Equation (2-5) therefore becomes

$$dE = T \, dS - p \, dv \tag{7-3}$$

This equation will be considered presently, but first it is advantageous to develop other similar equations. By the definition of enthalpy, $H = E + pv$, and

$$dH = dE + d(pv) = dE + p\,dv + v\,dp$$

This may be combined with Eq. (7-3) to give

$$dH = T\,dS + v\,dp \qquad (7\text{-}4)$$

It is convenient at this point to introduce two more thermodynamic properties, namely, the *work function*, or Helmholtz free energy A, and the *free energy*, or Gibbs free energy F. These quantities are defined mathematically, just as enthalpy was, as follows:

$$A = E - TS \qquad (7\text{-}5)$$
$$F = H - TS \qquad (7\text{-}6)$$

Both A and F are state functions for the reason that they are composites of other state functions. Their use is simply a matter of convenience. Instead of writing $E - TS$ and $H - TS$ each time they appear, one may write A and F, respectively. The free energy F is particularly useful in studies of phase and chemical equilibria and will be considered in detail in Chaps. 12 and 13.

Differentiation of Eq. (7-5) gives

$$dA = dE - T\,dS - S\,dT$$

Substitution for dE from Eq. (7-3) leads to

$$dA = -p\,dv - S\,dT \qquad (7\text{-}7)$$

In a similar fashion, Eq. (7-6) may be differentiated and combined with Eq. (7-4) to give

$$dF = v\,dp - S\,dT \qquad (7\text{-}8)$$

Equations (7-3), (7-4), (7-7), and (7-8) represent the four basic differential equations which relate the various thermodynamic properties to one another. They form the basis for a network of equations interconnecting these properties and are the starting point for the derivation of all such relationships.

In the following sections, a few of the most important equations for the determination of the thermodynamic properties of fluids will be presented. Many other relationships may be derived, some of which will be taken up in later chapters.

7-2. Thermodynamic Properties of a Single-phase System. According to the phase rule, a single-phase system of constant composition has but two degrees of freedom. Hence, the thermodynamic properties of such systems should be functions of temperature and pressure. The determination of the values of these properties as functions of temperature and pressure requires a certain minimum amount of experimental information. Usually, this consists of heat capacities at low pressure and p-v-T data.

There are two major problems in the determination of the thermodynamic properties of fluids. First is the experimental one of obtaining accurate data, and the second is the problem of calculating properties from this information. The calculational task will receive the major attention here, but first a word about the experimental problem.

The minimum experimental data required for the calculational procedures described below are low-pressure heat capacities as a function of temperature and p-v-T data over the complete range of temperatures and pressures. Heat capacities may be measured by direct calorimetric methods, but for gases the modern method is to determine them from spectroscopic data by statistical calculations. Low-pressure heat capacities are available for a large number of gases. On the other hand, p-v-T information is relatively rare, and measurements of these data must sometimes be made by chemical engineers before they can confidently carry out design calculations. The problem is one of measuring the volumes of a known mass of fluid over a range of temperatures and pressures. It is a difficult experimental task because of the high accuracy required. A summary of a number of the procedures used is given by Comings.[1]

To illustrate the derivation of the relationships for a single-phase system, suppose it is required to find how the enthalpy varies with pressure. Let Eq. (7-4) be used to evaluate the enthalpy change for a constant-temperature process. If the rate of change of enthalpy with respect to pressure is desired, each side of Eq. (7-4) may be divided by dp. The result is

$$\left(\frac{\partial H}{\partial p}\right)_T = T\left(\frac{\partial S}{\partial p}\right)_T + v \qquad (7\text{-}9)$$

The rate of change of enthalpy with respect to temperature at constant pressure is found by dividing both sides of Eq. (7-4) by dT and noting that the last term is zero:

$$\left(\frac{\partial H}{\partial T}\right)_p = T\left(\frac{\partial S}{\partial T}\right)_p \qquad (7\text{-}10)$$

Equations (7-9) and (7-10) are used to develop an expression for $(\partial S/\partial p)_T$ in terms of a quantity which can be evaluated from p-v-T data. This is accomplished by differentiating Eq. (7-9) with respect to temperature

[1] E. W. Comings, "High Pressure Technology," Chap. 7, McGraw-Hill Book Company, Inc., New York, 1956.

at constant pressure and Eq. (7-10) with respect to pressure at constant temperature.   Two equations will then be obtained for the second derivative of the enthalpy.

From (7-10)

$$\frac{\partial^2 H}{\partial T \, \partial p} = T \frac{\partial^2 S}{\partial T \, \partial p} \tag{7-11}$$

From (7-9)

$$\frac{\partial^2 H}{\partial p \, \partial T} = \left(\frac{\partial S}{\partial p}\right)_T + T \frac{\partial^2 S}{\partial p \, \partial T} + \left(\frac{\partial v}{\partial T}\right)_p \tag{7-12}$$

These second-order differentials must be equal even though they were taken in the opposite directions.   Hence combination of Eqs. (7-11) and (7-12) leads to an expression for $(\partial S / \partial p)_T$:

$$\left(\frac{\partial S}{\partial p}\right)_T = -\left(\frac{\partial v}{\partial T}\right)_p \tag{7-13}$$

Substituting this into Eq. (7-9) gives the required equation for the change in enthalpy with respect to pressure at constant temperature:

$$\left(\frac{\partial H}{\partial p}\right)_T = v - T \left(\frac{\partial v}{\partial T}\right)_p \tag{7-14}$$

Equations (7-13) and (7-14), along with experimental heat-capacity or specific-heat data at one pressure p_0 and p-v-T data, can be used to compute H and S throughout the single-phase region.   The method of calculation would be as follows:

1. First calculate the enthalpy and entropy for any temperature at the pressure p_0.   This can be accomplished by employing the following two equations developed in Chaps. 3 and 6:

$$(H - H_0)_{p_0} = \int_{T_0}^{T} C_{p_0} \, dT \tag{7-15}$$

$$(S - S_0)_{p_0} = \int_{T_0}^{T} \frac{C_{p_0}}{T} \, dT \tag{7-16}$$

H_0 and S_0 are the values of the enthalpy and entropy at T_0 and p_0 and are determined by an arbitrary choice of the condition for which H and S are taken to be zero.   The experimental data needed to compute H and S at p_0 are values of C_{p_0} (the heat capacity at p_0) over the desired temperature range.

2. Then compute H and S at any p and T by integrating Eqs. (7-13) and (7-14) at constant temperature between p_0 and p:

$$H - H_{p_0} = \int_{p_0}^{p} \left[v - T \left(\frac{\partial v}{\partial T}\right)_p \right] dp \tag{7-17}$$

and

$$S - S_{p_0} = - \int_{p_0}^{p} \left(\frac{\partial v}{\partial T}\right)_p dp \qquad (7\text{-}18)$$

H_{p_0} and S_{p_0} are the values of H and S determined from (7-15) and (7-16) at the pressure p_0. The quantities within the integrals are directly evaluated from p-v-T data. Note that $(\partial v/\partial T)_p$ is a state variable the same as the volume and therefore is, in general, a function of temperature and pressure. If the p-v-T data are available in the form of an equation of state (Chap. 4), the derivative may be obtained by differentiation and the integration of (7-17) and (7-18) accomplished analytically. If the p-v-T data are given in tabular form, the integrations may be carried out graphically. In this latter case the values of $(\partial v/\partial T)_p$ are first determined over the desired pressure range by plotting v vs. T for lines of constant pressure and measuring the slopes of these lines at the constant temperature involved. Then these values are plotted vs. p, and the area is evaluated to obtain the integral in Eq. (7-18). For the change in enthalpy with pressure [Eq. (7-17)] the whole term in brackets is plotted vs. the pressure, and the area is measured as before.

The evaluation of the integrals of Eqs. (7-17) and (7-18) by use of an equation of state can be illustrated for the simple case of the ideal-gas law. By the direct differentiation of $pv = RT$ (for 1 mole),

$$\left(\frac{\partial v}{\partial T}\right)_p = \frac{R}{p} = \frac{v}{T}$$

Substitution of this result in Eq. (7-17) yields

$$H - H_{p_0} = \int_{p_0}^{p} \left[v - T\left(\frac{v}{T}\right) \right] dp = 0 \qquad (7\text{-}19)$$

Also by Eq. (7-14)

$$\left(\frac{\partial H}{\partial p}\right)_T = 0 \qquad (7\text{-}20)$$

Similarly, Eq. (7-18) reduces to

$$S - S_{p_0} = - R \int_{p_0}^{p} \frac{dp}{p} = - R \ln \frac{p}{p_0} \qquad (7\text{-}21)$$

By Eq. (7-13)

$$\left(\frac{\partial S}{\partial p}\right)_T = - \frac{R}{p} \qquad (7\text{-}22)$$

Equations (7-19) and (7-20) show that the enthalpy of an ideal gas is independent of pressure, a conclusion reached previously (Sec. 3-3) by less direct means. On the other hand, Eqs. (7-21) and (7-22) indicate that the entropy of an ideal gas *is* a function of pressure.

Equations (7-17) and (7-18) apply to any single-phase single-component (or constant-composition) system. However, their application is most important in the case of gases. For liquids not near the critical point, the volume itself is small and does not change much with temperature. Thus it is seen from Eqs. (7-13) and (7-14) that pressure usually has little effect on the enthalpy and entropy of liquids. Therefore, for liquids at most conditions, Eqs. (7-15) and (7-16) can be used to determine the enthalpy and entropy at any temperature and pressure.

Example 7-1. Calculate the enthalpy and entropy of isobutane vapor at 190°F and 229.3 psia from the following information taken from the literature:[1]

1. Basis: H and S are zero for saturated liquid at 60°F.
2. The average specific heat of saturated isobutane liquid between 60 and 70°F is 0.558 Btu/(lb_m)(°F).
3. The heat of vaporization at 70°F is 143.4 Btu/lb_m.
4. The vapor pressure at 70°F is 45.0 psia.
5. The specific heat of the gas at a constant pressure of 45.0 psia is as follows:

t, °F	c_p, Btu/(lb_m)(°F)
70	0.430
100	0.420
130	0.423
160	0.430
190	0.442

6. The specific volumes of gaseous isobutane in cubic feet per pound *mass* are as follows:

p, psia	100°F	130°F	160°F	190°F	220°F
40	2.411	2.565	2.715	2.861	3.006
60	1.538	1.651	1.757	1.860	1.962
100	.....	0.9121	0.9888	1.060	1.128
150	.....	......	0.5983	0.6557	0.7091
200	.....	......	......	0.4505	0.4977
229.3	.....	......	......	0.3687	0.4137

Solution. Since enthalpy and entropy are state functions, the path chosen from the base state (saturated liquid at 60°F) to 190°F and 229.3 psia is arbitrary. However, from the nature of the data given, the following sequence of processes is suggested:

Sat liquid at 60°F $\xrightarrow{A}$ sat liquid at 70°F $\xrightarrow{B}$ sat vapor at 70°F, 45 psia
($H = 0$, $S = 0$)

Sat vapor at 70°F, 45 psia $\xrightarrow{C}$ vapor at 190°F, 45 psia $\xrightarrow{D}$ vapor at 190°F, 229.3 psia

The method of solution will be to evaluate ΔH and ΔS for each step and add the results.

[1] B. H. Sage and W. N. Lacey, *Ind. Eng. Chem.*, **30**, 673 (1938).

STEP a. This process follows the saturation curve, and both pressure and temperature are changing. However, the liquid is nearly incompressible at these conditions, so that $c_p = c_v = c_{sat} = 0.558$. Therefore

$$\Delta H = \int c \, dT = c \, \Delta T = 0.558(70 - 60) = 5.58 \text{ Btu/lb}_m$$
$$\Delta S = \int \frac{dQ}{T} = \int \frac{c \, dT}{T} = 0.558 \ln \frac{530}{520} = 0.0106 \text{ Btu/(lb}_m)(°R)$$

STEP b. The vaporization process occurs at constant temperature and pressure:

$$\Delta H = 143.4 \text{ Btu/lb}_m$$
$$\Delta S = \frac{\Delta H}{T} = \frac{143.4}{530} = 0.2707 \text{ Btu/(lb}_m)(°R)$$

STEP c. This is a constant-pressure heating process from 70 to 190°F. The given specific-heat data may be used in Eqs. (7-15) and (7-16):

$$\Delta H = \int_{530°R}^{650°R} c_p \, dT$$
$$\Delta S = \int_{530°R}^{650°R} \frac{c_p \, dT}{T}$$

Since the c_p data are presented in tabular form, the general procedure is to evaluate the foregoing integrals by graphic integration. In the first, c_p is plotted vs. T and the area is measured between the abscissa values of 530 and 650°R. In the second, c_p/T is plotted vs. T and the area is similarly evaluated. The results are

$$\Delta H = 51.2 \text{ Btu/lb}_m$$
$$\Delta S = 0.0872 \text{ Btu/(lb}_m)(°R)$$

STEP d. This process is one of compression at constant temperature. The effect of pressure on H and S is given by Eqs. (7-17) and (7-18). Consider (7-18) first:

$$\Delta S = - \int_{45}^{229.3} \left(\frac{\partial v}{\partial T} \right)_p dp$$

The partial derivative represents the slope of a curve of volume vs. temperature at constant pressure. Numerical values may be obtained by plotting the given volume data as curves of volume vs. temperature with pressure as parameter. A separate curve will result for each pressure, 40, 60, 100, 150, 200, and 229.3 psia. If the slope of each of these curves is measured at 190°F (for example, by drawing a tangent to each of the curves at 190°F), the numerical values will correspond to the desired partial derivative. Then, the value of the integral may be obtained graphically by plotting the derivative vs. the pressure (over the range 45 to 229.3 psia) at a constant temperature of 190°F and measuring the area under the curve. The results are as follows:

Pressure, psia	$\left(\dfrac{\partial v}{\partial T} \right)_p$ at 190°F
40	0.00530
60	0.00374
100	0.00247
150	0.00165
200	0.00118
229.3	0.00098

The area under the curve of $(\partial v/\partial T)_p$ vs. p between 45 and 229.3 psia is 0.388 [ft³/(lb$_m$) (°R)] (psi).   Then

$$\Delta S = -\frac{(0.388)(144)}{778} = -0.0719 \text{ Btu/(lb}_m)(°R)$$

For the enthalpy calculation, the same data for $(\partial v/\partial T)_p$ may be used in Eq. (7-17). This time it is necessary to plot the term in brackets vs. pressure.   The values are tabulated as follows:

Pressure, psia	$v - T\left(\dfrac{\partial v}{\partial T}\right)_p$ at 190°F, ft^3/lb_m
40	$2.861 - 650(0.00530) = -0.584$
60	$1.860 - 650(0.00374) = -0.571$
100	$1.060 - 650(0.00247) = -0.546$
150	$0.6557 - 650(0.00165) = -0.417$
200	$0.4505 - 650(0.00118) = -0.316$
229.3	$0.3687 - 650(0.00098) = -0.268$

The area under the curve is -85.0 (ft³/lb$_m$)(psia).   Therefore, ΔH for step d according to Eq. (7-17) is

$$\Delta H = -\frac{(85.0)(144)}{778} = -15.7 \text{ Btu/lb}_m$$

The desired values of H and S can be obtained by summing the results for the four steps:

$$H = 5.6 + 143.4 + 51.2 - 15.7 = 184.5 \text{ Btu/lb}_m$$
$$S = 0.0106 + 0.2707 + 0.0872 - 0.0719 = 0.2966 \text{ Btu/(lb}_m)(°R)$$

Although the calculations have been carried out for only one final state, the enthalpy and entropy can be evaluated for any temperature and pressure in the gas phase by a similar procedure, provided complete p-v-T data are available.

Once the enthalpy and entropy at any temperature and pressure are evaluated, the internal energy and free energy are simply obtained from these quantities by the defining equations

$$E = H - pv$$

and

$$F = H - TS$$

Example 7-2.   Extend the calculations of Example 7-1 to the liquid region by evaluating the enthalpy and entropy of liquid isobutane at 190°F and 1500 psia. Additional data are as follows:

Vapor pressure at 190°F = 229.3 psia

Heat of vaporization at 190°F = 101.7 Btu/lb$_m$

Pressure, psi	Liquid specific volume, ft³/lb$_m$				
	130°F	160°F	190°F	220°F	250°F
250	0.03100	0.03265	0.03499		
500	0.03066	0.03215	0.03421	0.03678	0.04112
1000	0.03009	0.03139	0.03300	0.03484	0.03730
1500	0.02966	0.03079	0.03212	0.03370	0.03549
2000	0.02926	0.03027	0.03145	0.03278	0.03431

Solution.   The answer to Example 7-1 gives the enthalpy and entropy for saturated isobutane vapor at 190°F.   The values for saturated liquid at 190°F would be

$$H_{liq} = H_{vap} - \Delta H_v = 184.5 - 101.7 = 82.8 \text{ Btu/lb}_m$$
$$S_{liq} = S_{vap} - \frac{\Delta H_v}{T} = 0.2966 - \frac{101.7}{650} = 0.1400 \text{ Btu/(lb}_m)(°R)$$

The final state can now be obtained by compressing the saturated liquid to 1500 psia at constant temperature.   The same equations as used for the gas-phase calculations are applicable, but the liquid-specific-volume data must be employed.

$$\Delta H_T = H_{1500} - 82.8 = \int_{229.3}^{1500} \left[v - T \left(\frac{\partial v}{\partial T} \right)_p \right] dp$$
$$\Delta S_T = S_{1500} - 0.1400 = - \int_{229.3}^{1500} \left(\frac{\partial v}{\partial T} \right)_p dp$$

The change of both v and $(\partial v/\partial T)_p$ with pressure for liquids is usually small.   Therefore, average values may be used without serious error, thus eliminating the need for graphic integration.   Calculating the derivatives as in Example 7-1 and taking an average value lead to the result

$$H_{1500} - 82.8 = \left[v - T \left(\frac{\partial v}{\partial T} \right)_p \right]_{ave} (1500 - 229.3) \left(\frac{144}{778} \right)$$
$$S_{1500} - 0.1400 = - \left[\left(\frac{\partial v}{\partial T} \right)_p \right]_{ave} (1500 - 229.3) \left(\frac{144}{778} \right)$$
$$H_{1500} = 82.8 + [0.03356 - 650(6.5 \times 10^{-5})](1500 - 229.3) \left(\frac{144}{778} \right)$$
$$= 82.8 - 2.0 = 80.8 \text{ Btu/lb}_m$$
$$S_{1500} = 0.1400 - (6.5 \times 10^{-5})(1500 - 229.3) \left(\frac{144}{778} \right)$$
$$= 0.1400 - 0.0153 = 0.1247 \text{ Btu/(lb}_m)(°R)$$

It is seen from this example that the effect of pressure on the thermodynamic properties of liquids is usually rather small.   For this reason the properties of liquids are frequently taken to be those of the saturated liquid at the same temperature regardless of the pressure, unless it is very high.   This procedure is satisfactory for most practical purposes except in the region near the critical point, where liquid properties change rapidly.

The accurate calculation of thermodynamic properties for the purpose of constructing a table or diagram is an exacting task.   Few engineers are called upon to make such calculations.   On the other hand, most engineers find frequent occasion to make practical use of thermodynamic properties calculated by methods such as those described.   If nothing more, a study of these methods should dispel any false notions of the absolute accuracy of tables and diagrams built up through their use. Even the tables for steam, which have received more attention than those for any other substance, are subject to appreciable uncertainty in certain regions.   There are two major reasons for this.   (1) The experimental data are subject to error because they are exceedingly difficult to measure. Moreover, data are frequently lacking in certain regions and must be improvised by interpolation and extrapolation procedures. This is seldom evident from a finished table or diagram of properties. (2) Even if the data are reasonably accurate, a serious loss of accuracy occurs in the differentiation process required in the calculations. This accounts for the fact that data of a very high order of accuracy are required to produce enthalpy and entropy values which are suitable for engineering calculations.

7-3. The Two-phase Region. In this section equations are developed which relate the thermodynamic properties of gas and liquid phases (or solid and liquid phases) in equilibrium. Under these conditions a single-component system is univariant; *i.e.*, the specification of a single intensive variable, such as pressure or temperature, completely determines the intensive state of the system. As a consequence of this, there exists a relationship between the latent heat of a phase change and the p-v-T data for the two-phase region. This relationship is the Clausius-Clapeyron equation, first introduced in Chap. 5. It is most easily derived from Eq. (7-8), applied to the two-phase system as a whole:

$$d\underline{F} = \underline{V}\,dp - \underline{S}\,dT \qquad (7\text{-}8)$$

Consider the case of a pure liquid and vapor in equilibrium in a piston-and-cylinder arrangement at temperature T and the corresponding vapor pressure p'. If a differential amount of liquid is caused to evaporate at constant temperature and pressure, Eq. (7-8) reduces to $d\underline{F} = 0$, since dp and dT are both zero. This equation applies to the entire system of liquid and vapor, and it means that the *total* free energy $\underline{F}$ of the system is unchanged by the vaporization of liquid at constant temperature and pressure. The only way this can be true is for the specific, or molal, free energy of the liquid to be identical with that of the vapor. Thus

$$F_g = F_f \qquad (7\text{-}23)$$

where F_g and F_f are the free energies of the gas and liquid phases, respectively, on a unit-mass or mole basis.

If the conditions of the system are changed in such a manner as to maintain two phases, then both the temperature and pressure must be altered in accordance with the vapor-pressure–temperature relationship of the system. Raising the temperature by dT requires that the pressure also be raised by dp'. Since equilibrium still exists, Eq. (7-23) still holds, and any change in F_g must be equaled by the change in F_f. Thus

$$dF_g = dF_f \qquad (7\text{-}24)$$

Equation (7-8) may now be applied to a unit amount of each phase:

$$dF_g = v_g\,dp' - S_g\,dT$$

CHEMICAL ENGINEERING THERMODYNAMICS [CHAP. 7

and

$$dF_f = v_f \, dp' - S_f \, dT$$

In view of Eq. (7-24) these expressions are equal. Thus

$$v_g \, dp' - S_g \, dT = v_f \, dp' - S_f \, dT$$

Rearrangement gives

$$\frac{dp'}{dT} = \frac{S_g - S_f}{v_g - v_f} = \frac{\Delta S_v}{\Delta v}$$

The quantity ΔS_v is the entropy change of vaporization at the conditions T and p'. Since $\Delta S_v = \Delta H_v / T$,

$$\frac{dp'}{dT} = \frac{\Delta H_v}{T \, \Delta v} \qquad (5\text{-}6)$$

which is the Clausius-Clapeyron equation.

The determination of the vapor-pressure curve (p' vs. T) is an important step in the development of the thermodynamic properties of a substance. In the first place, it provides the boundary between the single-phase regions of liquid and gas; secondly it provides data for use in the Clausius-Clapeyron equation, which links the properties of the gas and vapor regions.

A large number of empirical equations have been developed to represent the vapor-pressure curve. The most common type takes the form

$$\ln p' = A - \frac{B}{T} \qquad (7\text{-}25)$$

where A and B are constant for a given material. This equation indicates that a plot of the logarithm of vapor pressure vs. the reciprocal of absolute temperature should be a straight line. For many substances this is approximately true.

A more versatile equation is

$$\ln p' = A - \frac{B}{t + C} \qquad (7\text{-}26)$$

This three-constant expression is known as the Antoine equation. Temperatures in Eq. (7-26) may be measured on either the absolute scales or the common scales. If t is °C and $C = 273$, Eq. (7-26) becomes identical with Eq. (7-25). Thus Eq. (7-25) is seen to be a special case of the Antoine equation.

Many other methods have been proposed to represent vapor pressure as a function of temperature. Of these, the method of Othmer[1] appears to be the most convenient for engineering purposes.

[1] D. F. Othmer et al., *Ind. Eng. Chem.*, **49**, 125 (1957).

For the calculation of latent heats by the Clausius-Clapeyron equa[tion,] the derivative of vapor pressure with respect to temperature is con[ven-]iently expressed in equation form, and vapor-pressure equations ma[y be] differentiated for this purpose. However, the equation must repre[sent] the vapor-pressure data to a high order of accuracy, and the data th[em-]selves must be exact. Any inaccuracies in either equation or data [are] greatly magnified by differentiation. Neither Eq. (7-25) nor (7-26) [is] usually sufficiently accurate for this purpose, and a wide variety of mo[re] complicated relations have been suggested.

Up to this point only the properties of the individual phases (100 pe[r] cent vapor or 100 per cent liquid) have been considered. Frequently [the] properties of mixtures of the two phases must be evaluated. Since the intensive states of the phases are fixed when two phases are in equilib-rium, there exists a simple relationship among the properties of each phase and the mixture which depends only upon the extent of each phase. If the two phases are distinguished by subscripts g (gas) and f (fluid or liquid), the properties of the mixture on a unit basis are

$$v = v_f(1 - x) + v_g x \qquad (7\text{-}27)$$
$$H = H_f(1 - x) + H_g x \qquad (7\text{-}28)$$
$$S = S_f(1 - x) + S_g x \qquad (7\text{-}29)$$

where x is the weight or mole fraction of the gas phase (also often called the *quality*). All the thermodynamic quantities in these equations are on a unit basis, that is, v, H, and S are measured per unit mass or per mole of material. The values for the gas phase refer to saturated vapor (the gas when it is at its saturation point, or the point of incipient condensa-tion). Similarly, the thermodynamic properties of the liquid are those at the saturated state of the liquid as it is about to vaporize. The point at which condensation is about to occur is often called the *dew point*, while the point at which vaporization is about to occur is called the *bubble point.* For a pure component, the temperature and pressure of the dew point and bubble point are identical.

In tables of thermodynamic properties only values of the saturated phases are usually given, so that Eqs. (7-27) to (7-29) are necessary when the properties of a mixture of two phases are required. On the other hand, when the data are available in graphic form, values for various mixtures can sometimes be read directly from lines of constant values of x.

7-4. Types of Thermodynamic Diagrams. The thermodynamic dia-gram is one in which the temperature, pressure, volume, enthalpy, and entropy are shown on a single chart. (Sometimes data for all these var-iables are not included, but the term thermodynamic diagram is still retained.) The most common types are the following: temperature-entropy, enthalpy-entropy (this is commonly referred to as a *Mollier* *diagram*), pressure-enthalpy (often used in refrigeration work), and pressure-temperature. The designations refer to the variables chosen for the rectangular coordinates. Other charts are possible but are not in common use.

A pressure-temperature plot is especially useful for representing phase behavior. Such a diagram is shown for a single-component system in Fig. 7-1. Region *a* represents a solid phase; *b*, the liquid phase; and *c*, the gas phase. Region *d* (above the critical temperature and pressure) is often said to represent simply *fluid*. This region is marked off on Fig. 7-1 by dashed lines, which do not represent actual phase changes, but depend on rather arbitrary definitions of what constitute liquid and gas phases. A liquid is generally considered to be a phase which can be

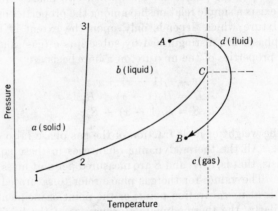

FIG. 7-1. Pressure-temperature diagram for a single-component system.

vaporized by lowering the pressure at constant temperature. A gas is considered a phase which can be condensed by reducing the temperature at constant pressure. The fluid in region *d* fits neither of these definitions; hence it can be called neither a gas nor a liquid. The gas phase *c* is sometimes considered to be divided in two parts, as shown by the dashed line of Fig. 7-1. A gas to the left of this line, which can be condensed by *both* compression at constant temperature and cooling at constant pressure, is frequently called a vapor.

It is interesting to note that it is possible to proceed from the liquid region to the gas region without crossing a phase boundary; *i.e.*, a liquid can be changed to a gas without any phase change being observed. Such a path is shown in Fig. 7-1 by the line connecting points *A* and *B*. This path represents a gradual transition from the liquid to the gas region rather than one which passes through a point of abrupt change of properties.

A state on the lines 1-2, 2-3, 2-C corresponds to the existence of at least two phases.   Along the line 1-2 solid and vapor are in equilibrium, along the line 2-3 liquid and solid are in equilibrium, and along the line 2-C liquid and vapor are in equilibrium.   The line 1-2 is the vapor-pressure curve of the solid material, while the line 2-C corresponds to the vapor-pressure curve of the liquid.   The point C is the critical point for the material, and for a single-component system it may be defined as the maximum temperature and pressure at which liquid and vapor phases can exist in stable equilibrium.   Line 2-3 is the melting or freezing curve, representing the relationship between the melting-point temperature and

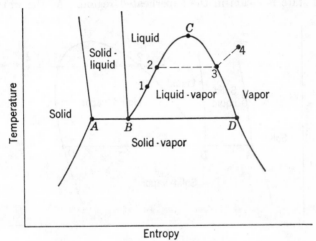

FIG. 7-2. Outline of a temperature-entropy diagram for a single-component system.

the pressure. On any of these lines the system is univariant; the specification of one property completely determines the intensive state.

The point 2 corresponds to equilibrium conditions where three phases are present, gas, liquid, and solid.   For a single-component system this is identified as a triple point, or nonvariant point.   None of the properties (phase-rule properties) of the system can be changed without the disappearance of a phase.   In engineering work the vapor, vapor-liquid, and liquid regions are most important.   However, in certain cases the solid-vapor region is also useful, as, for example, in processes for the manufacture of solid carbon dioxide (dry ice).

Figures 7-2 and 7-3 show the outlines of temperature-entropy and pressure-enthalpy diagrams.   It should be noted that the two-phase states, represented by lines in Fig. 7-1, become regions in these diagrams, and the triple point of Fig. 7-1 is represented by the horizontal lines ABD in Figs. 7-2 and 7-3.   Line DC represents the properties of the saturated vapor at the dew point, while line CB represents the properties of the saturated liquid at the bubble point.   Neither of these figures is a complete thermodynamic diagram since not all the variables are included. Examples of complete diagrams for the liquid, vapor, and liquid-vapor regions are given for air by the T-S diagram of Fig. 7-4, for methane by the p-H diagram of Fig. 7-5, and for steam by the H-S diagram of Fig. 7-6.

These charts are convenient for tracing the path of a process.   For example, consider the operation of the boiler in a steam power plant. The initial state is liquid water at a temperature below its boiling point; the final state is steam in the superheated region.   As the water goes

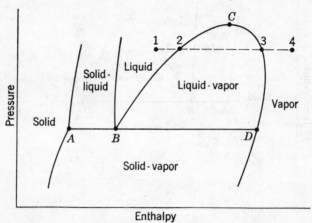

FIG. 7-3. Outline of a pressure-enthalpy diagram for a single-component system.

into the boiler and is heated, the temperature rises along a constant-pressure line (approximately) until saturation is reached—represented by line 1-2 in Figs. 7-2 and 7-3.   At point 2 the water begins to vaporize, the temperature remaining constant during the vaporization process.   The point of complete vaporization corresponds to point 3.   As more heat is added, the steam becomes superheated along the path 3-4.   On a pressure-enthalpy diagram the whole process is represented by the horizontal line (Fig. 7-3) corresponding to the boiler pressure.   Within the two-phase region the relation between any of the extensive properties and the quality x, or moisture content $(1 - x)$, is given by Eqs. (7-27) to (7-29). On a temperature-entropy diagram, in the liquid region to the left of the saturation curve (Fig. 7-2) the constant-pressure lines are close together; in fact, in most instances it is sufficiently accurate to use the saturation curve itself rather than a line of constant pressure which would lie very close to the saturation curve.   This situation occurs because liquids are

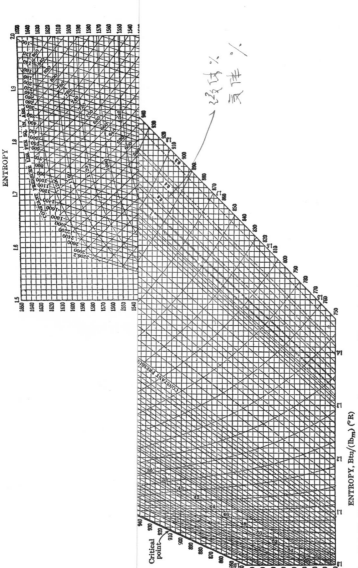

FIG. 7-6. Enthalpy-entropy diagram for steam. (Reproduced by permission from "**Steam Tables—Properties of Saturated and Superheated Steam,**" copyright 1940, Combustion Engineering, Inc.)

nearly incompressible so that their properties change only slightly with large changes in pressure.

The temperature-entropy diagram has the advantage that the transfer of energy to or from a system as heat may be represented on it by areas. In the boiler process the total heat absorbed by the water is equal to $\int T \, dS$. This is equivalent to the area between the line of zero temperature and the path followed by the process 1-2-3-4. A reversible adiabatic process is represented on a T-S diagram by a vertical line since it is characterized by no change in entropy. The path followed by the steam in reversible adiabatic turbines is simply a vertical line from the initial pressure down to the final pressure. This is also true on the H-S or Mollier diagram.

Although the behavior of multicomponent systems will not be taken up in this chapter, it is worthwhile to point out that the states represented by the solid lines in Fig. 7-1 occupy areas on p-T diagrams for multicomponent systems. For example, the vapor-pressure curve, line 2-C in Fig. 7-1, becomes a region bounded by dew-point and bubble-point lines in the case of a binary or ternary mixture. This is explained by the phase rule; *i.e.*, with the increase in number of components the system is no longer univariant. The phase behavior of multicomponent mixtures is considered in detail in Chap. 12.

7-5. Tables of Thermodynamic Properties. In many instances the thermodynamic properties of a material are reported in the form of tables. This method possesses the advantage that, in general, data can be read more accurately from tables than from charts, although interpolation may be required. In addition, there is a limitation to the number of variables that can be clearly represented in graphic form.

As an illustration of this method of presenting data, the complete tables for saturated and superheated steam are given in the Appendix. Because of the industrial importance of steam, the careful preparation of these data in tabular form is justified. Values are given at intervals close enough so that linear interpolation can be used to find properties at intermediate conditions.

Two kinds of tables are given. The first presents the properties of the saturated liquid and vapor phases in equilibrium. The enthalpy and entropy are arbitrarily assigned values equal to zero for the saturated liquid state at 32°F (*i.e.*, liquid at 32°F and 0.0886 psia). The range extends from 32°F to the critical point at 705.34°F.

The second table gives the properties of superheated steam, *i.e.*, steam at temperatures higher than the saturation temperature. This is actually the gas region. Pressure and temperature are taken as the independent variables, and volume, enthalpy, and entropy are tabulated as a function of pressure at various temperatures. In this table the pressure range is from 1 to 3206.2 psia, and the temperature range from the saturation temperatures up to 1200°F. In all instances units are in the English system, and the extensive properties are based on 1 lb_m of water.

Although the steam tables probably represent the most extensive and complete compilation of thermodynamic properties for any single material, a considerable amount of information is available for other substances.[1]

Example 7-3. Superheated steam originally at 150 psia and 500°F expands through a nozzle to an exhaust pressure of 30 psia. If the process is adiabatic and reversible and equilibrium is attained, what is the state of the steam at the nozzle exit?

Solution. From the fact that the process is both reversible and adiabatic, the change in entropy of the steam must be zero. There are two methods of solution; one makes use of the steam tables and the other, the Mollier diagram.

---

[1] Data for a number of substances are given by J. H. Perry (ed.), "Chemical Engineers' Handbook," 3d ed., pp. 249–281, McGraw-Hill Book Company, Inc., New York, 1950. These data are abstracted from other sources, and linear interpolation may not be satisfactory in certain regions of the tables.

A number of volumes are currently being prepared in England by F. Din (ed.), "Thermodynamic Functions of Gases," Butterworths Scientific Publications, London. As of 1958, the first two volumes had appeared, covering ammonia, carbon dioxide, carbon monoxide, air, acetylene, ethylene, propane, and argon. Subsequent volumes are to include butane, chlorine, ethane, Freons, helium, hydrogen, mercury, methane, nitrogen, oxygen, propylene, steam, and sulfur dioxide. This work presents a very comprehensive survey of the data available for each gas and includes data in both tabular and graphic form.

F. D. Rossini and the staff at the Carnegie Institute of Technology, Pittsburgh, in connection with Research Project 44 of the American Petroleum Institute have undertaken the task of preparing tables of the thermodynamic properties of hydrocarbons. These results are published periodically as they become available.

Other recent publications of thermodynamic tables and diagrams include:

1. *n*-Hexane: J. H. Weber, *AIChE J.*, **2**, 514 (1956). References to data for the lower normal paraffins are given in the bibliography of this article.

2. Ethylene: H. Benzer and A. V. Koch, *Chem.-Ing.-Tech.*, **27**, 71 (1955). This article contains a pressure-enthalpy diagram of special interest because it extends to the very high pressure of 10,000 atm.

3. Benzene: E. I. Organick and W. R. Studhalter, *Chem. Eng. Progr.*, **44**, 847 (1948).

4. Methyl alcohol: J. M. Smith, *Chem. Eng. Progr.*, **44**, 521 (1948).

5. Ethyl alcohol: R. C. Reid and J. M. Smith, *Chem. Eng. Progr.*, **47**, 415 (1951).

6. Diethyl ether: H. W. Schnaible and J. M. Smith, *Chem. Eng. Progr., Symposium Ser.* 7, **49**, 159 (1953).

7. Acetaldehyde: J. M. Smith, *Trans. AIChE*, **42**, 983 (1946).

8. Ethylene oxide: C. J. Walters and J. M. Smith, *Chem. Eng. Progr.*, **48**, 337 (1952).

9. Carbon dioxide: F. Cramer, *Chem.-Ing.-Tech.*, **27**, 484 (1955). The temperature-entropy diagram included in this article is particularly interesting because it covers the solid, liquid, gas, and two-phase regions as shown in Fig. 7-2 and extends to a pressure of 12,000 atm.

The initial state is as follows (data from the steam tables):

$$t_1 = 500°F$$
$$p_1 = 150 \text{ psia}$$
$$S_1 = 1.660 \text{ Btu/(lb}_m)(°R)$$
$$H_1 = 1274.1 \text{ Btu/lb}_m$$

At the final state,

$$p_2 = 30 \text{ psia} \quad \text{since } \Delta S = 0 \therefore \text{ adiabatic reversible,}$$
$$S_2 = 1.660 \text{ Btu/(lb}_m)(°R) \quad \longrightarrow 1.6/p_2$$

Since the entropy of saturated vapor at 30 psia is greater than S_2, the final state must be in the two-phase region. Equation (7-29) may be employed to solve for x, the fraction vapor in the mixture: $\longrightarrow$ S of water at 30 psia

$$1.660 = 0.368(1 - x) + 1.699x \qquad x = \text{mole fraction of vapor}$$

where 0.368 and 1.699 are the entropies of saturated liquid and saturated vapor at 30 psia. Solving,

$$x = 0.971$$

In other words the mixture contains 97.1 weight per cent vapor and 2.9 weight per cent liquid. The enthalpy of the mixture may be obtained from Eq. (7-28):

$$H = (0.029)(218.8) + (0.971)(1164.0)$$
$$= 1136.5 \text{ Btu/lb}_m \text{ of mixture}$$

To use the Mollier diagram, one locates the initial state and then follows a constant-entropy (vertical) line until the constant-pressure line of 30 psia is reached. The per cent moisture (liquid) is read directly from the chart as 2.9 and the enthalpy as 1136 Btu/lb$_m$.

7-6. Generalized Correlations of Thermodynamic Properties for Gases.

It frequently happens in the applications of thermodynamics that no tabulations or diagrams exist for the substance being considered and sufficient experimental data are not available for the calculation of the properties needed. In such cases one must resort to approximate methods. Frequently, sufficient heat-capacity data are available so that the effect of temperature on the enthalpy and entropy can be determined. It is the p-v-T data necessary to evaluate the effect of pressure that are lacking. Fortunately, the generalized compressibility-factor chart of Fig. 4-4 is available to supply volumetric information which is at least approximately valid for all substances. In theory, the procedure is to evaluate the integrals of Eqs. (7-17) and (7-18), using generalized compressibility-factor data. The values so obtained are then applicable to all gases as approximations, and generalized charts may be prepared as functions of T_r and p_r.

In practice, it is not accurate to prepare a chart for entropy showing the total effect of pressure as determined from Eq. (7-18). This is because its magnitude is large, as illustrated by Eq. (7-21) for an ideal gas. Instead, the difference between the actual entropy of the gas and the entropy of a hypothetical ideal gas at the same pressure and temperature is plotted. Then this result can be added to the effect of pressure on an ideal gas, as given by Eq. (7-21), to determine the total effect of pressure. For enthalpy, the same procedure is used, but it is not particularly significant, since pressure has no effect on the enthalpy of an ideal gas (Eq. 7-19).

The equations required for the preparation of the generalized charts can be derived in the following manner. Suppose Eq. (7-18) is integrated from a lower limit of pressure approaching zero (p^*) to any pressure p.

$$(S - S^*)_T = - \int_0^p \left(\frac{\partial v}{\partial T} \right)_p dp \qquad (7\text{-}30)$$

In this expression, S^* represents the entropy of the actual gas at T and a pressure approaching zero. Since any gas at this condition is ideal, the zero-pressure state, marked by an asterisk, is known as the ideal-gas state at zero pressure.

If the gas in the ideal-gas state at zero pressure is imagined to *remain* an ideal gas as it is compressed to a pressure p at constant temperature, its entropy change will be given by Eq. (7-21). If S' denotes the entropy of this hypothetical ideal gas, Eq. (7-21) may be integrated from zero pressure to pressure p to give

$$(S' - S^*)_T = - R \int_0^p \frac{dp}{p} \qquad (7\text{-}31)$$

If Eq. (7-30) is subtracted from Eq. (7-31), the zero-pressure entropy S^* is eliminated:

$$(S' - S)_{T,p} = \Delta S'_{T,p} = \int_0^p \left[\left(\frac{\partial v}{\partial T} \right)_p - \frac{R}{p} \right] dp \qquad (7\text{-}32)$$

The result $(S' - S)_{T,p}$ or $\Delta S'_{T,p}$ is the difference between the entropy of a hypothetical ideal gas and that of the actual gas at the same pressure and temperature. It is a relatively small value and may be conveniently plotted.

The corresponding expressions for enthalpy are obtained from Eqs. (7-17) and (7-19):

$$(H - H^*)_T = \int_0^p \left[v - T \left(\frac{\partial v}{\partial T} \right)_p \right] dp \qquad (7\text{-}33)$$

and

$$H' - H^* = 0 \qquad (7\text{-}34)$$

Subtracting Eq. (7-33) from (7-34) yields the expression for $\Delta H'_{T,p}$:

$$\Delta H'_{T,p} = (H' - H)_{T,p} = - \int_0^p \left[v - T \left(\frac{\partial v}{\partial T} \right)_p \right] dp \qquad (7\text{-}35)$$

The integrals in Eqs. (7-32) and (7-35) are evaluated at constant temperature.

The quantities $\Delta S'_{T,p}$ and $\Delta H'_{T,p}$ represent the differences between the properties of a material in the ideal-gas state and the actual properties at the same temperature and pressure. Their usefulness lies in the fact that they allow one to switch readily from the actual state of a gas to the ideal-gas state at the same temperature and pressure. This ideal-gas state is a hypothetical one, but this does not reduce its practical value, for property changes may be calculated along any convenient path, including paths along hypothetical states. Once the ideal-gas state is reached, property changes for it may be readily calculated by the simple equations for ideal gases [Eqs. (7-19) and (7-21)]. Then, after the required final temperature and pressure are reached in the ideal-gas state, one may convert back to the actual state of the gas by the use of Eqs. (7-32) and (7-35). The procedure can be summarized by writing the equations for the change in enthalpy and change in entropy for compressing a gas from p_1 to p_2 at the constant temperature T:

$$H_{p_2} - H_{p_1} = -(H' - H)_{T,p_2} + (H'_{p_2} - H'_{p_1})_T + (H' - H)_{T,p_1} \quad (7\text{-}36)$$
$$= -\Delta H'_{T,p_2} + 0 + \Delta H'_{T,p_1}$$

Similarly, for the entropy change,

$$S_{p_2} - S_{p_1} = -(S' - S)_{T,p_2} + (S'_{p_2} - S'_{p_1})_T + (S' - S)_{T,p_1}$$
$$= -\Delta S'_{T,p_2} - R \ln \frac{p_2}{p_1} + \Delta S'_{T,p_1} \quad (7\text{-}37)$$

The $\Delta H'$ and $\Delta S'$ values can be determined from Eqs. (7-32) and (7-35).

This method of evaluating properties by going through ideal-gas states is the one most commonly employed because heat-capacity data are usually known only at zero pressure. For this reason, the method described in Sec. 7-2 is limited in utility. Equations (7-32) and (7-35) can be used to obtain $\Delta H'$ and $\Delta S'$ by direct integration from experimental p-v-T data, or through the use of an equation of state. If this information is not available, integration may be accomplished through the use of generalized p-v-T data. To do this, Eqs. (7-32) and (7-35) are first written in terms of the compressibility factor. Since

$$v = \frac{ZRT}{p} \quad \text{(mole basis)}$$

$$\left(\frac{\partial v}{\partial T}\right)_p = \frac{R}{p}\left[Z + T\left(\frac{\partial Z}{\partial T}\right)_p\right]$$

Substituting these expressions into (7-35) gives

$$\Delta H'_{T,p} = RT^2 \int_0^p \left(\frac{\partial Z}{\partial T}\right)_p \frac{dp}{p} \quad (7\text{-}38)$$

and substituting the second into Eq. (7-32) gives

$$\Delta S'_{T,p} = R \int_0^p \left[Z - 1 + T \left(\frac{\partial Z}{\partial T} \right)_p \right] \frac{dp}{p} \tag{7-39}$$

Both integrals are evaluated at constant temperature. These expressions may now be converted to a reduced form through use of the relationships

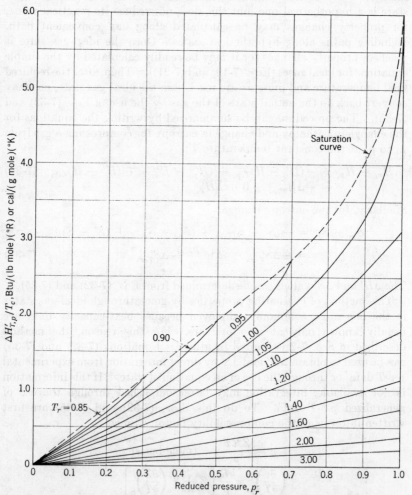

FIG. 7-7a. Generalized chart giving the difference between ideal and actual enthalpies of gases at the same temperature and pressure. Low-pressure range. (*Drawn by permission from the data of A. L. Lyderson, R. A. Greenkorn, and O. A. Hougen, Generalized Thermodynamic Properties of Pure Fluids, Univ. Wisconsin, Eng. Expt. Sta., Rept. 4, 1955.*)

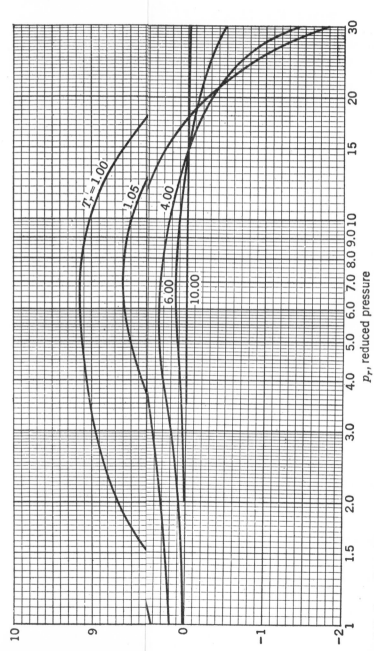

FIG. 7-7b. Generalized chart giving the difference between ideal and actual enthalpies of gases at the same temperature and pressure. High-pressure range. (Drawn by permission from the data of A. L. Lydersen, R. A. Greenkorn, and O. A. Hougen, Generalized Thermodynamic Properties of Pure Fluids, Univ. Wisconsin, Eng. Expl. Sta., Rept. 4, 1955.)

and
$$p = p_c p_r \qquad T = T_c T_r$$
$$dp = p_c \, dp_r \qquad dT = T_c \, dT_r$$

Making the logical substitutions in Eqs. (7-38) and (7-39) reduces them to

$$\frac{\Delta H'_{T,p}}{T_c} = RT_r^2 \int_0^{p_r} \left(\frac{\partial Z}{\partial T_r}\right)_{p_r} \frac{dp_r}{p_r} \tag{7-40}$$

and

$$\Delta S'_{T,p} = R \int_0^{p_r} \left[Z - 1 + T_r \left(\frac{\partial Z}{\partial T_r}\right)_{p_r} \right] \frac{dp_r}{p_r} \tag{7-41}$$

The terms on the right-hand side of these equations may be evaluated through the use of generalized compressibility-factor data. Their values

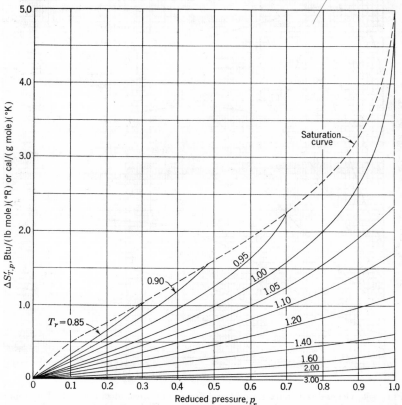

Fig. 7-8a. Generalized chart giving the difference between ideal and actual entropies of gases at the same temperature and pressure. Low-pressure range. (*Drawn by permission from the data of A. L. Lydersen, R. A. Greenkorn, and O. A. Hougen, Generalized Thermodynamic Properties of Pure Fluids, Univ. Wisconsin, Eng. Expt. Sta. Rept. 4, 1955.*)

are seen to depend only on the upper limit p_r of the integrals and on the reduced temperature at which the integrations are carried out. The quantities $\Delta H'_{T,p}/T_c$ and $\Delta S'_{T,p}$ may therefore be evaluated once and for all from generalized compressibility-factor data for a large number of reduced pressures and temperatures. Figures 7-7 and 7-8 show the results obtained when the generalized data of Fig. 4-4 are used. The values of $\Delta H'$ and $\Delta S'$ obtained from these figures can then be used in equations such as (7-36) and (7-37) to determine the effect of pressure upon the enthalpy and entropy of gases.

The correlations of Figs. 7-7 and 7-8 depend for their validity on the empirical principle of corresponding states, and they can be expected to

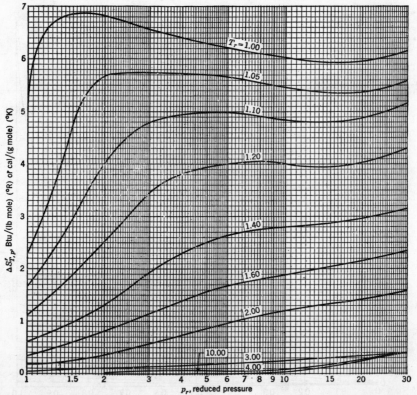

FIG. 7-8b. Generalized chart giving the difference between ideal and actual entropies of gases at the same temperature and pressure. High-pressure range. (*Drawn by permission from the data of A. L. Lydersen, R. A. Greenkorn, and O. A. Hougen, Generalized Thermodynamic Properties of Pure Fluids, Univ. Wisconsin, Eng. Expt. Sta., Rept. 4, 1955.*)

give no more than approximate results.   They are inherently less accurate than the generalized compressibility-factor chart on which they are based because deviations are magnified by the differentiations required in their development.   Furthermore, Figs. 7-7 and 7-8 give average values for gases having a critical compressibility factor Z_c of 0.27.   As mentioned in Sec. 4-3 in connection with the generalized compressibility-factor chart, the effect of this additional parameter can be taken into account only by preparing a series of charts, each for a different value of Z_c. Data of this sort are discussed by Lydersen, Greenkorn, and Hougen, and their report[1] should be consulted if more reliable values of generalized data are required for substances which have values of Z_c different from 0.27.

The use of the generalized charts is illustrated in the following example, which also gives some idea of their accuracy.

Example 7-4.   Estimate V, E, H, and S for 1-butene vapor at 400°F and 1000 psia if H and S are taken as zero for saturated liquid at 32°F.   Assume that the only information available is the critical pressure and temperature, the normal boiling point (267°K), and low-pressure heat capacities.

Solution.   The known data for 1-butene are

$$T_c = 420°\text{K} \qquad p_c = 39.7 \text{ atm} \qquad T_n = 267°\text{K}$$
$$C_p^* = 3.909 + 62.848 \times 10^{-3}T - 19.617 \times 10^{-6}T^2 \qquad (T = °\text{K})$$

The volume of 1-butene at 400°F and 1000 psia may be calculated by the equation

$$v = \frac{ZRT}{p}$$

where the value of Z is estimated from Fig. 4-4. Z is found to be 0.51, and the volume is

$$v = \frac{(0.51)(10.73)(860)}{1000} = 4.71 \text{ ft}^3/\text{lb mole}$$

The values of H and S cannot be calculated so simply, and a path must be devised, for purposes of calculation, which allows the use of available data.   The starting point is saturated liquid butene at 32°F, because H and S are taken as zero for this state.   The vapor pressure of butene at 32°F is not given and must be estimated. One method is to make use of the equation

$$\ln p' = A - \frac{B}{T}$$

According to this expression a plot of $\ln p'$ vs. $1/T$ is a straight line, as shown in the accompanying figure.   The vapor pressures at the normal boiling point (1 atm) and at the critical point (39.7 atm) may be employed to estimate p' at 32°F (273°K).

[1] A. L. Lydersen, R. A. Greenkorn, and O. A. Hougen, Generalized Thermodynamic Properties of Pure Fluids, *Univ. of Wisconsin, Eng. Expt. Sta., Rept.* 4, 1955.

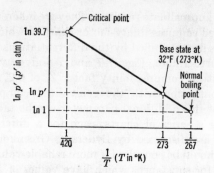

From the relations for similar triangles shown in the sketch above,

$$\frac{\ln p' - \ln 1}{\frac{1}{267} - \frac{1}{273}} = \frac{\ln 39.7 - \ln 1}{\frac{1}{267} - \frac{1}{420}}$$

Solution for p', the vapor pressure of butene in the base state, gives 1.25 atm.

The path chosen to lead from the base state of saturated liquid butene at 32°F and 1.25 atm to the required state of 400°F (478°K) and 1000 psia (68 atm) is shown schematically in the following diagram:

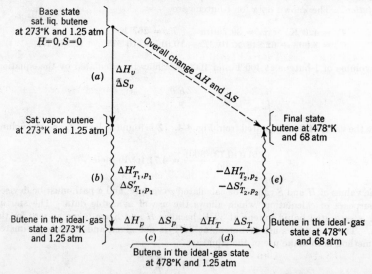

Step (a) represents the vaporization of butene at constant temperature and pressure. ΔH_v is the latent heat of vaporization, and $\Delta S_v = \Delta H_v/T$. The latent heat is not known and must be estimated. Equation (5-9) may be applied to calculate a value at the normal boiling point:

$$\frac{\Delta H_n}{T_n} = 8.75 + 1.987 \ln T_n = 8.75 + 1.987 \ln 267$$

$$\Delta H_n = 5290 \text{ cal/g mole}$$

Figure 5-3 may now be used to estimate the latent heat at 273°K. At the normal boiling point $T_r = 0.636$ and $\Delta H_n/\Delta H_0 = 0.858$. At the base conditions $T_r = 0.651$ and $\Delta H_{273}/\Delta H_0 = 0.847$. Thus

$$\frac{\Delta H_{273}/\Delta H_0}{\Delta H_n/\Delta H_0} = \frac{\Delta H_{273}}{5290} = \frac{0.847}{0.858}$$

$$\Delta H_{273} = \Delta H_v = 5230 \text{ cal/g mole}$$

and

$$\Delta S_v = \frac{5230}{273} = 19.16 \text{ cal/(g mole)(°K)}$$

Step (b) represents the fictitious process in which the real gas is transformed to an ideal gas at the same temperature and pressure. Figures 7-7 and 7-8 may be used to estimate $\Delta H'_{T1,p1}$ and $\Delta S'_{T1,p1}$ for this step. The reduced conditions are

$$T_r = 0.65 \qquad \text{and} \qquad p_r = 0.032$$

From Fig. 7-7

$$\frac{\Delta H'_{T1,p1}}{T_c} = 0.15$$

and

$$\Delta H'_{T1,p1} = (0.15)(420) = 63.0 \text{ cal/g mole}$$

This is the enthalpy change for step (b).

From Fig. 7-8

$$\Delta S'_{T1,p1} = 0.13 \text{ cal/(g mole)(°K)}$$

and this is the entropy change for step (b).

Step (c) results in a temperature change of the butene in the ideal-gas state from 273 to 478°K at a constant pressure of 1.25 atm. The enthalpy and entropy changes for this process are given by the equations

$$\Delta H_p = \int_{273}^{478} C_p^* \, dT \qquad \text{and} \qquad \Delta S_p = \int_{273}^{478} \frac{C_p^* \, dT}{T}$$

Substitution for C_p^* by the given equation and integration give

$$\Delta H_p = 5060 \text{ cal/g mole}$$

and

$$\Delta S_p = 13.56 \text{ cal/(g mole)(°K)}$$

Step (d) raises the pressure to its final value of 68 atm at a constant temperature of 478°K. Since the butene is still in the ideal-gas state, Eq. (7-19) is valid for the enthalpy change:

$$\Delta H_T = 0$$

Similarly Eq. (7-21) applies for the entropy change:

$$\Delta S_T = -R \ln \frac{p_2}{p_1} = -1.987 \ln \frac{68}{1.25} = -7.94 \text{ cal/(g mole)(°K)}$$

Step (e) takes the butene from the ideal-gas state to its actual state at the final conditions. The enthalpy and entropy changes are obtained from Figs. 7-7 and 7-8. Since the process is *from* the ideal-gas state *to* the actual state, $(H - H')_{T2,p2}$ or $-\Delta H'_{T2,p2}$ is required. At the final conditions,

$$T_r = 1.14 \qquad \text{and} \qquad p_r = 1.71$$

From Fig. 7-7,

$$\frac{\Delta H'_{T_2, p_2}}{T_c} = 4.3$$

and

$$-\Delta H'_{T_2, p_2} = (H - H')_{T_2, p_2} = (-4.3)(420)$$
$$= -1806 \text{ cal/g mole}$$

Similarly $(S - S')_{T_2, p_2} = -\Delta S'_{T_2, p_2}$, and this quantity can be determined from **Fig. 7-8**:

$$(S - S')_{T_2, p_2} = -\Delta S'_{T_2, p_2} = -2.9 \text{ cal/(g mole)(°K)}$$

The sums of the enthalpy and entropy changes for the various steps give the total enthalpy and entropy changes for the process leading from the base state to the required state. The results represent the enthalpy and entropy in the required state, since H and S were taken as zero in the base state. Hence

$$H = \Delta H = 5060 + 63 + 5230 + 0 - 1806 = 8547 \text{ cal/g mole}$$

or

$$(8547)(1.8) = 15,380 \text{ Btu/lb mole}$$
$$S = \Delta S = 19.16 + 0.13 + 13.56 - 7.94 - 2.90$$
$$= 22.0 \text{ cal/(g mole)(°K) or Btu/(lb mole)(°R)}$$

The internal energy is calculated from the equation

$$E = H - pv$$
$$= 15,380 - \frac{(1000)(144)(4.71)}{778}$$
$$= 14,510 \text{ Btu/lb mole}$$

Experimental values on the same basis may be obtained from the data given by Weber.[1] A comparison of the calculated and experimental values is given in the accompanying table.

	Calculated	Experimental
v, ft^3/lb mole...............	4.71	4.86
H, Btu/lb mole..............	15,380	14,960
E, Btu/lb mole..............	14,510	14,060
S, Btu/(lb mole)(°R).........	22.0	21.5

The agreement is good, much better than would have been the case had butene been assumed an ideal gas. Compared with this alternative, the generalized methods represent a striking improvement.

7-7. Thermodynamic Properties of Mixtures or Solutions. More often than not in practice it is necessary to deal with solutions or mixtures of gases and liquids, rather than with pure materials. Hence a method for determining the thermodynamic properties of solutions is of considerable practical importance. What is needed is an accurate general method of calculating the thermodynamic properties of solutions from

[1] J. A. Weber, *AIChE J.*, **1**, 210 (1955).

the properties of the pure components. This general problem has not been solved. However, a number of approximate methods are available.

One of the simplest relationships predicts the property of the solution to be the average of the properties of the pure components at the same temperature and pressure, each weighted according to its composition in the mixture. Suppose G is any molal property and x_A, x_B, etc., are the mole fractions of components A, B, etc., in a homogeneous mixture or solution. Then this relation between the molal property of the mixture G_m and the molal properties of the pure components G_A, G_B, etc., at the same temperature and pressure as the solution, is

$$G_m = x_A G_A + x_B G_B + \cdots + x_N G_N \qquad (7\text{-}42)$$

The simplicity of this equation is a strong recommendation for it, but, unfortunately, it is valid only in special cases. In order to make Eq. (7-42) universally valid a correction term ΔG is added. Thus

$$G_m = x_A G_A + x_B G_B + \cdots + x_N G_N + \Delta G \qquad (7\text{-}43)$$

where ΔG is the difference between the property of the solution G_m and the sum of the properties of the pure components which make it up, *all at the same temperature and pressure as the solution.* Hence ΔG is called the change in the property accompanying mixing. In the following paragraphs Eq. (7-43) will be applied to the properties v, E, H, and S for several special cases.

Ideal Gases. It was shown in Sec. 4-5 that for an ideal gas the total volume of a gas mixture is equal to the sum of its pure-component volumes. For a mole of mixture, the pure-component volumes are $y_i v_i$ and their sum is

$$v_m = y_A v_A + y_B v_B + \cdots + y_N v_N \qquad (7\text{-}44)$$

where y is used to represent the mole fraction in a gas mixture. This equation is identical with Eq. (7-42) if the property G becomes the volume. Thus for the case of ideal gases, Δv, the volume change of mixing, is zero.

One of the conditions for a gas to be ideal is that no forces exist between the molecules. If this is true, then the substitution of one kind of molecule for another at the same temperature cannot influence the energies of the original molecules that remain. Thus the internal energy of an ideal-gas mixture is simply the sum of the energies of the pure components which make it up. For a mole of mixture, these pure-component energies are $y_i E_i$, and their sum is

$$E_m = y_A E_A + y_B E_B + \cdots + y_N E_N \qquad (7\text{-}45)$$

This equation is also identical with Eq. (7-42), where the property G is taken as the internal energy. Hence ΔE, the internal-energy change of mixing, as defined in Eq. (7-43), is also zero for ideal gases.

By the definition of enthalpy, $H = E + pv$, and at constant pressure, $\Delta H = \Delta E + p\,\Delta v$. Since ΔE and Δv are zero for the constant-temperature and constant-pressure mixing of ideal gases, ΔH, the heat of mixing, must be zero. Applied to enthalpy, Eq. (7-43) becomes

$$H_m = y_A H_A + y_B H_B + \cdots + y_N H_N \qquad (7\text{-}46)$$

While the three property changes so far considered have all been zero for ideal gases, this is not true for entropy. When gases are mixed at constant temperature and pressure, there is always an entropy change, even for an ideal gas. Since the molecules of an ideal gas exert no forces on one another, each component in a mixture of such gases behaves as though it alone occupied the total volume at the temperature of the mixture, but at its own partial pressure. Thus, the net effect on each component of mixing the gases at the pressure p and the temperature T is the reduction of its pressure from p to the partial pressure it exerts in the mixture. The effect of pressure at constant temperature on the molal entropy of an ideal gas is obtained from Eq. (7-21):

$$\Delta S = -R \ln \frac{p_2}{p_1}$$

Suppose the gases are each at the pressure p and temperature T individually and then are mixed to form a mixture at the same pressure and temperature. Then

$$p_1 = p \qquad \text{and} \qquad p_2 = \bar{p}_i$$

where $\bar{p}_i$ is the partial pressure of component i in the mixture. If there are y_i moles of component i, the entropy change caused by mixing for component i is

$$\Delta S_i = -R y_i \ln \frac{\bar{p}_i}{p}$$

However, by Eq. (4-12a) $\bar{p}_i = y_i p$. Therefore

$$\Delta S_i = -R y_i \ln y_i = R y_i \ln \frac{1}{y_i}$$

The total entropy change when 1 mole of an ideal-gas mixture is formed from its pure components at the temperature and pressure of the mixture is the sum of such individual entropy changes of the components:

$$\Delta S = \sum \Delta S_i = R\left(y_A \ln \frac{1}{y_A} + y_B \ln \frac{1}{y_B} + \cdots \right.$$
$$\left. + y_N \ln \frac{1}{y_N} \right) = R \sum \left(y_i \ln \frac{1}{y_i} \right) \quad (7\text{-}47)$$

Hence the entropy of an ideal-gas mixture, according to Eq. (7-43), is

$$S_m = y_A S_A + y_B S_B + \cdots + y_N S_N + R \sum \left(y_i \ln \frac{1}{y_i} \right) \quad (7\text{-}48)$$

In summary, the properties of mixtures of ideal gases are

$$v_m = \sum y_i v_i \quad (7\text{-}44)$$

$$E_m = \sum y_i E_i \quad (7\text{-}45)$$

$$H_m = \sum y_i H_i \quad (7\text{-}46)$$

$$S_m = \sum y_i S_i + R \sum \left(y_i \ln \frac{1}{y_i} \right) \quad (7\text{-}48)$$

The Zero-pressure State of Real Gases. Since all gases approach ideality as the pressure approaches zero, it might seem that the equations developed in the preceding section for mixtures of ideal gases should apply to gas mixtures at zero pressure. This is indeed true for internal energy, enthalpy, and entropy, but it is not true in general for volume. The difficulty is that, as pressure approaches zero, the volume approaches infinity. Thus, at zero pressure Δv represents the difference between infinite quantities. Since $\infty - \infty$ is an indeterminate form, values of Δv cannot be predicted for mixing of actual gases at zero pressure. As a matter of fact, experimental data indicate that Δv approaches a finite value as p approaches zero.

Since the internal energy of an ideal gas is unaffected by pressure, ΔE at zero pressure is zero just as it is for any ideal gas. In the zero-pressure state, ΔH of mixing is given by the equation $\Delta H = \Delta E + p^* \Delta v$. If p^* approaches zero, ΔH also approaches zero regardless of the value of Δv, provided that it is zero or finite, as is indicated by experimental evidence.

Ideal Solutions. The ideal solution, like the ideal gas, is a hypothetical state. Solutions sometimes approximate the behavior postulated for the ideal solution, and for this reason the concept is valuable. An ideal solution is one for which the properties of the pure components may be combined to give the properties of the solution by the same equations as those derived for an ideal gas even though the solution is not an ideal gas, indeed, even though it be a liquid or solid. Thus for an ideal solution, $\Delta v = 0$, $\Delta E = 0$, $\Delta H = 0$, and $\Delta S = R \sum [x_i \ln (1/x_i)]$. The ideal solution is most closely approximated by solutions of components which are similar chemically, such as members of a homologous series. However, the equations for an ideal solution are often applied (especially to liquid solutions) where experimental data are lacking, simply because no better method is available.

It should be noted that the assumption that a system is an ideal solution is not so stringent as the assumption that it is a mixture of ideal gases. Many actual solutions approach ideal-solution behavior, but are not ideal gases, *e.g.*, liquid solutions such as benzene and toluene. Since the concept of an ideal solution is particularly helpful in the study of phase equilibria, this subject will be discussed again in Chap. 12.

Real Mixtures or Solutions. The enthalpy and entropy of gas mixtures in the ideal-gas state are correctly calculated from the ideal-gas-state values for the pure components by the equations already developed [*e.g.*, Eqs. (7-46) and (7-48)]. The rigorous method of passing between the ideal-gas state and the real state is the same as for pure gases. Equations (7-32) and (7-35) must be integrated through the use of experimental p-v-T data or an equation of state for the mixture.

An approximate method is to employ the equation of state based upon the law of corresponding states. Then the generalized charts for $\Delta H'$ and $\Delta S'$ (Figs. 7-7 and 7-8) together with pseudocritical constants may be used in the same way that the generalized compressibility-factor chart is used for volumes of gas mixtures. It should not be expected that the values so obtained will be very accurate. Nevertheless, the method is convenient and is probably as satisfactory as any available for mixtures for which no experimental data are at hand.

There is no generally satisfactory procedure for extending generalized properties of gaseous mixtures to the liquid region. Liquid solutions are often assumed to be ideal solutions, but where this assumption is not satisfactory recourse must be had to experimental data, as was discussed in Chap. 5 for heats of mixing.

Example 7-5. A vessel is divided into two equal compartments. One contains 0.1 lb mole of nitrogen at 70°F and 1 atm, and the other contains 0.1 lb mole of oxygen at the same conditions. The barrier separating the compartments is removed, and the gases are allowed to come to equilibrium. What is the change in entropy of the contents of the vessel?

Solution. Since the ideal-gas law will be closely followed at these conditions, the temperature and pressure after mixing will still be 70°F and 1 atm. The entropy change per mole of mixture formed under these conditions is given by Eq. (7-47). The total entropy change for 0.2 mole of the equimolal mixture is

$$\Delta S = 0.2R \left(0.5 \ln \frac{1}{0.5} + 0.5 \ln \frac{1}{0.5} \right) = 0.2R \ln 2$$

$$\Delta S = 0.276 \text{ Btu/}°\text{R}$$

This is the total entropy change resulting from the irreversible mixing of the gases. The loss in capacity of the system to do work because of the irreversibility of the process is given by Eq. (6-33):

$$W_{\text{lost}} = T_0 \, \Delta S_{\text{total}} = (70 + 460)(0.276) = 146 \text{ Btu}$$

Note that in this case the total change in entropy is the same as ΔS for the gases, because there is no change in entropy in the surroundings outside the vessel. The loss in capacity to do work as the result of irreversible mixing is also the minimum work required to separate the mixture into its components. Thus it would require a minimum of 146 Btu to separate the mixture of oxygen and nitrogen at 1 atm pressure into 0.1 mole of the separate gases, each at a pressure of 1 atm. In practice it would require a much greater quantity of work than this since the process of separation cannot be carried out reversibly. The low thermodynamic efficiency of actual processes is considered in Chap. 11.

PROBLEMS

1. Derive the equations

$$\left(\frac{\partial S}{\partial v}\right)_T = \left(\frac{\partial p}{\partial T}\right)_v$$

and

$$\left(\frac{\partial E}{\partial v}\right)_T = T\left(\frac{\partial p}{\partial T}\right)_v - p$$

for the case where T and v are taken as the independent variables.

2. (a) An ideal gas at 5000 psia and 200°F flows continuously through a pipe and emerges at a pressure of 2500 psia. If no work is accomplished and if the temperature is constant, calculate ΔE, ΔH, ΔS, ΔA, ΔF, $\int T\,dS$, and $\int p\,dv$ in units of Btu, pound moles, and degrees Rankine.

(b) An ideal gas, confined in a cylinder by a piston at 5000 psia and 200°F, expands isothermally against a constant resisting pressure of 500 psia until its volume has doubled. Calculate the same quantities for this process as in part (a) and also Q and W.

(c) An ideal gas, confined in a cylinder by a piston at 5000 psia and 200°F, expands isothermally against a resisting pressure, which is always equal to the pressure in the cylinder, until its volume doubles. Calculate the same quantities as in part (b).

3. Integration of Eqs. (7-32) and (7-35) may be accomplished through the use of an equation of state. Using van der Waals' equation, perform the required integrations and show that

$$-\Delta H'_{T,p} = pv - RT - \frac{a}{v}$$

$$-\Delta S'_{T,p} = R\ln\frac{p(v-b)}{RT}$$

Note that the terms v and $(\partial v/\partial T)_p$ in Eqs. (7-32) and (7-35) are inconvenient, because van der Waals' equation is a cubic in volume. This difficulty may be circumvented by use of the following relations (which should also be verified):

$$v\,dp = d(pv) - p\,dv$$

$$\left(\frac{\partial v}{\partial T}\right)_p dp = -\left(\frac{\partial p}{\partial T}\right)_v dv \qquad \text{(const } T\text{)}$$

4. The accompanying data for nitrogen gas were taken from Lunbeck, Michels, and Wolkers, *Appl. Sci. Research*, **A3**, 197 (1952). If H and S are taken as zero at 1 atm and 0°C, calculate from these data the values of H and S at 50°C for the pressure range from 0 to 1000 atm, and draw graphs showing H and S as a function of p at this temperature.

Z, COMPRESSIBILITY FACTOR

p, atm	0°C	25°C	50°C	75°C	100°C
0	1.000	1.000	1.000	1.000	1.000
1	1.000	1.000	1.000	1.000	1.000
3	0.999	0.999	1.000	1.000	1.001
5	0.998	0.999	1.000	1.001	1.001
10	0.996	0.998	1.000	1.001	1.002
30	0.989	0.996	1.001	1.005	1.007
50	0.985	0.996	1.004	1.009	1.014
100	0.984	1.004	1.018	1.027	1.033
200	1.036	1.057	1.072	1.082	1.089
300	1.134	1.146	1.154	1.160	1.163
400	1.256	1.254	1.253	1.250	1.247
600	1.524	1.495	1.471	1.450	1.432
800	1.798	1.723	1.697	1.658	1.625
1000	2.067	1.988	1.923	1.867	1.819
C_p^*	6.956	6.959	6.962	6.967	6.976

5. Calculate (where possible) the changes in E, H, S, A, and F (free energy) which occur when the following processes take place:

(a) Ten pounds *mass* of water at 212°F is vaporized at a constant pressure of 1 atm.

(b) One pound mole of an ideal gas expands isothermally and reversibly in a nonflow process from a pressure of 10 atm and a temperature of 70°F to a pressure of 1 atm.

(c) One pound mole of an ideal gas is expanded in a flow process from 10 atm and 70°F to 1 atm through an orifice. There is no heat exchanged with the surroundings, and the velocity change is negligible.

(d) One pound mole of an ideal monatomic gas is adiabatically and reversibly compressed in a nonflow process from 1 atm and 70°F to 5 atm. ($C_p = 5$.)

Ans. (a) $\Delta E = 8973$ Btu, $\Delta H = 9703$ Btu, $\Delta S = 14.446$ Btu/°R, $\Delta A = -730$ Btu, $\Delta F = 0$; (b and c) $\Delta E = \Delta H = 0$, $\Delta S = 4.61$ Btu/°R, $\Delta A = \Delta F = -2440$ Btu; (d) $\Delta E = 1440$ Btu, $\Delta H = 2394$ Btu, $\Delta S = 0$.

6. One pound *mass* of steam undergoes the following changes in state. Calculate the energy transferred as work and as heat in each case.

(a) Initially at 50 psia and 500°F, it is cooled at constant volume to 300°F.

(b) Initially at 50 psia and 500°F, it is cooled at constant pressure to 300°F.

7. Determine the differences between the enthalpy, internal energy, and entropy of steam at 900°F and 500 psia and at 300°F and 40 psia. Base your results on 1 lb mole. Compare answers obtained from the steam tables with those calculated, assuming steam to be an ideal gas.

8. Wet steam at 260 psia is expanded in a throttling calorimeter to a final pressure of 1 atm and a final temperature of 240°F. What is the quality of the 260 psia steam?

Ans. 95.5 per cent.

9. Steam at 80 psia and 400°F is expanded at constant enthalpy (as through a valve) to 14.7 psia.

(a) What is the temperature of the steam in the final state?   If steam under these conditions were an ideal gas, what would be the final temperature?

(b) What is its specific volume in the final state?

(c) What is the entropy change of the steam?

10. (a) One pound *mass* of steam is contained in a cylinder with a piston at 100 psia and 500°F.   Calculate the work done by the steam if it is allowed to expand isothermally and reversibly to 35 psia.   What is the heat absorbed by the steam from the surroundings during the process?

(b) Steam at 100 psia and 500°F is allowed to expand adiabatically and reversibly until its pressure is 35 psia.   Calculate the final temperature of the steam.   What is the work done by the steam?

(c) Explain the difference between the work values obtained in (a) and (b).

11. Steam at 380 psia leaves a boiler containing 4 per cent moisture but is subsequently superheated without change in pressure until its temperature is 800°F. What are the properties (v, H, and S) of the superheated steam, and how much heat was required for the process?

12. Steam at 300 psia and 90 per cent quality is reversibly and adiabatically expanded to 50 psia and is then treated isometrically until it becomes dry and saturated.   For each stage of the process as well as for the entire operation, what heat effects are involved and what work is done?   What are the final properties of the steam?

13. Steam of 75 per cent quality is expanded reversibly at constant quality from 400 to 100°F.   Determine Q and W.

14. One pound *mass* of water at 180 psia and 373°F drops in temperature to 200°F without any change in its internal energy.   What is the reversible work associated with this change?

15. At 450°F a mixture of saturated steam and liquid water exists in equilibrium. If the specific volume of the mixture is 0.6673 ft³/lb_m, calculate from data in the steam tables:

(a) Per cent moisture

(b) Enthalpy of the mixture, Btu/lb_m

(c) Entropy of the mixture, Btu/(lb_m)(°R)

16. Two boilers discharge equal amounts of steam into the same steam main.   The steam from one is at 200 psia and 420°F; from the other, at 200 psia and 96 per cent quality.

(a) What is the equilibrium condition after mixing?

(b) What is the loss of entropy of the higher-temperature steam?

(c) What is the gain of entropy of the lower-temperature steam?

17. Steam enters a turbine at 325 psia with 180°F of superheat and leaves at 1 atm.

(a) Show how the first-law flow equation is reduced to the simplified form usually used for obtaining the work of a turbine.

(b) Since work is produced, show on a sketch of the Mollier diagram where the path of the process *cannot* go.

(c) Making necessary (and usual) assumptions, show on the diagram where the path *cannot* go, based on the second law.

(d) If the process is irreversible to the extent that the work obtained is 90 per cent of that theoretically possible, what is the entropy of the outlet steam?   What is its enthalpy?

18. In an adiabatic turbine, the steam enters at 550 psia and 700°F.   It is necessary that the outlet steam have a quality of no less than 90 per cent.   An engineer claims that this can be achieved by controlling the outlet pressure.   Explain whether you agree or not, and why.

19. Steam enters a turbine at 240 psia with 400°F of superheat. It leaves the turbine at saturation. The vapors are condensed at constant pressure. During pumping, the liquid pressure is increased to 240 psia. It is then converted to the conditions at the turbine entrance as it passes through the boiler.

(a) What is the maximum efficiency of conversion of heat into work in this cycle?

(b) Show that pump work may be neglected.

20. Saturated steam at 125.3 psig expands adiabatically and reversibly to an absolute pressure of 10 in. Hg. Find the values of H, v, T, and the quality in the initial and final states. What is the work done?

21. Saturated steam at 200 psia expands continuously through a throttle to a constant pressure of 14.7 psia. What is the state of the expanded steam and the entropy change of the steam if the process is adiabatic and if potential- and kinetic-energy changes are negligible?

22. Describe the characteristics and sketch the paths of the following processes on p-v, p-H, T-S, and H-S diagrams:

(a) Continuous throttling of saturated liquid

(b) Condensing superheated vapor to subcooled liquid

(c) Adiabatic reversible expansion of saturated vapor

(d) Constant-volume heating of saturated liquid

(e) Isothermal expansion, starting at the critical point

23. A steam turbine is to operate reversibly and adiabatically, taking in superheated steam at 260 psia and discharging at a pressure of 3.5 psia. What is the minimum number of degrees of superheat required in the 260 psia steam so that the exhaust from the turbine will contain no moisture? What is the horsepower output of the turbine if it operates under these conditions and takes in 15 lb_m of steam per minute?

24. A steam turbine receives steam at 150 psia and 324°F superheat, and after doing work by expansion rejects the steam at 20 psia and 260°F. The operation of the turbine is essentially adiabatic. If in addition it is assumed to be reversible and if 2000 lb_m of steam per hour is used, calculate the horsepower developed by the turbine by two methods:

(a) Using only the first law

(b) Using the concept of entropy

25. Saturated steam at 140 psia expands through a turbine reversibly and adiabatically to an absolute pressure of 10 in. Hg. Find the values of H, v, T and the quality in the final state. Repeat for an initial condition of steam superheated 200°F at 140 psia. How much work is done by the turbine in each case?

If the saturated steam at 140 psia expands irreversibly and adiabatically through a throttle to a pressure of 10 in. Hg, what are the values of H, v, T and the quality in the final state? Repeat for an initial condition of wet steam at 140 psia, having a quality of 98 per cent.

26. (a) Steam initially at 200 psia expands at constant enthalpy to 14.7 psia. The temperature after expansion is 240°F. Determine the per cent moisture of the steam at 200 psia and also its temperature. What is the entropy change of the steam?

(b) Steam at 14.7 psia and 280°F is compressed to a condition in which it contains 10 per cent moisture. Its temperature is maintained constant during the compression. Calculate the changes in enthalpy and entropy.

27. A closed vessel of 10 ft³ capacity is filled with saturated steam at 250 psia. If subsequently 25 per cent of the steam is condensed, how much heat must be removed, and what is the final pressure? *Ans.* $Q = -1052$ Btu, $p = 186$ psia.

28. (a) An insulated evacuated tank having a volume of 50 ft³ is attached to a constant-pressure line containing steam at 50 psia, superheated 10°F. Steam is allowed to flow into the tank until the pressure has risen to 50 psia. Assuming the tank to be well insulated and to have a negligible heat capacity, how many pounds *mass* of steam will enter the tank?

(b) Prepare graphs showing the mass of steam in the tank and the temperature of the steam in the tank as a function of pressure.

29. A well-insulated closed tank of 1500 ft³ volumetric capacity contains 5 tons of heavy oil at 800°F. The oil is originally present as liquid with negligible vapor pressure and has a specific gravity of 0.70 and a specific heat of 0.60, both of which do not change appreciably with temperature. By accident 100 lb$_m$ of water at 70°F is added to the tank. What will be the pressure in the tank after equilibrium is attained?

30. A chemical plant has saturated steam available at 400 psia, but because of a process change has little use for steam at this pressure. The new process requires steam at 150 psia. To get the 150 psia steam it was first proposed to throttle the 400 psia steam to this pressure, but one of the plant engineers suggested a different scheme. He observed that the plant also had saturated steam available at a pressure of 40 psia and suggested that this steam be compressed from 40 psia to 150 psia, obtaining the required work by expanding the 400 psia steam to 150 psia. The two streams could then be mixed. If such a scheme could be carried out by a *completely reversible* process, what would be the quantities of 40 psia steam and 400 psia steam required to give enough 150 psia steam to supply 1,000,000 Btu/hr by condensing only (not subcooling)?

Ans. 679 lb$_m$/hr of 400 psia steam, 485 lb$_m$/hr of 40 psia steam.

31. Over the period of an hour the total steam demand of a certain plant is 12,000 lb$_m$, but because of batch operation of autoclaves, the demand fluctuates from 8000 to 20,000 lb$_m$/hr. To permit steady boiler operation at 12,000 lb$_m$/hr, a storage tank or accumulator is to be used. The boiler pressure is 130 psig, and the steam is saturated. The autoclaves operate with steam at 85 psig. Determine the volume of the accumulator necessary for this service. For safety, the liquid volume should not exceed 95 per cent of the tank volume. A drawing of the accumulator is shown in the accompanying sketch.   *Ans.* 1560 ft³.

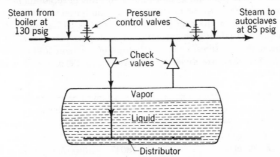

32. Making use of the appropriate generalized charts, calculate ΔH, ΔS, ΔE, and Δv for 1 lb mole of 1,3-butadiene when it is compressed from 25 atm and 260°F to 125 atm and 530°F.

33. Estimate the volume, entropy, enthalpy, and internal energy of 1 lb mole of propane at 200°F and 300 psia. The enthalpy and entropy are to be taken as zero at 1 atm and 0°F. Compare your results with the values calculated from the data for propane given by Perry.[1]

[1] J. H. Perry (ed.), "Chemical Engineers' Handbook," 3d ed., p. 274, McGraw-Hill Book Company, Inc., New York, 1950.

34. Estimate v, E, H, S, A, and F for 1 lb mole of propylene at 280°F and 800 psia. The enthalpy and entropy of propylene vapor are to be taken as zero at 1 atm and 0°F.

35. Determine the approximate values of v, E, H, and S for 1 lb mole of saturated acetylene vapor at 21°C and for saturated liquid acetylene at 21°C. Take H and S to be zero for acetylene in the ideal-gas state at 1 atm and 0°C. Report answers in cubic feet, pound moles, Btu, and degrees Rankine. The normal boiling point of acetylene is −84°C, and its vapor pressure at 21°C is 44 atm.

36. Assuming the enthalpy and entropy of chlorine to be zero at 300°K and 1 atm, what (approximately) are the enthalpy and entropy of chlorine at 100 atm and 500°K?

37. A closed tank having a volume of 10 ft³ holds ethane vapor at 62°F and 360 psia. The ethane is to be heated until it reaches a temperature of 310°F. How much heat must be transferred to the ethane during this process? Work the problem using generalized charts. Repeat, using data given by Perry.[1]

38. Carbon dioxide at 200 psig and 70°F is expanded to atmospheric pressure in two ways: reversibly and adiabatically through an engine, and through a throttle. Determine the temperature of the expanded gas in each case. Work the problem in three ways:

(a) Assuming the ideal-gas law
(b) Using the generalized charts
(c) Using data given by Perry[1]

39. Determine the horsepower required to compress, reversibly and adiabatically, 1 lb$_m$/min of ethylene oxide from 70°F and 1 atm to 250 psia. The molal heat capacity of ethylene oxide is given by the equation

$$C_p^* = 10.03 + 0.0184t \qquad (t = °F)$$

40. A process for the separation of an equimolal mixture of methane and ethane is being considered. It is necessary to have values for the enthalpy of this mixture (Btu per pound *mass*) at two conditions: (a) as a vapor at 100°F and 15 atm, (b) as a liquid at −150°F and 15 atm. Information for the pure components is given by Perry,[1] but data are lacking for mixtures. For the liquid an ideal solution may be assumed. For the vapor the pseudocritical method is to be used. It is desired to have all enthalpies based on zero enthalpy for each pure component at absolute zero in the ideal-gas state. Values for the enthalpies of methane and ethane in the ideal-gas state with this basis are given by the American Petroleum Institute Research Project 44 as follows:

	100°F	500°F
H for methane..........	281.1	531.7 Btu/lb$_m$
H for ethane...........	180.7	397.5 Btu/lb$_m$

Ans. (a) 208, (b) −92.6.

41. From the heat-of-formation data and heat capacities given in Chap. 5 and from the generalized charts given in this chapter, calculate the heat of dehydrogenation of propane to give propylene at 900°F and 500 psia.

42. According to a patent on the catalytic cracking of petroleum, hydrocarbons boiling above the gasoline range are cracked at temperatures of approximately 850

[1] *Ibid.*, pp. 249–281.

to 1050°F and pressures of approximately 75 to 600 psia.   In order to construct a proper catalytic reactor for this process, operating at 900°F and 600 psia, the heat of cracking at these conditions is needed.   Base your calculations on a feed of pure n-decane and the following reaction:

	$n\text{-}C_{10}H_{22} \rightarrow n\text{-}C_6H_{12}$	$+$ $2C_2H_4$	$+$	H_2
Molecular weight.................	142	84	28	2
T_n, normal boiling point, °R........	805	574		
T_c, °R..........................	1114	860	507	59 9
p_c, psia..........................	308	500	735	188
Heat of combustion, Btu/lb$_m$ at 25°C......................	20,480(l)	20,500(l)	21,600(g)	61,500(g)
Heat of vaporization, Btu/lb$_m$ at T_n	120	145		
Characterization factor, K..........	12.5	12	11.8	

The specific heats of liquid decane and liquid hexene may be taken as 0.6.   The specific heats of all three hydrocarbons in the gas phase are given by the equation

$$c_p^* = (0.045K - 0.233) + (0.44 + 0.0177K) \times 10^{-3}t - 0.153 \times 10^{-6}t^2$$

where t is degrees Fahrenheit, K is the characterization factor, and c_p^* is specific heat in Btu/(lb$_m$)(°F).

43. An insulated tank containing 1 lb mole of nitrogen at 100°C and 50 atm is connected to a similar tank containing 2 lb moles of carbon dioxide at 200°C and 10 atm. The contents of the two tanks are allowed to mix adiabatically, sufficient time being allowed for complete mixing.   Assuming the ideal-gas law, what is the change in entropy and why has the entropy changed?

44. What is the increase in entropy (Btu per degree Rankine) when 7.9 ft^3 of N$_2$ and 2.1 ft^3 of O$_2$, each at 1 atm and 70°F, diffuse together to form a mixture at 1 atm and 70°F?   Assume ideal gases.

45. Two gas streams, one of pure methane and the other of pure oxygen, are mixed at the essentially constant conditions of 1 atm and 70°F, preparatory to oxidation. If the stream flow rates are equal on a molal basis, what is the increase in entropy accompanying this process per pound mole of mixture?

46. A 50 mole per cent benzene–50 mole per cent toluene mixture is fed to a continuous fractionating column as a liquid at its boiling point.   The overhead product is essentially pure benzene, and the bottoms product is pure toluene.   The condenser and the cooler extract 150 Btu/lb$_m$ from the stream from the top of the tower.   The cooling water has an essentially constant temperature of 70°F, and the condensing-steam temperature in the still is 280°F.   The steam rate to the still is 5000 lb$_m$/hr, and the feed rate is 10,000 lb$_m$/hr.   The feed enters the column at a point where the liquid composition is 50 mole per cent benzene.   Neglecting sensible heat effects, calculate the total change in entropy resulting from the separation of 1 lb mole of benzene from the feed.   Is the process reversible?   Explain.

CHAPTER 8

THERMODYNAMICS OF FLOW PROCESSES

Nearly all equipment used in the chemical and related industries must be designed for the movement of fluids. Therefore, a knowledge of the fundamental relationships in fluid flow is essential to a chemical engineer. These relationships are based directly upon the following principles: the conservation of mass, Newton's second law of motion, and the first and second laws of thermodynamics. The utilization of the principles, along with empirical information to solve flow problems, constitutes the science of fluid mechanics.[1]

Many problems in fluid mechanics deal with the behavior of small elements of the fluid under various conditions of restraint. This kind of problem cannot be handled by the laws of thermodynamics, but involves instead the mechanics of the fluid particles. On the other hand, thermodynamic analysis is valuable in studying flow processes from an over-all viewpoint, particularly with regard to the energy transfer between the fluid and its surroundings.[2] The treatment of this latter type of problem is the objective of this chapter.

The thermodynamic analysis is based upon an examination of the initial and final states rather than the mechanism of the process itself. Applied to the flow of fluids this means that a knowledge of the mechanics of the flow process is not required. The thermodynamic treatment relates the change in state of the fluid from the entrance to the exit of the equipment to the energy exchange with the surroundings. Con-

[1] This subject is treated from an engineering viewpoint by R. L. Daugherty and A. C. Ingersoll, "Fluid Mechanics," 5th ed., McGraw-Hill Book Company, Inc., New York, 1954, and J. C. Hunsaker and B. G. Rightmire, "Engineering Applications of Fluid Mechanics," McGraw-Hill Book Company, Inc., New York, 1947. The relationship between thermodynamics and fluid mechanics is presented in detail by A. H. Shapiro, "The Dynamics and Thermodynamics of Compressible Flow," The Ronald Press Company, New York, 1953.

[2] The distinction between the two kinds of flow problems can be made more evident by an example. Suppose a liquid flows through a pipe at constant temperature. The nature of the velocity profile across the diameter of the pipe is not subject to thermodynamic analysis, but requires a momentum balance for its treatment. However, the amount of energy transfer between the pipe and its surroundings, necessary to maintain isothermal conditions, is a thermodynamic problem.

238

sider a gas flowing through a section of a pipeline at isothermal conditions. Application of the first law, coupled with a complete knowledge of the states of the fluid entering and leaving the section (and the thermodynamic properties of the fluid), is sufficient to establish the magnitude of the energy exchange with the surroundings.

In some problems, sufficient information is not available to obtain the solution from thermodynamic analysis alone. In this event information about the mechanics of the process may be necessary. Consider again the isothermal flow of a gas in a pipeline, but suppose the state at the exit is nòt fully known; for example, the exit pressure is not measured. By applying Newton's second law (with an empirical expression for the shear force between the fluid and the pipe wall) and the first law of thermodynamics, the energy transfer can be evaluated.

The fundamental equations are developed in Sec. 8-1, and the applications to specific flow processes are considered in subsequent sections.

8-1. Fundamental Equations. To be general, the equations for the flow of fluids should be expressed in three dimensions. However, for the thermodynamic analysis of the over-all flow process in pipes it is sufficient to consider the flow to be in one direction only. This means that quantities such as velocity, pressure, etc., vary only in one direction—the direction of flow. In addition only steady-state flow processes will be considered, thus eliminating time as a variable.

The Continuity Equation. The continuity equation expresses the conservation of mass. For steady flow this means that the mass flow rate is the same at all points along the conduit. If w is the mass flow rate, u the velocity, v the specific volume, and A the cross-sectional area, the continuity expression is

$$w = \frac{u_1 A_1}{v_1} = \frac{u_2 A_2}{v_2} = \frac{uA}{v} \tag{8-1}$$

where the subscripts represent different stations along the length of the conduit. If x is measured in the direction of flow, Eq. (8-1) may also be written

$$\frac{d}{dx}\left(\frac{uA}{v}\right) = 0 \tag{8-2}$$

The Equation of Motion. The equation of motion is based upon Newton's second law. For a fluid in motion this may be expressed as follows: the *net* rate of flow of momentum out of an element of the conduit in the x direction is equal to the net force acting on the element in the same direction. Suppose an element Δx of a circular conduit is chosen, as shown in Fig. 8-1.

The rate of flow of momentum into the element is wu and the flow out is $w(u + \Delta u)$, where Δu is the increase in velocity through the length

Δx. Then the net flow of momentum in the x direction is $w(\Delta u)$. According to the continuity equation this may be expressed as $(Au/v)(\Delta u)$.

The three forces acting on the element are indicated in Fig. 8-1. The pressure acts over an area A perpendicular to the direction of flow. The net force in the x direction is[1]

$$pA - (p + \Delta p)A = -A\,\Delta p$$

If the conduit is not horizontal, a gravitational force will act on the element. Its magnitude will be $(\Delta m)g$ acting vertically, or $-(\Delta m)g \sin\theta$ acting in the x direction. The mass of the element Δm is equal to

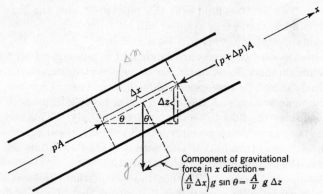

FIG. 8-1. Forces acting on an element of flowing fluid.

$(A/v)\,\Delta x$. Since $\Delta x(\sin\theta)$ is the change in elevation, Δz, the final form for the gravitational force, may be written

$$-\frac{A}{v}\,g\,\Delta x\,\sin\theta = -\frac{A}{v}\,g(\Delta z)$$

where g is the local acceleration of gravity.

The drag of the fluid against the wall as it flows along the conduit results in a shear force acting over the wall area parallel to the x direc-

[1] The cross-sectional area A has been taken constant in this formulation of the net force due to the pressure of the fluid. However, the same result would be obtained if the cross-sectional area changed. Under these conditions there would be a component in the x direction of the normal force at the wall of the conduit. The magnitude of this component would be the product of the average pressure and the projected area perpendicular to the x direction, or $\dfrac{p + (p + \Delta p)}{2}\,\Delta A$, where ΔA is the change in cross-sectional area over the length Δx. The net pressure force would then be

$$pA + \left(p + \frac{\Delta p}{2}\right)\Delta A - (p + \Delta p)(A + \Delta A) = -A\,\Delta p$$

as before.

$ft = \Delta(mv)$

$pA - (p + \Delta p)A - \frac{A}{v}g(\Delta z) - \tau(\pi D)\Delta x = w \cdot \Delta \mu$

tion. If this force per unit area is called τ, its magnitude in the x direction over the section of length Δx is

$$-\tau(\pi D)\, \Delta x$$

where D is the diameter of the conduit.

Equating the net momentum to the net force and multiplying by v/A yields

$$u(\Delta u) = -v\,\Delta p - g\,\Delta z - \frac{4\tau v}{D}\,\Delta x \qquad (8\text{-}3)$$

If it is desired to use pounds *force* in the units for pressure, and pounds *mass* in the units for specific volume, it is necessary to introduce the conversion factor g_c, as was done in Chap. 2. If the ratio g/g_c is taken equal to unity, and if the element is decreased to a differential length dx, Eq. (8-3) becomes

$$v\,dp + dz + \frac{u\,du}{g_c} + \frac{4\tau v}{D}\,dx = 0 \qquad (8\text{-}4)$$

All the terms in Eq. (8-4), which were originally forces, now represent energies per pound of fluid flowing through the conduit. This change occurred when the equation was multiplied by v/A, which has the units of feet per pound *mass*. Therefore, the last term refers to the energy associated with the shear force on the conduit wall. This energy term due to the shear or frictional force will be given the symbol F.†

Equation (8-4) is the equation of motion for one-dimensional steady flow of a fluid in a conduit. Suppose a device (for example, a turbine) is installed in the duct, against which the fluid will exert a force that is transmitted outside the walls. Then another term will be involved in Eq. (8-4). If the energy transferred to the surroundings as a result of this force is designated W_s, Eq. (8-4) may be written

$$v\,dp + dz + \frac{u\,du}{g_c} + dF + dW_s = 0 \qquad (8\text{-}5)$$

This equation is sometimes called the mechanical-energy balance. It expresses the concept that mechanical energy in a flow system is conserved, except for that part converted into other forms of energy as a result of friction, that is, dF.

Equation (8-5) is also known as the extended Bernoulli equation. When the flow is frictionless and there is no device in the conduit with which to exchange work with the surroundings, Eq. (8-5) reduces to

$$v\,dp + dz + \frac{u\,du}{g_c} = 0$$

† The same symbol is used to designate the free energy, but the two quantities seldom occur in the same problem.

If this expression is applied to the flow of an incompressible fluid (v constant), it may be integrated along the direction x to yield

$$vp + z + \frac{u^2}{2g_c} = \text{a const} \tag{8-6}$$

This is the classical Bernoulli expression presented over a century prior to the development of the first law of thermodynamics. It expresses the fact that the sum of the pressure, elevation, and velocity "heads" must be a constant at any point in the frictionless flow of an incompressible fluid.

The Energy Equation. The final fundamental equation for fluid flow is the expression for the first law, as developed in Chap. 2, Eq. (2-10):

$$\Delta H + \Delta z + \frac{\Delta u^2}{2g_c} = Q - W_s \tag{2-10}$$

In differential form this becomes

$$dH + dz + \frac{u\,du}{g_c} = dQ - dW_s \tag{8-7}$$

It is worthwhile to compare the extended Bernoulli equation (8-5) and the energy equation for *incompressible* flow. Under this restriction Eq. (8-5) can be integrated to the form

$$v\,\Delta p + \Delta z + \frac{\Delta u^2}{2g_c} + W_s + F = 0 \tag{8-8}$$

Replacing ΔH in Eq. (2-10) with its equivalent $\Delta E + \Delta(pv)$, or $\Delta E + v\,\Delta p$ for incompressible flow, gives

$$\Delta E + v\,\Delta p + \Delta z + \frac{\Delta u^2}{2g_c} + W_s = Q$$

Comparison of this expression with Eq. (8-8) indicates that the friction term is related to the change in internal energy and the heat transfer as follows:

$$F = \Delta E - Q \tag{8-9}$$

This relationship shows that the energy transferred because of friction at the conduit wall appears either as internal energy of the fluid or as heat transferred to the surroundings. If the flow is isothermal, $\Delta E = 0$,† and the frictional energy is transferred as heat to the surroundings ($-Q$). If the flow is adiabatic, the frictional energy appears entirely as internal energy.

One additional observation concerning Eqs. (8-7) and (8-5) is of inter-

---

† For an incompressible fluid the energy is a function of temperature only.

est.   For a reversible (or frictionless) flow process the two equations are identical.   This may be shown by utilizing the second law in the form

$$dH = T \, dS + v \, dp \tag{7-4}$$

If this expression is substituted in Eq. (8-7) and it is remembered that $dQ = T \, dS$ for a reversible process, the energy balance becomes

$$T \, dS + v \, dp + \frac{u \, du}{g_c} + dz = T \, dS - dW_s$$

or

$$v \, dp + \frac{u \, du}{g_c} + dz + dW_s = 0$$

This equation is the same as the mechanical-energy balance (Eq. 8-5) for the case of no friction.

The application of the energy equation to practical problems is simplified because it is available in integrated form [Eq. (2-10)], thus requiring no knowledge of the mechanism of the process.   However, it does not enable one to evaluate the friction in irreversible-flow processes.   The extended Bernoulli equation is suitable for determining the friction, but this differential equation also contains the term $v \, dp$.   In many irreversible processes this term cannot be integrated.   This difficulty was avoided in developing Eq. (8-9) by assuming incompressible flow.   For compressible flow with friction, the values of p and v along the flow path are usually unknown.   On occasion simplified flow conditions, such as constant temperature, may make integration possible.   In these cases Eq. (8-5) may be used to evaluate the friction, or it may be employed with the energy equation to determine other quantities.   Empirical expressions for dF have been developed for some situations (for example, flow in pipes).   These, employed along with the fundamental equations, are frequently helpful in the solution of practical problems.

The equations presented here are applied to several types of flow problems in the following sections.   Before proceeding to these applications, some mention should be made of the nature of the velocity occurring in Eqs. (2-10) and (8-5).   The quantity u in these expressions is the same bulk mean velocity that is defined by the continuity equation [Eq. (8-1)].   In flow through pipes the velocity varies from a maximum in the center to zero at the wall, because of the frictional force at the wall.   The problem of velocity variation across the diameter of the pipe is a basic one in fluid mechanics but, as previously mentioned, is not susceptible to thermodynamic analysis.   However, the variation in profile across the pipe does affect the kinetic-energy terms in Eqs. (2-10) and (8-8).   For the case of sharply changing velocities, such as in the parabolic profile for streamline flow, the kinetic-energy term is closer to u^2/g_c.   In highly turbulent flow the velocity across the central section of the pipe is nearly uniform, and here the expression $u^2/2g_c$, as used in the equations, is more nearly correct.[1]

8-2. Flow in Pipes. As an illustration of the method of applying the equations to flow in pipes, consider the situation depicted in Fig. 8-2, where a fluid is to be pumped from section (1) to section (3). In the analysis it is convenient to divide the process into two parts, the first corresponding to the pumping operation included between sections (1) and (2). If the assumption is made that there is no heat transfer with

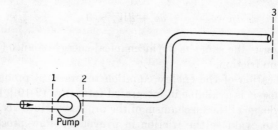

FIG. 8-2. Simple flow system.

the surroundings, the application of the energy-balance [Eq. (2-10)] and the momentum equation [Eq. (8-5)] to the pumping process leads to the following results:

$$-dW_s = dH \tag{8-10}$$
$$-dW_s = v\,dp + dF \tag{8-11}$$

The second equation shows that the energy required from the pump is equal to the sum of that necessary to increase the pressure and to overcome the friction in the pump. Equation (8-10) brings out the fact that the energy required as work is equal to the enthalpy change and could be evaluated in that manner if the initial and final states were known and if the thermodynamic properties of the fluid were available. Note that changes in potential energy and kinetic energy were neglected. In general these quantities are small in processes whose primary purpose is the production or utilization of external work or the transfer of energy as heat. In this particular problem the suction and discharge of the pump would be at nearly the same elevation so that Δz would be approximately zero. For pumping liquids and gases the sizes of the suction and discharge lines are frequently adjusted so that the velocities on the two sides of the pump are approximately the same, thus nearly eliminating the change in kinetic energy across the pump. The reason for maintain-

[1] W. H. McAdams reviews the available information on velocity gradients in turbulent flow in "Heat Transmission," 3d ed., Chap. 6, McGraw-Hill Book Company, Inc., New York, 1954.

ing approximately constant velocities in pipelines is that there is an optimum economic velocity for transporting a given fluid. Higher velocities result in excessive power costs (pumping costs) and lower velocities in excessive first costs (due to larger-sized pipe).

If the theoretical minimum work required for the pumping job is desired, friction may be neglected, and from (8-11)

$$-W_{s\min} = \int_{p_1}^{p_2} v \, dp \tag{8-12}$$

In general, the path of the process must be known before the term $v \, dp$ can be integrated and work quantities in Eq. (8-11) or (8-12) calculated. However, for liquids the specific volume is essentially constant and may be removed from the integral sign. The case of gases, where v changes considerably with the pressure, will be taken up in detail in Sec. 8-7 in connection with the discussion of compressors.

In any event the integration of Eq. (8-11) or (8-12) requires a knowledge of the discharge pressure p_2. This can be determined by analyzing the second part of the flow process. Between sections (2) and (3), again assuming adiabatic conditions, the energy and extended Bernoulli equations reduce to

$$dH + dz + \frac{u \, du}{g_c} = 0 \tag{8-13}$$

$$-v \, dp = dz + \frac{u \, du}{g_c} + dF \tag{8-14}$$

From Eq. (8-14) and the equation of continuity (8-1), the pressure p_2 can be evaluated, provided that conditions at the final state (3) are known and that the friction can be computed. This latter step requires going outside the scope of thermodynamics and using empirical means of calculating F. Since such calculations for pipe flow are of considerable importance, the procedure for evaluating the friction[1] will be briefly described along with introductory concepts of the mechanism of flow.

At low velocities, the flow in pipes is in one direction only; there exist no transient or steady components of velocity perpendicular to the axis of the pipe. Because of the viscosity of the fluid, the elements near the pipe wall are slowed down by the viscous shear (friction) force at the wall. Hence the velocity varies from a maximum at the center of the pipe to zero at the wall. Such flow is termed streamline, or viscous, and may be visualized as hollow cylinders of fluid slipping past each other down the

---

[1] For a more thorough treatment of friction calculations, reference should be made to standard texts such as W. L. McCabe and J. C. Smith, "Unit Operations of Chemical Engineering," McGraw-Hill Book Company, Inc., New York, 1956, or J. M. Coulson and J. F. Richardson, "Chemical Engineering," McGraw-Hill Book Company, Inc., New York, 1954.

pipe. As the flow rate is increased, transient components of velocity perpendicular to the pipe axis develop. These velocity fluctuations constitute what is termed *turbulence*. As the flow rate is increased further, the velocity fluctuations become more significant and the flow is described as turbulent. The degree of turbulence is greatest at the center of the pipe and decreases as the wall is approached. In the thin layer adjacent to the wall, the flow is still streamline. This region is known as the streamline, or laminar, boundary layer.

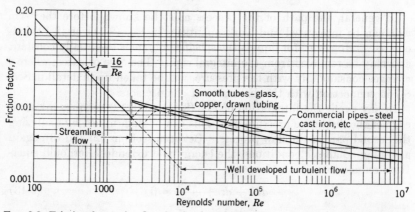

Fig. 8-3. Friction factor for flow in circular pipes. (*Reproduced by permission from W. H. McAdams, "Heat Transmission," 3d ed., McGraw-Hill Book Company, Inc., New York, 1954.*)

In turbulent flow the friction is due not only to the viscous force but to the shear stress (Reynolds stresses) arising from the velocity fluctuations. In fact the latter contribution is predominant. For both streamline and turbulent flow, the energy loss due to friction is given by the empirical expression, known as the Fanning equation,

$$dF = \frac{2fu^2}{g_c D} dL \tag{8-15}$$

where D = diameter of pipe
L = length of pipe
f = friction factor (dimensionless)

The friction has the units of energy per unit mass of fluid. Therefore, to measure F in foot-pounds *force* per pound *mass* the velocity should be in feet per second, the diameter in feet, the length in feet, and $g_c = 32.2$. The friction factor f depends upon whether the flow is streamline or turbulent. The Reynolds number (Re), defined by Eq. (8-16), has been found to characterize the nature of the flow. Below a value of about 2100 for this dimensionless quantity, the flow is streamline, while at higher values turbulence exists. Figure 8-3 shows the relationship between the friction factor f and the Reynolds number.   In the turbulent region, the friction depends upon the roughness of the pipe surface as well as Re. Hence two curves are indicated: one for smooth tubes such as glass and a second for a roughness corresponding to that of commerical metal pipes.

The Reynolds number is given by the expression

$$\text{Re} = \frac{Du\rho}{\mu} = \frac{DG}{\mu} \tag{8-16}$$

where ρ = density of fluid

μ = viscosity of fluid

G = mass velocity or mass flow rate per unit cross-sectional area

Equation (8-15) applies to flow in straight circular pipes.   The friction is increased by bends, valves, changes in pipe size, etc.   Empirical methods have been developed for estimating friction for these modifications of flow in pipes and also for flow with respect to other surfaces.[1] Applications of the fundamental equations and utilization of Eq. (8-15) are illustrated in Examples 8-1 and 8-2.

Example 8-1.   A centrifugal pump is being used to supply 100 gal/min of water to the condensers on a gasoline stabilizer unit.   The pump suction is 20 psig and the discharge pressure 200 psig.   The pump operates adiabatically; *i.e.*, no heat is exchanged with the surroundings.

The temperature of the water in and out of the pump is carefully measured and is found to rise from 60.0 to 60.35°F.   Calculate the fraction of the energy supplied to the pump that is dissipated through friction.   The suction and discharge lines to the pump are the same size.

Note any assumptions that are necessary regarding the physical behavior of liquid water under these conditions.

Solution.   Applying the energy balance [Eq. (2-10)] across the pump,

$$H_2 - H_1 + \frac{u_2^2 - u_1^2}{2g_c} = -W_s \tag{A}$$

Similarly, the extended Bernoulli equation (8-5) reduces to

$$\frac{u_2^2 - u_1^2}{2g_c} + \int_{p_1}^{p_2} v \, dp + F + W_s = 0 \tag{B}$$

The change in enthalpy in (A) may be evaluated from a knowledge of the initial and final states, *i.e.*, the state of the water entering and leaving the pump.   The actual change can be considered to take place in two steps, (1) a constant-pressure process in which the water is heated from 60.0 to 60.35°F and (2) a constant-temperature process during which the pressure is raised from 20 to 200 psig.   For the first step,

$$\Delta H_1 = Q_p = c_p(T_2 - T_1) = (1)(0.35) = 0.35 \text{ Btu/lb}_m$$

For the second step,

$$\Delta H_2 = \Delta E_2 + \Delta(pv)$$

---

[1] See texts on chemical engineering unit operations, fluid mechanics, and aerodynamics.

Since water is essentially incompressible at these conditions its energy depends only on the temperature. Therefore, for this isothermal process, ΔE will be zero, and the change in enthalpy is

(handwritten: → water at 60.35°F $\frac{1}{\rho} = v \frac{ft^3}{lbm}$)

$$\Delta H_2 = \Delta(pv) = v(p_2 - p_1) = \frac{(0.01604)(180)(144)}{778}$$
$$= 0.53 \text{ Btu/lb}_m$$

The change in kinetic energy across the pump will be zero; hence Eq. (A) gives the work required directly.

$$-W_s = H_2 - H_1 = 0.35 + 0.53 = 0.88 \text{ Btu/lb}_m \text{ of water}$$

Equation (B) can be solved for the friction by noting again that the specific volume is constant.

$$F = -W_s - v(p_2 - p_1)$$
$$= 0.88 - 0.53 = 0.35 \text{ Btu/lb}_m$$

Then the fraction of the energy supplied to the pump which is dissipated through friction is

$$\frac{F}{-W_s} = \frac{0.35}{0.88} = 0.40$$

The important point to note about the behavior of incompressible liquids is that the internal energy is not a function of pressure, just as in the case of ideal gases. However, in contrast, the enthalpy does change with the pressure at constant temperature.

Example 8-2. Air flows through a steam heater consisting of 36 ft of standard 1-in. iron pipe inside a standard 2-in. pipe. The air enters the 1-in. pipe at 70°F and leaves at 170°F. The air rate is 1000 lb$_m$/hr and the pressure at the entrance of the heater 20 psig. Estimate the friction and the rate of heat transfer to the air.

Solution. The total-energy balance [Eq. (2-10)] for this case reduces to

$$H_2 - H_1 + \frac{u_2^2 - u_1^2}{2g_c} = Q$$

The heater is horizontal so that there is no change in elevation. Even if the pipe had been vertical, the potential-energy term in Eq. (2-10) would have been negligible compared with Q and ΔH. For flow at ordinary velocities, the kinetic-energy changes would also be negligible in a heat exchanger. However, in this problem the rate of flow is high, and the velocity term may be appreciable. The initial velocity is

$$u_1 = w\frac{v_1}{A_1} = \left(\frac{1000}{3600}\right)\left(\frac{359}{28.9}\right)\left(\frac{460 + 70}{492}\right)\left(\frac{14.7}{34.7}\right)\frac{4}{\pi D^2} = 261 \text{ ft/sec}$$

If air is assumed to behave as an ideal gas under these conditions, the change in enthalpy is related to the change in temperature as follows:

$$H_2 - H_1 = \int c_p \, dT = c_{pm}(t_2 - t_1)$$

Then the total-energy balance becomes

$$c_{pm}(t_2 - t_1) + \frac{u_2^2 - u_1^2}{2g_c} = Q \qquad (A)$$

The downstream pressure is unknown, and hence u_2 and Q cannot be evaluated from this expression alone. However, the extended Bernoulli equation [Eq. (8-5)] provides a relation between the pressure and the friction.

$$\frac{u\,du}{g_c} + v\,dp + dF = 0 \qquad (B)$$

This is as far as thermodynamics can be applied toward the solution of the problem. Equations (A) and (B) are not sufficient to evaluate the three unknown quantities p_2, Q, and F.

An approximate solution can be obtained by using the Fanning equation (8-15) for the friction.

Combining this expression with Eq. (B),

$$\frac{u\,du}{g_c} + v\,dp + \frac{2fu^2}{g_cD}\,dL = 0 \qquad (C)$$

This equation cannot be integrated exactly, for the relationship between v and p for the air flowing through the heater is not known. However, an approximate solution is possible by rewriting (C) in such a way that the terms may be integrated, using average values, and still not introduce a large error. Since the mass velocity G or w/A is constant,

$$u = Gv$$

and

$$du = G\,dv$$

Replacing u in (C) with the above expressions and dividing by v^2 yields

$$\frac{G^2}{g_c}\frac{dv}{v} + \frac{dp}{v} + \frac{2fG^2}{g_cD}\,dL = 0$$

The first and third terms are directly integrable. If v is replaced by RT/pM in the second term, the equation may be integrated as follows:

$$\frac{G^2}{g_c}\ln\frac{v_2}{v_1} + \frac{M}{2RT_a}(p_2^2 - p_1^2) + \frac{2fG^2L}{g_cD} = 0 \qquad (D)$$

when T_a is the arithmetic average of T_1 and T_2. Since the total change in absolute temperature is only 19 per cent, the use of an average value should not introduce an error of more than a few per cent.

Equation (D) is most conveniently solved by trial, for example, by relating p_2 and v_2 from the ideal-gas equation and substituting the result in (D). The friction factor f can be determined from Fig. 8-3 and the Reynolds number.

$$G = \frac{w}{A} = \frac{(1000)(144)(4)}{(3600)(1.049)^2} = 46.3\ \text{lb}_m/(\text{ft}^2)(\text{sec})$$

The average viscosity of air between 70 and 170°F is approximately 0.019 centipoise or 0.046 $\text{lb}_m/(\text{hr})(\text{ft})$.

$$\frac{DG}{\mu} = \frac{(1.049)(46.3)(3600)}{(12)(0.046)} = 318,000\dagger$$

From Fig. 8-3, $f = 0.0042$.

† Note that consistent units must be used in evaluating the Reynolds number and that the term is dimensionless.

The correct value of R to use in Eq. (D) is 1545 ft-lb$_f$/(lb mole)(°R). Also, $T_a = 460 + 120 = 580$°R.

Substituting these numerical values in Eq. (D),

$$\frac{(46.3)^2}{32.2} \ln \frac{v_2}{v_1} + \frac{(144)^2[p_2^2 - (34.7)^2](28.9)}{(2)(1545)(580)} + \frac{(2)(0.0042)(36)(46.3)^2(12)}{(32.2)(1.05)} = 0$$

Since the air is assumed to behave as an ideal gas,

$$\frac{v_2}{v_1} = \frac{T_2 p_1}{T_1 p_2} = \frac{(630)(34.7)}{530 p_2} = \frac{41.2}{p_2}$$

Substituting for v_2/v_1,

$$\frac{(46.3)^2}{32.2} \ln \frac{41.2}{p_2} + \frac{(144)^2[p_2^2 - (34.7)^2](28.9)}{(2)(1545)(580)} + \frac{(2)(0.0042)(36)(46.3)^2(12)}{(32.2)(1.05)} = 0 \quad (E)$$

Solving (E) for p_2 gives

$$p_2 = 19 \text{ psia or } 4.3 \text{ psig}$$
$$u_2 = u_1 \left(\frac{34.7}{19}\right)\left(\frac{630}{530}\right) = (261)\left(\frac{34.7}{19}\right)\left(\frac{630}{530}\right) = 570 \text{ ft/sec}$$

Q can now be determined from Eq. (A), using a mean value of C_p read from Fig. 5-1.

$$Q = \left(\frac{7.0}{28.9}\right)(170 - 70) + [(570)^2 - (261)^2]\frac{1}{(32.2 \times 2)(778)}$$
$$= 24.2 + 5.1 = 29.3 \text{ Btu/lb}_m \text{ of gas flowing or } 29,300 \text{ Btu/hr}$$

About 17 per cent of the heat transfer is associated with the change in kinetic energy. This means that, of the total heat transferred, 17 per cent was needed to maintain the gas at constant temperature, despite the pressure drop, and 83 per cent of the heat was utilized in raising the temperature to 170°F.

With p_2 known, the friction can be computed approximately from Eq. (B).[1]

$$F = -\frac{u_2^2 - u_1^2}{2g_c} - \frac{RT_a}{M}\ln\frac{p_2}{p_1}$$
$$= -5.1 - \frac{(2)(580)}{28.9}\ln\frac{19}{34.7}$$
$$= -5.1 + 24.0 = 18.9 \text{ Btu/lb}_m \text{ or } 14,700 \text{ Btu/hr}$$

8-3. Maximum Velocity in Pipe Flow. Because the specific volumes of gases change rapidly with pressure at low pressures, unusual effects are observed in connection with the flow of gases. If a gas is flowing adiabatically at a steady mass rate within a horizontal pipe of constant cross-sectional area, the velocity will increase as the pressure drops because of friction. Equation (8-13) with dz equal to zero gives the relationship between the increase in velocity and decrease in enthalpy of the gas. A point in the flow process is ultimately reached where the increase in specific volume for a small decrease in pressure is so great that the pres-

---

[1] The approximation is introduced in integrating the $v \, dp$ term by using an average temperature.

sure and the enthalpy can no longer be lowered in a constant-cross-section pipe. Hence, at this point, the velocity cannot be increased further so that a maximum occurs. The conditions at this location in the pipe can be established by examining Eq. (8-13) with dz omitted:

$$-dH = \frac{u\,du}{g_c} \qquad (8\text{-}17)$$

It is clear from this equation that the maximum increase in velocity will result when the change in enthalpy is a maximum. Reference to a temperature-entropy diagram for gases shows that the maximum ΔH per unit pressure change corresponds to a constant-entropy process. A larger change in enthalpy for a given difference in pressure could result if the entropy decreased, but according to the second law this is not possible for an adiabatic process. Therefore, for the differential section at the very end of the pipe, the process is both adiabatic and isentropic. Under these conditions the friction will be zero, and the criterion for maximum velocity may be defined in terms of the extended Bernoulli equation (8-5):

$$-v\,dp = \frac{u\,du}{g_c} \qquad (\text{const } S) \qquad (8\text{-}18)$$

This expression can be written in somewhat different form by differentiating the continuity equation (8-1), remembering that the mass rate of flow is constant.

$$dw = 0 = \frac{A(v\,du - u\,dv)}{v^2}$$

or

$$du = \frac{u\,dv}{v}$$

Substituting this value of du into Eq. (8-18) and solving for the velocity leads to the result

$$u_{max}^2 = u_s^2 = -g_c v^2 \left(\frac{\partial p}{\partial v}\right)_s \qquad (8\text{-}19)$$

This is identical with the equation derived in physics for the velocity of sound in the fluid. Therefore, the maximum velocity of flow obtainable in a pipe of constant cross-sectional area is equal to sonic velocity. This does not imply that velocities above that of sound cannot be obtained, as will be seen in the discussion of nozzles (Sec. 8-6). However, it does mean that, starting with a subsonic velocity, the velocity of sound is the maximum value that can be reached in a conduit of constant cross section. The velocity of sound is obtained just at the exit of the pipe. If the pipe length is increased, the mass flow rate will decrease so that the sonic velocity will be obtained at the outlet of the lengthened pipe.

8-4. Flowmeters. The instruments for measuring flow rates which are of interest in the study of thermodynamics are based upon the determination of the kinetic energy of the fluid, *viz.*, the pitot tube, the orifice meter, and the venturi meter.

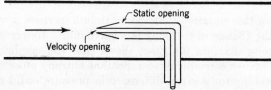

FIG. 8-4. Pitot tube.

The pitot tube (Fig. 8-4) is a device to determine the kinetic energy of the fluid stream by measuring the difference (on a manometer) between the sum of the so-called impact (velocity opening) head $u^2/2g_c + pV$ and the pressure (static opening) head pV. The reading h of the manometer then is equal to the kinetic energy,

$$h = \frac{u^2}{2g_c} \qquad (8\text{-}20)$$

Since the velocity opening must be small in order to affect the flow conditions as little as possible, the pitot-tube reading depends upon its position in the cross-sectional area available for flow. To obtain an average velocity and rate of flow, a series of readings must be taken across the diameter of the tube and averaged with respect to cross-sectional area.

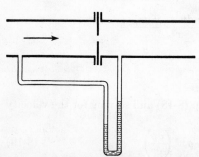

FIG. 8-5. Orifice meter.

The orifice meter (Fig. 8-5) is designed to convert part of the pressure head of the fluid into kinetic energy and measure this increment of kinetic energy by observing the change in pressure head. The extended Bernoulli equation (8-5) applied to this situation becomes

$$\frac{u_2^2 - u_1^2}{2g_c} = -v_a(p_2 - p_1) - F \qquad (8\text{-}21)$$

provided that the change in specific volume is small enough so that an average value may be used. If this assumption is not valid, as in the case of gases flowing under conditions such that the pressure drop across the orifice is a significant fraction of the absolute pressure, the term $v\,dp$ must be integrated by assuming a path for the process.

In applying (8-21), the friction is normally taken into account by introducing an empirical coefficient C and rewriting the equation as follows:

$$\frac{u_2^2 - u_1^2}{2g_c} = Cv_a(p_1 - p_2) \tag{8-22}$$

The discharge coefficient C is primarily a function of two variables, the ratio of the diameters of the pipe and the orifice and the Reynolds number. Further details concerning the relationship may be found in standard texts on chemical engineering.[1]

Flow through an orifice results in a permanent pressure drop due to friction. Most of this loss occurs as a result of the turbulence developed

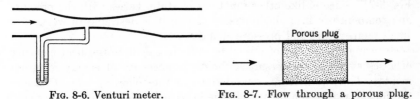

FIG. 8-6. Venturi meter.   FIG. 8-7. Flow through a porous plug. (Joule-Thomson expansion.)

downstream from the orifice. Equation (8-5) applied to sections both upstream and downstream from the orifice takes the form

$$\frac{u\,du}{g_c} + v\,dp + dF = 0 \tag{8-23}$$

In the upstream section the friction is small, and most of the decrease in pressure head is converted to kinetic energy. However, in the downstream section the friction is significant. Here the decrease in kinetic energy due to the increase in cross section of the flow stream is not entirely converted into pressure head but part is dissipated as turbulence or friction.

The flow equations applicable to the venturi meter (Fig. 8-6) are the same in form as those for orifices, but the friction term is much smaller. This results in a coefficient of discharge approaching unity. Well-designed venturi meters may have a coefficient of the order of 0.98.

8-5. Joule-Thomson Expansion. If a gas with an initial pressure p_1 and temperature T_1 flows through a porous plug or similar device designed to create friction, the pressure will decrease to p_2 and the temperature T_2 may be less, equal to, or greater than T_1. If the apparatus (Fig. 8-7) is

[1] For example, J. H. Perry (ed.), "Chemical Engineers' Handbook," 3d ed., pp. 404–406, McGraw-Hill Book Company, Inc., New York, 1950.

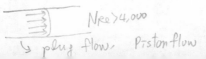

insulated from the surroundings and the changes in temperature and pressure through the porous section are small, variations in kinetic energy will not be significant. Under these conditions the energy equation (2-10) reduces to the simple form

$$\Delta H = 0 \tag{8-24}$$

The flow process is one of constant enthalpy, and the change in temperature with pressure is designated as the *Joule-Thomson coefficient* (after the early workers who first considered this type of process). Mathematically, the Joule-Thomson coefficient η is defined as

$$\eta = \left(\frac{\partial T}{\partial p}\right)_H \tag{8-25}$$

It is measured experimentally in an apparatus such as is illustrated in Fig. 8-7. Since η, like other functions of state, varies with the pressure and temperature in a single-phase system, it is desirable to work with small temperature and pressure changes.

Experimental values of η may be used to calculate the heat capacity of gases at constant pressure without the necessity of energy measurements. The equation may be derived in the following way: Consider the formal expression for the change in enthalpy for 1 mole accompanying a change in temperature and pressure,

$$dH = \left(\frac{\partial H}{\partial p}\right)_T dp + \left(\frac{\partial H}{\partial T}\right)_p dT \tag{8-26}$$

For a constant-enthalpy process ($dH = 0$), Eq. (8-26) may be written as

$$\left(\frac{\partial T}{\partial p}\right)_H = \eta = -\frac{(\partial H/\partial p)_T}{(\partial H/\partial T)_p} = -\frac{(\partial H/\partial p)_T}{C_p} \tag{8-27}$$

The general equation for the change in enthalpy derived in Chap. 7 is

$$dH = T\,dS + v\,dp$$

or

$$\left(\frac{\partial H}{\partial p}\right)_T = T\left(\frac{\partial S}{\partial p}\right)_T + v \tag{8-28}$$

Considering the entropy as a function of T and p,

$$dS = \left(\frac{\partial S}{\partial p}\right)_T dp + \left(\frac{\partial S}{\partial T}\right)_p dT = \left(\frac{\partial S}{\partial p}\right)_T dp + \frac{C_p}{T}\,dT$$

For a constant-entropy process, $dS = 0$. Hence

$$\left(\frac{\partial S}{\partial p}\right)_T = -\frac{C_p}{T}\left(\frac{\partial T}{\partial p}\right)_S \tag{8-29}$$

Combining Eqs. (8-27) to (8-29) to eliminate $(\partial H/\partial p)_T$ and $(\partial S/\partial p)_T$,

$$\eta = -\frac{v - C_p(\partial T/\partial p)_S}{C_p}$$

Solving this equation for C_p gives the desired expression, involving the Joule-Thomson coefficient and $(\partial T/\partial p)_S$.†

$$C_p = \frac{-v}{\eta - (\partial T/\partial p)_S} \tag{8-30}$$

A useful method of computing the variation of heat capacity with pressure may be obtained by differentiation of Eq. (8-27) with respect to temperature at constant pressure.

$$\left(\frac{\partial H}{\partial p}\right)_T = -\eta C_p \tag{8-27}$$

$$\frac{\partial^2 H}{\partial p\, \partial T} = \frac{\partial}{\partial p}\left(\frac{\partial H}{\partial T}\right)_p = \left(\frac{\partial C_p}{\partial p}\right)_T = -\left[\frac{\partial}{\partial T}(\eta C_p)\right]_p$$

or

$$\left(\frac{\partial C_p}{\partial p}\right)_T = -C_p\left(\frac{\partial \eta}{\partial T}\right)_p - \eta\left(\frac{\partial C_p}{\partial T}\right)_p \tag{8-31}$$

Sage and Lacey[1] have utilized Eq. (8-31) for evaluating specific heats at high pressures from experimental Joule-Thomson coefficients.

The expansion-valve process as encountered in practice approaches constant-enthalpy conditions. For example, the thermodynamic analysis of the vapor-compression refrigeration cycle is based upon the expansion-valve process occurring at constant enthalpy, an assumption which is frequently a good approximation (Chap. 10). The throttling calorimeter, which is frequently used to estimate the quality of steam, approaches a constant-enthalpy device. In it (Fig. 8-8) steam is bled from the main into a small cylinder which is open to the atmosphere. From a knowledge of the temperature of the steam in

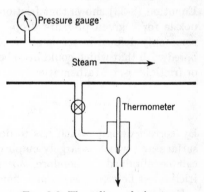

Pressure gauge

Steam ⟶

Thermometer

FIG. 8-8. Throttling calorimeter.

† $(\partial T/\partial p)_S$ is the isentropic temperature-pressure coefficient. It corresponds to the temperature change observed when a gas is expanded adiabatically and reversibly. The integrated relationship between T and p for an ideal gas was developed in Eq. (3-14).

[1] R. A. Budenholzer, B. H. Sage, and W. N. Lacey, *Ind. Eng. Chem.*, **31**, 1288 (1939).

the cylinder and the line pressure, the quality of the steam in the line may be evaluated by following a constant-enthalpy path from the final state back to the line pressure.

Example 8-3. A throttling calorimeter attached to a steam line reads 226°F. The line pressure is 15 psig. What is the steam quality?

Solution. In the exhaust chamber of the calorimeter the pressure is atmospheric. At 14.7 psia and 226°F the enthalpy, from the Mollier diagram for steam, is approximately

$$H = 1157 \text{ Btu/lb}_m$$

Since $\Delta H = 0$ for the process, at $H = 1157$ Btu/lb$_m$ and 29.7 psia the moisture content is 0.8 per cent and the quality 99.2 per cent.

8-6. Nozzles. A nozzle is a device for converting some of the energy of a flowing fluid into kinetic energy by changing the cross-sectional flow area. In practice, nozzles are used whenever a high-velocity stream is desired, as in turbines, jet engines, rocket motors, and ejectors, and in some cases as an instrument for measuring the rate of flow.

Flow in nozzles is nearly adiabatic. Hence, Eqs. (2-10) and (8-5) reduce to the forms

$$-dH = \frac{u \, du}{g_c} \tag{8-32}$$

$$-v \, dp = \frac{u \, du}{g_c} + dF \tag{8-33}$$

Equation (8-33) shows that friction reduces the velocity obtainable in a nozzle for a given pressure drop. Hence, the efficiency of a nozzle is commonly defined in terms of the actual increase in kinetic energy compared with that which could have been realized had the process been ideal or frictionless. Mathematically,

$$\text{Eff} = \frac{(u_2^2 - u_1^2)_{\text{actual}}}{(u_2^2 - u_1^2)_{\text{ideal}}} = \frac{\Delta H_{\text{actual}}}{\Delta H_{\text{ideal}}} \tag{8-34}$$

By correct design, which has to do mainly with the taper of the inside surface and which is largely empirical, efficiencies of 90 per cent or more can be obtained. Therefore, nozzle design based upon adiabatic and frictionless flow (*i.e.*, isentropic flow) is common practice.

For isentropic flow, Eqs. (8-32), (8-33), the continuity equation, and the properties of the fluid are sufficient to determine the nozzle. The design problem can take two broad forms: (1) determining the area of a new nozzle to suit specified conditions of flow rate, pressure, and velocity and (2) predicting the velocities, pressures, and flow rate for a given nozzle. Example 8-4 illustrates the design of a new nozzle for steam, using the steam tables for the required properties. Alternatively, it is frequently satisfactory to assume ideal-gas behavior for the fluid. Under these conditions Eq. (8-33) may be integrated to give the following equation for the velocity u_2 at any section of the nozzle:

$$u_2^2 = u_1^2 + \frac{2g_c\gamma p_1 v_1}{\gamma - 1}\left[1 - \left(\frac{p_2}{p_1}\right)^{(\gamma-1)/\gamma}\right] \qquad (8\text{-}35)$$

This result is obtained with the aid of the relation

$$pv^\gamma = \text{a const} = p_1 v_1^\gamma$$

where the subscript 1 refers to conditions at the nozzle inlet. In passing it may be noted that this equation is the same as that for evaluating the downstream velocity in an orifice for ideal-gas flow involving large changes in pressure (except for the omission of the coefficient of discharge C, which takes into account the friction).

For incompressible fluids, such as liquids at ordinary conditions, the nozzle area continues to decrease and the velocity to increase as the pressure decreases; *i.e.*, the nozzle is convergent. On the other hand, for compressible fluids, such as gases, the area first decreases and then increases, so that the nozzle consists of a converging section followed by a divergent one (Fig. 8-9). The reason for this is that at high pressures a given pressure drop causes a relatively small fractional increase in specific volume, while this increase becomes very large at low pressures. According to the continuity equation (8-1), this large specific volume must be compen-

FIG. 8-9. Converging-diverging nozzle.

sated for by an increase in area, even though the velocity is still increasing. In other words, the velocity increase is of the same order of magnitude per unit pressure drop throughout the whole range of pressures, while the increase in specific volume is very much larger at low pressures than high ones. To allow for this, the area of the nozzle must first decrease and then increase, as the velocity continually increases.

The velocity in the throat of the converging-diverging nozzle, the point of minimum area, is equal to the speed of sound in the fluid. This may be shown by writing the continuity equation in the form

$$vw = uA$$

If this is differentiated (w is constant) and rearranged, there is obtained

$$\frac{uA}{v}\,dv = u\,dA + A\,du \qquad (8\text{-}36)$$

At the throat of the nozzle the area is not changing. Therefore, $dA = 0$ at that point, and Eq. (8-36) may be written

$$\frac{uA}{v}\,dv = A\,du$$

or

$$du = u \frac{dv}{v}$$

Substituting this expression for du in Eq. (8-33), applied to frictionless adiabatic flow, gives

$$u_{th}^2 = u_s^2 = -g_c v^2 \left(\frac{\partial p}{\partial v}\right)_s \qquad (8\text{-}19)$$

which is the equation for the velocity of sound, as presented in Sec. 8-3.

It is also evident from this development that the maximum velocity obtainable in a converging nozzle is the velocity of sound. Suppose a given converging nozzle is supplied with a compressible fluid at a pressure p_1, and suppose the pressure p_2 in the chamber into which the nozzle discharges is variable. If this discharge pressure is p_1, the flow will be zero. As p_2 is decreased below p_1 the flow rate and the velocity increase. Finally a pressure ratio p_2/p_1 is reached such that the velocity in the throat is sonic. Further reduction in p_2 will have no effect on the conditions in the nozzle. The flow rate will remain constant, and the velocity in the throat will be that given by Eq. (8-19), regardless of the value of p_2/p_1.[†]

The value of the pressure ratio p_2/p_1 such that sonic velocity is obtained in the throat can be evaluated directly from Eqs. (8-35) and (8-19) if ideal-gas behavior is assumed. For an ideal gas Eq. (8-19) becomes

$$u_2^2 = u_s^2 = \gamma g_c p_2 v_2 \qquad \gamma = \frac{C_p}{C_v} \qquad (8\text{-}37)$$

Substituting this value of the throat velocity in Eq. (8-35) and solving for the pressure ratio gives[1]

$$\frac{p_2}{p_1} = \left(\frac{2}{\gamma + 1}\right)^{\gamma/(\gamma-1)} \qquad (8\text{-}38)$$

For steam the ratio is about 0.55 at moderate temperatures and pressures.

In summary, in a well-designed converging-diverging nozzle the velocity increases from a low entrance value to the velocity of sound at the throat. In the diverging section the velocity becomes supersonic while the pressure continues to decrease. This behavior is, of course, based upon the premise that the pressure at the discharge of the nozzle is low enough that the critical pressure ratio can be reached at the throat. If

[†] Such a sonic nozzle provides a means of obtaining a constant flow rate into a region of varying pressure. The only restriction is that the variations in p_2 are such that the critical value of p_2/p_1 is not exceeded.

[1] This derivation also depends upon the assumption that u_1^2 is negligible with respect to u_2^2. This is satisfactory because A_1 is much larger than the throat area A_2.

insufficient pressure drop is available in the nozzle for the pressure at the throat to reach the critical value and the velocity to become u_s, the nozzle will act like a venturi meter. That is, after the throat is reached the pressure will rise and the velocity decrease, according to conventional behavior for subsonic flow.

The converging-diverging nozzle offers a means of obtaining velocities greater than the velocity of sound (Mach numbers greater than unity). It is for this reason that they are used in jet-propulsion and ejector equipment. The relationships between velocity, area, and pressure in the nozzle are illustrated numerically in Example 8-4. Analytical relationships can also be derived (see Prob. 8 at the end of the chapter).

Example 8-4. A high-velocity nozzle is to be designed which will use steam at 100 psia and 580°F. At the nozzle inlet the velocity is to be 100 ft/sec. Calculate the values of the ratio A/A_1 (A_1 is the cross-sectional area of the nozzle at the inlet) for the sections where the pressure is 80, 70, 60, 50, 40, 30, and 20 psia. Assume that the nozzle operates adiabatically and without friction.

Solution. From the steam tables the initial enthalpy, entropy, and specific volume are

$$H_1 = 1319.2 \text{ Btu/lb}_m$$
$$S_1 = 1.7486 \text{ Btu/(lb}_m)(°R)$$
$$v_1 = 6.09 \text{ ft}^3/\text{lb}_m$$

From the equation of continuity (8-1),

$$\frac{A}{A_1} = \frac{u_1}{v_1}\frac{v}{u} = \left(\frac{100}{6.09}\right)\frac{v}{u} \tag{A}$$

In integrated form the energy equation (8-32) is

$$u^2 = u_1^2 - 2g_c(H - H_1)$$
$$u^2 = 10{,}000 - 50{,}700(H - 1319.2)† \tag{B}$$

Since the process is to be considered adiabatic and frictionless, it is isentropic. At 80 psia pressure

$$S = 1.7486 \text{ Btu/(lb}_m)(°R)$$
$$H = 1294.3 \text{ Btu/lb}_m$$
$$v = 7.22 \text{ ft}^3/\text{lb}_m$$

From Eqs. (B) and (A),

$$u = 1125 \text{ ft/sec}$$
$$\frac{A}{A_1} = \left(\frac{100}{6.09}\right)\left(\frac{7.22}{1125}\right) = 0.105$$

If the area ratios for the other pressures are evaluated in the same way, the results summarized in Table 8-1 are obtained. The pressure at the nozzle throat is about 55 psia; to obtain lower pressures the data show that the nozzle diverges and the velocity increases.

† The term $50{,}700(H - 1319.2)$ includes the conversion factor from Btu per pound *mass* to foot-pounds *force* per pound *mass*, that is, $50{,}700 = 2g_c(778) = (64.4)(778)$.

If the process were not reversible, the following equation could be used:

$$\frac{u^2 - u_1^2}{2g_c} = -K(\Delta H)_S \tag{C}$$

where the constant K allows for nonisentropic conditions (friction). The method of solution using (C) would be exactly the same, although the velocities obtained would be less than those of the ideal nozzle, since K is always less than unity.

TABLE 8-1

Pressure, psia	Specific volume, ft³/lb$_m$	u, ft/sec	$\dfrac{A}{A_1}$
100	6.09	100	1.0
80	7.22	1125	0.105
70	8.02	1400	0.094
60	9.16	1660	0.091
50	10.4	1910	0.089
40	12.3	2170	0.093
30	15.3	2450	0.103
20	20.8	2760	0.124

Example 8-5. Consider again the nozzle of Example 8-4, assuming that steam behaves as an ideal gas. Calculate:

(a) The critical pressure ratio and the velocity at the throat

(b) The discharge pressure if a Mach number of 2.0 is required at the nozzle exhaust

Solution. (a) The ratio of the specific heats for steam is about 1.3. Substituting in Eq. (8-38)

$$\frac{p_2}{p_1} = \left(\frac{2}{1.3 + 1}\right)^{1.3/(1.3-1)} = 0.55$$

The velocity at the throat, which is equal to that of sound, can be found from either Eq. (8-35) or (8-37). The former expression does not require a knowledge of the specific volume at the throat and, hence, is easier to use when entrance conditions only are known.

$$u_2^2 = u_{th}^2 = (100)^2 + \frac{2(32.2)(1.3)(100 \times 144)(6.09)}{1.3 - 1}[1 - (0.55)^{(1.3-1)/1.3}]$$

$$u_{th}^2 = (100)^2 + 3.18 \therefore 10^6$$

$$u_{th} = 1790 \text{ ft/sec}$$

These results compare favorably with the values obtained in Example 8-4 (Table 8-1) because steam closely approximates an ideal gas at these conditions.

(b) For a Mach number of 2.0 (based upon conditions at the nozzle throat) the discharge velocity will be 3580 ft/sec. If this value is utilized in Eq. (8-35), the pressure ratio can be computed.

$$(3580)^2 = (100)^2 + \frac{(2)(32.2)(1.3)(100 \times 144)(6.09)}{1.3 - 1}\left[1 - \left(\frac{p_2}{p_1}\right)^{(1.3-1)/1.3}\right]$$

$$\left(\frac{p_2}{p_1}\right)^{(1.3-1)/1.3} = 0.48$$

$$p_2 = (0.042)(100) = 4.2 \text{ psia}$$

8-7. Compressors. The movement of compressible fluids through the use of compressors, fans, blowers, ejectors, and vacuum pumps is an integral part of the unit operation of fluid flow.[1] Such equipment is used industrially in a number of ways: (1) to provide the proper pressure environment for chemical reactions, (2) to transport gases, and (3) to transfer mechanical energy to a fluid for the purpose of operating instruments, solids transport, agitation, etc.

Fans, blowers, and centrifugal and axial-flow compressors operate on the principle of transferring kinetic energy to the fluid from a rotating shaft equipped with blades, or impellers. In compressors this kinetic energy is converted partially into fluid pressure (pV energy) as is done in the diffusing section of a subsonic nozzle. Reciprocating compressors and vacuum pumps, by contrast, compress a fixed volume of gas enclosed momentarily in a cylinder.

Centrifugal and axial-flow compressors can efficiently handle large volumes of fluid in a minimum of space. Hence, these units are generally more economical than reciprocating compressors for large installations, at low or moderate discharge pressures (up to 4000 psia). Typical applications include gas compressors in butadiene, ethylene, and nitric acid plants and in catalytic cracking and re-forming operations in the petroleum industry. For small compressors (less than 500 ft^3/min at the discharge pressure) and for high pressures, the reciprocating type is still more economical. The design of centrifugal and axial-flow equipment requires the study of fluid flow against moving and stationary solid surfaces; hence more fluid mechanics than thermodynamics is involved.[2] However, thermodynamic analysis of reciprocating compressors does yield useful information, at least for ideal (reversible) operation. The important features of such analysis are considered briefly in the remainder of this section. The operation of ejectors is described in Sec. 8-8.

In a reciprocating compressor the gas is admitted through an intake valve into a cylinder equipped with a piston. The cylinder may be single-acting, open at one end, and capable of only one compression stroke per cycle, or it may be closed at both ends and means provided to supply gas at both ends. With the latter arrangement two compression strokes are obtained per cycle (double acting). During one cycle the following processes occur: (a) Low-pressure gas is admitted to the cylinder as the piston travels through its stroke (represented ideally in Fig. 8-10 as line 1-2). (b) The piston reverses its travel and compresses the gas to the

---

[1] For a summary of the operating characteristics and applications of equipment for moving fluids, reference may be made to a series of articles under the general title Handling Compressible Fluids, *Chem. Eng.*, June, 1956, pp. 178–238.

[2] For example, see R. L. Daugherty and A. C. Ingersoll, "Fluid Mechanics," 5th ed., McGraw-Hill Book Company, Inc., New York, 1954.

exhaust pressure (2-3). In practice the compression step is more nearly
adiabatic than isothermal. (c) The
high-pressure gas is exhausted (3-4)
by opening the exhaust valve and
maintaining the inlet valve closed.
At the end of the exhaust process,
the clearance volume (V_4) of the
cylinder still contains gas. (d) As
the piston retraces its path, the
pressure drops until the intake
value is reached, at which point
the intake valve opens and the cycle
is repeated. The valves are normally operated by the pressure
differences between the exhaust and
inlet lines and the gas within the
cylinder.

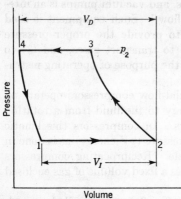

FIG. 8-10. Single-stage compressor cycle
with clearance.

Reciprocating compressors, besides being either single- or double-
acting, may be single- or multistage. In the single-stage type the entire
compression occurs in one step, while in multistage compression two or
more cylinders are involved and the
total pressure increase is obtained in
a series of steps, with cooling of the
gas between each in order to reduce
the total work requirement. In the
following paragraphs equations are
presented for calculating the minimum
(reversible) work of compression for
single- and multistage units.

Single-stage Compressors. In the
hypothetical case of negligible clearance, the compression cycle will be
as shown in Fig. 8-11. The total
work of the cycle is the sum of the

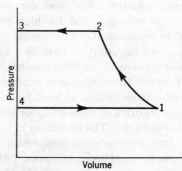

FIG. 8-11. Single-stage compressor
cycle with no clearance.

individual work terms for each of the three steps and is given by the
following equations:

$$W_s = p_1v_1 + \int_{v_1}^{v_2} p\,dv - p_2v_2 \qquad (8-39)$$

$$W_s = -\int_{p_1}^{p_2} v\,dp \qquad (8-40)$$

where W_s is the work per mole or unit mass of fluid. Also the work is
equivalent to the area 1-2-3-4 in Fig. 8-11. It may be noted that this is
the expression for flow work obtained from the extended Bernoulli equa-

tion [Eq. (8-5)] when changes in potential energy and kinetic energy and the friction can be neglected.

The evaluation of Eq. (8-40) depends upon the path followed during the compression process.   If it is *isothermal* and the ideal-gas law applies, integration yields

$$W_s = -RT \ln \frac{p_2}{p_1} \qquad (8\text{-}41)$$

If the pressures are high enough so that the gas is not ideal, but follows the law of corresponding states, Eq. (8-40) can be integrated graphically by evaluating v at a series of points between the initial and final values and plotting v vs. p.   This graphic integration can be carried out once and for all through use of Fig. 4-4.   Then the results may be plotted as a function of reduced temperature and reduced pressure as in Fig. 12-2. This figure introduces the term *fugacity*,[1] which will be given the symbol f.   The ratio of the fugacities in the final and initial states f_2/f_1 can be defined for an isothermal process in terms of the same integral, $\int_{p_1}^{p_2} v \, dp$, that is equal to the work [Eq. (8-40)].   The exact defining expression is

$$\ln \frac{f_2}{f_1} = \frac{1}{RT} \int_{p_1}^{p_2} v \, dp = \frac{-W_s}{RT} \qquad (8\text{-}42)$$

Hence the work may be determined by evaluating f_2 and f_1 from Fig. 12-2 without graphical integration.   If the gas does not follow the law of corresponding states but p-v-T data in the form of graphs or tables are available, the integrations can be carried out by plotting the specific volume vs. pressure for a series of pressures between the limits p_1 and p_2 and integrating graphically.   However, if complete thermodynamic data are available, it is simpler to use the following equation:

$$W_s = T \,\Delta S - \Delta H \qquad (8\text{-}43)$$

which follows from the first-law flow equation $Q - W_s = \Delta H$ [Eq. (2-10)] and the second law $Q = T \,\Delta S$.

Equations (8-41) to (8-43) are for the minimum isothermal work of compression, *i.e.*, for reversible operation.   For example, in the development of Eq. (8-43) it was possible to make the substitution $Q = T \,\Delta S$ only because it was postulated that the process was reversible.   Actual work requirements are larger than the minimum values in accordance with the degree of irreversibility.

In case the compression is *adiabatic* and the gas follows ideal behavior, Eq. (8-40) can be integrated using the relationship

$$pv^\gamma = \text{a const}$$

---

[1] The fugacity is another thermodynamic property like temperature and pressure. Its meaning and usefulness will be considered in detail in Chap. 12.

provided that $\gamma = C_p/C_v$ and this quantity is assumed to be constant over the pressure range from p_1 to p_2. The result in terms of the work per unit mass of gas compressed is

$$W_s = - \frac{\gamma p_1 v_1}{\gamma - 1} \left[\left(\frac{p_2}{p_1} \right)^{(\gamma-1)/\gamma} - 1 \right] \qquad (8\text{-}44)$$

where v_1 is the specific volume of the gas at compressor-inlet conditions.

If the gas does not follow ideal behavior but obeys the principle of corresponding states, the work can be evaluated by using Figs. 7-7 and 7-8. These charts show the effect of pressure on the enthalpy and entropy of gases. Since the total change in entropy must be zero (adiabatic and reversible compression) and since ΔS is a state function,

$$\Delta S = 0 = \Delta S_{\text{const } p} + \Delta S_{\text{const } T} \qquad (8\text{-}45)$$

where the terms represent the changes in S per mole for a two-step process (one at constant temperature, followed by another at constant pressure) for accomplishing the same change in state as occurs in the compressor. The first term is given by the equation

$$\Delta S_{\text{const } p} = \int_{T_1}^{T_2} \frac{C_p \, dT}{T} \qquad (8\text{-}46)$$

The second, $\Delta S_{\text{const } T}$, is obtainable from Fig. 7-8 and the expression for the change in entropy of an ideal gas with pressure. If C_p vs. temperature data are available at the compressor inlet pressure, $\Delta S_{\text{const } p}$ can be evaluated from (8-46) for any assumed compressor discharge temperature T_2. This assumption may be checked by obtaining $\Delta S_{\text{const } T}$ from Fig. 7-8 and applying Eq. (8-45). By this trial-and-error procedure the final temperature is evaluated. Then ΔH and the work can be computed by again dividing the actual change in state into two processes and computing ΔH for each.

$$\Delta H = \Delta H_{\text{const } p} + \Delta H_{\text{const } T} \qquad (8\text{-}47)$$

The separate contributions may be obtained from the equation

$$\Delta H_{\text{const } p} = \int_{T_1}^{T_2} C_p \, dT$$

and from Fig. 7-7. This total change in enthalpy is equal to the required work, since Eq. (2-10) applied to an adiabatic process reduces to

$$-W_s = \Delta H = H_2 - H_1 \qquad (8\text{-}48)$$

If a complete thermodynamic chart is available, the solution of the adiabatic compressor problem is very simple, since the final enthalpy H_2 in Eq. (8-48) can be evaluated directly at the final pressure along a constant-entropy line from the initial state.

If the expansion is neither isothermal nor adiabatic, the path of the process frequently can be represented adequately by the polytropic equation

$$pv^\delta = \text{const} \qquad (8\text{-}49)$$

where δ is determined by experiment and assumed to be constant throughout the process. Equation (8-49) may be used in exactly the same way as the adiabatic relationship between the pressure and the volume to integrate (8-40). It should be noted that γ is equal to the ratio of the heat capacity at constant pressure to that at constant volume, while δ has no theoretical significance.

The Effect of Clearance. The compressor cycle with clearance is shown in Fig. 8-10. The volume V_4 of gas remaining in the cylinder at the end of the exhaust process is termed the clearance volume. The displacement V_D is the volume corresponding to the complete stroke of the piston; V_I, the intake volume, is the volume of gas taken into the cylinder per cycle. The effect of clearance is to decrease the capacity of a compressor. By adding up the work terms for each step in the cycle an expression can be developed for the work per cycle. If the ideal-gas law is followed and the expansion is adiabatic, the equation obtained will be exactly the same as (8-44) provided that the actual volume of the gas taken into the cylinder, V_I, is used in the equation in place of v_1 (the specific volume at inlet conditions). It is apparent that the only effect of clearance under these circumstances is to decrease the capacity of the compressor.

In the event that the gas does not follow ideal behavior, development of equations for the work, including the effect of clearance, becomes more complicated. However, the same general procedure of evaluating the area included on the p-v plot, either by graphic integration or through the use of generalized tables of thermodynamic properties, is applicable. Illustrations of these methods are given in the problems at the end of the chapter.

A term often used in connection with the discussion of compressors is the *volumetric efficiency.* This is defined as the ratio of the intake volume V_I to the displacement volume V_D. The clearance C is normally defined as the ratio of the clearance volume V_4 to the displacement volume V_D. With these definitions, the volume of the intake gas can be evaluated from the pressure ratio, the clearance, and the displacement volume by the following equation (provided that the expansion is adiabatic and reversible):

$$V_I = V_D \left[1 + C - C \left(\frac{p_2}{p_1} \right)^{1/\gamma} \right] \qquad (8\text{-}50)$$

This expression is the result of setting $V_I = V_D - (V_1 - V_4)$ and utilizing the definition of C to replace V_4 in terms of V_D. The displacement volume corresponds to the total volume traversed by the piston in one direction (the volume corresponding to the stroke).

Multistage Compression. For several reasons the ratio of the discharge pressure to the suction pressure for a single-stage compressor is limited.

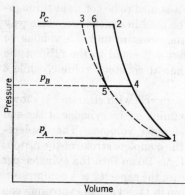

FIG. 8-12. Comparison of single- and two-stage compressor operation.

One reason is related to the efficiency of operation. Figure 8-12 illustrates the compression process for adiabatic (1-2) and isothermal (1-3) paths. The isothermal process requires less work by an amount equivalent to the area 1-2-3. Actually the compression step is more nearly adiabatic than isothermal, since it is impossible to transfer a large quantity of heat through the cylinder walls in the short time accompanying the stroke of the piston. Nevertheless, the benefits of isothermal operation can be partly achieved by dividing the process into two steps, that is, by limiting the discharge pressure from the first compressor cylinder to p_B, cooling the gas to the original temperature t_1 in an intercooler (a process occurring at essentially constant pressure, path 4-5), and finally completing the compression to p_C in a second cylinder. In this two-stage system a reduction of work equal to the area 2-4-5-6 has been accomplished. A further decrease in the work requirement would be obtained by increasing the number of stages to three or more. However, the maximum reduction in work is limited to the area 1-2-3; hence a point is soon reached at which the decrease in power costs is balanced by the increased first cost of the equipment. The number of stages employed in practice depends primarily upon the over-all pressure differential and the capacity. In large machines the pressure ratio per stage is seldom more than 5 or 6 and may be less. In small compressors, where power costs are of less importance, this ratio may be considerably higher.

Very-high-pressure machines operating with discharge pressures of the order of 10,000 psia are usually built with five or more stages. As the pressure is increased, the specific volume of the gas decreases and the cylinder size necessary for a given capacity decreases. This is an important reason why high compression ratios are not justified with single-stage machines; large cylinders would be required to handle the low-pressure intake gas, and the entire cylinder would have to be of expensive construction to withstand the high pressure existing at the end of the stroke.

The efficiencies of reciprocating compressors generally are between 70 and 90 per cent.   This means that the actual work required is 11 to 43 per cent greater than computed on the basis of reversible adiabatic operation.

Example 8-6.   Methane is to be compressed from 40°F, 20 psia to 80 psia in a single-stage unit.   If the compressor operates adiabatically, estimate the minimum power requirement to handle 100 ft³/min (at 60°F and 1 atm pressure) by the following methods:

(a) Assuming ideal-gas behavior

(b) Using the thermodynamic properties of methane

Solution.   (a) If methane is assumed to behave as an ideal gas under these conditions, Eq. (8-44) is applicable.   From Chap. 3, γ at 60°F and 1 atm pressure is 1.31. The variation in γ for an adiabatic compression to 80 psia will be small (γ increases with the pressure and decreases with temperature), and a constant value may be used without introducing an error greater than that involved in assuming ideal-gas behavior.

$$W_s = -\frac{1.31RT}{1.31 - 1}\left[\left(\frac{80}{20}\right)^{0.237} - 1\right]$$

$$= -\frac{(1.31)(1.98)(500)(0.389)}{0.31} = -1630 \text{ Btu/lb mole of gas}$$

$$\text{Power} = -(1630)\frac{(100)(492)(778)}{(359)(530)} = -326,000 \text{ ft-lb}_f/\text{min}$$

The work *required* would have the opposite sign, and hence the power requirement would be 326,000 ft-lb$_f$/min, or 9.9 hp.

(b) The minimum work would correspond to an isentropic process.   Reading the values of the enthalpy from Fig. 7-5 for methane at 40°F and 20 psia and at 80 psia, both at the same entropy, and using Eq. (8-48),

$$W_s = -\Delta H = -(H_2 - H_1) = -(488 - 389) = -99 \text{ Btu/lb}_m$$

The power requirement for 100 ft³/min would be

$$\text{Power} = \frac{(99)(16)(100)(492)(778)}{(359)(530)} = 319,000 \text{ ft-lb}_f/\text{min, or 9.7 hp}$$

In this case the assumption of ideal-gas behavior (and use of a constant value of γ) did not introduce a significant error in the results.   This would not necessarily be true at higher pressures.

Example 8-7.   Show that in multistage compressor operation the total work requirement is a minimum when the work in each stage is the same, provided that the gas is cooled to the initial temperature between each stage.

Solution.   If the assumption of ideal-gas behavior is justified, a simple analytical proof based upon Eq. (8-44) is possible.   For a two-stage unit with an interstage pressure p and volume v, the total work is

$$-W_s = \frac{\gamma RT_1\dagger}{\gamma - 1}\left[\left(\frac{p}{p_1}\right)^{(\gamma-1)/\gamma} - 1\right] + \frac{\gamma RT_1\dagger}{\gamma - 1}\left[\left(\frac{p_2}{p}\right)^{(\gamma-1)/\gamma} - 1\right]$$

or

$$-W_s = \frac{\gamma RT_1}{\gamma - 1}\left[\left(\frac{p}{p_1}\right)^{(\gamma-1)/\gamma} + \left(\frac{p_2}{p}\right)^{(\gamma-1)/\gamma} - 2\right]$$

† The term p_1v_1 in Eq. (8-44) may be replaced by RT_1 provided that the work per mole is desired and the gas is essentially ideal at inlet conditions.

Differentiating with respect to p and equating the result to zero (to satisfy the limitation for minimum total work) leads to the expression

$$p^{2(\gamma-1)/\gamma} = (p_2 p_1)^{(\gamma-1)/\gamma}$$

or

$$p^2 = p_2 p_1$$

The fact that the intermediate pressure is the geometric mean of the initial and final values means that the pressure ratio in each stage is the same and equal to $(p_2/p_1)^{1/2}$. Hence the work per stage will be the same, provided that the gases are cooled to the initial temperature T_1 in the intercooler.

That the conclusion reached in Example 8-7 must also be true for any number of stages can be seen by reference to Fig. 8-12. The minimum work of compression would be obtained if the operation were isothermal (line 1-5-3 in Fig. 8-12). The use of a number of stages with intercoolers tends to approach this condition. The figure shows that the farther the nonisothermal path (1-4-2) is followed, the greater the deviation from the isothermal line and, therefore, the greater the work (area in the figure) above the minimum isothermal value. Also, a given increase in pressure from point 4 on the adiabatic curve requires a much greater work input above the isothermal requirement than the same increase in pressure from point 1 on the adiabatic curve. In other words, for minimum work it is necessary to approach the isothermal path as closely as possible. The degree of divergence, measured as an increase in volume ΔV over the value at the same pressure on the isothermal path, depends upon the pressure ratio. Thus

$$V_B = V_A \left(\frac{p_A}{p_B}\right) \qquad \text{isothermal}$$

and

$$V_B' = V_A \left(\frac{p_A}{p_B}\right)^{1/\gamma} \qquad \text{adiabatic}$$

Hence

$$\Delta V = V_B' - V_B = V_A \left[\left(\frac{p_A}{p_B}\right)^{1/\gamma} - \frac{p_A}{p_B}\right]$$

Therefore the pressure ratio p_B/p_A in each stage must be as small as possible. This in turn requires that they all be equal.

The problem of optimum intermediate pressures for compressing non-ideal gases has been considered by York.[1] For most cases the assumption of equal pressure ratios in all stages is a close approximation to the minimum-total-work criterion.

Example 8-8. Pure propane gas is to be compressed from 1 atm pressure and 140°F to 42 atm pressure in a reciprocating compressor. Estimate the adiabatic

[1] R. York, Jr., *Ind. Eng. Chem.*, **34**, 535 (1942).

reversible work required per pound mole of propane handled. The molal heat capacity of propane at low pressure is given by the equation

$$C_p = 5.42 + 0.023T \qquad (T \text{ in } °R)$$

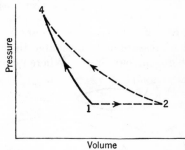

Solution. Since propane is not an ideal gas under these conditions, the method based upon Eqs. (8-45) to (8-48) should be used (in the absence of thermodynamic properties).

The first step is to assume a final temperature and calculate the change in entropy for the constant-pressure and constant-temperature processes chosen to replace the actual adiabatic compression. The processes are shown in the sketch: 1-4, the actual compression, is along a constant-entropy line. The same final state is attained by proceeding at constant pressure to 2 and then at constant temperature to 4.

If the final temperature is assumed to be 865°R,

$$\Delta S_{12} = \int C_p \frac{dT}{T} = \int_{600}^{865} \left(\frac{5.42}{T} + 0.023 \right) dT = 8.1 \text{ Btu/(lb mole)(°R)}$$

$\Delta S_{\text{const } T} = \Delta S_{24}$ can be evaluated from Fig. 7-8a and the isothermal change in entropy of an ideal gas. The latter value, according to Eq. (7-21), is

$$S_4' - S_1' = -R \ln {}^{42}\!/_1 = -7.3$$

From Fig. 7-8a at $T_r = {}^{865}\!/_{666} = 1.30$ and $p_r = {}^{42}\!/_{42} = 1.0$,

$$(S' - S)_4 = 0.8$$

Then, substituting in Eq. (7-37),

$$\Delta S_{24} = -(S' - S)_4 + (S_4' - S_2') + (S' - S)_2 = -0.8 - 7.3 + 0† = -8.1$$

Summing the two entropy changes,

$$\Delta S_{14} = \Delta S_{12} + \Delta S_{24} = 8.1 - 8.1 = 0$$

Since the total change in entropy is zero, 865°R is the correct final temperature.

The work required can now be determined from Eqs. (8-47) and (8-48):

$$\Delta H_{12} = \int C_p \, dT = \int_{600}^{865} (5.42 + 0.023T) \, dT = 5930 \text{ Btu/lb mole}$$

ΔH_{24} can be evaluated by first converting propane to the ideal-gas state at 1 atm, then compressing the ideal gas to 42 atm ($\Delta H = 0$), and finally converting to the actual state at 42 atm. The sum of the enthalpy changes for each step gives ΔH_{24}, according to Eq. (7-36),

$$\Delta H_{24} = -(H' - H)_4 + (H_4' - H_2') + (H' - H)_2 = H_4 - H_2$$

The first and third terms can be obtained from Fig. 7-7a. The result is

$$\Delta H_{24} = -(1.4)T_c + 0 + (0)(T_c) = -(1.4)(666) = -930 \text{ Btu/lb mole}$$

† In this calculation the small difference between the entropies of propane in the actual and ideal-gas states at 1 atm pressure has been neglected; that is, $S_2' - S_2 = 0$.

The work of compression is the sum of these enthalpy changes, or

$$\Delta H_{14} = 5930 - 930 = 5000 \text{ Btu/lb mole}$$

8-8. Ejectors. Ejectors are used to compress vapors to a small positive pressure or to discharge them from a vacuum chamber into atmospheric surroundings. Where mixing of the vapors with the driving fluid is allowable, ejectors are usually lower in first cost and maintenance costs than other types of compressors. The equipment (Fig. 8-13) consists of a converging-diverging nozzle, through which the driving fluid (commonly steam) is fed, and which is inside a second, larger nozzle, through which both the vapors and driving fluid pass. The thermodynamics of the inside nozzle have already been considered. The momentum of the high-velocity fluid leaving the driving nozzle is partly utilized to increase the velocity of the vapors to be compressed, and the mixture passes into the throat of the large nozzle at a velocity less than that of the driving fluid leaving the small nozzle. In the diverging section, the mixture is compressed to the discharge pressure at the expense of the kinetic energy of the stream by increasing the cross-sectional area. The velocity of the mixture in the converging section of the large nozzle must be above the velocity of sound, for otherwise the pressure would decrease going into the throat of the nozzle, defeating the purpose of the sonic ejector. The flow equations for nozzles apply. Although the actual mixing process itself is complicated when handled analytically, the maximum theoretical performance can be determined by assuming that momentum is conserved. Comparison of the actual performance with the ideal will give an efficiency value for the apparatus.

FIG. 8-13. Single-stage ejector.

8-9. Temperature Measurements at High Velocities. If an object is placed in a flowing stream, the velocity at the surface will approach zero because of friction. The slowing down of the stream results in a transfer of kinetic energy of the fluid to internal energy of the object. If the object is a thermometer or thermocouple, it will read a temperature higher than that of the flowing stream.

The quantitative relationships are given by applying the energy equation. For example, if Eq. (2-10) is applied to two nearby sections, one in the free stream and the other in the stream next to the surface of the object, there results

$$\frac{u^2}{2g_c} + H = \frac{u_0^2}{2g_c} + H_0 \qquad (8\text{-}51)$$

where the subscript 0 represents the section at the surface. If the flow is completely stopped at the surface, $u_0 = 0$ and Eq. (8-51) becomes

$$H_0 - H = \frac{u^2}{2g_c}$$

Since the pressure is constant, this expression may be written, with little error, in the form

$$C_p(T_0 - T) = \frac{u^2}{2g_c}$$

or

$$T_0 = T + \frac{u^2}{2g_c C_p} \tag{8-52}$$

The temperature T_0, defined by Eq. (8-52), is termed the stagnation or total temperature. For low velocities T_0 is essentially the same as the free-stream, or true, temperature T. However, at Mach numbers approaching unity the stagnation temperature will be significantly higher than T.

Measurement of temperatures in high-speed flow is complicated by this phenomenon. If a thermocouple is placed in the stream, part of its surface will be oriented so that it completely absorbs the kinetic energy of the fluid. At this point the temperature will be close to the stagnation value. At other parts of the surface, particularly those parallel to the direction of flow, all the kinetic energy will not be transferred to the surface and the temperature will be less than T_0. The thermocouple will indicate an average value which may be designated T_{obs}. The *recovery factor* ϵ has been used to relate the three temperatures T_0, T, and T_{obs}. It is defined as

$$\epsilon = \frac{T_{obs} - T}{T_0 - T} \tag{8-53}$$

If Eqs. (8-52) and (8-53) are combined to eliminate T_0, there is obtained

$$T = T_{obs} - \frac{\epsilon u^2}{2g_c C_p} \tag{8-54}$$

Equation (8-54) may be used to calculate the free-stream temperature provided the recovery factor may be estimated. The value of ϵ depends upon the construction of the thermocouple probe and the heat-transfer conditions. It is between 0.9 and 1.0 in most instances.[1]

PROBLEMS

1. Water at 70°F is pumped at the rate of 100 gal/min to the top of a storage tank open to the atmosphere. The discharge line emptying into the tank is 50 ft

[1] Temperature measurements in high-speed flow are considered in detail by E. R. G. Eckert, *J. Aero. Sci.*, **22**, 585 (1955).

above the pump, and the equivalent length of straight pipe from the pump to the tank is 150 ft. Calculate the required pressure on the discharge side of the pump, if the pipe is 2 in. ID and the pump suction (inlet pressure) is 5 psig. If the efficiency of the pump and electric motor drive is 70 per cent, calculate the horsepower of the motor.

2. A steam main has a 1-in.-ID insulated condensate drain line which extends a horizontal length of 50 ft and is open to the atmosphere. The steam enters the line at 15 psig and 20°F superheat. A valve at the end of the drain line is opened. What is the rate of flow of steam into the atmosphere when equilibrium is reached? The pressure drop through the valve is such that the pressure just upstream from the valve is 2 psig.

3. A throttling calorimeter is attached to a line containing steam at 15 psig with a quality of 98 per cent. What does the thermometer in the calorimeter read?

4. Air flows through a 1-in.-ID insulated steel pipe at the rate of 1700 lb_m/hr. At one point in the line the pressure is 50 psia, and the temperature 180°F. How far downstream from this point will the velocity reach a maximum value (the velocity of sound)? What will be the pressure at this point?

5. A reversible converging nozzle uses 1 lb_m/sec of steam entering at 100 psia and 500°F. Calculate the minimum pressure and area at the nozzle throat. Assume that the entrance velocity is negligible.

6. A reversible converging nozzle employs steam at a pressure p_1 in pounds per square inch absolute. Make a plot showing approximately the relation between the following variables:

(a) The velocity at the throat vs. the ratio of the variable pressure p_2 in the discharge chamber and p_1, that is, p_2/p_1

(b) The rate of flow in pounds mass per hour vs. the ratio p_2/p_1

7. Plot approximately to scale the ratio p/p_1 of the pressure at any section of a converging-diverging nozzle (reversible) to the initial pressure as abscissa with the following quantities as ordinates:

(a) The cross-section-area ratio A/A_1, where A is the area at the point where the pressure is p

(b) The velocity

(c) The mass rate of flow

Show by drawing dotted lines the curves which would be expected for an actual (irreversible) nozzle.

8. Derive a relationship between the velocity, area, and Mach number (M) for reversible flow in an adiabatic converging-diverging nozzle. Show that for Mach numbers less than unity the nozzle area will decrease as the velocity increases, while for Mach numbers greater than unity the area must increase as the velocity increases. In solving this problem, it is convenient to proceed as was done in deriving Eq. (8-19) for the nozzle throat, but this time use the complete continuity equation.

$$Ans. \quad \frac{du}{u} = \frac{1}{M^2 - 1} \frac{dA}{A}.$$

9. Carbon dioxide is flowing through a well-insulated, partly closed valve. The pressure and temperature on the upstream side of the valve are 100 psia and 100°F, while the downstream pressure is 20 psia. Evaluate the friction per pound of carbon dioxide.

10. An ideal gas with an initial pressure and temperature p_1, T_1 flows through a nozzle at such a rate that its pressure at the throat is p_2. Assuming that the nozzle operates adiabatically and without friction, derive an expression for the velocity at the throat in terms of the two pressures, the initial temperature, and other pertinent quantities.

NOTE: The ratio γ of the specific heats of the gas may be assumed to have a constant value.

11. A large steam main is carrying steam at 440°F. One end of an insulated 1-in.-ID steel pipe is connected to the main, and the other end is open to the atmosphere. The small pipe is 100 ft long, and the measured flow rate through the pipe is 2000 lb_m/hr. Calculate the pressure in the steam main, and discuss the changes which will occur in the system if an additional 100-ft length of 1-in. pipe is coupled to the open end of the present pipe.

12. A converging-diverging nozzle with throat and outlet areas A_t and A_0, respectively, is specifically designed to operate with inlet steam at T_1 and p_1 and to discharge to pressure p_2. Under these conditions, the pressure at the throat is p_t, about midway between p_1 and p_2.

Steam at p_1 and T_1 is admitted to the inlet, with the pressure in the discharge space initially at p_1. The discharge pressure is first gradually diminished to p_2, then further reduced to a pressure well below p_2. Draw curves showing the relation between pressure in the nozzle vs. distance from the nozzle inlet, for the following discharge pressures:

(a) Discharge pressure is 10 per cent below p_1.

(b) Discharge pressure is equal to p_t.

(c) Discharge pressure is 10 per cent above p_2.

(d) Discharge pressure is equal to p_2.

(e) Discharge pressure is well below p_2.

13. Compute the horsepower and cylinder volume ($V_D + V_4$ in Fig. 8-10) required to compress, adiabatically and reversibly, 400 ft³/min of air initially at 14.7 psia and 70°F to 100 psia. The clearance C is 0.03. The compressor is single-stage and double-acting and operates at 100 rpm.

14. What will be the minimum power requirement of a four-stage compressor handling 10 lb/min of nitrogen and operating with suction and discharge pressures of 20 and 1000 psia? Intercoolers between each stage cool the gas to its suction temperature of 70°F. The compression is not adiabatic or reversible but may be represented by the expression pV^δ = a const, with $\delta = 1.3$ in each stage.

15. Ammonia gas is to be compressed from 70°F and 14.7 psia to 80 psia in an adiabatic single-stage compressor.

(a) Calculate the work required per pound of ammonia if the compressor operates reversibly. The thermodynamic properties of ammonia are shown in Fig. 10-7.

(b) Compute the work necessary if the operation is irreversible and the actual enthalpy change is 1.15 times that for isentropic operation between the two pressures.

NOTE: In part (b) the discharge point is beyond the range of Fig. 10-7. Estimate the desired thermodynamic quantities at the discharge point by assuming that the specific heat at 100 psia and above 300°F is constant and equal to 0.60 Btu/(lb)(°F).

16. A compressor is to be designed for taking 500 ft³/min of ammonia at 40°F and 14.7 psia and discharging it at 175 psia. The operation is to be two-stage, with intercooling to 80°F. Compute the total power requirement when the intermediate pressure is chosen to give the minimum work requirement. Each stage operates reversibly and adiabatically. Also determine the heat absorbed from the gas in the intercooler (in Btu per hour).

17. A single-stage compressor for propane gas has a suction pressure of 45 psig and a discharge pressure of 400 psig. The temperature of the propane entering the compressor is 70°F. The capacity is 4000 ft³/hr measured at suction conditions. What is the minimum horsepower required if the compressor operates reversibly and adiabatically?

18. A single-stage compressor is designed to compress air at standard atmospheric pressure to a pressure of 80 psig. The clearance is 8 per cent. For the same discharge pressure, calculate the percentage change in capacity (on a weight basis) for the compressor and in the horsepower needed to drive it, if the unit is moved to an elevation where the air pressure is only 0.5 atm.

19. What is the maximum possible vacuum in inches of mercury that can be produced by a single-stage piston-type vacuum pump operating adiabatically and discharging at normal atmospheric pressure if the pump has a clearance of 5 per cent? Assume that air is being pumped.

20. Methane is to be compressed in a two-stage compressor from 20 psia and 80°F to 500 psia. The compressor operates adiabatically with complete intercooling and aftercooling and has an efficiency of 80 per cent (ratio of the minimum work to the actual work). Calculate the work per pound mole by each of the following methods:

    (a) Assuming methane to be an ideal gas with a constant specific-heat ratio equal to 1.31

    (b) Using generalized properties (Figs. 7-7 and 7-8)

    (c) Using Fig. 7-5

Tabulate for each method: T and p at the end of each stage, the work per stage, and the heat removed in the intercooler and aftercooler.

CHAPTER 9

PRODUCTION OF WORK FROM HEAT

Prior to the development of nuclear power plants, all the significant contributions to the mechanical energy used by man had the sun as their source. However, economical methods have not been developed as yet for directly converting solar radiation into work on a large scale. The amount of energy striking the earth from the sun is staggering when considered as a whole, but per unit surface the quantity is small. This introduces the serious difficulty of concentrating the heat gathered from a large surface and using it as an intensive source for conversion to work. Some progress has been made on the related problem of utilizing solar energy directly as heat; for example, solar radiation is being used to heat homes, to produce high temperatures for metallurgical operations (solar furnaces), and to concentrate aqueous solutions by evaporation.

The kinetic energy due to the mass movement of air has been used to some extent for the production of work, especially in rural areas (windmills). Variations and uncertainties in the wind velocity and the necessity for large-sized equipment to produce significant quantities of work are problems retarding progress in this field.

Conceivably, the available potential energy of tides could be concentrated and utilized. Attempts in this direction on a large scale have been made in several parts of the world where tides are extreme. However, the total power production in this manner is never likely to be significant in comparison with world demands for energy.

By far the most important sources of power are the potential energy of waterfalls, the chemical (molecular) energy of fuels, and nuclear energy. The utilization of water power simply involves the transformation of mechanical energy from one form to another; hence, a 100 per cent efficiency is theoretically possible. On the other hand, all present-day methods for the large-scale utilization of molecular and nuclear energy are based upon the evolution of the energy as heat and subsequent conversion of part of the heat into useful work. Accordingly, the efficiency of all such processes is destined to be low (values greater than 30 per cent are uncommon) despite improvements in the design of equipment. This is, of course, a direct consequence of the second law. If some means

275

could be devised to use the energy in fuels without going through the intermediate step of conversion to heat, this restriction on the efficiency could be eliminated. The usual device for directly utilizing chemical energy is the electrolytic cell in which the conversion is to electrical energy. Actually, some progress has been made in Germany in developing cells which will operate on carbonaceous fuels such as coal. In this country, a "fuel cell" has been produced in the laboratory in which hydrogen and oxygen are converted into water, and electrical energy is released directly.[1] The efficiency of the cell ranges from 65 to 80 per cent, more than twice the value obtained by the conventional process of first converting the chemical energy into heat.

The molecular energy of fuels is normally released by a combustion process. The function of the work-producing devices is then to convert part of this heat into mechanical energy. In the nuclear power plant the fission or fusion process releases the energy of the nucleus as heat, and then this heat is partially converted into work. Thus, the thermodynamic analysis of heat engines, as presented in this chapter, applies equally well to conventional (coal or oil fired) and nuclear power plants.

In one form of heat engine, the working fluid is completely enclosed and goes through a cyclical process, accomplished by vaporization and condensation. Heat is transferred to the fluid from another part of the apparatus across a physical boundary. A coal-fired power plant using steam is an example. Here, the combustion gases are separated from the steam by the boiler-tube walls. The internal-combustion engine is another form of heat engine, characterized by the direct evolution of heat within the work-producing device. Examples of this type are the Otto engine and combustion gas turbine.

THE STEAM POWER PLANT

9-1. Condensable-fluid Cycles. In the discussion of the second law, it was determined that the maximum efficiency of converting heat into work is obtained when the cycle of operation is a reversible one in which heat is absorbed at a constant high temperature and discarded at a constant low temperature. The efficiency increases as the temperature of the heat source increases. Hence, the fluid in the heat engine should absorb energy at the highest practical temperature for most efficient operation. For this to take place at constant temperature, the fluid that is being heated must undergo a phase change. At elevated temperatures this means, practically, that the fluid will evaporate from a liquid to a vapor phase and in so doing absorb the latent heat of evaporation. For a fuel-burning power plant, the most desirable fluid would be one

[1] *Chem. Eng. News*, Sept. 23, 1957, p. 25.

which can be vaporized at temperatures approximating those in the fuel bed and at pressures sufficiently low for mechanical equipment to be built without serious difficulty.   Mercury, having a low vapor pressure, approaches these characteristics.   However, its latent heat is low (requiring a high circulation rate per horsepower-hour of work developed), and its vapors are poisonous.   Steam has a much higher latent heat and is nontoxic, but the temperature and pressure at which water may be vaporized are limited by the structural strength of the boiler material. With modern alloys, this limit has been raised to about 2000 to 3000 psia, corresponding to evaporation temperatures of about 600 to 700°F (the steam leaving the boiler is usually superheated and hence is at a higher temperature, up to 1000 to 1500°F).   Although steam is used in general as the working medium in heat engines, mercury has been employed on some occasions in two-cycle systems, where the heat for evaporating the steam is supplied by condensation of mercury.   In this way increased efficiency can be realized by absorbing the heat from the fuel in the mercury boiler at a relatively high temperature.

The Carnot cycle has been found to be most efficient of all heat-engine cycles as long as it operates at the maximum temperature at which heat can be absorbed and the minimum temperature at which it may be rejected.   However, there are very serious mechanical problems involved in constructing a machine that would operate on the Carnot cycle. Single-phase mediums are not practical, first, because of the difficulty in building a satisfactory machine in which an adiabatic expansion follows an isothermal expansion.   Second, expansion processes in a cylinder are accompanied by substantial frictional effects, while the maximum work per cycle is relatively small.   Under these conditions, the net work effect of the cycle is very small and, indeed, may vanish if the friction is great.

These difficulties are eliminated by employing the evaporation and condensation of a fluid for the isothermal processes in the heat-engine cycle.   Even so, the ideal Carnot cycle cannot be achieved, primarily because of frictional effects and the properties of the medium.   These points will be brought out more clearly in the following discussion of a simple steam cycle.   The elements of equipment, schematically shown in Fig. 9-1, consist of a boiler, a work-producing device such as the steam turbine, a condenser, and a pump.   In the absence of preheaters, the liquid water enters the boiler below its boiling point and is heated in the liquid phase before vaporization occurs.   To utilize further the high-temperature source of heat in the fuel bed and to limit condensation in the work-producing device, the steam leaving the boiler is generally superheated several hundred degrees above the saturation temperature. The variation in pressure in the whole boiler process is small in comparison with other processes in the cycle and therefore can be approximated by following a constant-pressure path from the initial to the final temperature. On the T-S diagram in Fig. 9-1 this is indicated by the path 1-2-3-4.

The high-temperature steam from the boiler goes to a turbine or steam engine, where part of its energy is converted to work. If this process is to be reversible and adiabatic, it will correspond to the constant-entropy line 4-5. Actually the process can be made nearly adiabatic but not

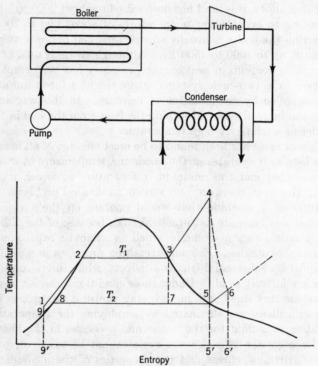

FIG. 9-1. Simple power-plant cycle.

frictionless, so that the entropy must increase (according to the second law). If the expansion proceeds to the same pressure, the actual irreversible path will be somewhat as indicated by the dashed line 4-6. The low-pressure steam from the turbine or steam engine is then condensed essentially at constant pressure by transferring heat to a cooling medium, which is normally water. This process is represented by the path 6-5-8-9 on the T-S diagram. The condensation step does not end upon the saturation curve (point 8), since it is desirable to be certain that the steam is always completely condensed. This necessitates normal operation in

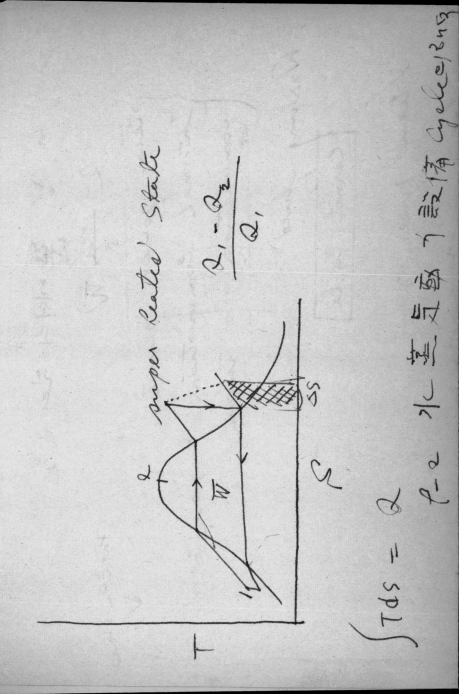

super heated State

$$\frac{Q_1 - Q_2}{Q_1}$$

$$\int T\,dS = Q$$

Boiler

$$\Delta H + \frac{\Delta u^2}{2 g_c} + \Delta z \frac{g}{g_c} = Q - W_s$$

$$\Delta H = Q$$

In enthalpy ∴

$\underline{\underline{Q}} = \underline{\underline{w}}$

100 ft

30.5 m

5 ft/sec   100 ft/sec

$$\boxed{\Delta H = -W_s}$$

pump

$$\boxed{\Delta H = -W_s}$$

$$-W_s = \int v \, dp + \boxed{F}$$

the subcooled-liquid region. The final step of the cycle is the pumping process, returning the liquid water from the condenser to the boiler. If the process were reversible and adiabatic, it would be represented by a vertical line (9-1). As will be seen later, the extent of this line on the T-S diagram is so small that its characteristics are relatively unimportant.

The cycle 1-2-3-7-8-9 (Rankine cycle) is of theoretical interest since it more closely approaches the ideal Carnot cycle between temperatures T_1 and T_2 than the actual cycle 1-2-3-4-6-8-9 just described. Practically, it is not feasible since excessive condensation would be involved during the work-producing process. This is undesirable in turbines because of erosion problems and is dangerous and inefficient in steam-engine operation.

An interesting consideration is the irreversibilities in each of the four processes. In the first, the chief deviation from reversibility occurs because the heat absorption is not at the temperature of the burning fuel. The diagram indicates that in the initial stage the temperature of the liquid water is increasing to its boiling point, and in the final stage of the process the temperature is increasing as a result of superheating. Since the temperature difference between the fuel and the water is a measure of the irreversibility, the heating of the liquid water prior to vaporization is the furthest removed from reversible conditions. This concept partly explains the desirability of superheating the steam in the boiler and of employing boiler-water preheaters.

In the expansion process the maximum work is obtained if the path is reversible; any irreversibilities represent an increase in entropy and decrease in work-producing capacity. The extent of this irreversibility can be reduced by exercising care in the design and maintenance of the equipment used.

In the condenser the process would be truly reversible only if the temperature difference between the condensing steam and the cooling water were negligible. Actually, for the heat to be transferred in a reasonable length of time, and therefore in equipment of a reasonable size, a finite temperature difference must be employed. This means that the temperature of the condensing steam must always be a few degrees above the temperature of the cooling water. The irreversibility resulting from the temperature difference between the condensing steam and the cooling water in this step is much less important than that resulting from the temperature difference between the fuel bed and the steam in the boiler.

In the last process, pumping the water up to the boiler pressure, the work involved is small compared with the other heat and work effects in the cycle. Therefore, irreversibilities are not of major significance. In pumping liquids under actual conditions, the increase in pressure would be accompanied by an increase in entropy; instead of a vertical line as is shown in Fig. 9-1, the line would slope upward to the right.

9-2. Analysis of the Steam-power-plant Cycle. Each process of the cycle 1-2-3-4-6-8-9 can be analyzed by using the flow equations of the previous chapter and the thermodynamic properties of steam. This analysis well illustrates how thermodynamics may be used to calculate work and heat effects in terms of changes in the properties of the system.

The Heat Absorbed in the Boiler. The primary purpose of the steam boiler is to transfer heat to the water; energy effects accompanying changes in elevation and velocity are small. Also, there is no mechanical-energy exchange with the surroundings so that the work term disappears. The total-energy-balance equation then reduces to the following form:

$$Q = \Delta H \tag{9-1}$$

In other words, the heat absorbed by the water is equal to its increase in enthalpy. From the state of the steam entering and leaving the boiler, this change in enthalpy can be obtained directly from the steam tables.

That the kinetic- and potential-energy effects are negligible in comparison with the heat may be seen by considering a numerical example. Suppose the liquid-water velocity entering the boiler is 5 ft/sec and the steam velocity leaving is 200 ft/sec. The kinetic-energy term $\Delta u^2/2g_c$ would be approximately 0.8 Btu/lb$_m$ of steam. Similarly, a change in elevation of as much as 100 ft would amount to only about 0.1 Btu/lb$_m$. Both these quantities are negligible in comparison with the heat absorbed in the boiler, which would be of the order of 1000 Btu/lb$_m$ of steam.

The Work-producing Step. By applying the total-energy balance to the turbine process and assuming adiabatic operation, the following result is obtained:

$$W_s = -\Delta H \tag{9-2}$$

This again neglects changes in kinetic energy and potential energy. Even in a turbine, which depends upon the conversion of kinetic energy into mechanical energy of a rotating shaft, the over-all changes in kinetic energy are relatively small; *i.e.*, the differences in velocity of the steam in the inlet line to the turbine and in the exhaust line from the turbine are such that the kinetic-energy effect is small in comparison with the work. Equation (9-2) indicates that the work obtained is entirely at the expense of the change in enthalpy of the expanding steam. It may be evaluated per pound of steam directly from the initial and final states, by using the steam tables. The work is equal to the change in enthalpy (except for sign) even though the process is not reversible. The only requirement is that the path be adiabatic. However, if the steam in a turbine expands in an irreversible manner, the change in enthalpy, and therefore the work, is less than if the process had been reversible to the same final pressure.

The Condenser. In the condenser the heat transferred from the condensing steam to the cooling water is equal to the change in enthalpy of the steam and may be evaluated from enthalpy values corresponding to conditions at the inlet and discharge of the condenser.

The heat transferred in the condenser as well as other heat and work effects can be conveniently represented on the temperature-entropy diagram. Referring to Fig. 9-1, the heat rejected to the condenser can be designated by the area 9'-5'-5-8-9, provided that the expansion process is reversible, *i.e.*, provided that it follows path 4-5. Likewise, the heat absorbed in the boiler can be indicated by the area 9'-5'-4-3-2-1-9'. By a total-energy balance, the work produced must be equal to the differences between the two areas, or 1-9-8-5-4-3-2-1. In the case of irreversible operation in the expansion process, as indicated along the dashed line 4-6, the heat rejected to the condenser is increased by an amount equal to the area 5'-6'-6-5. Since the heat absorbed in the boiler is the same as in the reversible case, there is a loss in work equivalent to the same area 5'-6'-6-5. It will be noted that this loss is also equal to the following expression:

$$W_{\text{lost}} = \int_6^5 T \, dS \qquad (9\text{-}3)$$

in which T is the variable temperature at which the heat is transferred in process 6-5. This is in agreement with the general principle (Chap. 6) developed in connection with the discussion of the second law, that the loss in work accompanying an irreversible process is equal to the total change in entropy accompanying that process times the lowest temperature at which heat can be discarded. In this instance this temperature was not constant but varied throughout the process.

The Pumping Process. If the pump returning the liquid water to the boiler operates adiabatically, the total-energy balance becomes

$$-W_s = \Delta H \qquad (9\text{-}4)$$

From a mechanical-energy balance the work of the pump can be expressed in the following manner:

$$-W_s = \int v \, dp + F \qquad (9\text{-}5)$$

Since the specific volumes of liquids are small, the pump work will be small even for relatively large changes in pressure. In general this work can be neglected in making an over-all analysis of the cycle. If necessary, W_s can be estimated for a reversible process by considering the specific volume to be constant and multiplying it by the change in pressure. For a pressure change of 1000 psia, W_s amounts to about 3 Btu/lb$_m$.

Example 9-1. The steam-power installation in a chemical plant must supply the following requirements:

(1) 10,000 lb/hr of process steam at 75 psia and 350°F

(2) 2000 lb/hr of process steam at 20 psia

(3) 1500 hp

The steam boiler will operate at 175 psia.   The power requirement is to be obtained from two turbines, one taking superheated steam from the boiler and discarding steam at 75 psia and 350°F.   Part of this will be returned to the boiler, where it will be superheated to 490°F, and then will enter the second turbine.   Two thousand pounds per hour of the exhaust steam (at 20 psia) will be bled off for requirement (2) and the remainder sent to the condenser.

Assume both turbines operate reversibly and adiabatically and that all parts of the power plant operate at constant pressure, except the two turbines and the feedwater pump.   Also assume that the make-up water for the boiler is added to the condensate from the condenser at the same temperature as the condensate.

(a) Draw a schematic flow diagram of the operations.

(b) Sketch the cycle on the T-S plane.

(c) Calculate the required water rate to the boiler.

(d) Calculate the heat that must be supplied by the boiler.

Solution

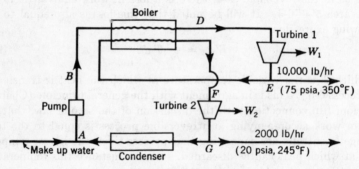

Schematic flow diagram

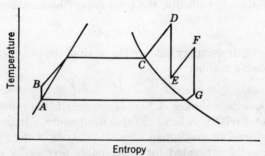

Entropy

Temperature-entropy diagram

FIG. 9-2. Diagrams for power plant of Example 9-1.

WATER RATE TO THE BOILER.   The steam leaving the first turbine is at 350°F and 75 psia.   Hence, from the steam tables,

$$H_E = 1205.3 \text{ Btu/lb}_m \qquad S_E = 1.6556 \text{ Btu/(lb}_m)(°R)$$

The entropy at D must be the same as at E, and the pressure is 175 psia.   Hence

$$H_D = 1285.5 \text{ Btu/lb}_m$$

The state at F, the entrance to the second turbine, is known.   Also the process FG is at constant entropy.   In this way the enthalpy at G can be evaluated.   The results are as follows:

$H_A =$ 196.2 Btu/lb$_m$ (assuming the water leaving the condenser is saturated)
$H_D =$ 1285.5 Btu/lb$_m$
$H_E =$ 1205.3 Btu/lb$_m$
$H_F =$ 1276.6 Btu/lb$_m$
$H_G =$ 1159.5 Btu/lb$_m$

Suppose the water rate through the boiler is m lb/hr.   The total work produced by both turbines is

$$W_s = -m(H_E - H_D) - (m - 10,000)(H_G - H_F)$$
$$W_s = (1500)\left(\frac{33,000}{778}\right)(60) = 3,820,000 \text{ Btu/hr}$$
$$3,820,000 = -m(1205.3 - 1285.5) - (m - 10,000)(1159.5 - 1276.6)$$
$$m = 25,300 \text{ lb}_m/\text{hr}$$

HEAT SUPPLIED BY THE BOILER (excluding the superheater section E-F)

$$Q = (H_D - H_A)(25,300) = (1285.5 - 196.2)(25,300) = 27,500,000 \text{ Btu/hr}$$

INTERNAL-COMBUSTION ENGINES

The steam power plant is characterized by large heat-transfer surfaces (1) for the absorption of heat at a high temperature in the boiler and (2) for the rejection of heat at a relatively low temperature in the condenser. This requirement is necessary because the steam power plant operates with an inert medium to which thermal energy must be transferred from an outside source, the fuel.   The combustion engine, on the other hand, employs the fuel mixture itself as the working medium, with the result that the thermal energy from the combustion process is available within the work-producing machine, for example, a piston-and-cylinder assembly, gas turbine, rocket motor, etc.

Another important distinction between the two types of power plant is that the medium in the steam power plant normally passes through a cycle of processes, returning to its original state after each cycle, while in the combustion engine this is not the case.   The fuel-air mixture is burned and the products of combustion rejected to the surroundings; thermodynamically, the process is not completely cyclical.   However, simple analyses of combustion engines are commonly carried out by representing the actual operation in an approximate way by a cyclical process.

Because of these differences, the internal-combustion engine may (1) be built as a small, compact power plant suitable for nonstationary applications and (2) operate at higher temperatures and therefore higher efficiencies. This second advantage follows from the necessity of heat transfer through a metal wall (the boiler tubes) in the steam power plant. The inability to develop materials to withstand unlimited temperatures and pressures thus places a restriction upon the temperature of heat absorption. In the combustion engine the high-temperature heat is available within the work-producing machine, eliminating the necessity for heat transfer at high temperatures through a retaining wall.

The thermodynamic analysis of the processes occurring in the actual internal-combustion engine is complicated by the fact that the burning step takes place in the engine. In the present treatment the actual cycles will be considered from a qualitative point of view and then a quantitative analysis made of an ideal cycle approximating the actual one. In the ideal cycle the working fluid will be an ideal gas (for example, air) and the actual combustion step represented by adding to the ideal gas an equivalent amount of heat.

9-3. The Otto Engine.   The ordinary Otto engine cycle used in automobiles is typical. It consists of an intake stroke at essentially constant pressure during which period the fuel-air mixture flows into the cylinder. This is represented by the line 0-1 in Fig. 9-3. During the second stroke all valves are closed, and the fuel-air mixture is compressed approximately adiabatically along the path 1-2. The mixture is then ignited, and the combustion process is so rapid with respect to the rate of piston movement

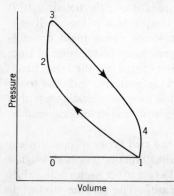

FIG. 9-3. Otto internal-combustion-engine cycle.

that the volume remains nearly constant, 2-3. Then follows the work-producing stroke, in which the high-temperature–high-pressure products of combustion expand along the path 3-4. When the exhaust valve is opened at the end of the expansion stroke, the pressure is rapidly reduced to a value just above the exhaust pressure. This is approximately a constant-volume process and is shown in Fig. 9-3 as line 4-1. Finally, during the exhaust stroke the piston pushes out the combustion gases remaining in the cylinder (except for the contents of the clearance volume) at about constant pressure. There are four strokes in each cycle of engine operation. Note that Fig. 9-3 is a plot of the pressure vs. the volume between the piston and cylinder head rather than the specific volume of the gases.

The effect of increasing the compression ratio, defined as the ratio of

the volumes at the beginning and end of the compression stroke, is to
increase the efficiency of the engine, *i.e.*, to increase the work produced per unit quantity of fuel. This may be seen by considering an approximate ideal cycle, called the air-standard cycle (Fig. 9-4). This consists of two adiabatic and two constant-volume processes, achieved by a heat engine employing air as a working medium. In the step DA (Fig. 9-4) heat is absorbed at constant volume in an amount sufficient to raise the temperature and pressure of the air to the values resulting from the combustion process in the actual internal-combustion engine.

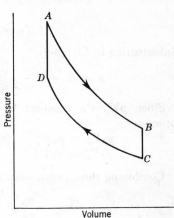

FIG. 9-4. Air-standard Otto cycle.

Then the air is expanded adiabatically and reversibly (AB), cooled at constant volume (BC), and finally compressed adiabatically and reversibly to the initial state, D.

The efficiency (the net work produced divided by the heat absorbed) of the air-standard cycle shown in Fig. 9-4 is, by a total-energy balance, equal to the following expression:

$$\frac{W}{Q_{DA}} = \frac{Q_{DA} + Q_{BC}}{Q_{DA}} \qquad (9\text{-}6)$$

If the heat capacity at constant volume is constant,

$$Q_{DA} = C_v(T_A - T_D) \qquad \text{(for 1 mole of air)} \qquad (9\text{-}7)$$
$$Q_{BC} = C_v(T_C - T_B) \qquad (9\text{-}8)$$

Substituting these values in Eq. (9-6),

$$\eta = \text{eff} = \frac{W}{Q_{DA}} = \frac{C_v(T_A - T_D) - C_v(T_B - T_C)}{C_v(T_A - T_D)}$$

$$\eta = 1 - \frac{T_B - T_C}{T_A - T_D} \qquad (9\text{-}9)$$

In this ideal cycle, air is an ideal gas so that $pV^\gamma = $ a constant for the two adiabatic reversible processes. The efficiency may then be simply related to the compression ratio $r = V_C/V_D$. Each temperature in (9-9) may be replaced by its value in terms of p and V.

$$T_B = \frac{p_B V_B}{R} = \frac{p_B V_C}{R}$$

$$T_C = \frac{p_C V_C}{R}$$

$$T_A = \frac{p_A V_A}{R} = \frac{p_A V_D}{R}$$

$$T_D = \frac{p_D V_D}{R}$$

Substituting in Eq. (9-9),

$$\eta = \text{eff} = 1 - \frac{V_C}{V_D}\frac{p_B - p_C}{p_A - p_D} = 1 - r\frac{p_B - p_C}{p_A - p_D} \quad (9\text{-}10)$$

Since pV^γ = a constant is applicable for the adiabatic reversible processes,

$$p_A V_D^\gamma = p_B V_C^\gamma \quad (\text{since } V_D = V_A \text{ and } V_C = V_B)$$
$$p_C V_C^\gamma = p_D V_D^\gamma$$

Combining these expressions to eliminate the volume,

$$\frac{p_B}{p_C} = \frac{p_A}{p_D} \quad (9\text{-}11)$$

Also,

$$\frac{p_C}{p_D} = \left(\frac{V_D}{V_C}\right)^\gamma = \left(\frac{1}{r}\right)^\gamma \quad (9\text{-}12)$$

Substituting (9-11) and (9-12) in (9-10) gives the desired expression for the efficiency in terms of the compression ratio.

$$\eta = 1 - r\frac{(p_B/p_C - 1)p_C}{(p_A/p_D - 1)p_D} = 1 - r\frac{p_C}{p_D}$$

$$\eta = 1 - r\left(\frac{1}{r}\right)^\gamma = 1 - \left(\frac{1}{r}\right)^{\gamma-1} \quad (9\text{-}13)$$

The equation shows that the efficiency increases rapidly with the compression ratio r at low values of r but more slowly at high compression ratios. This agrees with the results obtained in actual tests on internal-combustion engines.[1]

The treatment of the Otto engine given here, and that of other engines considered in subsequent sections, has been simplified and condensed since the chemical engineer seldom faces complex problems in this field. For detailed treatments of the subjects, more specific texts referred to in each section should be consulted.[2]

9-4. The Diesel Engine. The diesel engine differs from the Otto engine primarily in that the temperature at the end of the compression process is such that combustion is initiated without external means. This higher temperature is obtained by continuing the compression step

[1] J. H. Keenan, "Thermodynamics," p. 273, John Wiley & Sons, Inc., New York, 1941.

[2] C. F. Taylor and E. S. Taylor, "The Internal Combustion Engine," International Publishers Co., New York, 1938.

to a higher pressure, or higher compression ratio.   The fuel is not injected until the end of the compression process and then is added at such a slow rate in comparison with the rate of piston travel that the combustion process occurs, ideally, at constant pressure.   In general the Otto engine has a higher efficiency than the diesel for a given compression ratio. However preignition difficulties limit the compression ratio in the Otto engine, so that much higher ratios can be used in the diesel engine, and for that reason higher efficiencies obtained.

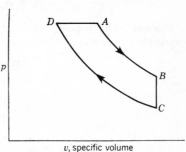

Example 9-2.   Sketch on the p-V plane the cycle for the air-standard diesel engine, and derive a relationship analogous to Eq. (9-13) for the efficiency of the air-standard diesel cycle.   Express the result in terms of a compression ratio r_c (ratio of volumes before and after the compression step) and the expansion ratio r_e (ratio of volumes after and before the expansion stroke).

FIG. 9-5. Air-standard diesel cycle.

Solution.   The air-standard diesel cycle is the same as the air-standard Otto cycle except that the heat-absorption step (corresponding to the combustion process in the actual engine) is at constant pressure as indicated by the line DA in Fig. 9-5.

The heat absorbed in the cycle is (per mole of air)

$$Q_{DA} = C_p(T_A - T_D)$$

provided that the specific heat is constant.

The heat rejected is

$$Q_{BC} = C_v(T_C - T_B)$$

By an energy balance, $W = Q_{DA} + Q_{BC}$ so that the efficiency is given by

$$\eta = \text{eff} = 1 - \frac{C_v}{C_p}\frac{T_B - T_C}{T_A - T_D} = 1 - \frac{1}{\gamma}\frac{T_B - T_C}{T_A - T_D} \tag{A}$$

If the air is assumed to behave as an ideal gas, then for the adiabatic processes AB and CD,

$$T_A(V_A)^{\gamma-1} = T_B(V_B)^{\gamma-1}$$

and

$$T_D(V_D)^{\gamma-1} = T_C(V_C)^{\gamma-1}$$

Since $r_c = V_C/V_D$ and $r_e = V_B/V_A$,

$$T_B = T_A \left(\frac{1}{r_e}\right)^{\gamma-1} \tag{B}$$

$$T_C = T_D \left(\frac{1}{r_c}\right)^{\gamma-1} \tag{C}$$

Substituting (B) and (C) in (A),

$$\eta = 1 - \frac{1}{\gamma}\frac{T_A(1/r_e)^{\gamma-1} - T_D(1/r_c)^{\gamma-1}}{T_A - T_D} \tag{D}$$

Also, from the ideal-gas law,

$$p_D V_D = RT_D$$
$$p_A V_A = RT_A$$

and

$$p_A = p_D$$

Hence,

$$\frac{T_D}{T_A} = \frac{V_D}{V_A} = \frac{V_D/V_C}{V_A/V_B} = \frac{r_e}{r_c}$$

This relationship between T_D and T_A may be used in Eq. (D) to give the desired expression for the efficiency in terms of the two ratios r_c and r_e.

$$\eta = 1 - \frac{1}{\gamma} \frac{(1/r_e)^{\gamma-1} - (r_e/r_c)(1/r_c)^{\gamma-1}}{1 - r_e/r_c}$$

or

$$\eta = 1 - \frac{1}{\gamma} \frac{(1/r_e)^{\gamma} - (1/r_c)^{\gamma}}{1/r_e - 1/r_c} \qquad (9\text{-}14)$$

THE COMBUSTION-GAS TURBINE[1]

Consideration of the Otto and diesel engines has shown that the direct utilization of the energy of high-temperature and high-pressure gases, without external transfer of heat, possesses some advantages in power production.   On the other hand, the turbine is more efficient in utilizing this energy than the reciprocating piston, primarily because of the friction accompanying the continual reversal of direction of the piston and friction in the valve operations.   The combustion-gas turbine is the result of attempts to combine in one unit the advantages o. the reciprocating engine and the steam turbine.

The gas turbine utilizes the high-temperature gases from the combustion space to operate an expansion turbine as indicated in Fig. 9-6.   To obtain high efficiencies the air must be compressed (supercharged) to several atmospheres pressure before combustion, just as it is in the internal-combustion engine.   This was a serious stumbling block in the development because of the low efficiency of centrifugal compressors (centrifugal equipment must be used if the complete unit is to operate from a single shaft as indicated in Fig. 9-6).   Recently, centrifugal compressors with efficiencies of the order of 80 per cent have been developed.   The combustion-gas turbine may then be built in a very compact manner, operating with the compressor on the same shaft as the turbine and using part of the work from the latter to operate the compressor.   The unit shown in Fig. 9-6 is a complete power plant, as is the Otto or diesel engine.   The gas turbine is simply one part of the assembly and performs

[1] A detailed treatment of gas-turbine power plants is given by B. H. Jennings and W. L. Rogers, "Gas Turbine Analysis and Practice," McGraw-Hill Book Company, Inc., New York, 1953.

the same function as the steam turbine in the steam power plant (Fig. 9-2).

9-5. The Efficiency of the Gas-turbine Power Plant. The higher the temperature of the combustion gases entering the turbine, the higher is

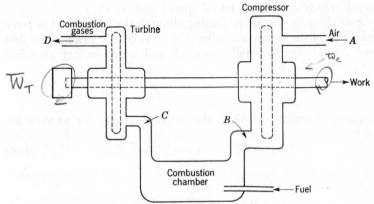

FIG. 9-6. Combustion-gas-turbine power plant.

the efficiency W/Q of the unit. The limiting value is determined by the strength of the metal turbine blades. Since this temperature depends upon the rate of heat transfer from the gases as well as on their temperature, any means of reducing the rate of heat transfer permits operation at higher gas temperatures. In any event operating levels are much lower than the adiabatic or flame temperature (Chap. 5). Therefore it is necessary to use low fuel-to-air ratios to provide sufficient diluent air to reduce the combustion temperature to a safe level.

The ideal cycle (based upon air) of the gas-turbine plant is shown on a pressure-volume plot in Fig. 9-7. The compressor process AB is represented as an adiabatic reversible (isentropic) step in which the pressure is increased from p_A (atmospheric pressure) to p_B. The actual combustion process is replaced by the constant-pressure addition of an amount of heat Q_{BC}. The turbine expansion produces work by an isentropic expansion to the pressure p_D. The hot gases from the turbine are exhausted to the atmosphere so that $p_D = p_A$. The ideal cycle can be completed by cooling of the air at constant pressure from D

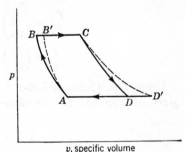

FIG. 9-7. Ideal cycle for gas-turbine power plant.

to A. The efficiency is given by the equation

$$\eta = \frac{W_{\text{net}}}{Q_{BC}} = \frac{W_{CD} + W_{AB}}{Q_{BC}} \tag{9-15}$$

where each energy quantity is based upon 1 mole of air.

The work done by the air in passing through the compressor is given by application of the energy equation [Eq. (2-10)] for a steady-state flow process. Neglecting the small potential- and kinetic-energy contributions, this expression reduces to

$$-W_{AB} = H_B - H_A$$

If the specific heat is constant, the enthalpy change for an ideal gas may be written

$$-W_{AB} = H_B - H_A = C_p(T_B - T_A) \tag{9-16}$$

Applying the energy equation to the combustion and turbine processes in a similar fashion yields

$$-W_{CD} = C_p(T_D - T_C) \tag{9-17}$$

$$Q_{BC} = C_p(T_C - T_B) \tag{9-18}$$

Substituting these expressions in the efficiency expression, and simplifying, leads to the result

$$\eta = 1 - \frac{T_D - T_A}{T_C - T_B} \tag{9-19}$$

Since the processes AB and CD are isentropic, the temperatures and pressures are related as follows [from (Eq. 3-14)]:

$$\frac{T_B}{T_A} = \left(\frac{p_B}{p_A}\right)^{(\gamma-1)/\gamma} \tag{9-20}$$

$$\frac{T_D}{T_C} = \left(\frac{p_D}{p_C}\right)^{(\gamma-1)/\gamma} = \left(\frac{p_A}{p_B}\right)^{(\gamma-1)/\gamma} \tag{9-21}$$

Using Eqs. (9-20) and (9-21) to eliminate T_A and T_D from Eq. (9-19) gives an expression for the efficiency in terms of the pressure ratio p_B/p_A:

$$\eta = 1 - \left(\frac{p_A}{p_B}\right)^{(\gamma-1)/\gamma} \tag{9-22}$$

Example 9-3. A gas-turbine power plant operates reversibly with a compression ratio p_B/p_A of 6. The temperature entering the compressor is 70°F, and the maximum permissible temperature in the turbine is 1400°F.

(a) What would be the efficiency of the power plant if it operates reversibly? Make the calculation for an ideal-gas cycle and assume $\gamma = 1.4$.

(b) In this case, suppose the compressor and turbine operate adiabatically, but irreversibly, with efficiencies of η_c and η_t. These efficiencies are defined in terms of the actual work and that produced by an isentropic machine operating between the same initial state and final pressure. The temperature entering the turbine will be limited to the same value as for part (a).

What will be the efficiency of the power plant if the values of η_c and η_t are 0.83 and 0.86?

$$\eta_c = 0.83 = \frac{\text{work required for isentropic compression}}{\text{work required for actual compression}}$$

$$\eta_t = 0.86 = \frac{\text{work produced by actual turbine}}{\text{work produced by isentropic turbine}}$$

Solution.   (a) Direct substitution in Eq. (9-22) gives the ideal cycle efficiency

$$\eta = 1 - \left(\frac{1}{6}\right)^{(1.4-1)/1.4} = 1 - 0.60 = 0.40, \text{ or 40 per cent}$$

(b) Irreversibilities in the compressor and turbine greatly reduce the over-all efficiency of the power plant since the net work is the *difference* between that required by the compressor and that produced by the turbine. This effect is shown by formulating the equation for the over-all efficiency.

The irreversible paths for the compressor and turbine are indicated in Fig. 9-7 as the dashed lines AB' and CD'. The point C remains the same as for the ideal cycle since the temperature entering the turbine is to be the same maximum value in both instances. The work required by the compressor is

$$-W_{AB'} = C_p(T_{B'} - T_A) \tag{A}$$

Since the isentropic work for the ideal cycle is given by Eq. (9-16), Eq. (A) may also be written

$$-W_{AB'} = C_p \frac{T_B - T_A}{\eta_c} \tag{B}$$

Similarly, the work produced by the turbine is

$$W_{CD'} = -C_p(T_{D'} - T_C) = -C_p\eta_t(T_D - T_C) \tag{C}$$

and the heat absorbed in the combustion is

$$Q_{B'C} = C_p(T_C - T_{B'}) \tag{D}$$

These equations are combined to give the over-all efficiency of the power plant:

$$\eta = \frac{W_{CD'} + W_{AB'}}{Q_{B'C}} = \frac{-\dfrac{T_B - T_A}{\eta_c} + \eta_t(T_C - T_D)}{T_C - T_{B'}}$$

The temperature $T_{B'}$ can be eliminated by using Eqs. (A) and (B). Doing this and simplifying yields

$$\eta = \frac{-(T_B/T_A - 1) + \eta_t\eta_c(T_C/T_A - T_D/T_A)}{\eta_c(T_C/T_A - 1) - (T_B/T_A - 1)} \tag{E}$$

The ratio of the temperatures T_B/T_A is related to the compression ratio by Eq. (9-20). The ratio T_C/T_A depends upon the maximum temperature T_C that the turbine can withstand. The quantity T_D/T_A can be written

$$\frac{T_D}{T_A} = \frac{T_C}{T_A}\frac{T_D}{T_C} = \frac{T_C}{T_A}\left(\frac{p_A}{p_B}\right)^{(\gamma-1)/\gamma} \tag{F}$$

Substituting these values for the temperature ratios in Eq. (E) gives

$$\eta = \frac{\eta_t \eta_c (T_C/T_A)(1 - 1/\alpha) - (\alpha - 1)}{\eta_c(T_C/T_A - 1) - (\alpha - 1)} \tag{9-23}$$

where

$$\alpha = \left(\frac{p_B}{p_A}\right)^{(\gamma-1)/\gamma}$$

It can be shown from Eq. (9-23) that the over-all efficiency of the gas-turbine power plant increases as the temperature entering the turbine increases and also as the component efficiencies η_c and η_t increase.

The numerical values for this particular example are

$$\eta_t = 0.86$$
$$\eta_c = 0.83$$
$$\frac{T_C}{T_A} = \frac{1400 + 460}{70 + 460} = 3.51$$
$$\alpha = (6)^{(1.4-1)/1.4} = 1.67$$

Substituting these quantities in Eq. (9-23),

$$\eta = \frac{(0.86)(0.83)(3.51)(1 - 1/1.67) - (1.67 - 1)}{(0.83)(3.51 - 1) - (1.67 - 1)} = 0.238$$

This analysis shows that even with a rather efficient compressor and turbine the ideal efficiency is drastically reduced, i.e., from 40 to 24 per cent.

JET-PROPULSION CYCLES

9-6. Jet Engines.[1]   In the power cycles considered up to this point the high-temperature high-pressure gas has been expanded in a turbine (steam power plant, gas turbine) or a reciprocating piston-cylinder assembly (Otto and diesel cycles).   In either case, the power has been available in the form of a rotating shaft.   Another device for expanding the hot gases is the jet or nozzle.   Here the power is available in the kinetic energy of the exhaust gases leaving the apparatus.   The entire power plant, consisting of compression device and combustion chamber as well as jet, is known as a jet engine.   Since the kinetic energy of the exhaust gases is directly available for propelling the engine and its attachments, such systems are most commonly used for aircraft propulsion.[2]   There are several types of jet-propulsion engines based upon different ways of accomplishing the compression and expansion processes.   Since the air

[1] M. J. Zucrow, "Jet Propulsion and Gas Turbines," John Wiley & Sons, Inc., New York, 1948.

[2] Note, however, that the ejector described in Sec. 8-8 utilizes the kinetic energy from a nozzle for another purpose, that is, to pump gases from a low pressure to a higher one.   The boiler (from which the steam is produced) and the ejector taken together may be regarded as a jet engine.

striking the engine has kinetic energy (with respect to the engine), its pressure may be increased in a diffuser.

The turbojet engine illustrated in Fig. 9-8 takes advantage of a diffuser to reduce the work of the compressor. The axial-flow compressor completes the job of compression, and then the fuel is introduced and burned

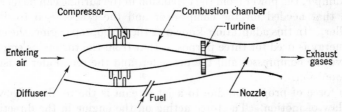

FIG. 9-8. The turbojet power plant.

in the combustion chamber. The hot combustion gases first pass through a turbine where the expansion is just sufficient to provide enough power to drive the compressor. The remainder of the expansion to the exhaust pressure is accomplished in the nozzle. Here, the velocity of the gases with respect to the engine is increased to a level above that of the entering air. This increase in velocity provides a thrust (force) on the engine in the forward direction. If the entire compression and expansion are reversible and adiabatic processes, the turbojet-engine cycle is identical to the ideal gas-turbine–power-plant cycle shown in Fig. 9-7. The only differences are that, physically, the compression and expansion steps are each carried out in two different types of apparatus.

If the compression in the diffuser can be carried to a high enough pressure, an efficient engine can be obtained without using a compressor. Under these conditions, the entire expansion process is accomplished in the exhaust nozzle, and all the energy output is in the kinetic energy of

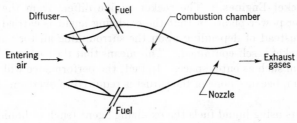

FIG. 9-9. The ram-jet power plant.

the exhaust gases. This type of engine (Fig. 9-9) is known as the *ram jet*. In order to obtain a high pressure at the exit of the diffuser, the entrance velocity (with respect to the engine) must be high. Ram-jet engines do not have an efficiency comparable to that of a turbojet unless the engine is moving in the atmosphere at supersonic velocities. For ideal operation, the cycle is again the same as that of the gas turbine (Fig. 9-7).

There are a number of combinations of compression and expansion devices that lead to modifications of the turbojet and ram-jet engines. For example, the power from the expansion in the turbine can be increased above that needed for the compressor and the excess used to drive a propeller. In this adaptation known as the turboprop engine, the expansion energy is used for three purposes: that from the turbine is employed to drive the compressor and the propeller, and the remainder is used for jet propulsion.

The force of propulsion due to a jet stream is the result of Newton's third law of motion. The force acting on the engine in the direction of motion is thus equal to the opposing force developed by the net increase in rate of momentum of the gases entering and leaving the engine. If the velocities (with respect to the engine) of the entering air and exit gases are u_a and u_g, and the corresponding mass rates of flow are w_a and w_g, the *thrust* in pounds force is

$$F = (w_g u_g - w_a u_a)\frac{1}{g_c} \tag{9-24}$$

Neglecting the mass of fuel with respect to that of the air, this expression may be simplified to the form

$$F = w_a(u_g - u_a)\frac{1}{g_c} \tag{9-25}$$

Part of this force must be used to balance the frictional, external (gravitational), and pressure forces exerted on the engine. The remainder is available for accelerating the engine and its supporting structure.

9-7. Rocket Engines.[1] The rocket engine differs from the turbojet and ram-jet power plants in that the oxidizing agent is carried with the engine. Instead of depending upon the surrounding air for burning the fuel, the rocket is self-contained. This means that the rocket will operate in a vacuum such as outer space. In fact, the performance will be better in a vacuum, because none of the thrust is required to overcome frictional forces.

In rockets using liquid fuels the oxidizing agent (such as liquid oxygen, nitric acid, fluorine) is pumped from tanks into the combustion chamber. Simultaneously, fuel (such as aniline, ethanol, petroleum fractions known as JP fuels, hydrazine) is pumped into the chamber and burned. The combustion takes place at constant pressure and produces high-temperature

[1] G. P. Sutton, "Rocket Propulsion Elements," John Wiley & Sons, Inc., New York, 1956.

exhaust gases. These are then expanded through a nozzle as indicated in Fig. 9-10.

In rockets using solid fuels the fuel and oxidizer are contained together in a solid mixture and stored in the forward end of the combustion chamber.

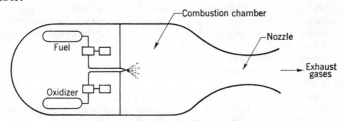

Fɪɢ. 9-10. Liquid rocket engine.

In the ideal rocket, the combustion and expansion steps are the same as those for an ideal jet engine (Fig. 9-7). The solid-fuel rocket requires no compression work, and in the liquid-fuel rocket the compression energy is small since the fuel and oxidizer are pumped as liquids.

Since there is no intake of air in a rocket engine, the thrust is given by setting $u_a = 0$ in Eq. (9-24). The mass of fuel and oxidizer that must be carried in the rocket is a major fraction of the total mass. Hence, an important criterion of a fuel-and-oxidizer system is the thrust divided by the mass flow rate. This quantity, the *specific impulse*, is related to the exhaust velocity by the expression

$$\frac{F}{w_g} = \frac{u_g}{g_c} \tag{9-26}$$

PROBLEMS

1. Steam is flowing through a horizontal, well-insulated 3-in.-ID iron pipe, 1500 ft long. The velocity at the entrance to the pipe, where the steam is dry and saturated at 150 psia, is 100 ft/sec. The steam discharges from the exit of the pipe into an adiabatic reversible turbine which exhausts at 14.7 psia. The steam leaving the turbine is in the dry-saturated condition.

(*a*) Calculate the horsepower produced by the turbine.

(*b*) Represent by a sketch on the *T-S* plane the change in state of the steam as it flows through the pipe and the turbine.

(*c*) What is the state of the steam entering the turbine?

2. A steam power plant operates as follows: Liquid water is pumped into the boiler at 150°F and 500 psia. The steam leaves the superheater coils at 900°F and 500 psia and is expanded in a noncondensing turbine which exhausts at 30 psia. The steam from the turbine is further utilized in an evaporator system, where it is condensed at 30 psia. The condensate is returned to the boiler through the pump, by which time its temperature has dropped to 150°F.

(*a*) Sketch the cycle of operations on the *T-S* diagram, assuming reversible adiabatic operation of the turbine and neglecting all pressure drops except those across the pump and the turbine.

(b) Calculate the ratio of the work produced to the heat absorbed in the boiler, assuming the turbine operation to be reversible and adiabatic.

(c) If the turbine operation were adiabatic but not reversible, indicate the general shape of the turbine process on the T-S diagram. Draw this path dotted for convenient comparison with the reversible path drawn in (a). Assume that the turbine exhaust is at 30 psia for irreversible operation as well as in the reversible case.

(d) Indicate as an area on the T-S diagram the loss in work-producing capacity which results if the turbine operates irreversibly as in (c) rather than reversibly as in (a). The steam from the turbine exhaust goes directly to the evaporator system in both types of operation.

  3. A power-plant cycle is as follows:

  1. Saturated liquid water from the condenser at 5 psig is pumped into a boiler operating at 175 psia.

  2. The steam leaves the boiler superheated 150°F.

(a) Assuming the condenser and boiler pressures are constant, calculate the maximum efficiency of the cycle (i.e., for a reversible adiabatic turbine).

(b) For comparison calculate the efficiency of a Carnot cycle operating between the saturation temperatures at the boiler and condenser pressures. Make the same calculation for the Carnot engine absorbing heat at the temperature of the steam leaving the boiler and discarding heat at the saturation temperature in the condenser.

(c) Calculate the efficiency of the cycle if the turbine operates adiabatically but irreversibly in such a way that the actual ΔH is 0.9 of the isentropic ΔH.

  4. Draw the cycle in Prob. 3a on the p-H plane and on the H-S plane. Compare the results with the Carnot cycle.

  5. Draw the air-standard Otto cycle and diesel cycle on the T-S and the p-H planes.

  6. An air-standard Otto cycle and diesel cycle both have the same compression ratio. Which has the higher efficiency? The diagrams of Prob. 5 may be helpful.

  7. Illustrate the conclusion reached in Prob. 6 by computing the efficiencies of air-standard Otto and diesel cycles operating with a compression ratio of 8, with both absorbing the same amount of heat per cycle.

  8. Calculate the efficiencies of an ideal gas-turbine cycle with pressure ratios of 4, 6, and 8. The ratio of the specific heats of the gas may be assumed constant at 1.39.

  9. The ideal gas-turbine cycle is modified by installing a heat exchanger to transfer energy from the gas leaving the turbine to the gas leaving the compressor. In the optimum countercurrent exchanger, the temperature of the gas leaving the compressor could be raised to T_D (Fig. 9-7) and that leaving the turbine cooled to T_B. Derive an equation for the efficiency of this regenerative ideal cycle in terms of the pressure ratio p_B/p_A and the temperature ratio T_C/T_A.

  Ans. $$\eta = 1 - \left(\frac{p_A}{p_B}\right)^{(\gamma-1)/\gamma} \frac{T_A}{T_C}$$

  10. On a T-S diagram sketch the following gas-turbine cycles:

(a) Ideal cycle corresponding to Fig. 9-6 (solid lines).

(b) Ideal cycle, except for compressor and turbine operating at efficiencies less than unity (Fig. 9-7, dashed lines).

(c) Ideal regenerative cycle (corresponding to the cycle described in Prob. 9).

  11. In Example 9-3 the effect of inefficiencies in the compressor and turbine on the over-all power-plant efficiency was illustrated. For the same pressure ratio and temperatures T_C and T_A, find the minimum efficiency of the compressor that will give a net power output. The efficiency of the turbine will always be 0.03 greater than that of the compressor.

CHAPTER 10

REFRIGERATION

Although refrigeration is applied most extensively in the treating, transportation, and preservation of foods and beverages, it is used on a considerable scale in a variety of chemical industries. Applications to petroleum refining include lubricating-oil purification, catalytic processes, and condensation of volatile hydrocarbons. Refrigeration is prominent in other industries concerned with the separation of volatile material by condensation. These include the production of nitrogen and oxygen from air, manufacture of ice, the dehydration of gases, and liquefaction of gases. The growth of air conditioning in houses and larger buildings has, in itself, created a great demand for refrigeration equipment, particularly small, compact units.

The chemical engineer should be familiar with both the practical aspects of common refrigeration methods and equipment and the fundamentals upon which the science is based. The second objective is the purpose of this chapter. No attempt will be made to discuss the details of equipment and refrigeration design. For a discussion of these subjects reference should be made to specialized books.[1]

The term *refrigeration* implies the maintenance of a temperature below that of the surroundings. Since the temperature must be not only reached but maintained, it is necessary to absorb heat continually at a low level. This necessitates a continuous or flow process. One way of absorbing heat at a low temperature is through the evaporation of a liquid whose properties are such that, at the pressure of evaporation, the boiling temperature is at a low value. For continuous operation, the evaporated fluid must be returned to its original liquid state so that it can again absorb heat at the low level. The complete series of steps through which the fluid passes constitutes the refrigeration cycle. A pure substance need not be employed in the machine. The evaporation of a component from a solution is accompanied by the absorption of heat.

[1] R. C. Jordan and G. B. Priester, "Refrigeration and Air Conditioning," Prentice-Hall, Inc., Englewood Cliffs, N.J., 1948; "The Refrigerating Data Book, Design Volume," 8th ed., American Society of Refrigerating Engineers, 1953; W. R. Woolrich and L. H. Bartlett, "Handbook of Refrigerating Engineering," 3d ed., D. Van Nostrand Company, Inc., Princeton, N.J., 1948.

Absorption refrigeration machines, of which the domestic gas refrigerator is an example, operate on this second principle.

These two methods of producing and maintaining low temperatures are the principal ones that are employed on a commercial scale. Before considering each scheme in detail a discussion of some of the general thermodynamic aspects of the problem of refrigeration may be helpful.

10-1. The Carnot Refrigeration Cycle. In a continuous refrigeration process, in which heat is absorbed at a low temperature, there must be a continuous rejection of heat to the surroundings at a higher temperature. Basically, the refrigeration cycle is a reversed heat-engine cycle. Heat

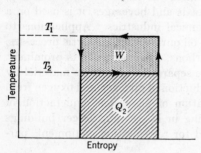

FIG. 10-1. Carnot refrigeration cycle.

is transferred from a low level to a higher one, and this, according to the second law, cannot be accomplished without utilizing external energy in the form of work. As was the case for the heat engine, the ideal refrigeration cycle would be of the Carnot type, consisting of two isothermal processes, in which the heat Q_2 is absorbed at the lower temperature T_2 and the heat Q_1 rejected at the higher temperature T_1, and two adiabatic processes, the result of which is the addition of the net work W to the system. According to the first law,

$$W = Q_1 - Q_2 \qquad (10\text{-}1)[1]$$

From Fig. 10-1, showing the Carnot cycle,

$$Q_1 = T_1 \, \Delta S \qquad (10\text{-}2)$$
$$Q_2 = T_2 \, \Delta S \qquad (10\text{-}3)$$

By combining Eqs. (10-1), (10-2), and (10-3), there is obtained

$$\frac{W}{Q_1} = \frac{T_1 - T_2}{T_1} \qquad (10\text{-}4)$$

which is the familiar expression for the Carnot efficiency of a heat engine and which also applies to the reversed cycle operating as a refrigeration machine. In terms of Q_2, Eq. (10-4) becomes

$$\frac{W}{Q_2} = \frac{T_1 - T_2}{T_2} \qquad (10\text{-}5)$$

from which may be computed the work required for a given quantity of

[1] Note that the usual sign convention, that heat is positive when absorbed by the system, has been disregarded here. Both Q_1 and Q_2 are positive so that W also becomes positive and is equal to the work added to the system.

refrigeration, Q_2. It is exact only for the Carnot cycle, but it does emphasize the point that the work required increases as the temperature of the refrigerator, T_2, goes down and as the temperature at which heat is rejected, T_1, increases.

To prove that the Carnot cycle is the most efficient of all refrigeration processes, consider Fig. 10-2, depicting another cycle, $ABCD$, operating in such a way that the temperature rises during the heat-absorption step and falls when heat is rejected. If the temperature of the refrigerator is not to be greater than T_A and that of the condenser not less than T_C, the Carnot cycle would be $AB'CD'$.

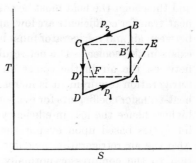

FIG. 10-2. Effect of deviations from the Carnot cycle; the air-refrigeration cycle.

The new cycle would have to operate in such a manner that the temperature of the fluid entering the refrigerator would be T_D so that it would not increase to a value higher than T_A when the fluid leaves the refrigerator. This new cycle would then be operating at an average temperature less than the Carnot cycle and, therefore, by Eq. (10-5), would be less efficient. Similarly, the maximum efficiency during the heat-rejection step would be for the isothermal process $B'C$ corresponding to the Carnot cycle, and not the process BC of the new cycle. Actually (although not shown in Fig. 10-2) a small, but finite, temperature difference in both the refrigerator and the heat-rejection step would be necessary to accomplish the transfer of heat to and from the refrigerant.

Since the Carnot cycle is reversible, the adiabatic steps are isentropic. If the processes were adiabatic but not reversible, there would be an increase in entropy as indicated by the dashed compression step AE and expansion step CF. The effect of these irreversibilities would be to increase the work required for compression, reduce the work obtained from the expansion process, and also reduce the quantity of refrigeration. This last result is evident from Fig. 10-2, since the value of $T \Delta S$ is less for process FA than for $D'A$.

10-2. The Air-refrigeration Cycle. The cycle $ABCD$ in Fig. 10-2, while not so efficient as the Carnot cycle, can be used to produce refrigeration. The air machine is an example (Fig. 10-3). In the refrigerator the air absorbs heat at the essentially constant pressure p_1 in the cold space and rejects heat to the surroundings in the cooler at the higher constant pressure p_2. The gas is compressed at constant entropy (ideally) from A to B, using as part of the energy required the work obtained from the expansion process CD.

Besides having a low efficiency, even on a reversible basis, the air cycle has additional disadvantages. First of all in both the refrigerator and the cooler the heat must be transferred through a gas film. Gas-film heat-transfer coefficients are low, and therefore the temperature difference between air and refrigerator must be relatively large. A similar condition exists in the cooler. The net result is that the difference in temperature between the air in the cooler and that in the refrigerator for a given refrigeration requirement is increased and the efficiency decreased. The heat-transfer coefficients for evaporating and condensing liquids are much higher; hence the loss in efficiency due to this effect is not so important for cycles based upon evaporation of a liquid in the refrigerator coils. Also the air refrigeration machine includes an expansion device in addition to the compressor normally used in common vapor-compression, evaporating-liquid cycles. Since the specific heat of air is small, relatively large quantities of air must be handled in these expansion and compression processes in order to achieve a significant amount of refrigeration.

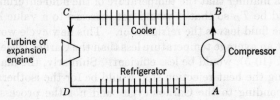

FIG. 10-3. Air refrigeration machine.

The air cycle was one of the first devices used for commercial refrigeration. However, the disadvantages mentioned previously have led to its replacement by other systems in most instances. When power for compression of the air is available from other sources, as in the case of aircraft with jet engines, the air machine may be practical. The thermodynamic analysis of the cycle is warranted since it provides a simple introduction to the type of calculations involved in the other, more practical cycles. Assuming that the specific heat of the gas is constant, the heats absorbed in the refrigerator and rejected in the cooler are (Fig. 10-2)

$$Q_2 = mc_p(T_A - T_D) \tag{10-6}$$
$$Q_1 = mc_p(T_B - T_C) \tag{10-7}$$

Since the pressure is constant (ideally) in the refrigerator coils and the cooler,

$$\frac{T_C}{T_D} = \left(\frac{p_2}{p_1}\right)^{(\gamma-1)/\gamma} = \frac{T_B}{T_A} \tag{10-8}$$

By an over-all balance [Eq. (10-1)]

$$W = mc_p[(T_B - T_C) - (T_A - T_D)] \tag{10-9}$$

Coefficient of Performance 标题 第三节

From Eqs. (10-6) to (10-9), the efficiency is

$$\frac{W}{Q_2} = \frac{T_B}{T_A} - 1 \tag{10-10}$$

The performance of a refrigeration machine is usually reported in terms of the *coefficient of performance*, defined as the ratio of the refrigeration obtained to the work required, Q_2/W.

For the air cycle,

$$\text{C.O.P.} = \frac{Q_2}{W} = \frac{T_A}{T_B - T_A} \tag{10-11}$$

If a refrigerator is to be maintained at 20°F with an air-cycle machine and a 10°F approach is possible, the coefficient of performance is given by the equation

$$\text{C.O.P.} = \frac{460 + 10}{T_B - (460 + 10)} \tag{10-12}$$

The temperature T_B and the coefficient of performance depend upon the quantity of air circulated and the refrigeration required. The maximum C.O.P. would be obtained when T_B had its lowest value, *i.e.*, when $T_B = T_C$. This would require an infinite circulation rate, or an infinitely small refrigeration capacity, and the process would correspond to a Carnot cycle. For a finite circulation, T_B would be greater than T_C, and the coefficient of performance would decrease.

10-3. The Vapor-compression Cycle. The evaporation of a liquid at constant pressure provides a means of absorbing heat at constant temperature. Likewise, the condensation process at a higher pressure provides a method of rejecting heat at constant temperature. The vapor leaving the refrigerator can be compressed to the higher pressure, not exactly by a constant-entropy process, but by one approaching that path, depending upon the care taken to eliminate irreversibilities in compressor operation. To complete the cycle, the liquid from the condenser must be returned to its original state by an expansion process. This could be done in an engine which operates approximately reversibly and from which work could be obtained (step CD, Fig. 10-4a). This sequence of processes results in the cycle $ABCD$ and is equivalent to the Carnot cycle except for the necessary cooling of the superheated vapor to its saturation point before condensation begins. Although the condensation and evaporation steps are drawn as constant-pressure processes, actually small pressure drops occur as a result of friction due to flow.

The heat absorbed in the refrigerator for the vapor-compression cycle per pound of fluid is given by the equation

$$Q_2 = \Delta H = H_A - H_D \tag{10-13}$$

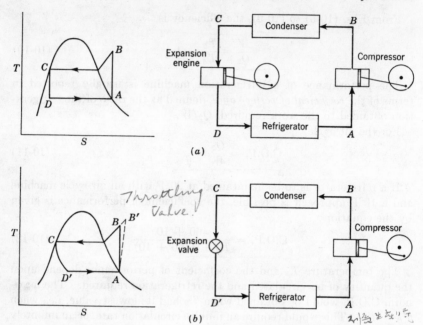

FIG. 10-4. Vapor-compression refrigeration cycles.

This equation follows from the total-energy balance for a flow process by neglecting the small changes in potential and kinetic energy. Likewise, the heat rejected in the condenser is

$$Q_1 = H_B - H_C \tag{10-14}$$

Then, from the first law,

$$W = (H_B - H_C) - (H_A - H_D) \tag{10-15}$$

Accordingly, the coefficient of performance is

$$\text{C.O.P.} = \frac{H_A - H_D}{(H_B - H_C) - (H_A - H_D)} \tag{10-16}$$

This process requires a turbine or expansion engine operating on a two-phase liquid-vapor mixture. Such a machine is relatively expensive and difficult to build for efficient operation. Therefore, the cycle shown in Fig. 10-4a is not used except for large installations. Instead, the expansion is accomplished by passing the liquid from the condenser through a partly opened valve. This throttling operation is highly irreversible, the pressure drop being due entirely to friction in the valve. However, in small plants, such as household refrigerators and air conditioners, the simplicity and lower cost of the throttle valve outweigh the greater effi-

$$R = \frac{c}{b}$$

$$R_p = R_3^\circ x_3$$
$$R_n = R_1^\circ x_1$$

coefficient of performance

$$\rho = R_3^\circ x_3 + R_1^\circ x$$

냉동 機械의 성능을 表示하는 尺도.

이들 냉동 機의 이론적 성능 尺도는 성능계수 (e.o.p)

Q_2/W로 정의된다.

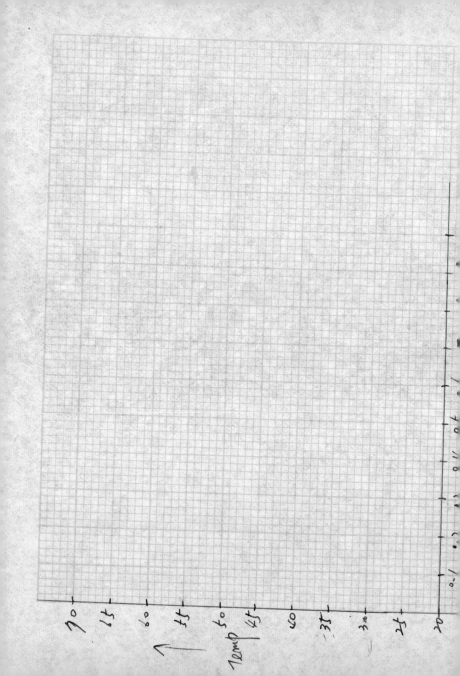

Temp

70
65
60
55
50
45
40
35
30
25
20

ciency of the turbine cycle. The thermodynamic path for the throttling
process can be approximated by applying the total-energy-balance flow
equation and neglecting kinetic-energy changes and the heat transferred
from the surroundings.[1] Under these conditions the process occurs at
constant enthalpy. This vapor-compression cycle is shown in Fig. 10-4b,
where the line CD' represents a constant-enthalpy process.

The equation for the coefficient of performance reduces to the simple
form

$$\text{C.O.P.} = \frac{H_A - H_{D'}}{H_B - H_A} \tag{10-17}$$

In addition to the coefficient of performance, it is necessary to know
the rate of circulation of refrigerant in order to design and size correctly
the compressor, condenser, refrigerator coils, and auxiliary equipment.
Refrigeration equipment is rated in tons of refrigeration; 1 ton is defined
as a rate of heat absorption of 12,000 Btu/hr. This quantity corresponds
approximately to the rate of heat removal necessary to freeze 1 ton of
water (initially at 32°F) per day.

With such a definition, the circulation in pounds per hour per ton of
refrigeration is given by the equation

$$m = \frac{12,000}{H_A - H_{D'}} \tag{10-18}$$

The ordinary vapor-compression cycle is also shown on the pressure-
enthalpy chart in Fig. 10-5. Such
plots are more commonly used in refrigeration work than T-S diagrams,
for the required enthalpy values are
easily read from such a chart. The
temperature-entropy diagram possesses the advantages that heat
effects and work effects can be represented as areas on the chart and
differences between reversible and
irreversible adiabatic processes can
be clearly brought out by the devia-

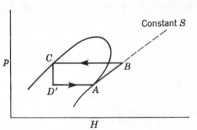

Fig. 10-5. Vapor-compression refrigeration cycle on a pressure-enthalpy
diagram.

tion from vertical lines. For example, an irreversible, but adiabatic,
compression process would deviate from the vertical as indicated by the
dashed line AB' in Fig. 10-4b.

10-4. Comparison of Refrigeration Cycles. The discussion of efficiency of refrigeration machines can be summarized as follows: The

---

[1] The expansion or throttling valve in commercial refrigeration plants is insulated
to reduce this heat transfer. Nevertheless the process is not entirely adiabatic, as is
indicated by the frost that collects on the valve stem and handle.

hypothetical Carnot cycle has the highest coefficient of performance; the vapor-compression process with a reversible expansion engine approaches this upper limit; the actual vapor-compression cycle has a somewhat lower value; and, finally, the air cycle has a still lower efficiency. As an indication of the magnitude of the coefficients of performance, consider the following example:

Example 10-1. The refrigerator (or cold room) is to be maintained at 10°F, and the available cooling water is at 70°F. Assume that the cold-room coils and the condenser are of sufficient size so that a 10°F approach can be realized in each. The refrigeration capacity is to be 10 tons. For the air cycle the operating pressures will be 14.7 and 60 psia. Freon-12 will be used in the vapor-compression machines. Calculate the coefficient of performance and the circulation rate [except for (a)] for the following cases:

    (a) Carnot cycle
    (b) Expansion engine, vapor-compression cycle
    (c) Ordinary vapor-compression cycle
    (d) Air machine

Solution. (a) For the Carnot cycle,

$$\text{C.O.P.} = \frac{T_2}{T_1 - T_2} = \frac{460 + 0}{(460 + 80) - (460 + 0)} = 5.75$$

(b) If Freon-12 is used in the vapor-compression cycles, the enthalpies in the various states of the cycle (Fig. 10-4a, *ABCD*) may be read from Fig. 10-6.

The Freon-12 vaporizing in the refrigerator coils at 0°F will be at 24 psia. The pressure in the condenser (saturated Freon-12 at 80°F) will be 99 psia.

$$H_A \text{ (sat vapor at 0°F)} = 78.2 \text{ Btu/lb}_m$$
$$S_A = 0.171 \text{ Btu/(lb}_m)(°R)$$
$$H_B \text{ (at 99 psia and } S_A) = 89.3 \text{ Btu/lb}_m$$
$$H_C \text{ (sat liquid at 99 psia)} = 26.3 \text{ Btu/lb}_m$$

The properties determining state *D* are the pressure (24 psia) and the entropy S_C. If Fig. 10-6 contained constant-entropy lines on the left-hand side of the chart, it would be a simple matter to locate *D*. Since these lines are not available, the point must be located analytically. The entropy at *C* is

$$S_C = S_{\text{sat}} - \Delta S_{\text{vap}} = S_{\text{sat}} - \left(\frac{\Delta H}{T}\right)_{\text{vap}}$$
$$= 0.167 - \frac{86.8 - 26.3}{460 + 80}$$
$$= 0.055 \text{ Btu/(lb}_m)(°R)$$

The state at *D* will consist of a mixture of liquid and vapor whose entropy is given by the expression

$$S_D = S_C = 0.055 = S_A - \left(\frac{\Delta H}{T_2}\right) x \qquad (A)$$

where *x* represents the fraction liquid at *D*. Similarly,

$$H_D = H_A - (\Delta H_{\text{vap}}) x \qquad (B)$$

Eliminating x from these equations,

$$H_A - H_D = T_2(S_A - 0.055)$$
$$H_D = H_A - T_2(S_A - 0.055)$$
$$H_D = 78.2 - (460)(0.171 - 0.055) = 24.9 \text{ Btu/lb}_m$$

The coefficient of performance may now be evaluated from Eq. (10-16),

$$\text{C.O.P.} = \frac{H_A - H_D}{(H_B - H_C) - (H_A - H_D)} = \frac{78.2 - 24.9}{(89.3 - 26.3) - (78.2 - 24.9)} = 5.5$$

The circulation rate for 10 tons of refrigeration is

$$m = \left(\frac{12,000}{78.2 - 24.9}\right)(10) = 2250 \text{ lb}_m/\text{hr}$$

(c) In the ordinary vapor-compression cycle $ABCD'$ (Fig. 10-4b), $H_{D'} = H_C = 26.3 \text{ Btu/lb}_m$. Using Eq. (10-17),

$$\text{C.O.P.} = \frac{H_A - H_{D'}}{H_B - H_A} = \frac{78.2 - 26.3}{89.3 - 78.2} = 4.7$$

The circulation rate is

$$m = \left(\frac{12,000}{78.2 - 26.3}\right)(10) = 2310 \text{ lb}_m/\text{hr}$$

(d) If air is the refrigerant, the cycle will be as shown in Fig. 10-2:

$$T_A = 460°\text{R}$$
$$T_C = 460 + 80 = 540°\text{R}$$

Temperatures at B and D are determined by the pressure range. Assuming adiabatic reversible operation during the compression and expansion processes AB and CD,

$$T_B = T_A \left(\frac{p_2}{p_1}\right)^{(\gamma-1)/\gamma} = (460)\left(\frac{60}{14.7}\right)^{(1.4-1)/1.4} = 687°\text{R}$$
$$T_D = T_C \left(\frac{p_1}{p_2}\right)^{(\gamma-1)/\gamma} = (540)\left(\frac{14.7}{60}\right)^{(1.4-1)/1.4} = 361°\text{R}$$

Then, according to Eq. (10-11),

$$\text{C.O.P.} = \frac{T_A}{T_B - T_A} = \frac{460}{687 - 460} = 2.0$$

The rate of heat removal in the cold room is 120,000 Btu/hr. Therefore the circulation rate m will be

$$m = \frac{120,000}{c_p(T_A - T_D)} = \frac{120,000}{(0.24)(460 - 361)} = 5000 \text{ lb}_m/\text{hr}$$

Table 10-1 illustrates the approach of each of the processes in (b), (c), and (d) to the ideal Carnot cycle.

10-5. The Choice of Refrigerant. A fundamental corollary of the second law of thermodynamics is that the maximum efficiency of a heat engine is independent of the medium employed in the engine. Similarly, the coefficient of performance of the ideal refrigeration process, the Carnot

TABLE 10-1 (EXAMPLE 10-1)

Cycle	C.O.P.	Circulation rate, lb/hr
Carnot...............................	5.75	
Vapor-compression (expansion engine)....	5.5	2250
Vapor-compression (expansion valve).....	4.7	2310
Air.................................	2.0	5000

cycle, is independent of the refrigerant.   However, the vapor-compression
cycle deviates from the ideal Carnot cycle, and therefore the efficiency
of actual refrigeration plants does depend to a certain extent upon the
refrigerant.   On the other hand, such characteristics of the material
as its vapor-pressure–temperature curve, toxicity, cost, explosiveness, and
corrosion properties are of greater importance than efficiency in choosing
a refrigerant.   The material should not have a subatmospheric vapor
pressure at the temperature in the refrigerator coils in order to avoid con-
tamination in the event of leaks.   The vapor pressure at the condenser

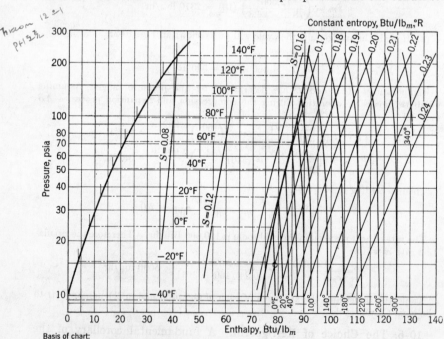

Basis of chart:
H and S = 0 for saturated liquid at −40°F

FIG. 10-6. Pressure-enthalpy diagram for Freon-12. (*By permission from "The Refrigerating Data Book Design Volume," 8th ed., American Society of Refrigeration Engineers,* 1953.)

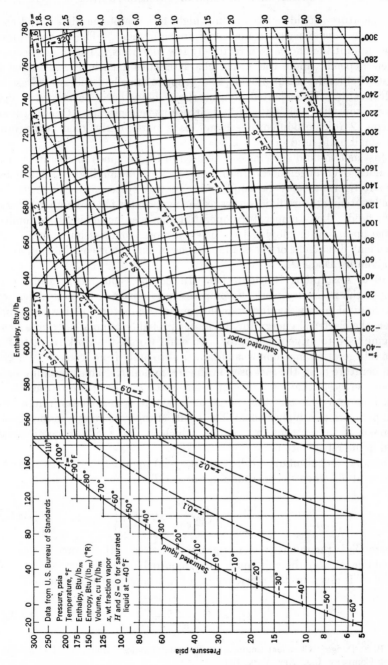

FIG. 10-7. Pressure-enthalpy diagram for ammonia.

307

temperature should not be unduly high, because of the high initial cost and operating expense for high-pressure equipment. These two requirements limit the choice to a relatively few materials. The final selection then depends upon the other characteristics mentioned. Ammonia, methyl chloride, sulfur dioxide, and propane have had widespread use as refrigerants. Halogenated hydrocarbons have been developed which have properties well suited for their use as refrigerants. One of these, Freon-12 (dichlorodifluoromethane), is a particularly good refrigerant for small units used in the home.

Just as two-fluid systems can be used in heat engines to operate across a higher over-all temperature difference and so obtain higher efficiencies, two refrigerants may be employed. In this system the condenser for the low-temperature fluid serves as the evaporator for the high-temperature fluid. Low-temperature operation can also be achieved by multistage operation employing two, or even more, compression stages. An excellent discussion of these adaptations of the vapor-compression cycle is given by Dodge.[1]

10-6. Absorption Refrigeration. In compression refrigeration machines the necessary work of compression is obtained from electrical or mechanical energy, as, for example, an electric motor. Going back further, the electrical energy for the motor probably originated from a heat engine used to drive a generator. In other words, the work required for the refrigeration machine was obtained ultimately from a source of high-temperature heat, the fuel used in the steam boiler. This reasoning naturally suggests the possibility of using heat directly in the refrigeration machine as a source of the energy necessary to transfer heat from a low temperature to a higher one. The result of this reasoning was the development of the absorption machine, which is used for both commercial and home refrigeration.

Ideally, the minimum work (Carnot cycle) required to operate a refrigerator at T_E when the surroundings are at T_C is

$$W = \frac{T_C - T_E}{T_E} Q_E \qquad (10\text{-}19)$$

where Q_E is the quantity of refrigeration desired. If a source of heat is available at T_R, the minimum heat required to obtain an amount of work W is given by the efficiency of a Carnot-cycle heat engine.

$$Q_R = W \frac{T_R}{T_R - T_C} \qquad (10\text{-}20)$$

[1] B. F. Dodge, "Chemical Engineering Thermodynamics," Chap. X, McGraw-Hill Book Company, Inc., New York, 1944.

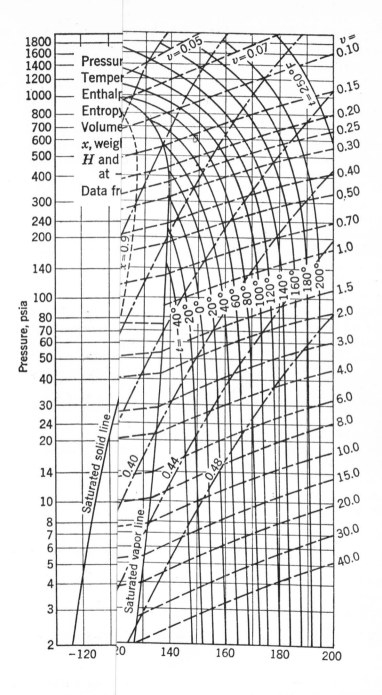

Pressure, psia

$v = 0.05$ $v = 0.07$ $v = 0.10$

$t = 250°$ F.

0.15
0.20
0.25
0.30
0.40
0.50
0.70
1.0

1.5
2.0
3.0
4.0
6.0
8.0
10.0
15.0
20.0
30.0
40.0

Pressur
Temper
Enthalp
Entropy
Volume
x, weig
H and
at —
Data fr

$x = 0.9$

$t = -40°$ $-20°$ $0°$ $20°$ $40°$ $60°$ $80°$ $100°$ $120°$ $140°$ $160°$ $180°$ $200°$

Saturated solid line

Saturated vapor line

0.40 0.44 0.48

1800
1600
1400
1200
1000
800
700
600
500
400
300
240
200
140
100
80
70
60
50
40
30
24
20
14
10
8
7
6
5
4
3
2

-120   140   160   180   200

The heat at the high temperature T_R required to obtain a refrigeration capacity of Q_E is then, by combination of Eqs. (10-19) and (10-20),

$$Q_R = Q_E \frac{T_R}{T_R - T_C} \frac{T_C - T_E}{T_E} \qquad (10\text{-}21)$$

Any actual absorption machine will have an efficiency (Q_E/Q_R) less than that given by Eq. (10-21), since Carnot-cycle operation cannot be completely achieved.

The schematic flow diagram for a typical absorption refrigeration machine is shown in Fig. 10-9. The essential difference between such a system and the vapor-compression cycle is that a heat engine has been substituted for the compressor. In other words, the section of the plant

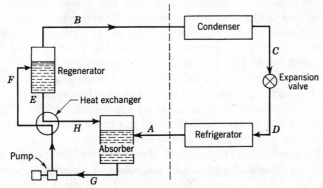

Fig. 10-9. Schematic diagram of an absorption refrigeration machine.

to the right of the dashed line is the same in both methods, while the section on the left represents a heat engine in the case of the absorption machine. In the absorption machine two substances are used, the refrigerant and a relatively nonvolatile solvent. The temperature difference between the source of heat (regenerator) and heat sink (absorber) is obtained by maintaining a different concentration of refrigerant in the solvent in the two parts of the apparatus. Heat is absorbed in the regenerator by evaporating the refrigerant from a concentrated solution of the nonvolatile solvent. Heat is rejected at a lower temperature by absorbing the refrigerant from the refrigerator coils in the low-concentration solution from the regenerator. The pressure in the regenerator is determined by the temperature of the condensing refrigerant in the condenser, and similarly the pressure in the absorber is fixed by the temperature of evaporating refrigerant in the refrigerator coils. The pressure will be higher in the regenerator, and a pump is needed to circulate the concentrated solution from the absorber to the regenerator. The temperatures in these two pieces of equipment are determined by the temperatures of the available cooling water and the heat supply. In commercial installations exhaust steam is commonly used as a source of heat in the regenerator, and an exchanger is installed between the absorber and regenerator as shown in Fig. 10-9. With definite temperature and pressure conditions in the regenerator and absorber, the solution concentrations can be evaluated from vapor-pressure—concentration data.

The system just described requires a source of mechanical energy to operate the pump. Although the actual power requirement of the pump is very small, it does contain moving parts and therefore introduces maintenance problems. This disadvantage has been ingeniously eliminated in the domestic gas refrigerator through the use of a third, extremely volatile component (hydrogen). As a result, the total pressure can be maintained essentially constant, and only the partial pressures of the refrigerant and the hydrogen vary between the refrigerator and absorber. The partial pressure of refrigerant is high in the regenerator and low in the absorber, but the total pressure is about the same as a result of the inverse variation of the hydrogen partial pressure. Since the driving force for evaporating the refrigerant in the regenerator is the difference between the partial pressure in the solution and the gas mixture above it, a higher total pressure in the gas has no appreciable effect. The source of heat in the gas refrigerator is a small gas flame under the regenerator and is the only energy source in the machine.

The thermodynamic treatment of absorption refrigeration is not complicated. In general, heats of solution, heats of absorption, and vapor-pressure data are necessary. The method of analysis is indicated in the following example:

Example 10-2. An absorption refrigeration machine employs ammonia as a refrigerant and water as an absorbent.

Heat is supplied to the regenerator by steam condensing at atmospheric pressure. The regenerator temperature is to be 175°F; with cooling water available at 60°F, the condenser and absorber temperatures are to be 70°F. The ammonia is to evaporate in the refrigerator at 10°F.

Assuming that the operation is adiabatic except where heat is intentionally added or rejected and neglecting the pressure drop due to fluid friction (except in the expansion valve), estimate the following:

(a) The pressure in each part of the system
(b) The composition of the strong and weak ammonia solutions
(c) The minimum pump work per ton of refrigeration
(d) The heat transferred in the regenerator, condenser, and absorber per ton of refrigeration

Neglect the vapor pressure of water.

Solution. (a) Refer to Fig. 10-9; pure ammonia vaporizes in the refrigerator and condenses in the condenser. Therefore, from Fig. 10-7 the pressures in the two parts of the system will correspond to the saturation pressures at 70 and 10°F:

$$p_2 \text{ (condenser and also regenerator)} = 128 \text{ psia}$$
$$p_1 \text{ (refrigerator and also absorber)} = 38 \text{ psia}$$

(b) It is necessary that the solution in the absorber have a vapor pressure of 38 psia at 70°F and that the solution in the regenerator have a vapor pressure of 128 psia at 175°F. The weight per cent ammonia in an aqueous solution having an ammonia pressure of 38 psia at 70°F is 46.5.† Similarly the concentration of the solution leaving the regenerator is 35.7 per cent.†

The circulation rate of ammonia through the refrigerator per ton of refrigeration will be

$$m = \frac{12,000}{H_A - H_D} = \frac{12,000}{613 - 122} = 24.4 \text{ lb}_m/\text{hr}$$

where H_A and H_D, taken from Fig. 10-7, refer to the enthalpy values leaving and entering the refrigerator.

(c) To determine the flow rates of the solutions, let y be the pounds per hour of weak solution flowing from the regenerator to the absorber and x the pounds per hour of strong solution flowing from the absorber to the regenerator. Then the ammonia and the total-material balances around the regenerator (Fig. 10-9) give equations

$$0.357y + 24.4 = 0.465x$$
$$y + 24.4 = x$$

Solving,

$$y = 121 \text{ lb}_m/\text{hr}$$
$$x = 145.4 \text{ lb}_m/\text{hr}$$

The pump work can be evaluated from the mechanical-energy-balance flow equation. Since potential- and kinetic-energy effects will be small,

$$V \, dp + dF + dW_s = 0$$

For the minimum work, $dF = 0$, and

$$W_s = -\int V \, dp = -V(p_2 - p_1)$$

The density of the 46.5 per cent solution† is 0.832. Hence the work required is

$$-W_s = \left[\frac{145.4}{(62.3)(0.832)} \right] (128 - 38)(144) = 36,300 \text{ ft-lb}_f/\text{hr}$$

$$\text{hp} = 0.018 \text{ per ton of refrigeration}$$

(d) Heat effects (taken as positive when heat is absorbed by the fluid in the machine):

(1) Refrigerator, $Q_E = 12,000$ Btu/hr   (1 ton of refrigeration)
(2) Condenser, $Q_C = 24.4(H_C - H_B)$

where H_B is the enthalpy of the ammonia leaving the regenerator at 175°F and 138 psia and H_C is the enthalpy leaving the condenser, corresponding to saturated liquid at 138 psia. Using the data in Fig. 10-7,

$$Q_C = 24.4(122 - 696) = -14,000 \text{ Btu/hr}$$

(3) Regenerator. An energy balance around the regenerator would include these streams (the capital-letter designations refer to those in Fig. 10-9):

Out	In
E—121 lb/hr of weak solution at 175°F	F—145.4 lb/hr of strong solution at 70°F
B—24.4 lb/hr of NH₃ at 175°F and 138 psia	Q_R (heat supplied by the condensing steam)

$$121H_E + 24.4H_B = 145.4H_F + Q_R \qquad (A)$$

† J. H. Perry (ed.), "Chemical Engineers' Handbook," 3d ed., Table 7, p. 1635, McGraw-Hill Book Company, Inc., New York, 1950

The enthalpies refer to the values per pound at the conditions indicated by the subscripts. Numerical values for H_E and H_F can be obtained from an enthalpy-concentration chart for ammonia and water. Such a chart is given by Hougen and Watson.[1] It is a thermodynamic diagram similar to Fig. 10-7, but it includes the additional variable of composition. Preparation of such a chart requires data concerning the heat effects accompanying mixing of ammonia and water at constant temperature and pressure, i.e., heats of solution. From Hougen and Watson's chart,

$$H_E = 80 \text{ Btu/lb}_m$$
$$H_F = -25 \text{ Btu/lb}_m$$

From Fig. 10-7, $H_B = 696$ Btu/lb$_m$. Enthalpies from both Hougen and Watson's chart and Fig. 10-7 may be used in the same equation since the basis for $H = 0$ is the same in both cases, viz., saturated liquid ammonia at $-40°F$. Care must be taken that this condition is satisfied in using data from a number of thermodynamic diagrams or tables. Substituting the values in Eq. (A),

$$Q_R = (121)(80) + (24.4)(696) - (145.4)(-25)$$
$$= 30{,}300 \text{ Btu/hr}$$

(4) Absorber. An energy balance around the absorber would include these streams:

Out	In
G—145.4 lb/hr of strong solution at 70°F	A—24.4 lb/hr of NH$_3$ at 0°F and 38 psia
Q_A (heat added from the cooling water)	H—121 lb/hr of weak solution at 175°F

$$145.4H_G - Q_A = 24.4H_A + 121H_H \qquad (B)$$

Since there is no exchanger in the present case, $H_H = H_E$ (Fig. 10-9) $= 80$ Btu/lb$_m$. As the pump is specified to operate adiabatically, the total-energy flow equation for the pump process is

$$\Delta H = -W_s = H_F - H_G$$
$$H_F - H_G = \frac{36{,}300}{(778)(145.4)} = 0.3 \text{ Btu/lb}_m$$

This is so small that, for all practical purposes,

$$H_G = H_F = -25 \text{ Btu/lb}_m$$

Then, from Eq. (B),

$$Q_A = (145.4)(-25) - (24.4)(613) - (121)(80)$$
$$= -28{,}300 \text{ Btu/hr}$$

The results are summarized as follows:

Heat in, Btu/hr	Heat out, Btu/hr
$Q_R = 30{,}300$	$-Q_C = 14{,}000$
$Q_E = 12{,}000$	$-Q_A = 28{,}300$
$\overline{42{,}300}$	$\overline{42{,}300}$

For each ton of refrigeration enough steam must be used in the regenerator to supply 30,300 Btu/hr. If a vapor-compression machine which had a C.O.P. of 4 were

[1] O. A. Hougen and K. M. Watson, "Chemical Process Principles," Part II, p. 584, Fig. 132, John Wiley & Sons, Inc., New York, 1947.

used in place of the absorption machine, the work requirement would be the equivalent of $(12,000)(\frac{1}{4})$ or 3000 Btu/hr. Whether or not the absorption machine would be advantageous would depend to a considerable extent upon the relative cost of 30,300 Btu/hr of heat from steam and 3000 Btu/hr of work.

The heat required in the absorption machine could have been decreased significantly by using a heat exchanger in the streams between the regenerator and absorber as illustrated in Fig. 10-9.

It is interesting to see what the minimum value of Q_R would be. This would correspond to Carnot-cycle operation for both the heat-engine and refrigeration parts of the apparatus. Hence the answer is given by Eq. (10-21).

$$Q_R, \min = Q_E \frac{T_R}{T_R - T_C} \frac{T_C - T_E}{T_E}$$
$$= (12,000) \left(\frac{635}{635 - 530} \right) \left(\frac{530 - 470}{470} \right)$$
$$= 9250 \text{ Btu/hr}$$

The actual cycle requires more than three times the theoretical minimum heat input.

10-7. The Heat Pump.[1] The heat pump is a device for heating houses and commercial buildings during the winter months and cooling them during the summer period. It is a reversed heat engine, or heat pump, which absorbs heat from a building during the summer and rejects it to the surroundings, operating much as any refrigeration machine. During the winter, when it is necessary to heat the building, the heat pump operates so as to absorb heat from the surroundings and reject heat in the building. This is done by evaporating a refrigerant in coils placed underground or in the outside air. The vapor is compressed to a pressure such that it may be condensed by an air or water stream at temperatures above room temperature. The heat transferred to the air or water during the condensation is used to heat the house. The operating cost of the installation is the cost of the electric power needed to run the compressor. If such a machine has a coefficient of performance of 4, considered as a refrigeration unit (that is, $Q_2/W = 4$), the heat available Q_1 for the house would be equivalent to five times the power input to the compressor. The economic feasibility of the heat pump as a heating device depends upon the cost of electrical energy compared with fuels such as coal, oil, and gas.

The unit may be operated as an air-conditioning machine during the summer by reversing the flow of refrigerant; heat is absorbed from air in the house at a low temperature and rejected to the underground heat reservoir or the outside air at a higher temperature.

Economic justification seems most likely in instances where the air-conditioning load is high and the heating load relatively low. This

[1] Philip Sporn, E. R. Ambrose, and Theodore Baumeister, "Heat Pumps," John Wiley & Sons, Inc., New York, 1947.

situation is approached in the warmer climates and in such commercial buildings as theaters.

Example 10-3. The heating requirement for a house in January is 100,000 Btu/hr, and the cooling requirement in July is 200,000 Btu/hr. A heat-pump installation is being considered which would maintain the house at 75°F in both winter and summer. To accomplish this, it is necessary to circulate the operating fluid through the radiator coils at 40°F in July and 140°F in January. An underground coil will be used to provide energy when the house is heated and to reject energy when it is cooled. The ground temperature will be about constant throughout the year at 55°F. The heat-transfer capacity of the coil is such that the fluid in it should be at 40°F during heating and at least 70°F during cooling.

What will be the theoretical minimum power requirements for cooling in July and heating in January?

Solution. For minimum power requirements a Carnot cycle is necessary. During heating, enough energy will be absorbed at 40°F to reject 100,000 Btu/hr at 140°F. The work required will be given by the expression for the efficiency of a Carnot cycle:

$$\frac{W}{Q_1} = \frac{T_1 - T_2}{T_1} = \frac{(140 + 460) - (40 + 460)}{140 + 460} = 0.167$$

$$W = (100,000)(0.167) = 16,700 \text{ Btu/hr}$$

or

$$W = (16,700)\left[\frac{778}{(60)(33,000)}\right] = 6.56 \text{ hp}$$

In the summer, 200,000 Btu/hr is to be absorbed at 40°F in the house and rejected at 70°F in the underground coil. The theoretical minimum work may be computed from the equation for the coefficient of performance for a Carnot cycle:

$$\text{C.O.P.} = \frac{Q_2}{W} = \frac{T_2}{T_1 - T_2} = \frac{40 + 460}{(70 + 460) - (40 + 460)} = 16.7$$

$$W = \frac{Q_2}{16.7} = \frac{200,000}{16.7} = 12,000 \text{ Btu/hr}$$

or

$$W = 4.71 \text{ hp}$$

10-8. Liquefaction Processes. The demand for liquefied gases has been steadily increasing through the years. A noteworthy example is the use of liquefied natural gas as a domestic fuel in rural areas and oxygen for rocket systems and blast-furnace operation. Also the growth of the synthetic-chemical industry has resulted in a greatly expanded market for pure gases. Perhaps the best way of transporting such gases, where pipelines are not available, is by liquefaction and bottling in cylinders under pressure. The methods used for separating gases from naturally occurring mixtures, such as oxygen and nitrogen from air, depend upon liquefaction followed by fractionation.

The essence of all liquefaction processes is to cool the gas until it passes into the two-phase region. This cooling may be accomplished in several ways:

1. Cooling at constant pressure, as in a heat exchanger
2. Cooling by expansion in an engine from which work is obtained
3. Cooling by an expansion-valve or throttling process

The first method requires a heat sink at a lower temperature than that to which the gas is to be cooled. In other words, an external refrigeration system is required if the gas temperature is to be reduced below normal surroundings temperature. This scheme is of no value in liquefying a gas such as helium since there is no known medium that could be evaporated in the refrigerator coils at such a temperature that the helium would be cooled into the two-phase region. Accordingly, the first method is normally used only as a means of precooling the gas.

The three methods are illustrated in Fig. 10-10. The constant-pressure path (1) approaches the two-phase region (and liquefaction) most closely for a given drop in temperature. In fact the isenthalpic expansion (3) will not result in liquefaction unless the initial state is at a high enough pressure and low enough temperature for the constant-enthalpy line to cut into the two-phase region. If the initial state is A, no liquefaction will occur by process (3). If the initial state is A', at the same temperature but considerably higher pressure than A, then a constant-enthalpy expansion along (3') will cause liquefaction. The process from A to A'

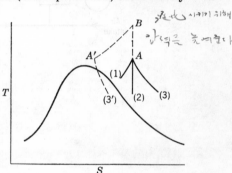

FIG. 10-10. Cooling processes on a temperature-entropy diagram.

is most easily accomplished, practically, by compressing the gas to the final pressure, AB, and then cooling at constant pressure, BA'. The isentropic process (2) does not require an initial state at as high a pressure (at a given temperature) in order that liquefaction may be obtained. For example, continuation of process (2) from an initial state A will ultimately result in liquefaction. On the other hand, there are difficulties encountered in attempting to construct an expansion engine which will operate efficiently at low temperatures and in the two-phase region.

The constant-enthalpy or Joule-Thomson expansion process (3) is the one commonly employed in small-scale commercial plants. If this method is to be useful, the gas must, of course, cool during the expansion. Hydrogen and helium initially at room temperature will increase in temperature as a result of the expansion. However, most gases have a positive Joule-Thomson coefficient[1] at ordinary conditions, and hydrogen

[1] The Joule-Thomson coefficient is defined as the rate of change of temperature with respect to pressure at constant enthalpy (Sec. 8-5).

and helium do at low temperatures (below about 100°K for hydrogen and 20°K for helium). Hence, for these two gases T must be first reduced below these values by external means, *i.e.*, method (1) or (2). Another requirement is that the temperature on the upstream side of the valve be low enough for the constant-enthalpy line to cut into the two-phase region. By reference to Fig. 7-4 it is seen that this temperature is dependent upon the pressure and is about 307°R for air at 100 atm pressure. In other words, if air can be compressed to 100 atm pressure and cooled to below 307°R, it can be partly liquefied by a Joule-Thomson expansion. The most economical way of cooling the air would be to pass it countercurrent to the unliquefied part of the air from the expansion

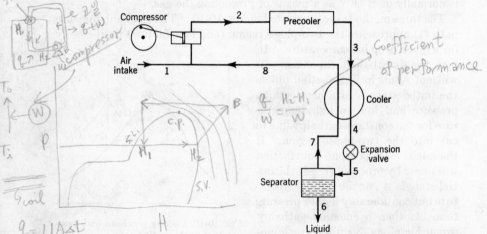

FIG. 10-11. Joule-Thomson liquefaction process.

process. This is the simplest type of machine used in practice (Fig. 10-11). The precooler can use either cooling water or an evaporating refrigerant as a heat sink. As is evident from Fig. 7-4, the lower the temperature of the air entering the expansion valve, the greater the fraction of air that will be liquefied. For example, evaporating a refrigerant in the precooler at −40°F will give a lower temperature into the valve than if water at 70°F is used as a cooling medium.

The maximum liquefaction is not obtained until steady-state conditions are reached. When the machine is first started, no liquid air will be produced. If the refrigerant described previously is used in the precooler and a 10°F approach is assumed, the first gas going into the expansion valve will be at −30°F. If the pressure in the separatory chamber is 2 atm and before the valve 100 atm, the air from the valve will be at about 372°R. No liquefaction will occur. Again assuming a 10°F approach, the high-pressure gas from the exchanger will be cooled to 382°R. Now the gas upon expansion to 2 atm pressure will cool to 310°R. This cooling of the gas will continue until steady-state conditions exist, at which time the following relationship must be satisfied:

$$H_6 z + H_8(1 - z) = H_3 \qquad (10\text{-}22)$$

where the enthalpy quantities refer to a unit mass of the fluid at the positions numbered in Fig. 10-11. From a knowledge of the enthalpies Eq. (10-22) may be solved for z, the fraction of the gas that is liquefied.

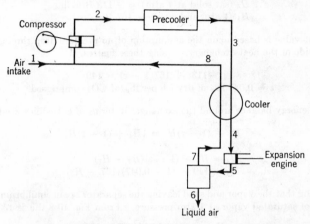

Fig. 10-12. Expansion-engine liquefaction process.

The flow diagram for the expansion engine (Fig. 10-12), the Claude process, is the same as for the Joule-Thomson expansion except that the engine replaces the expansion valve. The energy balance becomes

$$H_6 z + H_8(1 - z) + W_s = H_3 \qquad (10\text{-}23)$$

where W_s is the work per pound of fluid obtained from the expansion engine. If the operation is reversible and adiabatic, the work is given by the expression

$$W_s = -(H_5 - H_4) \qquad (10\text{-}24)$$

which follows from the total-energy balance for a flow process.

Equations (10-22) to (10-24) presuppose no heat leakage from the surroundings. This, of course, is never exactly true; such leakage may be a significant factor when the temperatures are very low, even with well-insulated apparatus.

The methods of calculation are illustrated in the example that follows:

Example 10-4. In a process for the manufacture of dry ice, carbon dioxide vapor at 1 atm pressure and 80°F is compressed in a four-stage compressor to 600 psia. The gas is cooled after each stage, leaving the intercoolers at 80°F. It then passes through a heat exchanger, where it is cooled still further.   Following the exchanger, the gas is partly solidified by throttling to atmospheric pressure.   The remaining cold gas is passed through the exchanger, leaving at 60°F.

(a) What is the production of dry ice per pound of carbon dioxide compressed?

(b) Assuming no losses, what is the temperature of the high-pressure carbon dioxide leaving the exchanger?

Solution.   (a) Figure 10-11 and Eq. (10-22) are applicable.   The enthalpy values may be read from Fig. 10-8.

$$H_3 \text{ (600 psia and 80°F)} = 149 \text{ Btu/lb}_m$$
$$H_6 \text{ (sat solid at 1 atm)} = -113 \text{ Btu/lb}_m$$
$$H_8 \text{ (1 atm and 60°F)} = 167 \text{ Btu/lb}_m$$

The last value is based upon the assumption of no pressure drop through the low-pressure side of the heat exchanger.   Using these figures,

$$-113z + 167(1 - z) = 149$$
$$z = 0.047 \text{ lb}_m \text{ of dry ice per lb}_m \text{ of } CO_2 \text{ compressed}$$

(b) An energy balance around the exchanger in terms of enthalpies would be

$$H_3 + (1 - z)H_7 = 1H_4 + (1 - z)H_8$$

or

$$H_4 = H_3 - (1 - z)(H_8 - H_7)$$
$$H_4 = 149 - (1 - 0.047)(167 - H_7)$$

Assuming that the vapor and solid leaving the separator are in equilibrium, H_7 is the enthalpy of saturated vapor at 1 atm pressure.   From Fig. 10-8 this is 133 Btu/lb$_m$.

$$H_4 = 149 - 0.953(167 - 133)$$
$$= 117 \text{ Btu/lb}_m$$

If the pressure drop in the high-pressure side of the exchanger is neglected, state 4 is characterized by an enthalpy of 117 Btu/lb$_m$ and a pressure of 600 psia.   According to Fig. 10-8 the temperature is 47°F, and the material leaving the exchanger consists of a mixture of about 80 per cent vapor and 20 per cent liquid.

PROBLEMS

1. A refrigeration machine requires 1 kw of power per ton of refrigeration.

(a) What is the coefficient of performance?

(b) How much heat is rejected to the condenser?

(c) If the condenser operates at 60°F, what is the lowest temperature the refrigerator could possibly maintain, assuming that the heat load is always 200 Btu/min?

2. A vapor-compression type of plant, employing water as refrigerant, is to be designed for a capacity of 5 tons of refrigeration when operating between a condenser temperature of 70°F and an evaporator (refrigerator) temperature of 40°F.   Assuming that the compression process is reversible and adiabatic and that the vapor leaving the evaporator is saturated,

(a) Sketch the cycle on the *T-S* and *p-H* planes.

(b) Compute the coefficient of performance and the circulation rate required.

(c) Compare the results in (b) with a Carnot cycle operating between the same temperature limits.

(d) Show by dotted lines how an actual cycle would deviate from the cycle drawn in (a).

3. A refrigerator using Freon-12 operates with a temperature of $-10°F$ in the cooling coils. The liquid Freon-12 from the condenser, at $60°F$, flows through an expansion valve into the refrigerator coils.

(a) How many pounds of Freon-12 must be circulated per hour for each ton of refrigeration produced?

(b) How much would the circulation rate be reduced if a reversible adiabatic expansion engine could be used instead of the expansion valve?

(c) Suppose the cycle is modified by inserting a countercurrent heat exchanger between the condenser and the expansion valve. The liquid from the condenser enters the exchanger at $60°F$ and is cooled by vapor from the refrigerator entering the exchanger at $-10°F$ and leaving at $50°F$. Compute the circulation rate for this modified cycle.

(d) Calculate the coefficient of performance in (a), (b), and (c).

4. An ice-manufacturing plant employs the standard vapor-compression cycle, using ammonia as the refrigerant. Compute the power requirement of the compressor and the refrigeration capacity in tons from the following information:

(a) The meter in the cooling-water line to the condenser indicates a flow of 50 lb_m/ sec. Thermometers in the inlet and exit water lines to the condenser read 60 and $80°F$.

(b) A rotameter in the liquid-ammonia line from the condenser shows a rate of 100 lb_m/min.

(c) The saturated liquid ammonia from the condenser is at $70°F$.

(d) The compressor operates adiabatically but irreversibly. Test data over a period of time indicate that the actual change in enthalpy in the compressor is 25 per cent greater than a reversible compression from the same initial state to the same final pressure. The efficiency of converting electrical energy to shaft work in the motor driving the compressor is 90 per cent.

(e) The vapor entering the compressor is saturated.

5. A vapor-compression refrigeration machine is to be used in an oil refinery to cool a solvent stream to $40°F$. The cycle will be conventional except that a countercurrent heat exchanger will be installed to subcool the liquid from the condenser with the vapor stream from the refrigerator coils. Ammonia is to be the refrigerant, and the heat load in the refrigerator coils is 200,000 Btu/min. The refrigerant is to evaporate at $32°F$ and liquefy in the condenser at $90°F$. The compressor will be adiabatic in its operation and be 80 per cent efficient compared with isentropic operation. The minimum temperature difference that can be attained in the exchanger is $10°F$.

What is the power requirement of the compressor? How does this result compare with the power for a conventional vapor-compression machine without the exchanger? Also compare the circulation rates for the two cases.

6. A house has an effective exposed area of 4000 sq ft. During the heating season of 160 days the average inside temperature should be $72°F$, while that outside is $49°F$. The over-all coefficient of heat transfer through the walls is 1.0 Btu/(hr)(sq ft)($°F$). Electricity costs \$0.03 per kilowatthour. Oil with a net heating value of 140,000 Btu/gal costs \$0.15 per gallon. Compare the seasonal costs for three heating methods:

(a) Using a conventional oil furnace

(b) Using an ideal heat pump, that is, one operating on a Carnot cycle, between 10 and $95°F$

(c) Using electrical energy directly for heating

7. An absorption refrigeration system employs benzene as refrigerant and diphenyl as an absorbent. The flow diagram of the system is the same as Fig. 10-9. The temperature of the available cooling water is such that the operating temperatures of the absorber T_A and condenser T_C will both be 30°C. The evaporator is to be operated at 6°C. The regenerator will be heated by condensing steam and operate at 95°C.

Assume that diphenyl is nonvolatile and that mixtures of benzene and diphenyl obey Raoult's law at both 30 and 95°C. Also neglect the heat of solution of benzene in diphenyl, and assume that other physical properties of the liquid mixtures, such as density and specific heat, are additive.

The operation of the system is adiabatic, except where heat is intentionally added or rejected. Neglect pressure drops due to flow except in the expansion valve and the pump. The heat exchanger operates in such a way that the temperature of the weak solution entering the absorber is 35°C.

(a) Tabulate the pressure in each part of the system and the composition of the liquid solution leaving the absorber (strong solution) and the regenerator (weak solution).

(b) Compute the theoretical minimum pump work per ton of refrigeration.

(c) Calculate the steam rate to the regenerator per ton of refrigeration, assuming that the steam condenses at 220°F and that only the latent heat is utilized.

(d) Compute the heat effects in the absorber, condenser, and evaporator per ton of refrigeration.

Data	Benzene	Diphenyl
1. Molecular weight..............................	78	154
2. Average liquid density, g/cm³....................	0.85	1.05
3. Average specific heat of liquid...................	0.45	0.45

4. Heat of vaporization of benzene, cal/g

t, °C....	20	40	80	100
ΔH......	104	101	94.4	90.6

5. Vapor pressure of benzene, mm Hg

t, °C...............	6	30	95
p, mm.............	36.7	118	1175

8. Pure dry air is supplied by a compressor and cooler system at a pressure of 160 atm and at 25°C. This air supply is used to produce liquid air by the process shown in Fig. 10-11. At steady-state conditions the low-pressure air leaves the exchanger at 5°C lower than the temperature of the incoming high-pressure air. The low-pressure side of the throttling valve is at 2 atm. The liquid air obtained in the separator in Fig. 10-11 must be further throttled through an expansion valve to atmospheric pressure to be recovered.

If the apparatus is well insulated to prevent heat exchange with the surroundings and the pressure drop in the exchanger is negligible for both fluids, what fraction of the air passing through the compressor is liquefied?

9. Liquid air is produced in a machine similar to that shown in Fig. 10-11, except that the high-pressure air from the precooler passes through cooling coils immersed in evaporating liquid ammonia before entering the cooler shown in the figure.   The ammonia evaporator is under a pressure of 6 psia.

The air leaving the precooler (entering the ammonia cooler) is at 2500 psia and 80°F. The temperature of the air leaving the ammonia evaporator is 5°F above that of the ammonia.   The pressure on the downstream side of the expansion valve is 30 psia, so that the liquid air must be further throttled to atmospheric pressure to be recovered. The pressure drops through pipes and equipment are negligible, except that on the low-pressure side of the cooler there is a 15-psia drop.   The unliquefied air is recycled from the cooler to the compressor after sufficient make-up air at 80°F and 15 psia is added.   The temperature of the low-pressure air leaving the cooler is 15°F below that of the incoming high-pressure air.

The air is compressed in three stages with equal compression ratios and cooling to 80°F after each stage.

If the plant is to produce 10 lb_m/min of liquid air at atmospheric pressure, compute the following quantities:

(a) The theoretical minimum horsepower required for each stage of the compressor.

(b) The quantity of ammonia evaporated per minute in the ammonia cooler.

(c) If the liquid ammonia for the cooler is obtained in a vapor-compression refrigeration machine whose condenser operates at 140 psia, what will be the maximum coefficient of performance?   Assume that the ammonia compressor is a two-stage unit with the same compression ratio in each stage and that the ammonia is cooled to 80°F between stages.

CHAPTER 11[1]

THERMODYNAMIC ANALYSIS OF PROCESSES

The object of this chapter is to develop a method for the evaluation of real processes from the thermodynamic point of view. No new fundamental ideas are needed; the method is based on a combination of the first and second laws. Hence, the chapter affords a review of the principles of thermodynamics so far considered.

In spite of the fact that many of the calculations of thermodynamics are based on the assumption of ideal conditions (*i.e.*, reversible processes), real or irreversible processes are nevertheless amenable to thermodynamic analysis. The object of such an analysis is to determine the over-all efficiency of the utilization of energy and to calculate the inefficiencies of the various steps of a process. The cost of energy is of concern in any manufacturing operation, and the first consideration in an attempt to reduce energy requirements is to determine where and to what extent energy is wasted through irreversibilities in the process.

11-1. The Calculation of Ideal Work. In any process requiring work, there is an absolute minimum amount which must be expended to accomplish the desired change. In a process producing work there is an absolute maximum amount which may be accomplished for a given change in the work-producing medium. In either case, this limiting value will be called the *ideal work*, or W_{ideal}. It is the work resulting when the change in state of the system is carried out in a *completely reversible* process. This requirement of complete reversibility can be divided into two parts as follows:

1. All changes within the system must be reversible.

2. Heat transfer between the system and surroundings must also be reversible.

It should be made clear at the outset of this discussion that the processes for which the following equations are developed are hypothetical. They are devised solely for the purpose of determining the ideal work associated with a given change of state. They have no connection with actual processes other than to bring about a change of state identical with

---

[1] Some of the material of this chapter was included in the paper by H. C. Van Ness, *Petrol. Refiner*, **35** (1), 165 (January, 1956), and is reprinted by permission.

the change accomplished by an actual process. The object is to compare the work of an irreversible process with the work required for the same change of state accomplished in a hypothetical reversible process. The system is selected to include the material undergoing the given change in state of the actual process, and in accordance with requirement 1 the change in state is now considered to be accomplished reversibly. Requirement 2 means that all heat transfer between the system and surroundings in the ideal process must occur at the temperature of the surroundings, T_0. Hence, at least the part of the system involved in heat transfer must be at the temperature level T_0. It may be necessary to include within the system reversible Carnot engines to accomplish heat transfer reversibly between the various temperature levels of the system and the temperature T_0. Since such engines are cyclic, they undergo no net change in state and do not contribute to any property changes in the system. An illustration of such a hypothetical process is given in Example 11-1.

As a matter of fact, it is not necessary to describe hypothetical processes for the purpose of calculating ideal work. All that is necessary is the realization that it is always possible to do so. The equations for ideal work can be developed in complete generality for any change in state from the first and second laws and the requirements of reversibility already listed. If the process is reversible and if all heat transfer between system and surroundings occurs at the temperature T_0, the second law requires that

$$dQ = T_0 \, dS \tag{11-1}$$

This equation holds for both nonflow and steady-flow processes meeting the stated requirements of reversibility.

For a nonflow process, the first law is written

$$dW = dQ - dE \tag{11-2}$$

Substitution for dQ by Eq. (11-1) gives

$$dW = T_0 \, dS - dE \tag{11-3}$$

where dW is the reversible work done by or on the system (according to the usual convention it will be positive in the former case and negative in the latter). Similarly, dS and dE are the entropy and internal-energy changes of the system, and T_0 is the absolute temperature of the surroundings.

In the nonflow process, the system may expand or contract, doing work on the atmosphere or receiving work from the atmosphere. In the former case such work cannot be used, but must be unavoidably expended; in the latter case it is free and need not be charged to the cost of operating the process. Thus to obtain what will be called ideal work, there must be subtracted from Eq. (11-3) the work exchanged with the surrounding atmosphere, $p_0 \, dV$, where p_0 is usually atmospheric pressure and dV is the volume change of the system. The result is

$$dW_{\text{ideal}} = T_0 \, dS - dE - p_0 \, dV \qquad (11\text{-}4)$$

This equation gives the ideal work for a differential nonflow process. It represents the maximum useful work which can be obtained from a work-producing process or the minimum work which must be expended for a work-requiring process for a given change in the properties of the system and for a given surroundings temperature and pressure.

More important in practice is the steady-state flow process. In this case the first law is

$$dH = dQ - dW$$

Both kinetic- and potential-energy changes have been neglected, as they are usually negligible when compared with the heat and work terms.

An analogous procedure to that used to derive Eq. (11-3) gives for the steady-flow process

$$dW = T_0 \, dS - dH$$

In this case the question of work done on or by the atmosphere does not arise, because the pV terms have already been taken into account in the dH term. Thus dW as given by the preceding equation is itself the ideal work, and

$$dW_{\text{ideal}} = T_0 \, dS - dH \qquad (11\text{-}5)$$

If T_0, the temperature of the surroundings, is considered constant, integration of Eq. (11-5) gives

$$W_{\text{ideal}} = T_0 \, \Delta S - \Delta H \qquad (11\text{-}6)$$

Example 11-1. Determine the maximum useful work that can be obtained in a flow process from 1 lb mole of nitrogen (assume ideal gas) at 1000°F and 50 atm. Take the temperature of the surroundings to be constant at 60°F. Would the result be any different if a nonflow process were considered?

Solution. The maximum possible work will be obtained from any completely reversible process which reduces the nitrogen to the temperature and pressure of the surroundings (60°F and 1 atm). The maintenance of a final temperature or pressure below the level of the surroundings would require work in an amount at least equal to any gain in work from the process as a result of the lower level. The result is obtained directly by solution of Eq. (11-6), where ΔS and ΔH are the entropy and enthalpy changes of the nitrogen as its state is changed from 1000°F and 50 atm to 60°F and 1 atm, and T_0 is $60 + 460 = 520$°R. For an ideal gas, enthalpy is independent of pressure. The enthalpy change may therefore be calculated from the heat-capacity equation for nitrogen given in Table 5-1:

$$\Delta H = \int C_p \, dT$$

$$= (1.8) \int_{T_1}^{T_0} (6.524 + 1.250 \times 10^{-3} T - 0.001 \times 10^{-6} T^2) \, dT$$

where T is in degrees Kelvin and ΔH is in Btu/lb mole. T_1 is 1000°F (811°K) and T_0 is 60°F (289°K). Integration gives $\Delta H = -6780$ Btu/lb mole.

$$\Delta S = \int \frac{C_p \, dT}{T} - R \ln \frac{p_0}{p_1}$$

$$= \int_{T_1}^{T_0} \left(\frac{6.524}{T} + 1.250 \times 10^{-3} - 0.001 \times 10^{-6} T \right) dT + 1.987 \ln 50$$

$$= 0.394 \text{ Btu/(lb mole)(°R)}$$

$$W_{\text{ideal}} = (520)(0.394) - (-6780) = 6980 \text{ Btu/lb mole}$$

To make clear the significance of this type of calculation, it may be helpful to consider a concrete process for accomplishing the change in state. Suppose the nitrogen is continuously changed to the final state ($T_0 = 60 + 460 = 520$°R and 1 atm pressure) by the following two-step process:

1. Expansion, reversibly and adiabatically, as in a turbine, from the initial state p_1, T_1, H_1 to 1 atm. Suppose the temperature at the end of this isentropic step is T_2.

2. Cooling (or heating if T_2 is less than T_0) to the final temperature T_0 at a constant pressure of 1 atm.

For step (1), the first-law equation for a flow process gives

$$Q - W_s = \Delta H$$

or, since the process is adiabatic,

$$W_s = -\Delta H = -(H_2 - H_1)$$

where H_2 is the enthalpy at the intermediate state of T_2 and 1 atm pressure.

To obtain the maximum work, step (2) must be reversible, and also all the heat transferred to the surroundings must be at T_0. These requirements can be met by employing a Carnot engine which receives heat from the nitrogen, produces work W_{Carnot}, and rejects heat to the surroundings at T_0. Since the temperature of the heat source, the nitrogen, varies from T_2 to T_0, the expression for the efficiency of the Carnot engine should be written in a differential form:

$$dW_{\text{Carnot}} = \frac{T - T_0}{T} (-dQ)$$

The minus sign preceding dQ is required in order that Q refer to the heat absorbed by the nitrogen. Integrating this expression yields

$$W_{\text{Carnot}} = -Q + T_0 \int_{T_2}^{T_0} \frac{dQ}{T}$$

The quantity Q, the heat transferred to the nitrogen, is equal to the enthalpy change $H_0 - H_2$. The integral is the change in entropy of the nitrogen going through the Carnot engine. Since step (1) occurs at constant entropy, the integral also represents ΔS for the entire process. Hence,

$$W_{\text{Carnot}} = -(H_0 - H_2) + T_0 \, \Delta S$$

The maximum or ideal work is the sum of W_s and W_{Carnot}.

$$W_{\text{ideal}} = -(H_2 - H_1) - (H_0 - H_2) + T_0 \, \Delta S$$
$$= -(H_0 - H_1) + T_0 \, \Delta S$$
$$= -\Delta H + T_0 \, \Delta S$$

which is the same as Eq. (11-6).

This method of derivation makes clear the difference between W_s, the shaft work of the turbine, and W_{ideal}. The ideal work includes not only the shaft work, but also all work obtainable by the operation of a reversible heat engine for the transfer of heat to the surroundings at T_0.

If the change in the nitrogen had been accomplished in a nonflow process, as in a piston-and-cylinder arrangement, with heat transfer to the surroundings again accomplished through a reversible heat engine, the ideal work would be calculated by Eq. (11-4), integrated for constant T_0 and p_0.

$$W_{ideal} = T_0 \, \Delta S - \Delta E - p_0 \, \Delta V$$

But for the nitrogen

$$\Delta E = \Delta H - \Delta(pV) = \Delta H - (p_0 V_2 - p_1 V_1)$$

Thus

$$
\begin{aligned}
W_{ideal} &= T_0 \, \Delta S - \Delta H + p_0 V_2 - p_1 V_1 - p_0 \, \Delta V \\
&= T_0 \, \Delta S - \Delta H + p_0 V_2 - p_1 V_1 - p_0 V_2 + p_0 V_1 \\
&= T_0 \, \Delta S - \Delta H - V_1(p_1 - p_0)
\end{aligned}
$$

or for an ideal gas

$$
\begin{aligned}
W_{ideal} &= T_0 \, \Delta S - \Delta H - \frac{RT_1}{p_1} (p_1 - p_0) \\
&= 6980 - \frac{(1.987)(1460)(50 - 1)}{50} \\
&= 4140 \text{ Btu/lb mole}
\end{aligned}
$$

Example 11-2. Rework Example 6-5, making use of the equation for ideal work.

Solution. In this method of solution, the procedure is to calculate the maximum possible work W_{ideal} which can be obtained from 1 lb_m of steam in a flow process as it undergoes a change in state from 212°F and 1 atm (saturated) to liquid water at 32°F and 1 atm. Now the problem reduces to the question of whether this amount of work is sufficient to operate a reversible Carnot heat pump delivering 800 Btu as heat at 350°F and taking heat from the unlimited supply of cooling water at 32°F.

For the steam,

$$
\begin{aligned}
\Delta H &= 0 - 1150.4 = -1150.4 \text{ Btu/lb}_m \\
\Delta S &= 0 - 1.7566 = -1.7566 \text{ Btu/(lb}_m)(°R)
\end{aligned}
$$

Therefore, by Eq. (11-6),

$$
\begin{aligned}
W_{ideal} &= T_0 \, \Delta S - \Delta H = (492)(-1.7566) - (-1150.4) \\
&= 286.2 \text{ Btu/lb}_m
\end{aligned}
$$

If this amount of work, the maximum attainable from the steam, is used to drive a reversible Carnot heat pump operating between the temperatures of 32 and 350°F, the heat transferred at the higher temperature is

$$Q = W \frac{T}{T_0 - T} = (286.2) \left(\frac{350 + 460}{350 - 32} \right) = 729 \text{ Btu}$$

This represents the maximum possible heat release at 350°F, and is less than the claimed value of 800 Btu. Thus it is concluded that the process described is *not* possible, in agreement with the result reached in Example 6-5.

11-2. Lost Work. In Sec. 6-7 an equation (6-33) was derived for the lost work resulting from the irreversible transfer of heat from one temperature to a lower one. However, the equation is not restricted, and is applicable to any kind of irreversible process.   A brief, general derivation is considered here.

Actual processes are irreversible, and every irreversibility results in lost work.   Thus, processes which produce work deliver less than the ideal, and processes which require work must be supplied with more than the ideal.   The expression for lost work is the same for all processes, and will be derived for the nonflow case.

Suppose that a differential irreversible process occurs in a nonflow system.   The objective is to relate the lost work resulting from the irreversibility of the process to the entropy change of the process.   This is done by considering the work which would accompany the same change in state of the system accomplished by a completely reversible process.   The difference between the work done by the reversible process and the work done by the irreversible process is the lost work.   The work done by the system in the irreversible process is given by the first law:

$$dW = dQ - dE$$

The reversible work is given by Eq. (11-3):

$$dW_{rev} = T_0\,dS - dE$$

The difference is the lost work:

$$dW_{lost} = dW_{rev} - dW = T_0\,dS - dE - (dQ - dE)$$

or

$$dW_{lost} = T_0\,dS - dQ \qquad\qquad (11\text{-}7)$$

where dQ is the heat transfer with respect to the system and dS is the entropy change of the system.

Sometimes it is more convenient to refer the heat transfer to the surroundings rather than the system.   In this case Eq. (11-7) becomes

$$dW_{lost} = T_0\,dS + dQ_0 \qquad\qquad (11\text{-}8)$$

where dQ_0 is heat absorbed by the surroundings.   Since the entropy change of the surroundings is dQ_0/T_0, the *total* entropy change accompanying the process is

$$dS_{total} = dS + \frac{dQ_0}{T_0} = \frac{T_0\,dS + dQ_0}{T_0}$$

Hence

$$dW_{lost} = T_0\,dS_{total}$$

This is Eq. (6-33), developed in Chap. 6 for the special case of irreversible heat transfer.   Although it has been developed for a nonflow process, it holds also for flow processes, as may be shown by an entirely analogous derivation.

For finite processes, if T_0 is constant, integration of Eq. (11-7) gives

$$W_{lost} = T_0 \Delta S - Q \qquad (11\text{-}9)$$

Example 11-3. A steam turbine takes in superheated steam at 220 psia and 900°F and exhausts at 10 psia. The turbine is neither reversible nor adiabatic, but delivers 85 per cent of the shaft work of a reversible adiabatic machine. Small heat losses to the surroundings at 70°F result from imperfect insulation and amount to 3.0 Btu per pound *mass* of steam. What is the lost work of the process?

Solution. The initial properties of the steam as given in the steam tables are

$$H_1 = 1474.2 \text{ Btu/lb}_m$$
$$S_1 = 1.7928 \text{ Btu/(lb}_m)(°R)$$

If expansion occurred reversibly and adiabatically to 10 psia, the entropy of the steam in the final state would still be 1.7928 Btu/(lb$_m$)(°R), and at this condition the enthalpy as read from the steam tables is 1146.7 Btu/lb$_m$. Thus, the reversible adiabatic work is

$$1474.2 - 1146.7 = 327.5 \text{ Btu/lb}_m$$

The actual shaft work of the turbine is

$$W_s = (0.85)(327.5) = 278.4 \text{ Btu/lb}_m$$

By the over-all energy balance for a flow process

$$\Delta H = Q - W_s$$

Hence

$$H_2 = H_1 + Q - W_s = 1474.2 - 3.0 - 278.4 = 1192.8 \text{ Btu/lb}_m$$

Thus the *actual* final state of the steam is

$$p_2 = 10 \text{ psia}$$
$$H_2 = 1192.8 \text{ Btu/lb}_m$$
$$S_2 = 1.8579 \text{ Btu/(lb}_m)(°R) \qquad \text{(from steam tables)}$$

The lost work of the process is calculated by Eq. (11-9):

$$W_{lost} = T_0 \Delta S - Q = (530)(1.8579 - 1.7928) + 3.0$$
$$= 37.5 \text{ Btu/lb}_m \text{ of steam}$$

This figure is *not* the difference between the reversible adiabatic work of the turbine and the actual work, but represents the additional work which could have been done had the expansion of the steam occurred reversibly to the *actual* final state and if the heat losses from the turbine had been used to operate reversible Carnot engines discarding heat to the surroundings at 70°F.

The lost work is also the difference between the ideal work and the actual work for the process as described. In this case, the ideal work is

$$W_{ideal} = T_0 \Delta S - \Delta H$$
$$= (530)(1.8579 - 1.7928) - (1192.8 - 1474.2)$$
$$= 315.9 \text{ Btu per pound } mass \text{ of steam}$$

Hence

$$W_{lost} = W_{ideal} - W_s = 315.9 - 278.4 = 37.5 \text{ Btu per pound } mass \text{ of steam}$$

In the preceding example a single-step process was considered, and the lost work was calculated for the over-all process. For more complicated processes, consisting of several steps, it is more useful to calculate the lost work for each step separately, so as to determine the locations of the major irreversibilities. The actual work is then the difference between the ideal-work and the lost-work terms. Thus

$$W = W_{ideal} - \Sigma W_{lost} \tag{11-10}$$

where W is the actual work of the process (shaft work for a flow process).

11-3. Thermodynamic Analysis of Practical Processes. If T_0 is constant, the terms of Eq. (11-10) may be evaluated by the application of Eq. (11-6)[1] to the over-all process for the calculation of W_{ideal} and Eq. (11-9) for the calculation of the lost work associated with each step. It should be noted that Eq. (11-10) is not ordinarily used to calculate the actual work of a process, but rather provides a check on the calculations.

The thermodynamic efficiency of a work-requiring process is defined as the ratio of the ideal work to the actual work:

$$\text{Thermodynamic efficiency (work required)} = \frac{W_{ideal}}{W} \tag{11-11}$$

In this case the actual work requirement is greater than the work ideally required. A thermodynamic analysis of the process would show what fraction of the actual work went into bringing about the desired change (ideal work) and what fraction was lost in each step of the process as a result of its irreversibility or inefficiency. For a work-producing process the thermodynamic efficiency is defined as the ratio of the actual work to the ideal work:

$$\text{Thermodynamic efficiency (work produced)} = \frac{W}{W_{ideal}} \tag{11-12}$$

The actual procedure for the analysis of processes is probably best illustrated by examples.

Example 11-4. Methane is to be liquefied in a simple Linde system, as shown in the figure on page 330. The methane is taken into the apparatus at 1 atm and 80°F, compressed to 1000 psia, and cooled again to 80°F. The product is saturated liquid methane at 1 atm. The unliquefied methane, also at 1 atm, is returned through a heat exchanger where it is heated to 75°F by the high-pressure methane. A heat leak into the exchanger from the surroundings of 2.5 Btu will be assumed for each pound *mass* of methane entering the compressor. Heat leaks to other parts of the apparatus will be assumed negligible.

---

[1] For the less important case of a nonflow process, the integrated form of Eq. (11-4) is used.

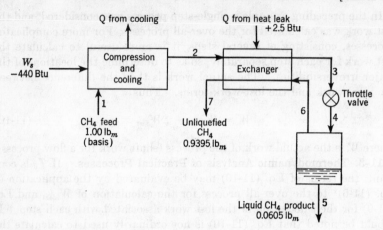

Make a thermodynamic analysis of the process, *i.e.*, determine the thermodynamic efficiency of the process, calculate the lost work in each step of the process, and express each as a percentage of the actual work.

Solution. For most practical problems the exact value chosen for T_0 makes little difference so long as it is approximately the ambient temperature. In this solution, T_0 will be taken as 80°F (540°R). Methane compression from 14.7 to 1000 psia will be assumed to be carried out in a three-stage machine with intercooling and aftercooling to 80°F. The compressor efficiency is 75 per cent compared with reversible adiabatic operation. The actual work of this compression has been calculated with the aid of the pressure-enthalpy diagram for methane to be 440 Btu per pound *mass* of methane. The fraction of the entering methane that is liquefied is readily calculated by an energy balance to be 0.0605 [see Eq. (10-22)]. The properties at the various key points of the process, calculated by the usual methods, are given in the accompanying table. Data were taken from Matthews and Hurd.[1] The basis for all calculations is 1 lb_m of methane entering the process.

Point	State of the CH_4	T, °F	p, psia	H, Btu/lb_m	S, Btu/(lb_m)(°R)
1	Superheated vapor	80.0	14.7	410.4	1.6890
2	Superheated vapor	80.0	1000	381.6	1.1273
3	Superheated vapor	−88.0	1000	223.6	0.7725
4	Wet vapor	−258.6	14.7	223.6	1.1118
5	Saturated liquid	−258.6	14.7	17.7	0.0877
6	Saturated vapor	−258.6	14.7	236.9	1.1777
7	Superheated vapor	75.0	14.7	407.7	1.6840

The heat transfer for the compression and cooling step is calculated by application of the first law:

$$Q = \Delta H + W_s = (381.6 - 410.4) - 440.0 = -468.8 \text{ Btu} \qquad (11\text{-}13)$$

[1] C. S. Matthews and C. O. Hurd, *Trans. AIChE*, **42**, 55 (1946).

The system is comprised of the methane and the equipment which contains it. Since the equipment undergoes no change, only the methane need be considered in calculating the ideal work.   This is done by Eq. (11-6) applied to the over-all process:

$$W_{ideal} = T_0\,\Delta S - \Delta H$$
$$= (540)[(0.0605)(0.0877) + (0.9395)(1.6840) - 1.6890]$$
$$- [(0.0605)(17.7) + (0.9395)(407.7) - 410.4]$$
$$= -28.6 \text{ Btu}$$

The various lost-work terms are calculated by Eq. (11-9) applied to each part of the process separately.   For the compression and cooling system,

$$W_{lost} = T_0\,\Delta S - Q = (540)(1.1273 - 1.6890) + 468.8$$
$$= 165.5 \text{ Btu}$$

For the exchanger,

$$W_{lost} = (540)[(0.9395)(1.6840 - 1.1777) + (0.7725 - 1.1273)] - 2.5$$
$$W_{lost} = 62.8 \text{ Btu}$$

For the throttle valve,

$$W_{lost} = (540)(1.1118 - 0.7725) - 0 = 183.2 \text{ Btu}$$

These results are summarized in the accompanying table.

	Btu/lb$_m$	Per cent of W
Ideal work..........................	28.6	6.5
W_{lost} in compression and cooling.......	165.5	37.6
W_{lost} in exchanger...................	62.8	14.3
W_{lost} in throttling...................	183.2	41.6
Total W........................	440.1	100.0

As required by Eq. (11-10), the sum of the first column of figures in this table is the actual work.   Also from Eq. (11-11) the first figure of the second column (6.5 per cent) is the thermodynamic efficiency of the process.

The largest loss occurs in the throttling process.   By eliminating this completely irreversible process in favor of an expansion engine, a considerable increase in efficiency can be achieved.

Example 11-5.   Consider the operation of a simple power cycle generating steam to run a steam turbine under the following conditions: The fuel is to be coke (considered to be pure carbon in these calculations), and it is to be burned completely to CO_2

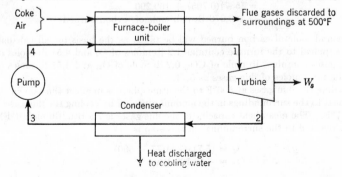

with 20 per cent excess air. Steam will be generated at 500 psia and superheated to 900°F. The turbine will have an efficiency of 75 per cent compared with an isentropic turbine, and it will exhaust to a condenser at 1 psia. It will be assumed that no subcooling of the condensate occurs in the condenser and that the condensate is returned to the boiler directly. The work of pumping the condensate to the boiler is negligible. The stack gases from the furnace will have a temperature of 500°F, and cooling water is available at 77°F. Make a thermodynamic analysis of the process.

Solution. The power cycle is represented in the figure on page 331, and the conditions and properties of the steam (as taken from the steam tables) are given for various key points of the cycle in the accompanying table.

Point	State of the steam	T, °F	p, psia	H, Btu/lb$_m$	S, Btu/(lb$_m$)(°R)
1	Superheated vapor	900	500	1465.1	1.6975
2	Wet vapor, $x = 0.973$	101.74	1	1077.5	1.9275
3	Saturated liquid	101.74	1	69.7	0.1326
4	Subcooled liquid	101.74	500	69.7	0.1326

The system consists of the material passing through the furnace and the steam cycle. However, the cycle remains invariant, and the only changes which need be considered for the calculation of ideal work are in the material passing through the furnace. In an ideal process the flue gases would be cooled to the temperature of the surroundings before leaving the system. Thus for the calculation of ideal work, we have for the property changes of the system only the *isothermal* ΔH and ΔS values for the combustion reaction. This assumes that the coke and air are also at T_0, an assumption that cannot be far from right.

The reaction occurring is

$$C + O_2 \rightarrow CO_2$$

For this reaction at 77°F (25°C),

$$\Delta H = -94,050 \text{ cal/g mole}$$
$$= -169,290 \text{ Btu/lb mole}$$
$$\Delta S = 0.705 \text{ Btu/(lb mole)(°R)}$$

ΔH is the standard heat of reaction at 25°C, and ΔS is the corresponding standard entropy change. Application of Eq. (11-6) to the process gives

$$W_{\text{ideal}} = T_0 \Delta S - \Delta H$$
$$= (537)(0.705) + 169,290$$
$$= 169,670 \text{ Btu/lb mole of carbon burned}$$

One pound mole of carbon burned will be taken as the basis for all calculations. The air supplied to the furnace contains 1.2 lb moles of O_2 and 4.51 lb moles of N_2. The flue gases contain 1 lb mole of CO_2, 0.2 lb mole of O_2, and 4.51 lb moles of N_2, giving the total moles of flue gases as 5.71.

Discarding the flue gases at 500°F to the atmosphere is in effect the same as transferring heat to the surroundings in the amount given off by cooling the flue gases from 500 to 77°F. The mean heat capacity of the flue gases is 7.5 Btu/(lb mole)(°F), and the heat rejected to the surroundings in this step is

$$Q = (5.71)(7.5)(77 - 500)$$
$$= -18,100 \text{ Btu}$$

The heat transferred to the boiler for generating steam is the heat of reaction minus the heat loss from discarding the flue gases at 500°F. This amounts to

$$169,290 - 18,100 = 151,190 \text{ Btu}$$

The amount of steam generated is therefore

$$\frac{151,190}{1465.1 - 69.7} = 108.35 \text{ lb}_m$$

The actual work produced by the turbine is

$$W_s = (108.35)(1465.1 - 1077.5) = 42,000 \text{ Btu}$$

The heat rejected to the surroundings (cooling water) in the condenser is

$$Q = (108.35)(69.7 - 1077.5)$$
$$= -109,200 \text{ Btu}$$

The lost-work quantities may now be calculated for the various steps of the process. For the furnace and boiler,

$$W_{\text{lost}} = T_0 \,\Delta S - Q$$
$$= (537)[(108.35)(1.6975 - 0.1326) + 0.705] + 18,100$$
$$= 109,530 \text{ Btu}$$

For the turbine,

$$W_{\text{lost}} = (537)(108.35)(1.9275 - 1.6975) - 0$$
$$= 13,380 \text{ Btu}$$

For the condenser,

$$W_{\text{lost}} = (537)(108.35)(0.1326 - 1.9275) + 109,200$$
$$= 4770 \text{ Btu}$$

In this case work is produced, and the actual work is less than the ideal work. Hence, it is the ideal work which must be apportioned between the actual work and the several lost-work terms. Here Eq. (11-10) is best written as

$$W_{\text{ideal}} = W + \Sigma W_{\text{lost}}$$

The results, which satisfy this equation, are summarized in the accompanying table.

	Btu per pound mole of carbon burned	Per cent of W_{ideal}
Actual work W	42,000	24.8
W_{lost} in furnace and boiler............	109,530	64.5
W_{lost} in turbine....................	13,380	7.9
W_{lost} in condenser..................	4,770	2.8
W_{lost} in pump......................	Neglected	
Total W_{ideal}......................	169,680	100.0

Since work is produced, the thermodynamic efficiency of the process is given by Eq. (11-12). From the table of results, it is 24.8 per cent.

From the standpoint of energy conservation, the thermodynamic efficiency of a process should be as high as possible, and the lost work should be as low as possible. However, the final design of a process depends on economic considerations, of which the cost of energy is only one factor. It frequently happens that for a stage in the development of technology a process of low thermodynamic efficiency is more economical than another process of higher efficiency. The thermodynamic analysis of a specific process shows the locations of the major inefficiencies, and hence the pieces of equipment or steps in the process which could be altered or replaced to advantage. However, this sort of analysis gives no hint as to the nature of the changes that might be made. It merely shows that the present design is wasteful of energy and that there should be a better one. It is one of the functions of the chemical engineer to try to devise a better process and to use his ingenuity to keep the capital expenditure low. Each newly devised process may, of course, be analyzed to determine what improvement has been made. This search for an improved process deals with the details of operation and is therefore not within the province of thermodynamics.

11-4. Application to Fluid Flow. The only integrated forms of Eqs. (11-5) and (11-7) considered so far have been those for which T_0 is constant. For most practical problems, T_0 is chosen as the maximum ambient temperature, *i.e.*, the highest temperature at which nature forces us to discard heat. However, calculations can be made for any value of T_0, even one which varies. To understand this, it is helpful to note that a given change within a system can be carried out regardless of the temperature of the surroundings. However, it is apparent from the equations given that W_{ideal} and W_{lost} depend on the value of T_0. In fact, it is convenient when speaking of ideal or lost work to regard them as being *with respect to* some particular temperature.

In the general case the value or values of T_0 may be selected at will. This is equivalent to considering the system to exist in imaginary surroundings. For example, the surroundings might be considered to consist of an infinite number of heat reservoirs, each at a different temperature. Then heat could always be transferred reversibly between the system and surroundings by choosing different heat reservoirs for different parts of the system or for different times as changes occur in the system. The surroundings temperature would then be variable and would always equal the temperature of the system. Equations (11-5) and (11-7) would then be integrated to give

$$W_{ideal} = \int T \, dS - \Delta H \qquad (11\text{-}14)$$

and

$$W_{lost} = \int T \, dS - Q \qquad (11\text{-}15)$$

where T is the absolute temperature of the system.

Ideal work and lost work calculated by these equations are always with respect to the temperature of the system, and this is presumed to be uniform (though not necessarily constant) throughout the system. This is equivalent to neglecting any work that could be obtained by operating a heat engine between the system and the *actual* surroundings. The integration of the equations requires a knowledge of the temperature-entropy relationship actually existing throughout the process.

The most interesting application of these equations is the development of the mechanical-energy balance of fluid flow (*i.e.*, the extended Bernoulli equation). One approach was given in Chap. 8. The following alternative is a purely thermodynamic derivation.

Here, potential- and kinetic-energy effects cannot be neglected, and the complete energy balance for a steady-flow process must be used. This is Eq. (2-10):

$$\Delta H + \Delta z \frac{g}{g_c} + \frac{\Delta u^2}{2g_c} = Q - W_s \qquad (2\text{-}10)$$

The basic differential equation relating enthalpy changes to changes in other properties is Eq. (7-4):

$$dH = T\,dS + v\,dp \qquad (7\text{-}4)$$

In integral form this becomes

$$\Delta H = \int T\,dS + \int v\,dp \qquad (11\text{-}16)$$

Objection is sometimes made to the application of this equation to irreversible or actual processes (such as fluid flow) on the basis that integration is possible only if the path of the process is known and an exact path cannot be defined for an irreversible process. In the strictest sense this is true, but for most engineering purposes the path can be adequately defined so that results of the required accuracy are obtained.

By Eq. (11-15),

$$\int T\,dS = Q + W_{\text{lost}}$$

Substituting this in Eq. (11-16),

$$\Delta H = Q + W_{\text{lost}} + \int v\,dp \qquad (11\text{-}17)$$

ΔH may now be eliminated between Eqs. (2-10) and (11-17) to give

$$Q + W_{\text{lost}} + \int v\,dp + \Delta z \frac{g}{g_c} + \frac{\Delta u^2}{2g_c} = Q - W_s$$

or

$$-W_s = \int v\,dp + \Delta z \frac{g}{g_c} + \frac{\Delta u^2}{2g_c} + W_{\text{lost}} \qquad (11\text{-}18)$$

The W_{lost} term represents the total lost work as a result of fluid friction taken with respect to the temperature of the flowing fluid. It is customary to divide it into two parts: the lost work in the pump, turbine, compressor, or other machine and the lost work from friction in pipes, valves, fittings, etc. Thus

$$W_{\text{lost}} = W_{\text{lost pump}} + \Sigma W_{\text{lost}}$$

Equation (11-18) then becomes

$$-W_s = \int v \, dp + \Delta z \frac{g}{g_c} + \frac{\Delta u^2}{2g_c} + W_{\text{lost pump}} + \sum W_{\text{lost}}$$

or

$$-(W_s + W_{\text{lost pump}}) = \int v \, dp + \Delta z \frac{g}{g_c} + \frac{\Delta u^2}{2g_c} + \sum W_{\text{lost}}$$

The quantity $W_s + W_{\text{lost pump}}$ is the ideal work of the pump, turbine, compressor, or other machine and is designated by W^*. It is the shaft work of an ideal machine, operating without friction. Thus

$$-W^* = \int v \, dp + \Delta z \frac{g}{g_c} + \frac{\Delta u^2}{2g_c} + \sum W_{\text{lost}}$$

In the nomenclature of fluid flow, ΣW_{lost} is replaced by ΣF, the summation of mechanical-energy losses through friction in pipes, valves, fittings, etc., but does not include friction losses in the pump, turbine, compressor, or other machine. The final form of the mechanical-energy balance is then written

$$-W^* = \int v \, dp + \Delta z \frac{g}{g_c} + \frac{\Delta u^2}{2g_c} + \sum F$$

This is the same equation developed in Chap. 8 [Eq. (8-5)] from purely mechanical principles. The derivation given here shows it to be in accord with thermodynamic principles.

W^* is not the actual shaft work (W_s) of the pump, compressor, turbine, or other machine. However, W_s may be calculated by multiplying or dividing (depending on whether work is produced or required) W^* by an appropriate efficiency.

PROBLEMS

1. Determine the maximum amount of useful work that can be obtained in a flow process from 1 lb mole of steam at 200 psig, superheated 100°F. $T_0 = 60°F$.

2. One pound *mass* of water is heated at a constant pressure of 1 atm from 70°F to the boiling point and is completely vaporized at this temperature. What is the maximum percentage of the heat added to the water that can be converted into work if the temperature of the surroundings is 70°F? What happens to the rest of the heat? What is the entropy change of the surroundings during the process? Of the system? Total?

3. Suppose that the heat required in the preceding problem came from a furnace at a temperature of 500°F. What is the total entropy change resulting from this heating process? How much work is lost because of the irreversibility of the process? Recalculate the lost work by making use of the result of the preceding problem.

4. In a test of a reciprocating air compressor, air at 1 atm and 40°F was taken from the surroundings and compressed to 147 psia. The cylinder of the compressor was water-cooled. In this particular test, water circulated through the cooling jacket at a rate of 100 lb_m/lb mole of air compressed. It entered at 40°F and left at 60°F. The temperature of the air leaving the compressor was 290°F. Assuming all other heat transfer to the surroundings to be negligible, calculate the ratio of the work actually delivered to the compressor to the ideal work of the process. Assume air to be an ideal gas with a constant $C_p = 7$ Btu/(lb mole)(°F).

5. As an initial step in considering a process to separate methane and ethane by low-temperature distillation, the minimum work requirement is to be calculated. The feed mixture is to contain 60 mole per cent methane and 40 mole per cent ethane, and will enter the apparatus at 90°F and 1 atm. The product streams are to be essentially pure methane and ethane at 1 atm and 70°F. What is the minimum work requirement for this process per mole of feed mixture? Assume ideal gases. Cooling water is available at 50°F.

6. (a) Calculate the minimum work in kilowatthours and per lb mole of O_2 to separate dry air at 1 atm and 70°F into its pure components (consider N_2 and O_2 only) at 1 atm and 70°F. Assume the gases to be ideal.

(b) Repeat for the separation into two streams, one 50 mole per cent oxygen and the other 98 mole per cent nitrogen.

(c) Repeat for the separation into pure liquid oxygen and impure gaseous nitrogen, with 90 per cent oxygen recovery.   *Ans.* (a) 0.757; (b) 0.140; (c) 3.17.

7. An ideal gas is expanded adiabatically through an orifice from a pressure of 300 psia to 15 psia without doing any work. Heat transfer and changes in potential and kinetic energy are negligible. How much work is lost because of this process? State any assumptions.

8. A gas with a heat capacity given by the equation

$$C_p = 6.30 + 1.01 \times 10^{-3}T - 0.107 \times 10^{-6}T^2$$

where T is degrees Rankine and C_p is Btu/(lb mole)(°F), is cooled at constant pressure from 2000 to 100°F. The surroundings temperature is 60°F. What is the work lost as a result of the process? Show that the same result is obtained by calculating the work which can be derived by operating reversible heat engines with the gas serving as the source of heat.

9. Exhaust gas at 650°F and 1 atm from an internal-combustion engine is to be used in a waste-heat boiler to generate saturated steam at a pressure of 140 psia. Water enters the boiler at 70°F, the temperature of the surroundings. The boiler is designed for a minimum heat-transfer driving force of 50°F. The steam generated is to be used to operate a turbine having an efficiency of 80 per cent, and it exhausts to a condenser maintained at a pressure of 2 in. Hg abs.

(a) What is the work output of the turbine?
                                        Ans. 404 Btu per pound mole of exhaust gas.

(b) What is the thermodynamic efficiency of the boiler-turbine combination?
                                        Ans. 47.6 per cent.

(c) What is the work lost in the boiler?

> *Ans.* 276 Btu per pound mole of exhaust gas.

For the exhaust gas, take the molal $C_p = 6.38 + 0.00118T$ (°R).

10. An ice plant is to produce 1 ton of flake ice per hour in a continuous process. What is the minimum power requirement for this process if water is cooled from 70 to 32°F and frozen at this temperature? Heat rejection is at 70°F. The latent heat of fusion of ice at 32°F is 143.3 Btu/lb$_m$. *Ans.* 10.0 hp.

11. With reference to the preceding problem, the required refrigeration might be accomplished with an absorption refrigeration machine using condensing steam to supply the heat. Determine the minimum steam requirement for such a process. Assume that exhaust steam is available, saturated at 30 psia, and that heat is again rejected at 70°F. *Ans.* 106 lb$_m$/hr.

12. It is necessary in a certain steady-state process to cool 100,000 ft³/hr of air at 60°F and 1 atm to 20°F by refrigeration. If cooling water is available at 60°F, what is the minimum work requirement in Btu per hour?

13. A flue gas is cooled from 2000 to 300°F, and the heat is used to generate steam continuously in a boiler. The steam is to be saturated at 212°F. The flue gas has a molal heat capacity given by the equation

$$C_p = 7.00 + 0.00300T \text{ (°R)}$$

Water enters the boiler at its boiling point, 212°F, and is vaporized at this temperature.

(a) With reference to a surroundings temperature of 60°F, what is the lost work of this process per mole of flue gas?

(b) What is the maximum work per mole of flue gas that can be accomplished by the saturated steam at 212°F if it condenses only and does not subcool? The temperature of the surroundings is again 60°F.

(c) How does the answer in part (b) compare with the maximum work theoretically obtainable from the flue gas itself as it is cooled from 2000 to 300°F?

14. One million cubic feet of methane (as measured at 1 atm and 60°F) is to be compressed per hour from 100 psia and 80°F to 500 psia in a single-stage compressor operating adiabatically. The compressor may be assumed to operate with an efficiency of 80 per cent. After leaving the compressor, the gas is cooled at constant pressure of 500 psia to a temperature of 100°F by cooling water. Water is available at a temperature of 60°F.

(a) What will be the power required to drive the compressor?

(b) Assuming the temperature rise of the water in the cooler to be 20°F, how much water will be required per hour?

(c) What is the thermodynamic efficiency of the over-all process (compression plus cooling)?

15. An inventor has developed a complicated process for making heat continuously available at an elevated temperature. Saturated steam at 220°F is used as the only source of energy. Assuming that there is plenty of cooling water available at 75°F, what is the maximum amount of heat which could be made available at a temperature level of 400°F per Btu of heat given up by the steam?

16. An ice plant is to produce 3000 lb$_m$ of ice per hour. What is the absolute minimum power requirement to cool the water from 80 to 32°F and freeze it at this temperature, if heat rejection is at 80°F? What would be the power required by a single Carnot heat pump operating between 32 and 80°F? What is the minimum power requirement if an ideal ammonia cycle is used? What is the power requirement if a practical ammonia cycle is used, if the compressor is 80 per cent efficient, and if the minimum temperature approaches in the condenser and evaporator are

8°F? The condenser is water-cooled, and the rise in the water temperature is to be 30°F. At what rate must ammonia circulate in the practical cycle? In all cases the process is one of steady flow. The condenser is to operate countercurrently.

17. Consider the following reaction: $CO + \frac{1}{2}O_2 \rightarrow CO_2$. The standard heat of this reaction at 25°C is $-67,640$ cal, and the standard entropy change is -20.8 cal/°K.

(a) What is the maximum work which can be obtained in a flow process at 1 atm through the use of this reaction? The surroundings are at 25°C.

(b) If carbon monoxide is burned in an adiabatic reactor at 1 atm with the theoretical amount of air, what is the maximum amount of work which can be obtained from the flue gases if the reaction goes to completion? The surroundings are again at 25°C. The gases may be assumed ideal. Where is the irreversibility in this process? How much work is lost because of this irreversibility? What has increased in entropy? By how much?

(c) If the flue gases are discarded to the atmosphere at a temperature of 300°C after being used to generate saturated steam continuously in a boiler at 400 psia, what is the maximum work which can be obtained from the steam in a flow process per gram mole of carbon monoxide burned? Water enters the process at 1 atm and 25°C, the temperature of the surroundings. What are the irreversible features of this process?

18. It is proposed that a stream of cold CO_2 can be obtained in the following manner: CO_2 at 15 psia and 50°F is to be compressed to a pressure of 250 psia, cooled to 50°F, and then expanded to 15 psia once again by a Joule-Thomson expansion. The compression is to be accomplished in two stages with intercooling. The compressor efficiency may be taken as 80 per cent. Calculate:

(a) The work required per mole of CO_2 compressed.

(b) The amount of heat removed per mole of CO_2 in the intercooler and aftercooler.

(c) The final state of the CO_2 after expansion. Make a thermodynamic analysis of the process.

19. A chemical plant has saturated steam available at 400 psia, but because of a process change has little use for steam at this pressure. The new process uses steam at 150 psia. In addition, the plant also has exhaust steam available, saturated at 40 psia. It has been suggested that the 40-psia steam be compressed to 150 psia, obtaining the required work by expanding the 400-psia steam to 150 psia. The two streams at 150 psia could then be mixed. Calculate the amounts of each kind of steam required to give enough steam at 150 psia to supply 1,000,000 Btu/hr by condensation only (*i.e.*, no subcooling). Perform these calculations for an ideal system. Rework the problem for a practical process, and suggest a method or methods for carrying out the process.

20. A conventional vapor-compression refrigeration cycle is to be installed in an oil refinery to cool a solvent oil from 70 to 40°F. The oil rate is 16,670 lb_m/min, and the oil has a specific heat of 0.40. Ammonia is to be used as the refrigerant. The evaporator is to operate at 32°F and the condenser at 90°F. The compressor will operate adiabatically and will be assumed 80 per cent efficient, compared with isentropic operation. Cooling water is available at 75°F. Make a thermodynamic analysis of the process.

Ans. The actual work is subdivided as follows: W_{ideal}, 24.7 per cent; loss in condenser, 25.3 per cent; loss in throttling, 5.7 per cent; loss in evaporator, 27.5 per cent; loss in compression, 16.8 per cent.

21. A single-effect evaporator (with feed at the boiling point) in which water is being vaporized from a colloidal solution discharges 1000 lb_m of steam per hour at 212°F, dry and saturated. The boiling-point elevation is negligible. A plant engineer proposes the installation of a compressor which will take this vapor, compress it, and return it to the heating coils. It is necessary to maintain at least a 50°F heat-transfer driving force across the coils. Assume no subcooling of the condensate from the coils.

(a) With adiabatic and reversible operation of the compressor, how much could one afford to pay for the compressor to operate 24 hr a day, 300 days a year? The total fixed charges are 25 per cent; power costs 1 cent per kwhr; steam costs 40 cents per 1000 lb_m. Would make-up steam be necessary to augment the compressed steam? What would be the exit temperature from the compressor?

(b) Rework the problem for an 80 per cent compressor efficiency and a 90 per cent motor efficiency.

(c) Make a thermodynamic analysis of the process of part (b).

22. Refrigeration at a temperature level of 150°R is required for a certain process. A cycle using helium gas has been proposed to operate as follows: Helium at 1 atm is compressed adiabatically to 5 atm, water-cooled to 60°F, and sent to a heat exchanger where it is cooled by returning helium. From there it goes to an adiabatic expander which delivers work to be used to help drive the compressor. The helium then enters the refrigerator, where it absorbs enough heat to raise its temperature to 140°R. It returns to the compressor by way of the heat exchanger.

Helium may be considered an ideal gas with a constant molal heat capacity at constant pressure of 5. If the efficiencies of the compressor and expander are 80 per cent and if the minimum temperature difference in the exchanger is 10°F, at what rate must the helium be circulated to provide refrigeration at a rate of 100 Btu/min? What is the net power requirement of the process? Sketch the cycle, and show the temperatures at the various points. What is the coefficient of performance of the cycle? How does it compare with the Carnot C.O.P.? Make a thermodynamic analysis of the process.

CHAPTER 12

PHASE EQUILIBRIA

The composition of phases in equilibrium is of paramount importance in a great number of physical and chemical processes. The temperature-pressure-composition relationships in multiphase systems at equilibrium form the basis for the quantitative treatment of all distillation, absorption, and extraction processes. The nature of equilibrium between phases also may be an important factor in many other problems, for example, in the mixed-phase flow of liquid and gas in pipes. Many chemical reactions are carried out industrially at conditions where more than one phase exists. In these instances the equilibrium conditions are determined by the restrictions of both phase equilibrium and chemical-reaction equilibrium (Chap. 13).

Although thermodynamics is of considerable value in determining the pressure-temperature-composition relationships at equilibrium, experimental data are also necessary to provide the information required for the solution of practical problems. These problems are commonly of two types: (1) the determination of the composition of phases which exist in equilibrium at a known temperature and pressure; (2) the determination of the conditions of temperature and pressure required to obtain equilibrium between phases of specified compositions. Thermodynamics provides the system of equations relating the necessary experimental data and the unknown phase compositions, temperature, and pressure. By far the largest number of industrial problems involve only liquid and vapor phases, although vapor-solid, liquid-solid, solid-solid, and vapor-liquid-solid systems are sometimes encountered. The material in this chapter will be limited to liquid-vapor and liquid-liquid systems and will be divided into three parts. First is a general discussion of the concept of equilibrium, then a more detailed treatment of mixtures of miscible materials, and finally a brief treatment of partially miscible and immiscible liquid systems.

12-1. The Nature of Equilibrium. Equilibrium implies a situation in which there is no change with respect to time. In thermodynamics, where attention is focused upon a particular quantity of material, this means no change in the properties of that material with time. Actually, a true state of equilibrium is probably never reached owing to continual variations in the surroundings and to retarding resistances. Equilibrium requires a balance of all potentials that may cause a change. However, the rate of change, and hence the rate of approach to equilibrium, is proportional to the difference in potential between the actual state and the equilibrium state. Therefore the rate of change becomes very slow as equilibrium is approached. Actually, equilibrium is assumed in scientific studies when changes can no longer be detected with the available measuring devices. In engineering problems, the assumption of equilibrium is justified when the results computed according to equilibrium methods are of satisfactory accuracy. For example, in the still of a distillation system, equilibrium between liquid and vapor phases is commonly assumed. This is not exactly true because the vaporization process occurs rapidly. However, the compositions of liquid and vapor evaluated by equilibrium calculations are within a few per cent of the actual results.

As an example of phase equilibrium, consider the boiling of liquid water at atmospheric pressure. Suppose the operation is carried out in such a way that the liquid and vapor are intimately mixed at all times. If the supply of heat is removed and the vessel is completely insulated, there would be no further tendency for changes to occur. The temperature, pressure, volume, etc., of each phase would not vary with time. The system is in equilibrium. Nevertheless, conditions are not static. The molecules comprising the liquid phase at one instant are not the same molecules as those in the liquid at a later time. Those molecules which possess exceptionally high velocities in comparison with the average value and which are near the interphase boundary will overcome the surface forces and pass into the vapor phase. Similarly, molecules in the vapor phase with much less than the average velocity will be captured by the liquid phase. However, the average rate of passage of molecules is the same in both directions so that there is no net transfer of material between the phases.

Throughout the earlier chapters the reversible or equilibrium process has been used in illustrating the first and second laws. From the foregoing discussion it is evident that an actual process cannot occur at equilibrium. For example, if the transfer of material between phases is to take place at an appreciable rate, a finite difference in potential must exist. This is contrary to the concept of equilibrium.[1]

The equilibrium process can be approached very closely in practice by conducting operations at a slow rate. As an illustration refer again to

[1] The principle of the equilibrium process was retained in the formulation of the first and second laws by postulating a differential change in potentials and not restricting the time allowed for a change to take place.

the example of boiling water. Suppose heat is supplied at a constant rate and water is evaporated at constant pressure. If the rate of heat absorption is held to a low value and the liquid and vapor phases are intimately mixed, the transfer of water from the liquid to the vapor phase will approach an equilibrium process. It will not occur exactly at equilibrium because there must exist a driving force that results in more molecules leaving the liquid than returning to it from the vapor.

12-2. Criteria of Equilibrium. The next step in the development is to inquire what the defining characteristics of this equilibrium process are in terms of thermodynamic variables.

When liquid water is evaporated at conditions approaching equilibrium, the temperature and pressure of the two phases are observed to be the same. This is a necessary condition for equilibrium between phases and will be accepted here without further discussion. In addition to this condition there are other restraints placed by thermodynamics on multiphase systems at equilibrium. These were first deduced by Gibbs.[1] He showed that a quantity, which he called the *chemical potential* μ, must have the same value for a given component in each phase at equilibrium. The term *potential* is a good one, for it indicates that this quantity is a driving force in the transfer of material from one phase to another. The equality of these driving forces or potentials in all phases for each component indicates that no tendency for material transfer exists. Hence, this is also a basic criterion for phase equilibrium and may be indicated mathematically by the expression

$$\mu_k' = \mu_k'' = \mu_k''' = \mu_k''''$$
(12-1)

where k refers to any one component of the system and the primes refer to different phases.

While a complete and rigorous proof of the equality of the chemical potentials will not be attempted in this text, Eq. (12-1) can be easily verified for the simple example of boiling water considered in the previous paragraphs. Gibbs defined the chemical potential of a pure component in the following manner:

$$\mu = F = H - TS$$
(12-2)

where the enthalpy and entropy refer to a single mole of material. The free energy F for 1 mole is equivalent to the chemical potential and is perhaps more generally used. However, the latter term emphasizes the existence of a potential for the transfer of mass, just as there is a potential (temperature) for the transfer of energy as heat.

[1] J. W. Gibbs, "Collected Works," Vol. I, pp. 55–354, Longmans, Green & Co., Inc., New York, 1931.

Applying Eq. (12-2) to the equilibrium process of evaporating a mole of liquid water,

$$\Delta\mu = \Delta H - T\,\Delta S \tag{12-3}$$

From the first law for a constant-pressure process [Eq. (2-21)],

$$\Delta H = Q$$

From the second law for a constant-temperature reversible process,

$$Q = T\,\Delta S \tag{12-4}$$

Combining Eqs. (12-3) and (12-4),

$$\Delta\mu = 0 \tag{12-5}$$

or

$$\mu_L = \mu_G \tag{12-6}$$

Equations (12-5) and (12-6) are restricted forms of the general equation (12-1). They indicate that, for the equilibrium process, there is no change in the chemical potential of a substance as a result of its transfer from liquid to gas. Equation (12-6) was developed on the basis of a transfer of material actually taking place. It applies also to the cases where two phases are in equilibrium with no net change occurring.

The chemical potential is an intensive quantity. Free energy, like internal energy and enthalpy, is basically an extensive quantity. However, the difference is eliminated if the free energy per mole is taken as the basis of comparison. Thus Eq. (12-2) is true only for a single mole of material, while the following relationship is applicable to any quantity:

$$F = H - TS \tag{12-2}$$

A complication is introduced in the study of phase equilibria when multicomponent systems are involved. In such systems the molal enthalpy, entropy, and chemical potential are not determined entirely by the temperature and pressure but are functions of a certain number of additional intensive quantities as required by the phase rule. Normally concentrations of components in the phases are chosen for these additional variables since they are easily measured. For example, in a binary single-phase system the energy for 1 mole of one of the components depends upon the temperature, pressure, and the composition. The molal energy of alcohol in a liquid containing water and ethanol depends upon the mole fraction ethanol as well as on T and p. The same situation exists with regard to the entropy, enthalpy, and free energy or chemical potential. Hence, the chemical potential of a component in a mixture is not equal to the chemical potential of the pure component at the same temperature and pressure as that of the mixture. Nor is it generally possible to calculate, from thermodynamics alone, the chemical potential in a multicomponent system from the temperature, pressure, and composition of the mixture. Experimental information concerning the effect of changes in composition upon these properties is necessary. Because of this effect of composition, the energy, enthalpy, entropy, and free energy for 1 mole of a component in the mixture are normally defined in the following way:

partial quantity

$$\bar{E}_k = \left(\frac{\partial \underline{E}}{\partial n_k}\right)_{T,p,n} \tag{12-7}$$

$$\bar{H}_k = \left(\frac{\partial \underline{H}}{\partial n_k}\right)_{T,p,n} \tag{12-8}$$

$$\bar{S}_k = \left(\frac{\partial \underline{S}}{\partial n_k}\right)_{T,p,n} \tag{12-9}$$

$$\bar{F}_k = \left(\frac{\partial \underline{F}}{\partial n_k}\right)_{T,p,n} \tag{12-10}$$

In Eqs. (12-7) to (12-10) $\underline{E}$, $\underline{H}$, $\underline{S}$, and $\underline{F}$ refer to *total quantities* for the homogeneous mixture. The specific quantities written with the bar above are called *partial quantities*. Physically, the partial derivative means the change in energy (enthalpy, entropy, or free energy) occurring when 1 mole of component k is added to the phase under conditions of constant temperature, pressure, and composition n. For example, if a mole of component k is added to a very large quantity of mixture of composition n at constant pressure and temperature, the change in energy of the mixture would be $\bar{E}_k$. The composition would not change significantly during the addition of a single mole to a very large quantity of mixture. The partial quantities represent intensive properties of the solution just like the temperature and pressure.

The chemical potential of component k in the mixture would be equivalent to its partial free energy,

$$\mu_k = \bar{F}_k \tag{12-11}$$

These ideas can be summarized by stating that the chemical potential is equivalent to the free energy when the latter is on a molal basis, *i.e.*, an intensive property, and that the free energy of a component in a mixture, the partial free energy, is a function of the composition as well as the temperature and pressure.

12-3. The Fugacity. The use of the chemical potential in problems in phase equilibria is somewhat inconvenient. This is evident from Eq. (12-12), which may be obtained by differentiating Eq. (12-2) and combining the result with the first and second laws. For a pure component,

$$d\mu = dH - T\,dS - S\,dT$$

From the first and second laws,

$$dH = dE + d(pv) = T\,dS + v\,dp$$

Then

$$d\mu = -S\,dT + v\,dp$$

For a constant-temperature process, $dT = 0$, and

$$\left(\frac{\partial \mu}{\partial p}\right)_T = v \tag{12-12}$$

Equation (12-12) shows that at low pressures the chemical potential decreases rapidly as the pressure decreases. If the chemical potential is finite at 1 atm, it will approach a very high negative value at pressures near zero because the volume tends toward infinity. On the other hand, if μ is finite at a low pressure, it will have a very large positive value at ordinary pressures. This is an important consideration, for at very low pressures certain generalizations (for example, the ideal-gas law) can be made regarding the behavior of all substances. For this reason a new variable, related to the chemical potential and called the *fugacity f*, is in widespread use. It was first proposed by G. N. Lewis and may be partially defined for a pure component as follows:[1]

$$\mu = RT \ln f + \theta \tag{12-13}$$

where θ is a function of temperature only and μ is based upon 1 mole of material. This equation does not determine the absolute value of the fugacity, except in terms of the unknown constant θ. The definition can be completed by considering what happens as the pressure approaches zero.

By differentiating Eq. (12-13) at constant temperature and combining the result with (12-12) the following relationship is obtained:

$$\frac{d(\ln f)}{dp} = \frac{v}{RT} \tag{12-14}$$

As the pressure at which (12-14) is applied approaches zero, the behavior of all substances approaches that of an ideal gas. Hence, at very low pressures,

$$d(\ln f) = d(\ln p) \tag{12-15}$$

If upon integration the constant of integration is chosen equal to zero, the fugacity is equal to the pressure, or

$$f^* = p^* \tag{12-16}$$

[1] G. N. Lewis and Merle Randall, "Thermodynamics and the Free Energy of Chemical Substances," McGraw-Hill Book Company, Inc., New York, 1923.

where the superscript symbolizes a pressure approaching zero. Equation (12-16), stating that the fugacity is equal to the pressure at a pressure near zero (or at any pressure where the ideal-gas law is valid), completes the definition of this new thermodynamic potential. Note that the fugacity does not have the disadvantage of the chemical potential; *i.e.*, as the pressure is decreased, it remains finite, approaching a value equal to the pressure itself.

From Eqs. (12-1) and (12-13) and the fact that the temperature must be equal in all phases at equilibrium, an alternative criterion of equilibrium in terms of fugacities is

$$\bar{f}_k' = \bar{f}_k'' = \bar{f}_k''' = \bar{f}_k'''' \qquad (12\text{-}17)[1]$$

With the aid of Eq. (12-17) the basic problem of determining the composition of phases in equilibrium is, in principle, quite simple. It is necessary only to evaluate the compositions so that the fugacity of each component is the same in all phases. For example, in a liquid-vapor mixture of ethanol and water at a definite temperature and pressure, the mole fraction ethanol in the liquid and vapor must be such that the fugacity of ethanol is the same in both phases, or, in terms of Eq. (12-17),

$$\bar{f}_{\text{gas}} = \bar{f}_{\text{liquid}}$$

In order to evaluate quantitatively these equilibrium compositions it is necessary to relate the fugacity of a component to its mole fraction in the mixture. Equations (12-12) to (12-16) are not directly applicable to this problem, for they apply only to pure substances. For multicomponent single-phase systems Eqs. (12-12) and (12-13) become

$$\left(\frac{\partial \mu_k}{\partial p}\right)_T = \bar{v}_k \qquad (12\text{-}18)$$

and

$$\mu_k = RT \ln \bar{f}_k + \theta \qquad (12\text{-}19)$$

where μ_k is the chemical potential of component k in the mixture and $\bar{v}_k$ is the partial molal volume of component k, defined in the same manner as the partial energy [Eq. (12-7)]. Thus the partial molal volume is the change in volume of a very large quantity of the mixture when 1 mole of the pure component is added at constant pressure and temperature.

Differentiating Eq. (12-19), combining with Eq. (12-18), and integrating at constant temperature and composition leads to the result

$$\ln \frac{\bar{f}_k}{\bar{p}_k^*} = \frac{1}{RT} \int_{p^*}^{p} \bar{v}_k \, dp \qquad (12\text{-}20)$$

---

[1] In this text f_k will denote the fugacity of pure component k and $\bar{f}_k$ will mean the fugacity of k in a solution.

In this expression the partial pressure $\bar{p}_k^*$ has been substituted for the fugacity $\bar{f}_k^*$ at the very low pressure p^*, in accordance with Eq. (12-16).

For the same component in the pure state Eq. (12-14), upon integration at constant temperature, becomes

$$\ln \frac{f_k}{p^*} = \frac{1}{RT} \int_{p^*}^{p} v_k \, dp \tag{12-21}$$

where v_k is the molal volume of pure k. The asterisk in Eqs. (12-20) and (12-21) refers to a pressure approaching zero.

At the very low pressure the mixture will exhibit a behavior closely approaching that of an ideal gas. Therefore the partial pressure of the component k in the mixture will be given by the following equation (Dalton's law), developed in Sec. 4-5,

$$\bar{p}_k^* = p^* y_k \tag{12-22}$$

where y_k is the mole fraction of component k in the gaseous mixture.

Then combining Eqs. (12-20), (12-21), and (12-22) to eliminate $\bar{p}_k^*$ and p^*, there is obtained[1]

$$\ln \frac{\bar{f}_k}{f_k y_k} = \frac{1}{RT} \int_0^p (\bar{v}_k - v_k) \, dp \tag{12-23}$$

The term within the integral in Eq. (12-23) is the difference between the partial molal volume of component k in the mixture and its molal volume in the pure state at the same pressure and temperature. It represents the change in *total* volume when 1 mole of k is added to a mixture, or, more simply, the volume change on mixing. The integration is carried out at constant temperature and composition but variable pressure from zero to p.†

If $\bar{v}_k = v_k$ at all pressures and compositions, Eq. (12-23) gives a simple relationship for the effect of composition on the fugacity of a gas, namely,

$$\boxed{\bar{f}_k = f_k y_k} \tag{12-24a}$$

The partial volume $\bar{v}_k$ will be equal to v_k if the volume change on mixing is zero. When this is true for all pressures from zero to p, the system is called an ideal solution. For example, a mixture of ideal gases is an ideal solution. If Eq. (12-24a) is applied to a vapor phase which follows ideal-gas behavior, the fugacities may be replaced by pressures in accordance

[1] B. H. Sage and W. N. Lacey, "Thermodynamics for Multi-component Systems," copyright, 1940.

† While both v_k and $\bar{v}_k$ approach infinity as the pressure approaches zero, their difference remains a finite quantity. Hence, in Eq. (12-23) the value of the integral is essentially independent of the lower limit of integration p^*, as long as it approaches zero. Under these circumstances the convenient value of $p^* = 0$ can be chosen.

with Eq. (12-16). The result is Dalton's law, stating that the partial pressure of a component in a gas is equal to the total pressure multiplied by the mole fraction y_k, that is,

$$\bar{p}_k = \text{partial pressure} = py_k \qquad (12\text{-}25)$$

Equation (12-22) is an application of this equation at pressures approaching zero.

The concept of an ideal solution is also applied to liquid solutions. To interpret the requirements necessary for a liquid mixture to be an ideal solution, it is best to look upon the fugacity as the escaping tendency of molecules from the solution.[1] This escaping tendency of component k should depend upon the volume fraction of k molecules in the mixture and the effect of the other substances present. This second factor is determined by the intermolecular forces between the molecules of k and the other components. If these forces were the same for all the kinds of molecules present, the escaping tendency of k would depend only upon the volume fraction of k. If, further, the molecular volumes of all the components were the same, the mole fraction would represent the sole effect of composition, and an equation similar to Eq. (12-24a) would be applicable. These requirements for an ideal-liquid solution are not so severe as those for a mixture of ideal gases. For ideal gases, the intermolecular forces and molecular volumes are both zero. For ideal solutions, it is only necessary that the intermolecular forces and molecular volumes be the same for all the components. Thus, liquid benzene and toluene form an ideal solution but have finite force fields and molecular volumes so that their mixtures are, obviously, not ideal gases.

For *ideal*-liquid solutions, then, the general equation (12-23) reduces to the simple form

$$\bar{f}_k = f_k x_k \qquad (12\text{-}24b)$$

Equation (12-24b) means that the fugacity of a component in an ideal solution is equal to the mole fraction times the fugacity of the pure component, evaluated at the same pressure and temperature and in the same kind of phase. It is known as the *Lewis and Randall rule.*

The liquid fugacities $\bar{f}_k$ and f_k in Eq. (12-24b) can be replaced with gas-phase fugacities through the application of Eq. (12-17). Thus the fugacity $\bar{f}_k$ is equal to the fugacity of k in the gas phase in equilibrium with the liquid solution. If this gas phase is assumed to be ideal, then $\bar{f}_k$ is equivalent to the partial pressure $\bar{p}_k$ of k in the gas. Applying the same reasoning to the liquid phase of pure k, f_k is equal to the vapor pres-

---

[1] As described by G. N. Lewis and Merle Randall, *op. cit.*

sure p_k' of the ideal gas over the liquid. Under these conditions Eq. (12-24b) may be written

$$\bar{f}_k = \bar{p}_k = p_k' x_k \tag{12-26}$$

This expression is known as *Raoult's law.*

The results of the preceding paragraphs may be summarized as follows:

1. Equation (12-23) is the general expression relating the fugacity $\bar{f}_k$ of a component in a homogeneous mixture to its mole fraction in the mixture. It involves the fugacity of the pure component at the same temperature and pressure, f_k, and also partial volumes of the component from zero pressure to p. This last information must generally be obtained experimentally.

2. If the partial molal volume of the component in the gaseous mixture is always equal to the molal volume of the pure component (at the same pressure and temperature), the gas is an ideal solution and the fugacity $\bar{f}_k$ is given by Eq. (12-24a). Similarly, if the liquid phase is an ideal solution, Eq. (12-24b) is valid. Application of these simplified expressions does not require experimental partial volumetric data.

3. If a gaseous mixture, in addition to being an ideal solution, behaves as an ideal gas, Eq. (12-24a) becomes equivalent to Dalton's law of partial pressures. If the liquid phase is an ideal solution and the gas phase in equilibrium with it is an ideal gas, Eq. (12-24b) is equivalent to Raoult's law.

12-4. The Composition of Phases in Equilibrium. Equations (12-23) to (12-26) provide, in various degrees of generality, methods of computing the fugacity of a component in a homogeneous mixture from its composition. By applying these results to each of the phases and utilizing the criterion of equilibrium as described by Eq. (12-17), the problem of evaluating the composition of phases in equilibrium can be solved.

In the rigorous approach, Eq. (12-23) or its equivalent, Eq. (12-20), is used to describe the fugacity of a component in each phase. Applying Eq. (12-20) to a liquid with a mole fraction of component k equal to x_k and to a vapor with a composition y_k, there is obtained

$$\ln \left(\frac{\bar{f}}{\bar{p}^*} \right)_L = \frac{1}{RT} \int_{p^*}^{p} \bar{v}_{k_L} \, dp \tag{12-27}$$

$$\ln \left(\frac{\bar{f}}{\bar{p}^*} \right)_G = \frac{1}{RT} \int_{p^*}^{p} \bar{v}_{k_G} \, dp \tag{12-28}$$

At a pressure approaching zero, the liquid phase will become an ideal gas so that $\bar{p}_L^*$ is given by Eq. (12-22), or $p^* x_k$. Similarly $\bar{p}_G^*$ is equal to $p^* y_k$. Making these substitutions and subtracting the second equation from the first gives

$$\ln \left(\frac{\bar{f}/x}{\bar{f}/y} \right)_k = \frac{1}{RT} \int_{0}^{p} (\bar{v}_L - \bar{v}_G)_k \, dp \tag{12-29}$$

$(12\text{-}27) - (12\text{-}28)$

$\ln \bar{f}_{kL} - \ln x - \ln p^* - (\ln \bar{f}_{kG} - \ln y - \ln p^*) = \ln \frac{y}{x}$

Equation (12-29) may be further simplified to the form[1]

$$\ln \left(\frac{y}{x}\right)_k = \ln K_k = \frac{1}{RT} \int_0^p (\bar{v}_L - \bar{v}_G)_k \, dp \qquad (12\text{-}30)$$

since the fugacity $\bar{f}_k$ is the same in the two phases at equilibrium.

Equation (12-29) or (12-30) represents a thermodynamically rigorous method of evaluating the composition of phases in equilibrium from p-v-T data. The first term within the integral is the partial molal volume of k in the liquid phase and the second that of k in the gas phase. Both depend upon the composition, so that the resultant equilibrium constant is a function of composition as well as pressure and temperature. Since the integration must be carried out from zero pressure up to the equilibrium pressure p, partial-volume data are required over this entire pressure range. The equation applies at a constant temperature, and, of course, a separate one may be written for each of the n components in the system. These n equations along with material balances provide the framework for determining the composition of the phases in equilibrium.

Generally experimental p-v-T data are unavailable, so that Eq. (12-29) cannot be applied rigorously. However, for hydrocarbons the Benedict-Rubin-Webb equation of state[2] has been employed to predict partial volumes. These results have been used for estimating fugacity coefficients and phase equilibrium constants by Eq. (12-29)[3] for a number of the light hydrocarbons.

If both gas and liquid phases are assumed to be ideal solutions, a much less complex equation for the equilibrium constant is obtained. Equation (12-24a) may be applied to the gas and Eq. (12-24b) to the liquid, giving

$$\bar{f}_k = f_{k_L} x_k = f_{k_G} y_k$$

or

$$K_k = \frac{y_k}{x_k} = \left(\frac{f_L}{f_G}\right)_k \qquad (12\text{-}31)$$

Equation (12-31) in contrast to Eq. (12-30) requires no volume data as a function of composition but only the fugacities of pure k in the gas f_{k_G} and in the liquid phase f_{k_L}.

If, in addition, the vapor phase behaves as an ideal gas, combination

---

[1] K, the ratio of the mole fraction of a component in the gas and liquid phases, has been called equilibrium ratio, distribution coefficient, as well as vaporization equilibrium constant, or simply equilibrium constant. The last term will be used here in accordance with common industrial usage.

[2] M. Benedict, G. B. Webb, and L. C. Rubin, *J. Chem. Phys.*, **8**, 334 (1940); **10**, 747 (1942); and *Chem. Eng. Progr.*, **47**, 419 (1951).

[3] M. Benedict, G. B. Webb, and L. C. Rubin, *Chem. Eng. Progr.*, **47**, 449 (1951).

of Eqs. (12-25) and (12-26) gives a still simpler expression for the equilibrium constant:

$$py_k = p'_k x_k$$

or

$$K = \frac{y_k}{x_k} = \frac{p'_k}{p} \tag{12-32}$$

The only experimental data required in order to compute K from Eq. (12-32) is the vapor pressure of the component and the total pressure p of the system. To achieve this degree of simplification, it is necessary to make the stringent assumptions of an ideal-liquid solution and an ideal-gas phase.

The application of Eqs. (12-30) to (12-32) to quantitative problems of obtaining the composition of phases in equilibrium will be considered in Sec. 12-8.

12-5. The Fugacity of a Pure Component. Phase-equilibria problems for single-component systems are relatively simple since composition is not a variable. However, approximate methods of treating multicomponent systems frequently are based upon data for each of the components in the pure state, as illustrated by Eq. (12-31). For this reason, it is necessary to discuss the methods of evaluating the fugacity of pure components.

Upon integration of Eq. (12-14) between the limits p^* and any pressure p, there is obtained

$$\ln \frac{f}{f^*} = \frac{1}{RT} \int_{p^*}^{p} v \, dp \tag{12-33}$$

This is a general expression for the effect of pressure upon the fugacity. It may be employed to evaluate the fugacity of a substance at a given temperature T and pressure p, from a knowledge of the fugacity at p^* and T and pressure-volume data from p^* to p at that temperature. If the volume follows the ideal-gas law, Eq. (12-33) reduces to $f = p$. For a real gas no such simplification exists and the equation must be integrated with the aid of volume data. There is no difficulty in evaluating the fugacity f^* at the lower limit, for at p^* ideal-gas behavior is approached, and $f^* = p^*$. However, Eq. (12-33) is not in a convenient form for integration since the volume approaches infinity as $p^* \to 0$. This difficulty can be avoided by one of two methods.

The first depends upon the fact that the residual volume α, the difference between the ideal-gas volume and the actual volume, retains a finite value as the pressure approaches zero.

$$\alpha = \frac{RT}{p} - v \tag{12-34}$$

$$\frac{1}{RT} \int_{p*}^{p} \left(\frac{RT}{p} - \alpha \right) dp$$

Introducing Eq. (12-34) in Eq. (12-33) and integrating,

$$\ln \frac{f}{f*} = \ln \frac{p}{p*} - \frac{1}{RT} \int_0^p \alpha \, dp$$

or, since $f* = p*$,

$$\ln \frac{f}{p} = - \frac{1}{RT} \int_0^p \alpha \, dp \qquad (12\text{-}35)$$

From a knowledge of the actual volumetric behavior of the gas, Eq. (12-35) can be integrated graphically to give the fugacity at any temperature and pressure.

The second method is based upon the concept of the compressibility factor. Since

$$Z = \frac{pv}{RT} \qquad \text{(1 mole of gas)}$$

Eq. (12-33) may be written as

$$\ln \frac{f}{f*} = \int_{p*}^{p} \frac{Z \, dp}{p}$$

At zero pressure the term Z/p is infinity. However, if dp/p is added and subtracted from the equation, there is obtained

$$\ln \frac{f}{f*} = \int_{p*}^{p} \frac{dp}{p} - \int_{p*}^{p} \frac{1 - Z}{p} \, dp$$

Integrating and recalling that $p* = f*$,

$$\ln \frac{f}{p} = - \int_0^p \frac{1 - Z}{p} \, dp \qquad (12\text{-}36)$$

Like α, the term $(1 - Z)/p$ is finite as the pressure approaches zero, so that there is no difficulty in integrating Eq. (12-36). If the volume of the substance is known from zero pressure to p, the compressibility factor can be calculated and Eq. (12-36) solved for the fugacity.

If experimental data are unavailable, an equation of state may be used to predict the residual volume or compressibility factor. Then Eq. (12-35) or (12-36) can be used to estimate fugacities in the same manner as described in the preceding paragraph. If a generalized equation of state is employed, such as that represented by the compressibility-factor chart, Fig. 4-4, a single graph for predicting the fugacity of all gases can be prepared. This is accomplished by writing Eq. (12-36) in reduced form:

$$\ln \frac{f}{p} = - \int_0^{p_r} \frac{1 - Z}{p_r} \, dp_r \qquad (12\text{-}37)$$

This expression can be integrated graphically (at constant temperature)

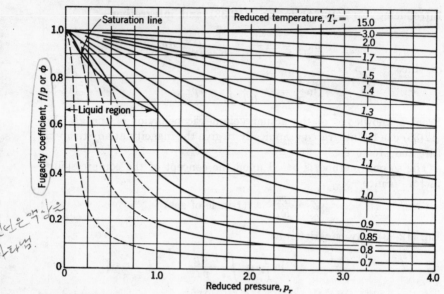

FIG. 12-1. Fugacity of gases and liquids for $Z_c = 0.27$. (*Data reproduced by permission from A. L. Lydersen, R. A. Greenkorn, and O. A. Hougen, Univ. Wisconsin, Eng. Expt. Sta., Rept. 4, October, 1955.*)

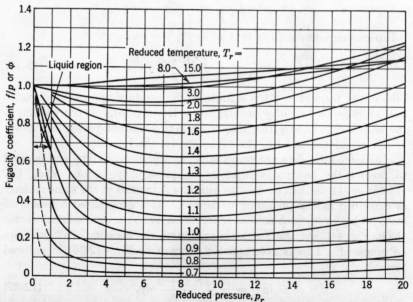

FIG. 12-2. Fugacity of gases and liquids for $Z_c = 0.27$. High-pressure range. (*Data reproduced by permission from A. L. Lydersen, R. A. Greenkorn, and O. A. Hougen, Univ. Wisconsin, Eng. Expt. Sta., Rept. 4, October, 1955.*)

by taking compressibility factors from isotherms in Fig. 4-4. Figures 12-1 and 12-2 represent the results of these computations over a wide range of temperature and pressure. Where experimental volumetric data are not available, or for approximate calculations, Figs. 12-1 and 12-2 can be used to evaluate the fugacity of any pure gas for which the critical pressure and temperature are known. The accuracy of the results depends upon how closely the compressibility-factor charts predict the actual p-v-T behavior of the gas.[1]

According to the requirements of equilibrium [Eq. (12-17)], the fugacity in a liquid phase is equal to that in the gas phase in equilibrium with it. Accordingly, fugacities of pure liquids at their boiling points can be obtained by applying Eq. (12-36) or Figs. 12-1 and 12-2 at the vapor pressure of the boiling liquid. The fugacity of a liquid at a pressure above the vapor pressure can be determined by adding to the value at saturation the contribution obtained by compressing the liquid to the desired pressure. This latter calculation requires liquid-volume data and, hence, necessitates applications of an equation such as Eq. (12-14) to the liquid phase. As for gases, generalized correlations of liquid-volume data in terms of reduced temperature and pressure can be employed. Figures 12-1 and 12-2 include liquid regions evaluated in this fashion from the reduced-density chart, Fig. 4-5.

Fugacity calculations for pure components in the gas and liquid phases are illustrated by the following examples.

Example 12-1. Estimate the fugacity of gaseous propane at 175 psia and 100°F by the following methods:

(a) Assuming propane is an ideal gas
(b) Employing the principle of corresponding states (Fig. 12-1)
(c) Using the following p-v-T data[2] at 100°F

Pressure, psia	Specific volume, ft^3/lb_m
25	5.307
50	2.578
100	1.208
150	0.7494
175	0.6118
200	0.0337
500	0.0331
700	0.0328
1000	0.0323

[1] Note that both the compressibility-factor charts and Figs. 12-1 and 12-2 are based upon a critical compressibility factor Z_c of 0.27. Similar results are available for other values of Z_c. (A. L. Lydersen, R. A. Greenkorn, and O. A. Hougen, *Univ. Wisconsin, Eng. Expt. Sta., Rept.* 4, October, 1955.) For the most precise calculations, fugacities should be obtained from the tables or charts corresponding to the value of Z_c for the particular gas in question.

[2] B. H. Sage and W. N. Lacey, *Ind. Eng. Chem.*, **26**, 1218 (1934).

Solution. (a) If propane is assumed to behave as an ideal gas at 175 psia and 100°F, the fugacity will be equal to the pressure, that is, $f = 175$ psia.

(b) To use Fig. 12-1, the critical temperature and pressure are required. Using the data in Table 4-1,

$$p_r = \frac{175}{(14.7)(42)} = 0.284$$

$$T_r = \frac{100 + 460}{(1.8)(370)} = 0.84$$

From Fig. 12-1, f/p is estimated to be 0.83. Hence the fugacity is

$$f = (0.83)(175) = 145 \text{ psia}$$

(c) Since experimental p-v-T data are available, Eq. (12-35) should be used. The residual volume over the whole pressure range from 0 to 175 psia can be determined from Eq. (12-34). It may be computed either on a molal or unit-mass basis. Since the specific volumes are given per pound, it is convenient to evaluate α in cubic feet per pound.

$$\alpha = \frac{RT}{Mp} - v = \frac{10.73(460 + 100)}{44.06p} - v$$

where 44.06 is the molecular weight of propane. Applying this expression to the data, the following values of the residual volume are obtained:

Pressure, psia	α, ft^3/lb$_m$
0	(0.147)
25	0.148
50	0.149
100	0.156
150	0.160
175	0.167

The value of α at zero pressure is not known experimentally. However, it is finite and can be obtained by extrapolation of the curve α vs. p determined by the above points. If this is done, α at zero pressure is estimated to be 0.147 ft^3/lb$_m$.

The value of the integral

$$\int_0^p \alpha \, dp$$

in Eq. (12-35) can be determined graphically by evaluating the area under the α vs. p curve between the limits 0 and 175 psia. This area is equal to 27.2 (ft^3/lb$_m$)(psi).

Substituting in Eq. (12-35),

$$\ln \frac{f}{p} = -\frac{M}{RT} \int_0^{175} \alpha \, dp$$

$$\ln \frac{f}{175} = -\frac{44.06}{(10.73)(560)} (27.2) = -0.200$$

$$f = (0.82)(175) = 143 \text{ psia}$$

In this particular example the assumption of the ideal-gas law resulted in an error of about 30 per cent, while Fig. 12-1 gave an answer in good agreement with the value based upon actual data.

Example 12-2. From the p-v-T data given in Example 12-1 compute the fugacity of propane at 100°F and 1000 psia. The vapor pressure of propane at 100°F is 190 psia.

Solution. At 1000 psia and 100°F propane is a liquid. Equation (12-35) may be used (as in Example 12-1) to calculate the fugacity of the saturated vapor at 190 psia. Since propane liquid and vapor are in equilibrium at this pressure, the fugacity of liquid propane at 100°F and 190 psia will be equal to this same value [see Eq. (12-17)]. Then Eq. (12-14) may be employed to find the change in fugacity upon compressing the liquid to 1000 psia. The calculations are as follows:

By evaluating the area under the α vs. p curve from 0 to 190 psia, Eq. (12-35) yields the following value for the fugacity of the saturated gas:

$$\ln \frac{f_G}{190} = -\frac{M}{RT} \int_0^{190} \alpha \, dp = -\frac{44.06}{(10.73)(560)}(29.7) = -0.218$$
$$f_G = (190)(0.80) = 152 \text{ psia}$$

Now, applying Eq. (12-14) to the liquid from 190 to 1000 psia,

$$\ln \frac{f_{1000}}{f_L} = \frac{1}{RT} \int_{190}^{1000} v_L \, dp$$

where v_L is the volume of the liquid, f_L is the fugacity of saturated liquid at 190 psia, and f_{1000} is the required fugacity at 1000 psia.

Since $f_L = f_G = 152$ psia, the preceding equation becomes

$$\ln \frac{f_{1000}}{152} = \frac{1}{RT} \int_{190}^{1000} v_L \, dp$$

The specific volumes given in Example 12-1 for the liquid region do not vary greatly, and the change is approximately linear. Hence, the integration can be carried out without serious error, using an average value of v_L,

$$\ln \frac{f_{1000}}{152} = \frac{44.06}{(10.73)(560)}(0.0330)(1000 - 190) = 0.196$$
$$f_{1000} = (152)(1.22) = 185 \text{ psia}$$

As the volume of liquids (not near the critical point) is relatively small, the effect of pressure on the fugacity of a liquid is likewise small. In this example a pressure increase of over 800 psia caused a change in fugacity of only 33 psia.

MISCIBLE SYSTEMS—QUALITATIVE TREATMENT

Miscible mixtures of two or more components characterize the type of system most frequently found in practice. The important problems concerned with vapor-liquid equilibria are the calculation of the compositions of the phases in equilibrium, the quantity of each phase, and the conditions for the appearance or disappearance of a phase. The quantitative methods of handling these problems through the utilization of the concept of fugacity will be considered after a brief discussion of the qualitative aspects of the subject.

The treatment of equilibrium between gas and liquid would be simple provided that each phase exhibited the properties of an ideal solution. Under these ideal conditions no information about the mixture is required. To compute the composition of the phases in equilibrium, all that is necessary is the fugacities of the pure components, as illustrated by Eq. (12-31).

Actually large deviations from ideal-solution behavior are likely in either the gas or liquid phase. The fundamental reason for these deviations is the forces that exist between molecules. If the forces between unlike molecules are same as those between like molecules, the behavior of the phase is not dependent on the kind of substances involved, *i.e.*, the phase is an ideal solution. If the forces are not the same, deviations occur. The magnitude of the intermolecular forces depends upon the nature of the molecules (kind of substance) and the average distance between them.

Since the molecules in a liquid phase are relatively close together, the force fields are strong. Hence, the different molecules in a liquid mixture must be very similar in shape and charge distribution if ideal-solution behavior is to be expected. Benzene and toluene satisfy these conditions at ordinary pressures. However, most liquid mixtures contain molecules that are sufficiently different to cause deviations from the ideal-solution concept. For example, aqueous solutions nearly all exhibit significant deviations.

In a gaseous mixture the force fields are less strong, and ideal-solution behavior is a good assumption at low pressure. At higher pressures, the molecules are closer together and the differences in molecular shape and charge distribution exert an effect on the intermolecular forces. For example, recent studies[1] of the benzene-methanol system at pressures of several hundred pounds per square inch show large deviations from ideal-solution behavior.

From the standpoint of vapor-liquid equilibria this discussion may be summarized as follows:

1. At low pressures, deviations from ideal-solution performance will be primarily due to the liquid phase. The gas phase will approach an ideal solution, and indeed may be well described by the ideal-gas law.[2]

2. At high pressures both gas and liquid phases may deviate from ideal-solution behavior. The extent of the deviations will depend upon the dissimilarity of the components in the mixture.

---

[1] P. G. McCracken and J. M. Smith, *AIChE J.*, **2**, 498 (1956).

[2] It is important to note the distinction between an ideal gas and an ideal solution. In an ideal gas the forces between molecules are negligible. The ideal-solution assumption is less severe and requires only that the forces between like and unlike molecules be the same. A gas phase can approximate an ideal solution but still deviate significantly from the ideal-gas law.

3. The most difficult problem of vapor-liquid equilibria involves mixtures of chemically dissimilar substances at high pressures. Here large deviations from Eq. (12-31) would be expected in both phases.

It is convenient to illustrate phase behavior qualitatively by graphical means, dividing the treatment into two sections, depending upon the pressure.

12-6. Phase Behavior at Elevated Pressures. Perhaps the most helpful graph for examining the effect of pressure on the phase behavior of liquids is the pressure-temperature chart. Figure 12-3 is an example for a binary system. The curves OC_A and OC_B are the ordinary vapor-pressure curves for the pure components, terminating at the critical temperature and pressure corresponding to points C_A and C_B for the two

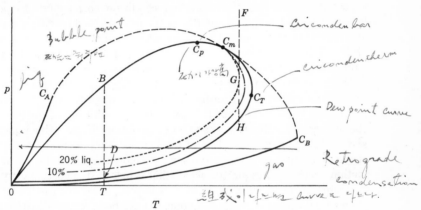

FIG. 12-3. Phase behavior of a binary system represented on a pressure-temperature diagram.

substances. The phase behavior of multicomponent systems differs from that of pure components in that the pressure is not constant during the vaporization of a liquid at constant temperature. The pressure at which the liquid first starts to vaporize is termed the *bubble point* and that at complete vaporization, or initial condensation, the *dew point*. Hence, the phase boundary is not a single line but a region such as that enclosed by the curve OBC_mHO. At the temperature T, p_B is the bubble-point and p_D the dew-point pressure. Within the region bounded by the curve OBC_mHO, both liquid and gas phases exist. Above and to the left of the bubble-point curve OBC_m is a liquid region, and below and to the right of the dew-point curve C_mHO is a vapor region. C_m is the critical point of the mixture and may be defined for multicomponent systems as the state at which the properties of the gas and liquid phases in equilibrium are identical. This definition is also valid for single-component systems, but in this case the critical pressure is also the highest at which liquid and gas phases can exist at equilibrium and the critical temperature is the maximum at which two phases can exist. These corollaries are not true for multicomponent systems, as is evident from Fig. 12-3. The maximum temperature at which two phases can exist is at C_T and is called the *cricondentherm.* The maximum pressure for two phases is at C_p, a point for which Dodge[1] has suggested the name *cricondenbar.*

The dashed lines in Fig. 12-3 refer to the per cent liquid in the two-phase mixture of gas and liquid. From their position it is evident that, under certain conditions, the unusual behavior of an increase in per cent liquid may accompany a reduction in pressure. To the left of the critical point C_m a reduction of pressure along a line such as BD is accompanied by vaporization from the bubble point to the dew point, as would be expected. However, if the original condition corresponds to point F, liquefaction occurs upon reduction of the pressure and reaches a maximum at G, after which vaporization takes place until the dew point is reached at H. This phenomenon was first considered by Kuenen[2] and given the name *retrograde condensation.* It has become of considerable importance in the production of petroleum from certain deep wells where the pressure in the underground formation is high enough to be in the region of F. Under these conditions it is possible, by maintaining the pressure at the surface at a value near the point G, to obtain considerable liquefaction and hence a partial separation of the heavier components of the mixture. If the pressure is reduced at the surface below the dew point H, no liquefaction occurs and the initial separation is lost. It is customary to practice repressuring operations in such cases, *i.e.*, to return the lean gas (gas from which the less volatile components have been removed) to the underground reservoir or formation and thus maintain the reservoir pressure at a high value. If this were not done, the drop in pressure as the reservoir contents are removed would result in condensation in the sand formation underground and would reduce the ultimate recovery from the formation.

The phase boundary curve OC_mO is for a definite total composition. In Fig. 12-4 are shown curves for several compositions of A and B. The dashed line represents the locus of the critical points C_m of the various mixtures. The shape of the envelope explains how the critical point may have different locations with respect to the cricondentherm and cricondenbar, since the envelope and phase boundary curves are tangent at the critical points.

For a two-phase two-component system the specification of the tem-

---

[1] B. F. Dodge, "Chemical Engineering Thermodynamics," McGraw-Hill Book Company, Inc., New York, 1944.

[2] J. P. Kuenen, "Theorie der Verdampfung und Verflüssigung von Gemischen, und der fraktionierten Destillation," Johann Ambrosius Barth, Munich, 1906.

perature and pressure completely determines the intensive state of the system and, therefore, the compositions of the phases in equilibrium. Referring to Fig. 12-4, the compositions of the two phases in equilibrium at the point p_0, T_0 would be given by the composition of mixture required to give the dew-point curve III and the composition corresponding to the bubble-point line II. The former is the gas composition and the latter

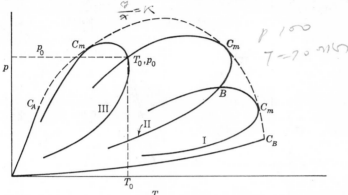

FIG. 12-4. Phase diagrams for binary systems of different composition.

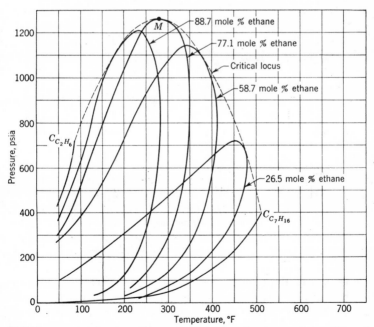

FIG. 12-5. Pressure-temperature diagram for the ethane-heptane system. [*Reproduced by permission from F. H. Barr-David, AIChE J.*, **2**, 426 (1956).]

the composition of the liquid in equilibrium with it.   A similar point of
equilibrium is at B.

Figures 12-5 and 12-6 are specific illustrations of the nature of Fig.
12-4 for the ethane-heptane and the benzene-methanol systems.   The

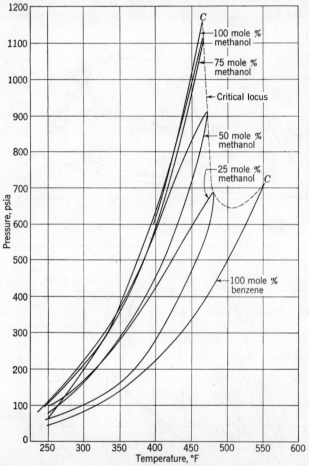

FIG. 12-6. Pressure-temperature diagram for the methanol-benzene system.   [*Reproduced by permission from P. G. McCracken and J. M. Smith, AIChE J.*, **2**, 498 (1956).]

first is typical of the phase behavior of the relatively nonpolar hydrocarbon mixtures.   The second, Fig. 12-6, represents a polar (methanol)–
nonpolar (benzene) system.   The complex and specific nature of the
curves in these figures illustrates the difficulty in predicting phase behavior at high pressures.   While both systems deviate from ideal-solution

behavior, the methanol-benzene system is particularly irregular, and different from the ethane-heptane case, because of the dissimilarity between methanol and benzene.

Pressure-temperature curves for mixtures of more than two components are similar to Fig. 12-4.   However, the equilibrium state is not determined solely by the temperature and pressure but also depends upon the composition.

In addition to p-T diagrams, temperature-composition and y-x (y is the molal composition of the more volatile component in the vapor and x that of the same component in the liquid) charts are of importance. Figure 12-7 includes temperature-composition diagrams for three pressures.   Set I shows the liquid and vapor composition as a function of

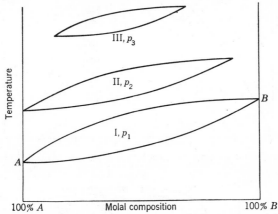

Fig. 12-7. Temperature-composition diagram for a binary system at three different total pressures.

temperature at a pressure below the critical pressure of either of the components A or B.   At any temperature a horizontal line relates the composition of the liquid and vapor in equilibrium.   Point A is the boiling point of pure A, and B the boiling point of pure B, at the given pressure. These curves would be obtained by drawing a horizontal line on Fig. 12-4 at the constant pressure p_1 and plotting the composition of the dew-point and bubble-point curves that intersect that line.   Curves II are for a pressure between the critical pressures of the two components and curves III for a pressure above the critical pressures of both components.

The same information plotted on a y-x diagram is illustrated in Fig. 12-8.   It is clear from Figs. 12-7 and 12-8 that the maximum concentration of the more volatile component that can be obtained in a distillation process conducted at a pressure p_3 would be given by the point $x_1 = y_1$ and the minimum concentration of this component at the point $x_2 = y_2$.

Figure 12-9 is a y-x diagram for the ethane-heptane system and is based upon data identical to those in Fig. 12-5. The maximum pressure at which liquid and vapor phases can exist is indicated by the point A and corresponds to 1263 psia and a liquid composition of about 77 mole per cent ethane. This same point is labeled M in Fig. 12-5. Barr-

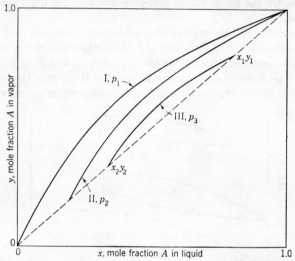

FIG. 12-8. Equilibrium y-x diagram for a binary system at three different total pressures.

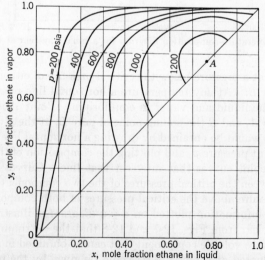

FIG. 12-9. y-x diagram for ethane-heptane system. [*Reproduced by permission from F. H. Barr-David, AIChE J.*, **2**, 426 (1956).]

David[1] has prepared a consistent set of charts for this system, including p-T, T-x, y-x, and p-x diagrams.

12-7. Phase Behavior at Low Pressures. As stated previously, the deviation from ideal behavior at low pressures is primarily due to the fact that the liquid solution does not follow the ideal-solution laws, since the vapor phase will generally closely approach ideal-gas behavior. The concept of an ideal liquid solution resulted in Eq. (12-24b), relating the fugacity in a mixture to the fugacity of a pure component at the same temperature and pressure. If Eq. (12-24b) is applied to a liquid phase

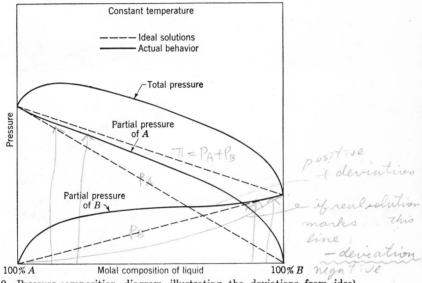

FIG. 12-10. Pressure-composition diagram illustrating the deviations from ideal solutions.

at low pressure, the fugacity of a component will be equal to the partial pressure and will be given by Raoult's law [Eq. (12-26)]. Therefore, a plot of partial pressure against the mole fraction would result in a straight line for an ideal liquid solution. Such a case is illustrated by dashed lines in Fig. 12-10 for a binary system of components A and B. The upper dashed line represents the total pressure on the system and is given by the sum of the two lower curves. The system benzene-toluene would be closely represented by the dashed lines. The solid lines illustrate one type of behavior of nonideal systems in which the partial pressure of both components is larger than predicted by Raoult's law.

If the deviations are sufficiently large, the total-pressure curve may

[1] F. H. Barr-David, *AIChE J.*, **2**, 426 (1956).

exhibit a maximum or minimum.[1]   Both cases are illustrated in Fig.
12-11, system I having a minimum total pressure and system II, a maximum.   The solid lines represent the total pressure of the liquid solution
of any composition at the fixed temperature, *i.e.*, bubble-point pressure
lines.   Dew-point pressure curves (dashed) representing the pressure of
the saturated vapor as a function of composition are also indicated.

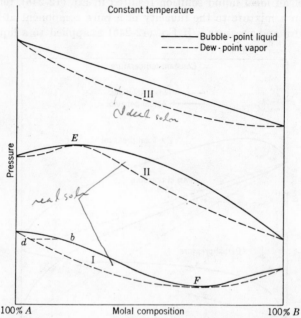

FIG. 12-11. Pressure-composition diagram illustrating maximum and minimum boiling
mixtures (azeotropes).

Compositions of liquid and vapor in equilibrium are found by horizontal
tie lines such as *db*.   It is evident that the maximum concentration of *A*,
obtainable by distilling a dilute mixture of a system which has a minimum
pressure, is the composition at that pressure, for example, *F* in Fig. 12-11.

[1] Such positive deviations from Raoult's law can be interpreted roughly as an
instance of strong intermolecular forces between like molecules and relatively weak
forces between unlike molecules.   Thus, in a solution of *A* and *B*, if the attractive
forces between two *A* molecules and between two *B* molecules are relatively stronger
than between an *A* and a *B* pair, the partial pressures of *A* and *B* should be greater
than predicted by the concept of ideal solutions.   If this difference in forces is large,
a maximum in total pressure and azeotropic behavior will occur, as shown in Fig.
12-11, II.   Going to the extreme case, the forces between unlike molecules may be
so slight in comparison with those between like pairs that the two components will
separate into two liquid phases.   This results in partially miscible and immiscible
systems, as described in Sec. 12-13.

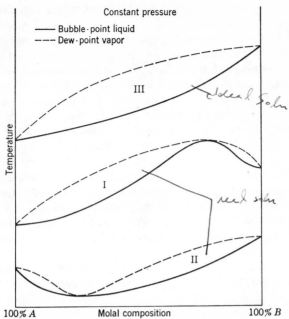

FIG. 12-12. Temperature-composition diagram illustrating maximum and minimum boiling mixtures (azeotropic mixtures).

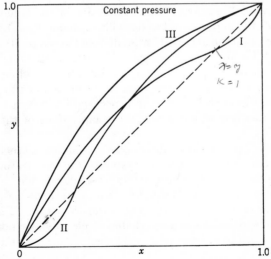

FIG. 12-13. Equilibrium y-x diagram illustrating maximum and minimum boiling mixtures.

At this point liquid and vapor in equilibrium have the same composition, and further purification by distillation is not possible. Systems exhibiting this constant-boiling behavior are known as azeotropes. 天津過空份

Since most distillation processes are carried out at constant pressure rather than constant temperature, the temperature-composition curves in Fig. 12-12 (corresponding to the p-x curves in Fig. 12-11) are more useful in discussing azeotropic mixtures. A maximum pressure in Fig. 12-11 becomes a minimum boiling point in Fig. 12-12. Ethyl alcohol and water exhibit this behavior, having a minimum point at 78.15°C at 760 mm corresponding to composition of 89.43 mole per cent alcohol.

Curves III in Figs. 12-11 and 12-12 are typical of ideal solutions such as benzene and toluene. It is evident that complete separation is possible by vaporization and condensation operations. The curve for ideal solutions can be easily determined from a knowledge of the vapor pressures of the components (see Sec. 12-10), while those for nonideal liquids require more experimental information, since simplifying equations, such as Eq. (12-26), cannot be utilized.

The y-x plots for the three systems shown in Fig. 12-12 take the form illustrated in Fig. 12-13. The points where the curves cross the diagonal line (dashed) designate azeotropes, since liquid and vapor phases are identical in composition at those locations.

MISCIBLE SYSTEMS—QUANTITATIVE TREATMENT

12-8. Elevated Pressures. The complexity of the behavior of nonideal systems at high pressures has been illustrated in Figs. 12-5 and 12-6. Methods have not been achieved for predicting the compositions of phases in equilibrium for all types of systems. Equation (12-30) offers a sound method of evaluating the equilibrium constant, but it seldom can be used because the necessary volumetric data as a function of composition are not available. In such instances it is necessary to resort to the direct experimental method of measuring the compositions of the vapor and liquid.

Progress has been made in developing prediction methods for a restricted, though important, class of systems—the hydrocarbons. These systems all seem to possess phase diagrams similar to that shown in Fig. 12-5. The Benedict-Rubin-Webb equation of state has been used with Eq. (12-29) to compute fugacity-composition ratios for 12 light hydrocarbons. These calculations give reliable values of vaporization equilibrium constants up to a pressure of 3600 psia. Benedict and coworkers[1]

[1] M. Benedict, G. B. Webb, and L. C. Rubin, *Chem. Eng. Progr.*, **47**, 419, 449, 571, 609 (1951).

have summarized the results in a series of 324 charts,[1] the essential feature of which is the use of a single parameter, the molal average boiling point, to represent the complete effect of composition. These charts can be used to estimate the equilibrium constant K from the temperature, pressure, and molal average boiling point of each phase.

The same approach has been applied to a nonhydrocarbon mixture, nitrogen–carbon monoxide.[2] The predicted results agree well with the experimental data available for this system, but the two molecules are similar. When applied to a more dissimilar system, propane–carbon dioxide, computed equilibrium constants deviated as much as 100 per cent from the predicted values.[3]

The numerous charts of Benedict have been reduced in number and made easier to apply by DePriester[4] and by Edmister and Ruby.[5] The DePriester charts include two for each hydrocarbon, one giving the fugacity ratio for the gas and the second that for the liquid phase.[6]

Instead of molal average boiling point, a number of correlations[7–9] use the critical pressure to represent the effect of composition. It is clear from Figs. 12-5 and 12-6 that the location of the critical point varies greatly with the composition and nature of the components. At the critical pressure the composition of vapor and liquid are identical, making the equilibrium constant unity for each component. Hence curves of K vs. pressure must converge to a value of 1.0 at the critical pressure, as illustrated in Fig. 12-16. On this graph the equilibrium-constant curves for components A (more volatile) and B are shown for two different mixtures of a multicomponent system. The solid curves with a critical convergence pressure of C correspond to one mixture. The dashed curves represent a second mixture with a convergence pressure C_2. This type of plot clearly shows how the composition of a mixture can affect the equilibrium constant near the critical pressure.

The use of correlations requiring the molal average boiling point or the convergence pressure is generally tedious and frequently necessitates trial calculations. Hence, to illustrate the application of equilibrium constants to practical problems, limited nomographs showing

---

[1] Known as the Kellogg charts.

[2] F. C. Schiller and L. N. Canjar, *Chem. Eng. Progr., Symposium Ser.* 7, **49**, 67 (1953).

[3] E. J. Cullen and K. A. Kobe, *AIChE J.*, 1, 453 (1955).

[4] C. L. DePriester, *Chem. Eng. Progr., Symposium Ser.* 7, **49**, 1 (1953).

[5] W. C. Edmister and C. L. Ruby, *Chem. Eng. Progr.*, **51**, 95-F (1955).

[6] To reduce the number of charts it also was necessary to reduce the pressure to a maximum value of 1000 psia.

[7] S. S. Hadden, *Chem. Eng. Progr., Symposium Ser.* 7, **49**, 53 (1953).

[8] J. M. Lenoir and H. S. Myers, *Petrol. Refiner*, **36**(2), 167 (1957).

[9] F. W. Winn, *Chem. Eng. Progr., Symposium Ser.* 2, **48**, 121 (1952).

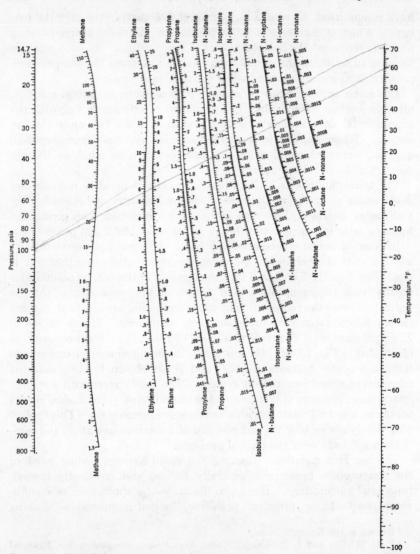

FIG. 12-14. Equilibrium constants in light-hydrocarbon systems. Low-temperature range. [*Reproduced by permission from C. L. DePriester, Chem. Eng. Progr., Symposium Ser. 7, 49 (1953).*]

K values for hydrocarbons as a function of temperature and pressure alone are presented in Figs. 12-14 and 12-15. These were prepared by De Priester,[1] and are based on the Kellogg charts. Dependence of the K values on composition has been avoided by the use of average values.

[1] C. L. De Priester, *Chem. Eng. Progr., Symposium Ser.* **7, 49,** 1 (1953).

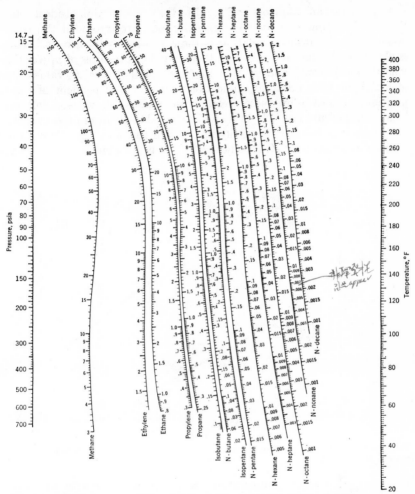

Fig. 12-15. Equilibrium constants in light-hydrocarbon systems.   High-temperature range.   [*Reproduced by permission from C. L. De Priester, Chem. Eng. Progr., Symposium Ser. 7,* **49** (1953).]

Hence results based on this correlation are approximate but are adequate for many purposes.   In the sense that these K values are independent of composition, they are like K values determined from Eq. (12-31), which is derived on the assumption that both phases are ideal solutions. Although used in exactly the same manner, they are not necessarily the same, because the De Priester values allow for an *average* effect of composition while the ideal values allow for *no* effect.

At pressures not too close to the critical, the assumption of ideal solutions in both phases may be reasonably accurate, provided the components are chemically similar, as is the case with hydrocarbons. This is illustrated by the curves in Fig. 12-16. Below pressures of p_1 (for the volatile component) and p_2 (for the less volatile), the K values are identical for both mixtures, indicating that K is independent of composition. Hence below these pressures the phases behave essentially as ideal solutions and Eq. (12-31) is applicable. At still lower pressures, the gas phase may behave essentially as an ideal gas, and Eq. (12-32), the simplest expression for K, becomes valid. It is apparent from this equa-

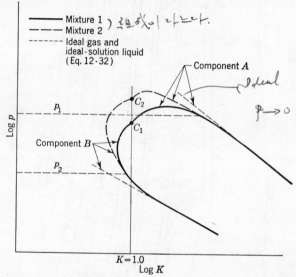

FIG. 12-16. Effect of pressure and composition on the equilibrium constant in a binary system of A and B.

tion that, at constant temperature, K varies inversely with the total pressure. On a logarithmic plot such as Fig. 12-16, Eq. (12-32) is represented by a straight line, as is indicated in the figure by the dashed lines.

The apparent simplicity of Eqs. (12-31) and (12-32) is misleading, because practical complications make them difficult to apply effectively. Eq. (12-31), $K_k = (f_L/f_G)_k$, requires values for the fugacity of pure component k both as a liquid and as a vapor *at the equilibrium temperature and pressure*. However, pure k can actually exist as either a liquid or a vapor, but not as both, at these conditions. Hence one of these conditions of pure k is a fictitious state, and the properties for this state are, at best, difficult to determine. Moreover, the fictitious state required for at least one pure component is the vapor state, while that for another component is the liquid state. Thus correlations are required for both fictitious liquid and vapor states. Figs. 12-1 and 12-2, however, show fugacities for the real liquid and vapor states only. Generalized correlations are available for K values based upon the extrapolation of both liquid and vapor states into the fictitious or unstable region. The most general of these is given by Hougen, Watson, and Ragatz.[1]

The application of Eq. (12-32), $K_k = p_k'/p$, is even more tenuous, for it usually requires the extrapolation of the vapor-pressure curve beyond the critical point for at least one of the components of the system. The vapor pressure for pure k, p_k', must be for the temperature of the system at equilibrium, and this may be well above the critical temperature for component k. Such extrapolations are uncertain.

Example 12-3. Calculate the equilibrium constants for methane and for n-pentane for the binary system in phase equilibrium at 400 psia and 160°F. Use the following methods:

(a) Assume an ideal solution for the liquid phase and an ideal gas for the liquid phase.

(b) Assume both phases are ideal solutions.

(c) Obtain K values from Fig. 12-15.

Solution. (a) The vapor pressure of n-pentane at 160°F is 43.4 psia. Extrapolation of the vapor pressure curve for methane beyond the critical point gives a value for the fictitious vapor pressure of methane at 160°F of approximately 7400 psia. Application of Eq. (12-32) gives for methane

$$K_{C_1} = \frac{p_{C_1}'}{p} = \frac{7400}{400} = 18.5$$

For n-propane

$$K_{C_5} = \frac{p_{C_5}'}{p} = \frac{43.3}{400} = 0.11$$

(b) If both phases are assumed to be ideal solutions, Eq. (12-31) is applicable. For methane, the gas-phase fugacity can be obtained directly from Fig. 12-1.

$$p_r = \frac{400}{(45.8)(14.7)} = 0.60$$

$$T_r = \frac{160 + 460}{(191)(1.8)} = 1.80$$

$$\frac{f_G}{p} = 0.98$$

$$f_G = (0.98)(400) = 392 \text{ psia}$$

Equation (12-31) also requires the fugacity of methane as a liquid at the equilibrium conditions. However, pure methane does not exist as a liquid at 400 psia and 160°F. Clearly, data for the liquid phase must be extrapolated beyond the region in which it actually exists. The most direct procedure is to plot the f/p data for the liquid region

---

[1] O. A. Hougen, K. M. Watson, and R. A. Ragatz, "Chemical Process Principles," 2d ed., Part II, pp. 937–942, John Wiley & Sons, Inc., New York, 1959.

of Fig. 12-1 versus T_r for a constant reduced pressure of 0.60 and to extrapolate the resulting curve to $T_r = 1.80$. The result from this procedure is:

$$\frac{f_L}{p} = 4.6$$
$$f_L = (4.6)(400) = 1840 \text{ psia}$$

Then by Eq. (12-31)

$$K_{C_1} = \frac{1840}{392} = 4.7$$

For pentane, the liquid-phase fugacity is directly obtained from Fig. 12-1:

$$p_r = \frac{400}{(33.3)(14.7)} = 0.82$$
$$T_r = \frac{160 + 460}{(470)(1.8)} = 0.73$$
$$\frac{f_L}{p} = 0.12$$
$$f_L = (0.12)(400) = 48 \text{ psia}$$

Pentane does not exist as a gas at 400 psia and 160°F. Again an extrapolation procedure is required. In this case f/p data for the gas region of Fig. 12-1 can be plotted versus T_r for a constant reduced pressure of 0.82 and extrapolated to a reduced temperature of 0.73. The result is

$$\frac{f_G}{p} = 0.40$$
$$f_G = (0.40)(400) = 160 \text{ psia}$$

Then by Eq. (12-31)

$$k_{C_5} = \frac{48}{160} = 0.30$$

(c) Values of K are determined from the nomograph of Fig. 12-15 by constructing a straight line to connect the given pressure and temperature points.

$$\text{For methane, } K_{C_1} = 8.1$$
$$\text{For } n\text{-pentane, } K_{C_5} = 0.17$$

Sage, Lacey, and coworkers[1] have measured K values for this system by analysis of the gas and liquid phases in equilibrium. Their K values, along with the computed results of (a), (b), and (c), are given in Table 12-1.

TABLE 12-1. EQUILIBRIUM CONSTANTS AT 160°F, 400, PSIA

	Methane	n-Pentane
(a) Ideal gas and ideal-solution liquid	18.5	0.11
(b) Ideal-solution gas and liquid	4.7	0.30
(c) De Priester nomograph (Fig. 12-15).........	8.1	0.17
(d) Experimental.........................	7.93	0.17

[1] B. H. Sage, H. H. Reamer, R. H. Olds, and W. N. Lacey, *Ind. Eng. Chem.*, **34**, 1108 (1942).

12-9. Applications of Equilibrium Constants. Once K values are decided upon, the mechanics of calculating the compositions of the phases in equilibrium, the dew-point and bubble-point temperatures and pressures, and the distribution of the mixture between liquid and vapor are relatively simple.

The boiling-point, or bubble-point, temperature of a given liquid mixture at a definite pressure is characterized by the condition that

$$\Sigma y_i = 1 \tag{12-39}$$

where the y value for each component is evaluated from the equation

$$y_k = K_k x_k \tag{12-40}$$

This calculation also gives the composition of the vapor in equilibrium with the liquid. Analogously, the dew-point temperature of a given gas mixture at a fixed pressure is determined by the equations

$$\Sigma x_i = 1 \tag{12-41}$$

$$x_k = \frac{y_k}{K_k} \tag{12-42}$$

If a mixture is in equilibrium at a temperature between its bubble point and dew point, it must consist of two phases. In such two-phase problems it is convenient to take as a basis 1 mole of the total mixture, consisting of L moles of liquid and $1 - L$ moles of vapor. The number of moles of each constituent in the total mixture will be given the symbols $n_1, n_2, \ldots, n_k$, and these will also be the mole fractions in the total mixture. The relationship between the mole fraction n_k in the total mixture and the compositions and amounts of the individual phases can be obtained by combining a material balance with the equilibrium equation. The material balance for component k is

$$n_k = L x_k + (1 - L) y_k$$

and the equilibrium relation is $y_k = K_k x_k$. Solving these two expressions for the mole fraction in the liquid gives

$$x_k = \frac{n_k}{L + K_k(1 - L)} \tag{12-43}$$

Example 12-4. In a proposed natural-gasoline fractionation column, the product taken from the top of the tower will contain 20 mole per cent ethane, 40 per cent propane, 15 per cent isobutane, and 25 per cent n-butane. This material is to be completely liquefied in a condenser, with cooling water entering at a temperature of 70°F. Assuming a 10°F approach, what must be the pressure in the condenser?

Solution. The problem is essentially one of calculating the bubble-point pressure of the given mixture at $70 + 10 = 80°F$. Equations (12-39) and (12-40) are applicable. The K values are obtained from Fig. 12-15. It is convenient to carry out the operations in tabular form:

	x	K at 150 psia	$y = Kx$	K at 220 psia	$y = Kx$
Ethane........	0.20	3.1	0.62	2.1	0.42
Propane.......	0.40	1.0	0.40	0.74	0.30
Isobutane......	0.15	0.44	0.07	0.34	0.05
n-Butane	0.25	0.30	0.07	0.23	0.06
Total........	1.00	....	$\Sigma y_i = 1.16$	....	$\Sigma y_i = 0.83$

Σy_i 은 맞춰야지 1이 줘야.

The assumption of a pressure of 150 psia gave K values too high, so that $\Sigma y_i = 1.16$. This means that the mixture would partially vaporize at 80°F and 150 psia. At 220 psia $\Sigma y_i = 0.83$, indicating that the mixture would be a subcooled liquid. A third trial at 175 psia should be close to the required answer.

	x	K at 175 psia	$y = Kx$
Ethane..........	0.20	2.17	0.54
Propane..........	0.40	0.87	0.35
Isobutane.........	0.15	0.39	0.06
n-Butane.........	0.25	0.27	0.07
Total..........	1.00	....	$\Sigma y_i = 1.02$

Therefore, the desired pressure is slightly more than 175 psia, or about 180 psia.

If the vapor phase were assumed to behave as an ideal gas, the pressure could be obtained from Eq. (12-26) and the fact that the sum of the vapor pressures must be equal to the total pressure.

$$p = \Sigma p_i' x_i = 0.20(620) + 0.40(145) + 0.15(54) + 0.25(37)$$
$$= 124 + 58 + 8 + 9 = 199 \text{ psia}$$

The numbers in parentheses are the vapor pressures of the pure components at 80°F. In this case the error due to assuming that the gas phase was ideal amounted to about $[(199 - 180)/(180)](100)$, or 10 per cent.

Example 12-5. The product drawn from the still of a fractionation column contains 75 mole per cent n-pentane, 20 per cent n-butane, and 5 per cent isobutane. If the pressure is 75 psia and equilibrium is assumed, what is the composition of the vapor returned to the column from the still and what is the still temperature?

Solution. This is again a bubble-point calculation if it is assumed that the vapor and liquid leaving the still are in equilibrium. A trial-and-error solution is again required. Start the computations by assuming a temperature. In this case try, first, 150°F and, second, 200°F.

	x	K at 150°F (and 75 psia)	$y = Kx$	K at 200°F	$y = Kx$
Isobutane......	0.05	1.8	0.09	2.8	0.14
n-Butane......	0.20	1.4	0.28	2.3	0.46
n-Pentane.....	0.75	0.53	0.40	0.97	0.73
Total.......	1.00	....	$\Sigma y_i = 0.77$	....	$\Sigma y_i = 1.33$

The required temperature is between 150 and 200°F, probably about 170°F. A third trial at this temperature gives the following results:

	x	K at 170°F	$y = Kx$	Vapor composition
Isobutane........	0.05	2.2	0.11	0.11
n-Butane........	0.20	1.7	0.34	0.36
n-Pentane........	0.75	0.68	0.51	0.53
Total..........	....	....	$\Sigma y_i = 0.96$	1.00

The final temperature will be approximately 175°F and the vapor composition that shown in the last column of the preceding table.

Example 12-6. A mixture of hydrocarbons (10 mole per cent methane, 20 per cent ethane, 30 per cent propane, 15 per cent isobutane, 20 per cent n-butane, and 5 per cent n-pentane) is flashed into a separator at 80°F and 150 psia. What fraction leaves the separator as liquid, and what is its composition?

Solution. Equation (12-43) is applicable. Successive values of the fraction liquid L are assumed until $\Sigma x_i = 1.0$.

	n	K at 150 psia and 80°F	$x (L = 0.4)$	$x (L = 0.50)$	$y = Kx$
Methane........	0.10	17	0.01	0.01	0.18
Ethane..........	0.20	3.1	0.09	0.10	0.30
Propane........	0.30	1.0	0.30	0.30	0.30
Isobutane.......	0.15	0.44	0.22	0.20	0.10
n-Butane........	0.20	0.32	0.34	0.30	0.10
n-Pentane.......	0.05	0.096	0.11	0.09	0.01
Total.........	1.00	......	$\Sigma x_i = 1.07$	$\Sigma x_i = 1.00$	0.99

The calculation of x values for $L = 0.4$ was carried out using Eq. (12-43) in the following way:

For methane,

$$L + KV = 0.4 + 17(1 - 0.4) = 10.6$$
$$x = \frac{0.10}{10.6} = 0.01$$

For ethane,

$$L + KV = 0.4 + 3.1(1 - 0.4) = 2.2$$
$$x = \frac{0.20}{2.2} = 0.09$$

Liquid mole fractions for the remaining components are calculated in a similar fashion.

Since $\Sigma x_i = 1.0$ for $L = 0.5$, 50 per cent (molal basis) of the mixture leaving the separator is liquid and 50 per cent vapor. The composition of the liquid is represented by the x values in the next to the last column. The vapor composition $y = Kx$ is given in the last column. The sum of the vapor mole fractions should add up to unity. The fact that $\Sigma y_i = 0.99$ indicates that a more exact calculation of the fraction liquid would have given slightly different values.

12-10. Low Pressures. In Sec. 12-8 the equilibrium constant K was considered under three sets of restraints:

1. Using the rigorous equation (12-29) with an empirical equation of state for mixtures. This development led to the Kellogg charts and was satisfactory for hydrocarbons over a wide range of pressures.

2. Assuming that the liquid and gas phases form ideal solutions [Eq. (12-31)].

3. Assuming that the liquid is an ideal solution and the gas follows ideal-gas behavior [Eq. (12-32)].

There is a *fourth* classification of considerable importance in which the liquid phase is not an ideal solution, but the pressure is low enough that the vapor phase is an ideal gas. Distillation at atmospheric pressure of chemically dissimilar components introduces phase-equilibria problems in this classification. Azeotropic distillation involves a ternary system of this type. Qualitatively, problems of this type were discussed in Sec. 12-7.

The equilibrium constant lumps together in one quantity deviations from ideality in both the liquid and gas phases. In this fourth classification, the deviations are localized in the liquid. Hence, instead of using the equilibrium-constant concept, problems in this group are treated by considering deviations from Raoult's law. These deviations are taken into account by incorporating a correction factor γ into Eq. (12-26). The purpose of γ, the *activity coefficient*, is to account for the departure of the liquid phase from ideal-solution behavior. It is introduced into Eq. (12-26) as follows:

$$\bar{p}_k = \gamma_k p'_k x_k \tag{12-44}$$

The activity coefficient is a function of liquid-phase composition and temperature. Through its use phase-equilibrium problems of this type are reduced to evaluating values of γ. Consideration of the general features of multicomponent systems provides one equation between these variables. This relationship (the Gibbs-Duhem equation) is an important tool in studying the suitability of proposals for predicting γ and for testing the consistency of experimental phase-equilibria data. The development of the equation and of schemes for predicting the activity coefficient is taken up in the next section. It is worthwhile to preface these developments with the treatment of the special case where $\gamma = 1.0$.

When the activity coefficient is unity, Eq. (12-44) is the same as (12-26) and the problem reduces to the third classification listed earlier. Under these circumstances the equilibrium constant is given by the simple expression Eq. (12-32). However, problems of this type are perhaps easier to solve directly in terms of pressures. For example, suppose it is required to predict, for a binary system, T-x and p-x diagrams such as those in Figs. 12-11 and 12-12 (curves III). Equations (12-25) and (12-26) give the partial pressures in terms of the vapor and liquid compositions, respectively,

$$\bar{p}_k = p y_k \tag{12-25}$$
$$\bar{p}_k = p'_k x_k \tag{12-26}$$

A point on the bubble-point (liquid) line in Fig. 12-11 is given by the sum of the partial pressures of the two components evaluated from Eq. (12-26),

$$p = p'_A x_A + p'_B x_B \tag{12-45}$$

Here p'_A and p'_B are the vapor pressures of pure A and B. The point at the same temperature on the dew-point (vapor) curve is given by dividing the partial pressure of component B from Eq. (12-26) by the total pressure.

The temperature-composition curves can be determined from a knowledge of the vapor pressure of each component as a function of temperature. At any composition, x_A and x_B are known; hence Eq. (12-45) may be used to estimate, by trial, the temperature such that the sum of the partial pressures is equal to the known total pressure. This determines the bubble-point curve in Fig. 12-12 (III). Once the bubble-point curve has been located, the dew-point curve is found by the equation

$$y_A = \frac{p'_A x_A}{p} \tag{12-46}$$

Note that for the pressure-composition curves (Fig. 12-11) the temperature is constant, while in the temperature-composition curves the total pressure is constant. In plant-scale operations the latter case is more common.

The y-x diagram (Fig. 12-13, III) is also prepared on the basis of constant total pressure. It can be evaluated from the temperature-composition diagram by plotting points read from the bubble-point and dew-point curves at the same temperature. An approximate curve can be obtained directly by making use of the fact that the ratio of the vapor pressures of the two components does not vary greatly with temperature. Applying Eq. (12-46) to the two components and designating the ratio p'_A/p'_B as β, there results

$$\frac{y_A}{1 - y_A} = \frac{\beta x_A}{1 - x_A}$$

or

$$y_A = \frac{\beta x_A}{1 - x_A + \beta x_A} \tag{12-47}$$

Although Eq. (12-47) is not exact over a range in temperature without considering the variation in β, the effect is sufficiently small that an average value of β may be used in many cases for the whole y-x diagram.

The use of these equations based upon an ideal liquid phase is illustrated by the following example:

Example 12-7. Benzene and toluene form ideal-liquid solutions. Compute the composition of the vapor and liquid in equilibrium at 1 atm total pressure and temperatures of 80.0, 92.0, 100.0, and 110.4°C. Vapor-pressure data for the pure components are as follows:

Temperature, °C	Vapor pressure of benzene, mm	Vapor pressure of toluene, mm
80.0	760	300
92.0	1078	432
100.0	1344	559
110.4	1748	760

Solution. At 1 atm pressure the vapor phase may be regarded, without serious error, as an ideal gas. Equations (12-45) and (12-46) are then applicable. At 80°C, by Eq. (12-45),

$$760 = 760 x_B + 300(1 - x_B)$$
$$x_B \text{ (benzene)} = 1 \qquad x_T \text{ (toluene)} = 0$$

From Eq. (12-46),

$$y_B = \frac{(760)(1)}{760} = 1 \qquad y_T = 0$$

At 80°C and 1 atm pressure, only pure benzene can be present in vapor and liquid phases in equilibrium.

At 92°C,

$$760 = 1078 x_B + 432(1 - x_B)$$
$$x_B = 0.51 \qquad x_T = 0.49$$
$$y_B = \frac{(1078)(0.51)}{760} = 0.72 \qquad y_T = 0.28$$

At 100°C,

$$760 = 1344 x_B + 559(1 - x_B)$$
$$x_B = 0.256 \qquad x_T = 0.744$$
$$y_B = \frac{(1344)(0.256)}{760} = 0.45 \qquad y_T = 0.55$$

At 110.4°C,

$$760 = 1748x_B + 760(1 - x_B)$$
$$x_B = 0 \qquad x_T = 1.0$$
$$y_B = 0 \qquad y_T = 1.0$$

The calculations summarized in the accompanying table provide the necessary information for constructing the bubble-point and dew-point lines on a temperature-composition diagram (similar to Fig. 12-12, III).

Temperature, °C	Dew-point (vapor) curve		Bubble-point (liquid) curve	
	Benzene, y_B	Toluene, y_T	Benzene, x_B	Toluene, x_T
80	1.0	0.0	1.0	0.0
92	0.72	0.28	0.51	0.49
100	0.45	0.55	0.256	0.744
110.4	0.0	1.0	0.0	1.0

12-11. The Gibbs-Duhem Equation. The Gibbs-Duhem equation relates the partial pressures, or activity coefficients, and the composition of the liquid phase. It may be derived by considering the expression for the free energy F of 1 mole of the liquid. From the discussion in Sec. 12-2, it is clear that the contribution of each component in the mixture will be $x_i \bar{F}_i$, where x_i is the mole fraction of the component and $\bar{F}_i$ is its partial molal free energy. Summing these contributions gives

$$F = x_1 \bar{F}_1 + x_2 \bar{F}_2 + \cdots = \Sigma x_i \bar{F}_i \qquad (12\text{-}48)$$

For any change in state this equation may be differentiated generally.

$$dF = \bar{F}_1 \, dx_1 + x_1 \, d\bar{F}_1 + \bar{F}_2 \, dx_2 + x_2 \, d\bar{F}_2 + \cdots$$
$$= \Sigma \bar{F}_i \, dx_i + \Sigma x_i \, d\bar{F}_i \qquad (12\text{-}49)$$

Another way of evaluating the change in free energy of a mixture accompanying any variation in state is to consider that such a change must be due to a difference in either temperature or pressure or to the addition or subtraction of mass of any of the components. In differential form this would be

$$dF = \left(\frac{\partial F}{\partial T}\right)_p dT + \left(\frac{\partial F}{\partial p}\right)_T dp + \left(\frac{\partial F}{\partial n_1}\right) dn_1 + \left(\frac{\partial F}{\partial n_2}\right) dn_2 + \cdots$$
$$= \left(\frac{\partial F}{\partial T}\right)_p dT + \left(\frac{\partial F}{\partial p}\right)_T dp + \sum \bar{F}_i \, dn_i \qquad (12\text{-}50)$$

where the summation term represents the effect of adding dn_1 moles of component 1, dn_2 moles of component 2, . . . , at constant temperature and pressure.

If the change is restricted to one occurring at constant temperature and pressure, Eq. (12-50) becomes

$$dF = \Sigma \bar{F}_i \, dn_i$$

If both sides of this expression are divided by the total number of moles,

$$dF = \Sigma \bar{F}_i \, dx_i \qquad (12\text{-}51)$$

A comparison of (12-49) and (12-51) leads to the result

$$\Sigma x_i \, d\bar{F}_i = 0 \qquad (12\text{-}52)$$

Equation (12-52) applies rigorously at constant temperature and pressure. It shows the restriction that is placed on the variation of the partial free energies of the components in the solution with the composition. If the variations of the $\bar{F}_i$'s are considered with respect to a change in the mole fraction of component 1, the equation becomes

$$\sum_{i=1}^{n} x_i \left(\frac{\partial \bar{F}_i}{\partial x_1} \right)_{T,p} = 0 \qquad (12\text{-}53)$$

This is the general form of the Gibbs-Duhem equation. It may be written in terms of fugacities by differentiating Eq. (12-19) at constant temperature and pressure and substituting in Eq. (12-53). The result is

$$\sum x_i \left[\frac{\partial (\ln \bar{f}_i)}{\partial x_1} \right]_{T,p} = 0 \qquad (12\text{-}54)$$

Under the low pressures considered in this section, the vapor phase approaches an ideal-gas mixture. Then the fugacity $\bar{f}_i$ in the liquid is equal to the partial pressure $\bar{p}_i$ in the gas, and (12-54) becomes

$$\sum x_i \left[\frac{\partial (\ln \bar{p}_i)}{\partial x_1} \right]_{T,p} = 0 \qquad (12\text{-}55)$$

Equation (12-44) can be used along with (12-55) to present the Gibbs-Duhem equation in terms of activity coefficients. If logarithms are taken of Eq. (12-44) and the result is differentiated, there is obtained

$$\ln \bar{p}_k = \ln x_k + \ln \gamma_k + \ln p'_k$$
$$d(\ln \bar{p}_k) = d(\ln x_k) + d(\ln \gamma_k) \qquad (12\text{-}56)$$

Combining Eqs. (12-56) and (12-55),

$$x_1 \left[\frac{\partial (\ln \gamma_1)}{\partial x_1} \right]_{T,p} + x_2 \left[\frac{\partial (\ln \gamma_2)}{\partial x_1} \right]_{T,p} + x_3 \left[\frac{\partial (\ln \gamma_3)}{\partial x_1} \right]_{T,p} + \cdots$$
$$+ 1 + x_2 \left[\frac{\partial (\ln x_2)}{\partial x_1} \right]_{T,p} + x_3 \left[\frac{\partial (\ln x_3)}{\partial x_1} \right]_{T,p} + \cdots = 0 \qquad (12\text{-}57)$$

The second series of Eq. (12-57) may be written as

$$1 + \frac{dx_2}{dx_1} + \frac{dx_3}{dx_1} + \cdots = \frac{dx_1 + dx_2 + dx_3 + \cdots}{dx_1} = \frac{0}{dx_1} = 0$$

Therefore the equation in terms of activity coefficients is

$$x_1 \left[\frac{\partial(\ln \gamma_1)}{\partial x_1} \right]_{T,p} + x_2 \left[\frac{\partial(\ln \gamma_2)}{\partial x_1} \right]_{T,p} + x_3 \left[\frac{\partial(\ln \gamma_3)}{\partial x_1} \right]_{T,p} + \cdots = 0$$

or

$$\sum x_i \left[\frac{\partial(\ln \gamma_i)}{\partial x_1} \right]_{T,p} = 0 \qquad (12\text{-}58)$$

It is important to note that the various forms of the Gibbs-Duhem equation (12-54), (12-55), and (12-58) are strictly true only at constant-temperature and constant-pressure conditions. That is, these expressions relate the effect of composition changes, at constant T and p, on the fugacities of the components in the liquid. For systems of three or more components, phase-rule requirements present no difficulty in the application of these equations to vapor-liquid equilibria problems. However, when there are only two components, the specification of constant pressure and temperature completely fixes the system, including the composition of the liquid phase. If composition is to vary, then either temperature or pressure must change too, and Eq. (12-58) cannot be valid when applied rigorously to a binary system. Many actual processes involving vapor-liquid equilibrium, such as distillation, occur at constant pressure. Then the temperature varies with the liquid composition, as illustrated in the T-x diagrams of Fig. 12-12. The other, less practical case is the constant-temperature one, where the pressure varies with x, as shown in Fig. 12-11. Correct equations for both cases and their differences from the approximate Eq. (12-58) have been presented by Dodge and Ibl.[1] If pressure only is constant, the magnitude of the error is dependent upon the heat of mixing of the liquid and the rate of change of temperature (boiling point) with composition. In most examples of binary distillation the temperature change is small enough that Eq. (12-58) can be employed without serious error, except perhaps at liquid compositions x_1 near zero or unity.

Equations (12-54), (12-55), and (12-58) are primarily useful in checking the consistency of experimental phase-composition data and in reducing the quantity of experimental work required to determine completely the composition of gas and liquid phases in equilibrium. This is particularly well illustrated by binary systems since, for two phases to be present at equilibrium, only two properties need be specified to fix the state. Equation (12-55) becomes in this case

[1] B. F. Dodge and N. V. Ibl, *Chem. Eng. Sci.*, **2**, 120 (1953).

$$x_1 \frac{d(\ln \bar{p}_1)}{dx_1} + x_2 \frac{d(\ln \bar{p}_2)}{dx_1} = 0$$

or

$$x_1 \frac{d(\ln \bar{p}_1)}{dx_1} + (1 - x_1) \frac{d(\ln \bar{p}_2)}{dx_1} = 0 \qquad (12\text{-}59)$$

If the partial pressure of component 1 is known over a range of x_1 values at a constant temperature, Eq. (12-59) provides a method of computing the partial pressure of the other component over the same range of composition. If both $\bar{p}_1$ and $\bar{p}_2$ are measured experimentally, the consistency of the data can be evaluated.

The expression analogous to Eq. (12-59) but in terms of activity coefficients is, according to Eq. (12-58),

$$x_1 \frac{d(\ln \gamma_1)}{dx_1} + x_2 \frac{d(\ln \gamma_2)}{dx_1} = 0 \qquad (12\text{-}60)$$

An adaptation of this which is useful in testing the consistency of experimental data is

$$\int_0^1 \ln \frac{\gamma_1}{\gamma_2} \, dx_1 = 0 \qquad (12\text{-}61)[1]$$

According to Eq. (12-61), if $\ln (\gamma_1/\gamma_2)$ is plotted vs. x_1, the net area under the curve must be zero. Hence, if experimental data are available

[1] Redlich and Kister [*Ind. Eng. Chem.*, **40**, 345 (1948)] derived this equation by considering the *excess* free energy of mixing ΔF_{ex} per mole. This quantity is the difference between the free energies of mixing for a real solution and for an ideal solution. The free energy for 1 mole of a binary solution is given by Eq. (12-48),

$$F = x_1 \bar{F}_1 + x_2 \bar{F}_2$$

The free energy prior to mixing the two components would be $x_1 F_1 + x_2 F_2$, where F_1 and F_2 are the molal free energies of the pure components. Hence the free energy of mixing is, in general,

$$\Delta F_m = x_1 (\bar{F} - F)_1 + x_2 (\bar{F} - F)_2$$

This can be written in terms of fugacities by employing Eqs. (12-13) and (12-19).

$$\Delta F_m = RT \left[x_1 \ln \left(\frac{\bar{f}}{f} \right)_1 + x_2 \ln \left(\frac{\bar{f}}{f} \right)_2 \right]$$

If this last expression is applied to a liquid phase at low pressures so that the ideal-gas law is valid, the fugacities may be replaced by pressures, giving

$$\Delta F_m = RT \left[x_1 \ln \left(\frac{\bar{p}}{p'} \right)_1 + x_2 \ln \left(\frac{\bar{p}}{p'} \right)_2 \right]$$

Introducing the activity coefficient through Eq. (12-44), there is obtained

$$\Delta F_m = RT[x_1 \ln (\gamma x)_1 + x_2 \ln (\gamma x)_2] \qquad (12\text{-}62)$$

Equation (12-62) gives the free energy of mixing of a real solution. For an ideal

from which to compute γ values by Eq. (12-44), the consistency of the data can be checked by plotting a curve of $\ln (\gamma_1/\gamma_2)$ vs. x_1. Figures 12-17 and 12-18 illustrate applications of Eq. (12-61) for two binary systems at 1 atm pressure. In Fig. 12-17 there is a net positive area, indicating uncertainties in the data. In contrast the net area under the curve in Fig. 12-18 is essentially zero, demonstrating that the requirements of the Gibbs-Duhem equation are satisfied.

Other forms of the Gibbs-Duhem equation are sometimes of value. For example, the partial pressures in Eq. (12-59) may be eliminated with the aid of the following equations:

$$\bar{p}_1 = py_1 \qquad d\bar{p}_1 = p\,dy_1 + y_1\,dp$$
$$\bar{p}_2 = p(1 - y_1) \qquad d\bar{p}_2 = -p\,dy_1 + (1 - y_1)\,dp$$

where p is the total pressure and y refers to the composition of the vapor phase. Substitution of these expressions in Eq. (12-59) yields

$$\frac{dp}{p} = \frac{y_1 - x_1}{y_1(1 - y_1)}\,dy_1 \qquad (12\text{-}66)$$

This relationship between the total pressure and the composition of the vapor and liquid phases may be employed for such problems as evaluating y from total-pressure and liquid-composition data.

The Gibbs-Duhem equation does not permit the independent evalua-

---

solution the activity coefficient would be unity, *i.e.*,

$$(\Delta F_m)_{\text{ideal}} = RT(x_1 \ln x_1 + x_2 \ln x_2) \qquad (12\text{-}63)$$

Subtracting the ideal from the real free energy of mixing yields the *excess* free energy of mixing:

$$\Delta F_{\text{ex}} = RT(x_1 \ln \gamma_1 + x_2 \ln \gamma_2) \qquad (12\text{-}64)$$

If Eq. (12-64) is differentiated with respect to x_1, there results

$$\frac{d(\Delta F_{\text{ex}})}{dx_1} = RT\left[\ln \gamma_1 - \ln \gamma_2 + x_1 \frac{d(\ln \gamma_1)}{dx_1} + (1 - x_1)\frac{d(\ln \gamma_2)}{dx_1}\right]$$

According to the Gibbs-Duhem equation (12-60), the sum of the last two terms is zero. Hence,

$$\frac{d(\Delta F_{\text{ex}})}{dx_1} = RT\left(\ln \frac{\gamma_1}{\gamma_2}\right) \qquad (12\text{-}65)$$

If now Eq. (12-65) is integrated between the definite limits $x_1 = 0$ and $x_1 = 1.0$, there is obtained

$$(\Delta F_{\text{ex}})_{x_1=1} - (\Delta F_{\text{ex}})_{x_1=0} = 0 = RT\int_0^1 \left(\ln \frac{\gamma_1}{\gamma_2}\right) dx_1$$

The excess free energy of mixing is zero at both $x_1 = 0$ and $x_1 = 1$ because at these end points only pure components are involved, and so no mixing effects occur. The equation can be further simplified to agree with Eq. (12-61) by dropping the RT term.

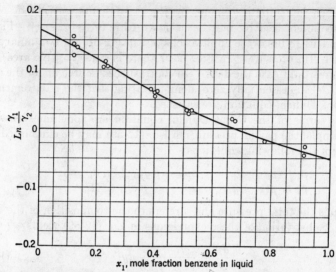

FIG. 12-17. Gibbs-Duhem test of data for benzene–*n*-octane system at 1 atm. [*Reproduced by permission from O. Redlich, A. T. Kister, and C. E. Turnquist, Chem. Eng. Progr., Symposium Ser. 2, 48, 49 (1952).*]

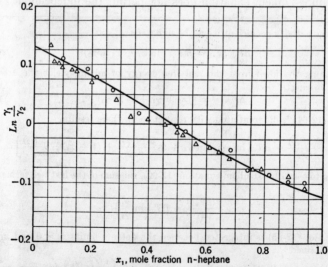

FIG. 12-18. Gibbs-Duhem test of data for *n*-heptane–toluene system at 1 atm. [*Reproduced by permission from O. Redlich, A. T. Kister, and C. E. Turnquist, Chem. Eng. Progr., Symposium Ser. 2, 48, 49 (1952).*]

tion of partial pressures or activity coefficients, but merely provides a relationship between those quantities for the components in the solution. Methods of predicting activity coefficients directly are discussed in the next section.

Example 12-8. The following data are available for mixtures of acetone and water:[1]

Liquid composition, mole per cent acetone	Partial pressure of acetone, mm Hg		
	60°C	45°C	30°C
0.0	0	0	0
3.3	190	101	47.5
11.7	443	253	134
31.8	588	346	189
55.4	672	400	225
73.6	711	423	236
100.0	860	505	281

Using the Gibbs-Duhem equation, calculate the partial pressure of water over the above solutions at the three temperatures 30, 45, and 60°C.

Solution. Since the total pressures will be relatively small, Eq. (12-59), based upon ideal-gas behavior for the vapor phase, is satisfactory.

If subscript W refers to water and A to acetone Eq. (12-59) may be written so as to separate the variables.

$$\frac{d\bar{p}_W}{\bar{p}_W} = -\frac{x_A}{1-x_A}\frac{d\bar{p}_A}{\bar{p}_A}$$

Integrating between states 1 and 2 at constant temperature,

$$\ln\frac{\bar{p}_{W_2}}{\bar{p}_{W_1}} = -\int_{\bar{p}_{A_1}}^{\bar{p}_{A_2}}\frac{x_A}{1-x_A}\frac{d\bar{p}_A}{\bar{p}_A} \tag{A}$$

If the initial state 1 is chosen so that $x_{A_1} = 0$, $x_{W_1} = 1.0$ and $\bar{p}_{W_1}$ is the vapor pressure of pure water at the given temperature. Also, $\bar{p}_{A_1}$ will be zero. At 60°C the vapor pressure of pure water is 149.4 mm. Hence Eq. (A) becomes

$$\ln\frac{\bar{p}_{W_2}}{149.4} = -\int_0^{\bar{p}_{A_2}}\frac{x_A}{1-x_A}\frac{d\bar{p}_A}{\bar{p}_A} \tag{B}$$

where $\bar{p}_{W_2}$ is the partial pressure of water above a solution which exerts an acetone partial pressure $\bar{p}_{A_2}$. All the quantities within the integral sign are known from the data given in the example. Therefore, the partial pressure of water at any liquid composition can be obtained by plotting $x_A/(1-x_A)\bar{p}_A$ vs. $\bar{p}_A$ and evaluating the integral graphically from $\bar{p}_A = 0$ to the $\bar{p}_A$ corresponding to the desired liquid composition. It is important to note that the integration indicated in (B) is to be carried out at constant temperature for variations in liquid composition from zero acetone up

[1] A. E. Taylor, *J. Phys. Chem.*, **4**, 675 (1900).

to the desired concentration. The results of the graphic integration are shown in the accompanying table under the columns labeled $\bar{p}_W$ [Eq. (B)].

Liquid composition, mole fraction acetone, x_A	Partial pressure of water, mm Hg					
	60°C		45°C		30°C	
	$\bar{p}_W$ [Eq. (B)]	$\bar{p}_W$ (exp)	$\bar{p}_W$ [Eq. (B)]	$\bar{p}_W$ (exp)	$\bar{p}_W$ [Eq. (B)]	$\bar{p}_W$ (exp)
0.0	149.4	149.4	71.5	71.5	31.5	31.5
0.033	144.9	149	69.2	76	30.5	34.5
0.117	137.1	134	65.2	66	28.4	30.5
0.318	127.5	126	61.2	67.5	26.2	35
0.554	115.7	102	54.3	47	23.0	20
0.736	104.3	97	48.9	45.5	20.8	21.5
1.0	0.0	0.0	0.0	0.0	0.0	0.0

The values labeled (exp) were taken from the reference given in the statement of the example. In general, the agreement between computed and experimental results is good. Large deviations suggest inconsistencies in the data, and such a comparison as shown in the table may often be of value in determining the points which are in error.

Example 12-9. Show that Raoult's law is valid for component A of a binary solution over the range of composition for which Henry's law holds for component B. That is, show that $p_A = p_A' x_A$ when $p_B = k x_B$.

Solution. If $\bar{p}_B = k x_B$, where k is a constant at a fixed temperature (that is, k is Henry's-law constant),

$$\ln \bar{p}_B = \ln k + \ln x_B$$

and

$$\frac{d(\ln \bar{p}_B)}{dx_B} = \frac{1}{x_B}$$

If this relation is substituted in the Gibbs-Duhem equation (12-59),

$$1 + (1 - x_B)\frac{d(\ln \bar{p}_A)}{dx_B} = 0$$

or

$$d(\ln \bar{p}_A) = d(\ln x_A)$$

Integrating,

$$\ln \bar{p}_A = \ln x_A + \ln C$$

where $\ln C$ is the constant of integration. When $x_A = 1$, the partial pressure of A is its vapor pressure p_A'. Hence $C = p_A'$ and the equation may be written

$$\ln \bar{p}_A = \ln x_A + \ln p_A'$$

or

$$\bar{p}_A = p_A' x_A$$

which is Raoult's law.

This result is applicable as long as Henry's law is valid. Therefore, Raoult's law is satisfactory for component A over the same range of composition that Henry's law is valid for B. Henry's law is satisfied for any system when the component is present in very low concentrations. Hence Raoult's law is always satisfied for a component present at very high concentrations. It should be noted that an ideal-gas phase has been assumed in these considerations.

12-12. Evaluation of Activity Coefficients. A number of methods have been proposed for predicting the activity coefficient.[1-6] Their objective is to permit the evaluation of γ, as a function of liquid-phase composition, from a minimum of experimental data. In particular it is important to minimize the information needed for the mixture, since this is generally not available and is difficult to measure. These methods are based upon empirical expressions for the excess free energy of mixing, and two of them are discussed here. Both are thermodynamically sound in that they are in agreement with the Gibbs-Duhem equation; that is, the equations for γ represent solutions to the differential equation expressed by Eq. (12-60). The first proposal[4] results in the following expressions:

$$\ln \gamma_1 = x_2^2[B + C(3x_1 - x_2) + D(x_1 - x_2)(5x_1 - x_2) + \cdots] \quad (12\text{-}67)$$
$$\ln \gamma_2 = x_1^2[B + C(x_1 - 3x_2) + D(x_1 - x_2)(x_1 - 5x_2) + \cdots] \quad (12\text{-}68)$$

where B, C, and D are constants to be evaluated from experimental data. These equations have been found to correlate data for varied systems. The more nonideal the liquid phase, the more terms are required. If B, C, and D, etc., are chosen equal to zero, $\gamma_1 = \gamma_2 = 1$, so that this is equivalent to assuming an ideal liquid phase. If B is the only constant not equal to zero, the equations are satisfactory for treating systems that form an almost-ideal liquid phase, such as n-hexane and toluene. For mixtures containing an associating molecule such as methanol or acetic acid, three or four constants may be required. With only two constants $(B$ and $C)$ retained, Eqs. (12-67) and (12-68) are equivalent to the Margules[7] solutions of the Gibbs-Duhem equation.

A second empirical method of correlating activity coefficients results from the van Laar[8] equations:

$$\ln \gamma_1 = \frac{a}{[1 + (x_1/x_2)(a/b)]^2} \quad (12\text{-}69)$$

$$\ln \gamma_2 = \frac{b}{[1 + (x_2/x_1)(b/a)]^2} \quad (12\text{-}70)$$

[1] M. Benedict, C. A. Johnson, E. Solomon, and L. C. Rubin, *Trans. AIChE*, **41**, 371 (1945).

[2] H. C. Carlson and A. P. Colburn, *Ind. Eng. Chem.*, **34**, 581 (1942).

[3] O. Redlich and A. T. Kister, *Ind. Eng. Chem.*, **40**, 345 (1948).

[4] O. Redlich, A. T. Kister, and C. E. Turnquist, *Chem. Eng. Progr., Symposium Ser.* 2, **48**, 49 (1952).

[5] G. Scatchard, *Chem. Rev.*, **44**, 7 (1949).

[6] K. Wohl, *Trans. AIChE*, **42**, 215 (1946).

[7] M. Margules, *Sitzber. Akad. Wiss. Wien, Math.-naturw. Kl.*, **104**, 1243 (1895).

[8] J. J. van Laar, *Z. physik. Chem.*, **72**, 723 (1910); **83**, 599 (1913).

These expressions also involve two arbitrary constants a and b. For two-constant equations, such as those of Margules or van Laar, a minimum of one experimental point for the mixture is required. That is, the vapor and liquid compositions in equilibrium at one point are necessary to evaluate the activity coefficients, and then the constants may be calculated from Eqs. (12-67) and (12-68) or (12-69) and (12-70). Thus, if the mole fraction of component 1 in the liquid is x_1 and in the vapor y_1, Eq. (12-44) for the liquid and Eq. (12-25) for an ideal gas give

$$\bar{p}_1 = \gamma_1 p_1' x_1$$

and

$$\bar{p}_1 = p y_1$$

Solving for γ_1 gives

$$\gamma_1 = \frac{p y_1}{p_1' x_1} \tag{12-71}$$

Similarly,

$$\gamma_2 = \frac{p(1 - y_1)}{p_2'(1 - x_1)} \tag{12-72}$$

If the binary system forms an azeotrope at that point, $y_1 = x_1$. Then γ_1 and γ_2, and hence a and b, can be evaluated from an experimental determination of either y_1 or x_1. If the composition of liquid and vapor phases is known at a number of points, statistical methods can be used to evaluate more accurate values of the constants.

Equations of the Margules and van Laar types have been developed for ternary systems.[1] The objective of these proposals is to allow the prediction of the activity coefficients in such systems from data on the three possible binary combinations. However, at least some ternary information appears necessary if reasonably accurate results are to be obtained.

Example 12-10. Using the van Laar method, calculate the y-x equilibrium compositions at atmospheric pressure for a mixture of chloroform and acetone. Chloroform and acetone form an azeotrope which contains 66.6 mole per cent chloroform and boils at 64.5°C. The vapor pressures (millimeters of mercury) of the pure components are as follows:

Temperature, °C	Acetone, p_A', mm	Chloroform, p_C', mm
45	510.5	439.0
50	612.6	526.0
55	. . . . . .	625.2
56.3	760.0	
60	860.6	739.6
60.9	. . . . . .	760.0
70	1190	1019
80	1611	1403

[1] K. Wohl, *Trans. AIChE*, **42**, 215 (1946).

Solution. In order to determine a and b in the van Laar equations it is first necessary to evaluate single values of the activity coefficients from Eqs. (12-71) and (12-72). In this case the data concerning the constant-boiling mixture are sufficient for the purpose.

At the constant-boiling point $x_C = y_C$ (subscript C designates chloroform and A, acetone), so that Eqs. (12-71) and (12-72) reduce to

$$\gamma_C = \frac{p}{p_C'} = \frac{760}{858} = 0.886$$

$$\gamma_A = \frac{p}{p_A'} = \frac{760}{1000} = 0.760$$

p_C' and p_A' are the vapor pressures of pure chloroform and acetone at 64.5°C. These values of γ_C and γ_A can be used in Eqs. (12-69) and (12-70) to determine the constants a and b. Solving the two expressions simultaneously,

$$a = \ln \gamma_C \left(1 + \frac{x_A \ln \gamma_A}{x_C \ln \gamma_C}\right)^2 = \ln 0.886 \left(1 + \frac{0.334 \ln 0.760}{0.666 \ln 0.886}\right)^2$$

$$= -0.552$$

$$b = \ln \gamma_A \left(1 + \frac{x_C \ln \gamma_C}{x_A \ln \gamma_A}\right)^2 = \ln 0.760 \left(1 + \frac{0.666 \ln 0.886}{0.334 \ln 0.760}\right)^2$$

$$= -0.970$$

The final working equations for the activity coefficients at any composition are

$$\ln \gamma_C = \frac{-0.552}{[1 + 0.570(x_C/x_A)]^2}$$

$$\ln \gamma_A = \frac{-0.970}{[1 + 1.759(x_A/x_C)]^2}$$

The accompanying table gives the values of γ_C and γ_A computed from these equations.

Liquid composition, mole fraction chloroform, x_C	Activity coefficients		Vapor composition, chloroform	
	Chloroform, γ_C	Acetone, γ_A	y_C (calc)	y_C (exp)
0.0	0.576	1.000	0.0	0.0
0.2	0.655	0.985	0.125	0.126
0.4	0.748	0.930	0.316	0.320
0.6	0.856	0.814	0.577	0.585
0.666	0.886	0.760	0.666	0.666
0.8	0.950	0.626	0.840	0.835
1.0	1.000	0.379	1.000	1.000

The composition of the vapor phase, mole fraction chloroform (y_C), can be determined from the activity coefficients by Eqs. (12-71) and (12-72).

$$y_C = \frac{\gamma_C p_C' x_C}{p} \qquad (A)$$

$$y_A = 1 - y_C = \frac{\gamma_A p_A'(1 - x_C)}{p} \qquad (B)$$

If Eq. (A) is divided by (B), the total pressure drops out, giving the following expression for y_C in terms of the activity coefficients:

$$\frac{y_C}{1 - y_C} = \frac{\gamma_C p_C' x_C}{\gamma_A p_A'(1 - x_C)}$$

$$y_C = \frac{1}{1 + (\gamma_A/\gamma_C)(x_A/x_C)(p_A'/p_C')} \tag{C}$$

The advantage of Eq. (C) over (A) for determining the vapor composition from the liquid composition and activity coefficients is that, if the vapor-pressure ratio is nearly constant, it is unnecessary to calculate the boiling temperature. This is a simplification, for the calculation of boiling points involves trial-and-error work. For example, at the point where $x_C = 0$, the temperature corresponds to the boiling point of pure acetone, or 56.3°C. At $x_C = 1.0$, $t = 60.9$°C. The vapor-pressure ratios at 50 and 60°C are (from the data given in the statement of the example)

$$t = 50°C \qquad \frac{p_A'}{p_C'} = \frac{612.6}{526} = 1.16$$

$$t = 60°C \qquad \frac{p_A'}{p_C'} = \frac{860.6}{739.6} = 1.16$$

Since this ratio is constant over the entire temperature range, Eq. (C) may be written as

$$y_C = \frac{1}{1 + 1.16(\gamma_A x_A/\gamma_C x_C)}$$

Values of y_C so calculated are shown in the next to the last column of the preceding table. The experimental results given in the last column were taken from data obtained by Rasanoff and Easley.[1] The calculated and experimental results agree exactly at the constant-boiling point $x_C = 0.666$, since the method was based upon that experimental point. The agreement between the values at the other compositions is a measure of the accuracy of the method.

If the vapor-pressure ratio had not been constant, the boiling temperature would have had to be determined at each composition in order to evaluate the correct vapor pressures. This calculation would have involved the assumption of a temperature, calculation of the separate partial pressures by Eq. (12-44), and finally checking the assumed temperature by noting whether or not the sum of the pressures was equal to the total pressure, 760 mm.

SYSTEMS OF LIMITED MISCIBILITY

Many mixtures form more than one liquid phase. In industry such systems occur primarily in distillation and solvent-extraction operations. They contain two or more components, and the liquid phases may be essentially immiscible or may exhibit a significant mutual solubility. Such systems represent a further degree of deviation from the concept of an ideal solution than miscible systems. In an approximate way the components of an immiscible system may be imagined to be so dissimilar

[1] *J. Am. Chem. Soc.*, **30**, 953 (1909).

chemically that they are completely incompatible.   This situation results when the forces of attraction between like molecules are very large with respect to those between unlike molecules.

12-13. Partially Miscible Systems.   For a two-component system consisting of two liquid phases and one vapor phase in equilibrium, there is but one variant.   At a fixed pressure, the temperature (and compositions) of all three phases is determined.   On a temperature-composition diagram the points representing the states of the three phases in equilibrium fall on a horizontal line.   In Fig. 12-19, points C and D represent the two liquid phases, and point E represents the vapor phase.   If more of either component is added to the system, and if the three-phase equilibrium is maintained, the compositions of the three phases must remain

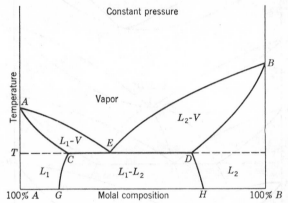

FIG. 12-19. Temperature-composition diagram for a binary system of partially miscible liquids at constant pressure.

the same.   However, the relative amounts of the phases will change to reflect the alteration in total composition.   For the case shown the total composition must lie between the compositions of points C and D.

At temperatures above T on Fig. 12-19, the system can exist either as two phases (liquid and vapor) or as a single phase, depending on the total composition.   In region L_1-V, a liquid and a vapor phase are in equilibrium.   The states of the individual phases are indicated by points on lines AC and AE at the particular temperature considered.   In region L_2-V, liquid and vapor phases, designated by the lines BD and BE, exist at equilibrium.   Finally, in the region designated as vapor, the system is a single gaseous phase.   Below the three-phase temperature T, no vapor phase can be present.   A mixture having a total composition within the region L_1-L_2 would consist of two liquid phases of compositions given by the intersections of a horizontal line corresponding to the temperature of the system and the lines CG and DH.   It is to be noted that in all sections of the diagram the tie lines connecting the compositions of phases in equilibrium are horizontal. Figure 12-19 applies for one particular pressure. The compositions of the phases in equilibrium, and hence the locations of the lines, will change with pressure, although the general appearance of the diagram will remain the same over a range of pressures.

For most systems the components become more soluble in one another as the temperature increases. This is indicated by lines CG and DH of

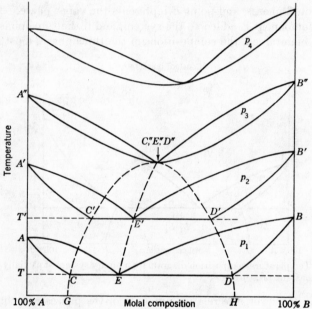

FIG. 12-20. Temperature-composition diagram at several pressures.

Fig. 12-19. However, these lines terminate at the three-phase equilibrium temperature T. If this diagram is drawn for successively higher pressures, the corresponding three-phase equilibrium temperature will increase, and lines CG and DH will extend further and further until they meet at a point. The temperature at which this occurs is known as the *upper critical solution temperature*, and at this temperature the two liquid phases become identical and merge into a single phase. For the pressure at which this point is reached, the line CED becomes a point, and the vapor-liquid equilibrium lines AEB and $ACDB$ take the form shown in Fig. 12-12 (curve II, minimum-boiling azeotrope). At higher pressures three-phase equilibrium cannot exist, and the only diagram possible is for the two-phase vapor-liquid equilibria. Figure 12-20 summarizes the foregoing treatment and shows graphically the situation described.   The dashed lines are the loci of points representing three-phase equilibrium.

Not all systems behave as described in the preceding paragraph. Sometimes the upper critical solution temperature is never attained because a vapor-liquid critical temperature is reached first.   In other cases the liquid solubilities increase with a *decrease* in temperature.   In this event a *lower critical solution temperature* will be found, unless solid phases appear first.   There are also systems which exhibit *both* upper and lower critical solution temperatures.

The problem of predicting the compositions of equilibrium phases for partially miscible systems is similar to that encountered for miscible systems.   Comparison of Figs. 12-12 and 12-19 indicates that the relation between the vapor and liquid compositions for each liquid in the partially miscible system is of the same type as that for miscible substances.   The essential difference is that a region of two stable liquid phases is present for the partially miscible system.   If the liquid solutions are ideal and the vapor phase is an ideal gas, Eqs. (12-25) and (12-26) apply.   They may be used to construct a temperature-composition diagram, provided that information concerning the compositions of the two liquid phases in equilibrium is available.   It is not necessary to make such stringent assumptions as these if Henry's-law constants are available for the components.   In general, Raoult's law is more accurate for a component when its concentration is high and Henry's-law more accurate when its concentration is low.   If Raoult's law holds for one component, then Henry's law must be true for the other (Example 12-9).   Hence all that is necessary is to assume that Raoult's law holds for the component present in the larger concentration in each of the liquid phases.   From Fig. 12-19 this will be component A for liquid phase 1 and component B for liquid phase 2.   With these assumptions the equations for determining the temperature-composition diagram are as follows: For liquid phase 1,

$$p = \text{total pressure} = \bar{p}_A + \bar{p}_B = \text{sum of partial pressures}$$
$$= p_A' x_A + (1 - x_A)k_B$$

or

$$x_A = \frac{p - k_B}{p_A' - k_B} \tag{12-73}$$

$$y_A = \frac{p_A' x_A}{p} \tag{12-74}$$

Equations (12-73) and (12-74) determine the lines AC and AE, describing the equilibrium between vapor and liquid 1.   The constant k_B is the Henry's-law constant for component B in A.   For liquid phase 2 exactly analogous relations apply.   Here Raoult's law is assumed for component B, and Henry's law applies to component A.

$$x_B = \frac{p - k_A}{p_B' - k_A} \qquad (12\text{-}75)$$

and

$$y_B = \frac{p_B' x_B}{p} \qquad (12\text{-}76)$$

These equations determine the lines BD and BE in Fig. 12-19. Since the total pressure is known and the temperature is to be evaluated, the solution of Eqs. (12-73) to (12-76) involves a trial-and-error procedure. The method is illustrated by the following example:

Example 12-11. Construct a t-x diagram for the ether-water system at 1 atm total pressure from the following data:

t, °C	Total pressure, atm	Saturated water phase, x_B	Saturated ether phase, x_B	p_A'	p_B'
34.15	1.005	0.0122	0.9451	0.053	0.983
40	1.250	0.0116	0.9416	0.073	1.212
50	1.744	0.0103	0.9348	0.121	1.679
60	2.381	0.0093	0.9271	0.196	2.271
70	3.195	0.0075	0.9212	0.306	3.018
80	4.229	0.0069	0.9158	0.467	3.935
90	5.514	0.0058	0.9107	0.691	5.040
100	7.040	......	......	1.000	6.390

x_B = mole fraction ether.
p_A' = vapor pressure of pure water, atm.
p_B' = vapor pressure of pure ether, atm.

Assume Raoult's law is valid for ether in the ether phase and for water in the water phase.

Solution. From the data, the temperature at which the two liquid phases and the vapor phase are in equilibrium at 1 atm total pressure will be about 34.0°C. The composition of the ether phase is approximately 0.9456 mole fraction ether and that of the water-rich phase 0.0123 mole fraction ether. These conditions fix points C and D and the horizontal line CED in Fig. 12-19.

The dew-point and bubble-point lines AE and AC may be located with the aid of Eqs. (12-73) and (12-74), assuming that Raoult's law is valid for the rich component. Applying Eq. (12-73),

$$x_A = \frac{p - k_B}{p_A' - k_B}$$

where A refers to water and B refers to ether. This expression may be used at any constant temperature to determine x_A and hence locate curve AC. However, k_B, Henry's-law constant for ether in this water-rich liquid, must be evaluated. This constant depends upon the temperature, but since total pressure-composition data are given at a series of temperatures, k_B may be evaluated at a series of temperatures. For example, at 50°C, from Eq. (12-73),

$$x_A = 1 - x_B = 1 - 0.0103 = \frac{1.744 - k_B}{0.121 - k_B}$$

or

$$k_B = 168 \text{ at } 50°C$$

Now x_A may be found by applying (12-73) at a total pressure of 1 atm and 50°C.

$$x_A = 1 - x_B = \frac{1 - 168}{0.121 - 168}$$

$$x_B = 0.0052 \quad \text{(mole fraction ether)}$$

The vapor composition (on line AE) in equilibrium with this liquid is given by Eq. (12-74).

$$y_A = 1 - y_B = \frac{p'_A x_A}{p} = \frac{(0.121)(0.9948)}{1} = 0.120$$

$$y_B = 0.880$$

The same scheme is applicable at any temperature between 34.0 and 100°C to calculate points on the curves AC and AE. The results for three intermediate temperatures are given in the accompanying table.

Temperature, °C	Mole fraction ether	
	Liquid, x_B	Vapor, y_B
34.0	0.0123	0.947
50	0.0052	0.880
70	0.0019	0.672
90	0.0005	0.307
100	0.0	0.0

The composition of the vapor at point E (in Fig. 12-19) at 34.0°C in the table is given directly by Eq. (12-74) without computing a k value. This is because x_B is known. For example,

$$y_A = 1 - y_B = \frac{(0.053)(1 - 0.0123)}{1} = 0.053$$

$$y_B = 0.947$$

In principle the x-y data for the ether-rich phase (lines BD and BE) can be obtained in an analogous manner by using Eqs. (12-75) and (12-76). However, the difference between the temperature of pure ether at B and the temperature at D is so small, $34.5 - 34.0$°C, that accurate evaluation of the differences between x and y in this region is not possible. Actually, this difference is probably quite small so that the y and x curves (lines BE and BD) nearly coincide.

The temperature-composition diagram is shown in Fig. 12-21. Two different composition scales are used in order to magnify the results.

12-14. Immiscible Systems. Probably no two liquids are totally immiscible. However, this condition is so closely approached in many cases that the assumption of complete immiscibility does not lead to appreciable error.

The essential feature of an immiscible system is that each liquid phase exerts its own total vapor pressure regardless of the quantity of the other liquid present. The phase characteristics of such a system are well illustrated on the temperature-composition diagram shown in Fig. 12-22. This phase diagram is the special case of Fig. 12-19, occurring when the

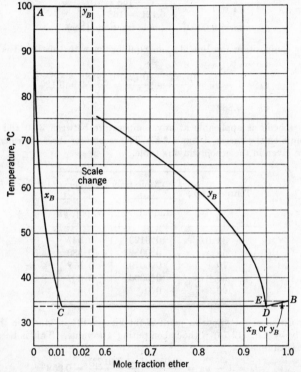

FIG. 12-21. Temperature-composition diagram for the ether-water system at 1. atm pressure.

two liquid phases L_1 and L_2 are the pure components A and B. Suppose initially the mixture is entirely in the vapor phase at the given pressure. This would be represented by a point such as J in Fig. 12-22. Upon cooling at constant pressure, a point M is reached such that the vapor pressure of pure A is equal to the partial pressure of A in the mixture. With continued cooling, pure liquid A will be condensed and the vapor composition will decrease in A along the line ME. When the temperature T is reached, the partial pressure of B in the vapor will have become equal to the vapor pressure of pure B. At this temperature, there will be three phases in equilibrium, pure liquid A, pure liquid B, and vapor of composition E.   Upon further heat removal, the temperature will remain constant at T until the vapor phase disappears.   Continued cooling will be represented by line NP.   If the original composition had been at H, the sequence of events would have been the same except that pure liquid B would have condensed out first.

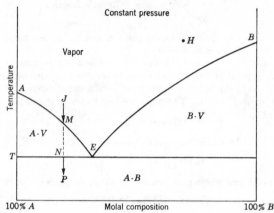

FIG. 12-22. Temperature-composition diagram for a binary system of immiscible liquids.

If the vapor phase is an ideal gas, Fig. 12-22 can be determined from a knowledge of vapor-pressure–temperature data for the two liquids.   The calculations are illustrated in Example 12-12.

Example 12-12.   Prepare a temperature-composition diagram for benzene-water mixtures at a total pressure of 760 mm from the following vapor-pressure data:

t, °C	Pure benzene, mm Hg	Pure water, mm Hg
50	269	93
60	389	149
70	547	233
75	640	285
80	754	355
90	1016	526
100	1344	760
110	1748	1075

Solution.   The point where both benzene and water will start to condense from a vapor mixture (point E in Fig. 12-22) corresponds to a temperature such that the sum of the vapor pressures is equal to the total pressure (760 mm).   From the data, this is seen to be slightly below 70°C, or about 69°C. The partial pressures in the vapor phase are

$$\bar{p}_B = 534$$
$$\underline{\bar{p}_W = 226}$$
$$\bar{p}_B + \bar{p}_W = 760$$

The composition of the vapor is

$$y_B = {}^{534}\!/_{760} = 0.70 \text{ mole fraction}$$
$$y_W = 1 - 0.70 = 0.30$$

This temperature and composition locate point E and fix the horizontal temperature line below which no vapor can exist.

To locate points on the dew-point line EB, choose temperatures between 69 and 100°C (the boiling point of water), and compute the compositions of the vapor. For example, if water is at the point of condensing from a vapor mixture at 80°C, its partial pressure must be 355 mm. The mole fraction water in the vapor will be

$$y_W = {}^{355}\!/_{760} = 0.47 \qquad y_B = 0.53$$

Similarly at 90°C, to be on the dew-point line corresponding to EB,

$$y_W = {}^{526}\!/_{760} = 0.69 \qquad y_B = 0.31$$

On the dew-point line where pure benzene is about to condense at 80°C,

$$y_B = {}^{754}\!/_{760} = 0.992$$

At 75°C

$$y_B = {}^{640}\!/_{760} = 0.84$$

This information is sufficient to locate the T-x diagram at 760 mm total pressure. The data are summarized in the table that follows.

Dew-point line for vapor–liquid water		Dew-point line for vapor–liquid benzene	
Temperature, °C	Mole fraction benzene	Temperature, °C	Mole fraction benzene
100	0	80.3	1.0
90	0.31	80	0.99
80	0.53	75	0.84
69	0.70	69	0.70

Nomenclature

a and b Constants in the van Laar equations (12-69) and (12-70).

B, C, and D Constants in the extended Margules equations (12-67) and (12-68).

Z Compressibility factor, pv/RT.

F Free energy $= H - TS$. $\bar{F}_k$ is the partial free energy of component k in a homogeneous phase defined as $(\partial \underline{F}/\partial n_k)_{T,p,n}$, where n_k may represent either moles or mass. The subscripts T, p, n signify constant temperature, pressure, and composition. $\bar{E}_k$, $\bar{H}_k$, $\bar{S}_k$, and $\bar{v}_k$ are similar partial quantities defined in an analogous manner.

f Fugacity; $\bar{f}$ is the fugacity of a component in a solution.

k Henry's-law constant, $p = kx$.

K Equilibrium constant, $K = y/x$.

L Mole fraction liquid in a vapor-liquid mixture.

p Partial pressure.
p Total pressure.
p' Vapor pressure.
x Mole fraction in the liquid phase, or mole fraction in general when no phase is specified.
y Mole fraction in the vapor phase.
α Residual volume, $\alpha = RT/p - v$.
β Ratio of the vapor pressures, p'_A/p'_B, of components A and B.
γ Activity coefficient.
θ Temperature function in defining equation for fugacity,
      $F \doteq RT \ln f + \theta$.
μ Chemical potential.
ϕ Fugacity coefficient, f/p.

Subscripts and Superscripts

k A subscript referring to a particular component in the mixture.
i A subscript referring to any component in the mixture.
G Vapor phase.
L Liquid phase.
$*$ A superscript designating a pressure p^*, approaching zero.
$'$ Primes designate separate phases, except when used with p.

PROBLEMS

1. Calculate the fugacity of isobutane at 190°F and 175 psia from the following p-v-T data:[1]

Pressure, psia	Specific volume, ft^3/lb_m	Pressure, psia	Specific volume, ft^3/lb_m
10	11.854	150	0.6557
14.7	8.023	175	0.5391
20	5.860	200	0.4504
30	3.861	225	0.3794
40	2.861	250	0.03499
50	2.260	500	0.03421
60	1.860	750	0.03352
80	1.360	1000	0.03200
100	1.060	1500	0.03212
125	0.8183	2000	0.03145

Also calculate the fugacity at 190°F and 1500 psia.   The vapor pressure at 190°F is 229.3 psia.   Compare the result obtained at 175 psia with that predicted from Fig. 12-1.

2. Calculate the equilibrium constant of n-butane at 150°F and 250 psia in a system containing 50 mole per cent n-butane and 50 mole per cent ethane by the following methods:

(*a*) Assuming the liquid phase is an ideal solution and the gas phase is an ideal gas.

[1] B. H. Sage and W. N. Lacey, *Ind. Eng. Chem.*, **30**, 673 (1938).

(b) Assuming that both liquid and gas phases form ideal solutions and using Fig. 12-1 to evalute the pure component fugacities

(c) Using the nomograph of Fig. 12-15

Would the true equilibrium constant be changed if the system consisted of 50 per cent methane and 50 per cent n-butane? Would the values computed by methods (a), (b), and (c) be changed for this new system? Explain.

3. Calculate the dew-point and bubble-point pressures of a mixture of 5 mole per cent methane, 10 per cent ethane, 30 per cent propane, and 55 per cent isobutane at 80°F. Also determine the fraction in the vapor phase at 150 psia.

4. The overhead vapor stream (from a fractionating column) going to the condenser has the following analysis:

Mole fraction

Ethane.................	0.15
Propane................	0.20
Isobutane..............	0.60
n-Butane...............	0.05
Total.................	1.00

It is desired to operate so that 75 mole per cent of the total stream is liquefied in the condenser. If the material leaving the condenser is at 80°F, what is the pressure required?

5. Assuming that the overhead vapor stream described in Prob. 4 is in equilibrium with the liquid leaving the top bubble plate in the column, compute the temperature on the top plate. Assume that the pressure drop between the top plate of the column and the exit of the condenser is 5 psia.

6. At 50°C the vapor pressures of pure ether and pure ethyl alcohol are 1276.4 and 221.1 mm Hg, respectively. Measured total pressures above liquid mixtures of ether and alcohol at 50°C are as follows:

Mole per cent ether	Total pressure p, mm Hg
6.5	400.3
14.0	558.1
21.1	693.2
29.3	804.6
38.3	903.5
48.3	995.0
58.7	1072.7
71.3	1136.0
85.4	1208.4

Using the Gibbs-Duhem equation, compute from these data the partial pressures of ether and alcohol over liquid solutions of various compositions at 50°C.

7. Employing the data determined in Prob. 6, evaluate Henry's-law constant for ether in an ether-alcohol system at 50°C. Over what range of liquid composition would Henry's law be satisfactory (i.e., predict partial pressures within 5 per cent of those determined in Prob. 6)? Make a plot of partial pressure of ether vs. liquid composition, including lines for Henry's and Raoult's laws.

8. From the results of Prob. 6 calculate activity coefficients for ether and alcohol at 50°C for each of the liquid compositions given in that problem. Make a plot of activity coefficient vs. mole fraction ether in the liquid for each component.

Assuming that Eqs. (12-67) and (12-68) are applicable for this system with $D = 0$, evaluate the best values of constants B and C by the least-mean-square technique.

PHASE EQUILIBRIA **403**

Using the results, evaluate computed activity-coefficient curves, using Eqs. (12-67) and (12-68). Comment on the suitability of these equations for the ether-alcohol system at 50°C.

9. Prepare a y-x diagram for the ether–ethyl alcohol system at a constant temperature of 50°C.

10. Using the van Laar method compute the y-x curve for ethyl alcohol–water mixtures at a total pressure of 760 mm. Base the computations upon the composition of the azeotropic mixture.

$$\text{Mole per cent alcohol} = 89.43$$
$$\text{Temperature} = 78.15°C$$
$$\text{Vapor pressure of alcohol at } 78.15°C = 755 \text{ mm}$$
$$\text{Vapor pressure of water at } 78.15°C = 329 \text{ mm}$$

Compare the results with the following experimental data:

Temperature, °C	Mole per cent alcohol	
	Liquid, 100x	Vapor, 100y
100	0	0
89.0	7.21	38.91
85.3	12.38	47.04
81.5	32.73	58.26
79.7	51.98	65.99
78.4	74.72	78.15
78.15	89.43	89.43

11. In a steam distillation, the vapor leaving the top of the fractionating column and entering the condenser is at 230°F and 30 psia and has the following analysis:

Component	Mole fraction
n-Butane	0.20
n-Pentane	0.40
Water	0.40
Total	1.00

Assuming no pressure drop in the condenser calculate these data:

(a) The temperature and composition of the condensate at the dew point of the mixture

(b) The temperature at which the hydrocarbon material first starts to condense and when 50 mole per cent of it has condensed

(c) The bubble-point temperature

It is satisfactory to neglect the small mutual solubility of the hydrocarbons and water in the liquid phase.

12. Benzene and water are essentially immiscible. A vapor containing 75 mole per cent water and 25 mole per cent benzene originally at 100°C and a total pressure of 780 mm is cooled slowly at constant pressure until all the vapor has condensed. At any time during the process the residual vapor is in equilibrium with the liquid. Construct a plot of temperature vs. the mole fraction benzene in the residual vapor.

CHAPTER 13

CHEMICAL-REACTION EQUILIBRIA

The transformation of material into products of greater value by means of chemical reaction is a major industry. The number of commercial products obtained by chemical synthesis increases by hundreds each year. The manufacture of synthetic rubber from petroleum is an outstanding example, but merely one of many based upon hydrocarbons as a source material. Polyethylene, ammonia, ethanol, isopropanol, and ethylene oxide are others made in great quantities. The same development of synthetic chemicals has occurred in industries utilizing other raw materials. Butadiene was made during the Second World War from ethanol produced by fermentation of molasses and grain. Acetaldehyde and acetic acid came from the same source. Phenol and phthalic anhydride are examples of commercial chemicals derived from coal-tar distillation products by controlled chemical reactions.

In view of this it is important that the chemical engineer understand the problems involved in the design and operation of reaction equipment. The primary consideration in the development of a commercial chemical reaction is the effect of controllable variables upon the progress and extent of the reaction. For example, data are necessary on how the time during which the reactants are in the reaction vessel affects the conversion to the desired product. This problem depends upon the rate of the reaction and is not susceptible to thermodynamic treatment. In addition, it is important to ascertain how the temperature, pressure, and composition of reactants[1] affect the conversion. In this case the answer depends upon both the rate of reaction and the equilibrium result (corresponding to an infinite reaction time). This is true because temperature, pressure, and reactant composition may affect both the rate of conversion to the desired product and the equilibrium conversion. As an illustration, consider the effect of temperature upon the oxidation of sulfur dioxide to sulfur trioxide. This reaction requires a catalyst if a reasonable rate of oxidation is to be achieved. The rate becomes appreciable with a platinum catalyst at about 300°C and increases rapidly at higher tempera-

---

[1] For example, in the synthesis of methyl alcohol from CO and H_2 the relative quantities of the reactants will affect the extent of the conversion to methanol.

tures. On the basis of rate alone, it would appear desirable to operate a reactor at a high temperature level. However, an examination of the equilibrium of the reaction shows that below 520°C the conversion to sulfur trioxide is greater than 90 per cent, but at higher temperatures it falls off rapidly, reaching 50 per cent at about 680°C. This means that, regardless of time or catalyst, the maximum conversion at 680°C is only 50 per cent. The evident conclusion from this example is that both equilibrium and rate must be considered in developing a commercial process for a chemical reaction. It is the purpose of this chapter to develop and apply the methods of determining the effect of temperature, pressure, and reactants ratio upon the equilibrium conversion.

Many reactions in industry are not carried to equilibrium. Under these circumstances the reaction equipment must be designed, not on the basis of thermodynamics and the equilibrium yield, but by considering the reaction rate. However, even in these cases the restrictions of equilibrium may influence the choice of operating conditions as illustrated in the oxidation of sulfur dioxide. In addition, the equilibrium conversion of a reaction provides a goal by which to measure improvements in the process. Similarly, it may determine whether or not an experimental investigation of a new process is worthwhile. For example, if the thermodynamic analysis indicates that a yield of only 20 per cent is possible at equilibrium and a 50 per cent yield is required for the process to be economically attractive, there is no purpose in further work on the problem, experimental or otherwise. On the other hand, if the equilibrium yield is 80 per cent, an experimental program to determine the rate under various conditions may be warranted.

The calculation of the equilibrium conversion consists in combining fundamental equations of chemical-reaction equilibria, free-energy data, and the principle of conservation of mass.[1] The basic equations are developed in Secs. 13-1 to 13-3, including the relationship between the standard free energy of reaction and the equilibrium constant. The evaluation of the free energy and the equilibrium constant from thermodynamic data is considered in Sec. 13-4. Finally, application of this information to computing the conversion is taken up in Sec. 13-6.

13-1. Criteria of Equilibrium. In the discussion of phase equilibria (Chap. 12) the transfer of material from one phase to another, under equilibrium conditions, was found to be accompanied by no change in free energy. Similarly, there is no change in free energy when a chemical reaction occurs at equilibrium.[2] As in the case of transfer of material

---

[1] In nonisothermal reactors, the law of conservation of energy (first law) may be needed to determine the temperature, and therefore the conversion, at equilibrium.

[2] The general proof of this statement is given by J. Willard Gibbs, "Collected Works," Vol. I, p. 65, Longmans, Green & Co., Inc., New York, 1931. That ΔF must

between phases, the temperature and pressure of all the components must be identical when two or more chemical species are in equilibrium. These criteria may be stated mathematically by the equation

$$\Delta F = 0 \qquad \text{at const } T \text{ and } p \qquad (13\text{-}1)$$

13-2. The Standard Free-energy Change and the Equilibrium Constant. The criteria of chemical-reaction equilibrium expressed by Eq. (13-1) can be related to the equilibrium constant and the composition at equilibrium by introducing the fugacity. Suppose the reaction is written

$$aA + bB \rightarrow cC + dD \qquad (13\text{-}2)$$

where the lower-case letters refer to the number of moles of the substances (designated by the capital letters) taking part.

---

be zero for a chemical reaction occurring at equilibrium conditions can be simply illustrated with the defining equation for free energy,

$$F = H - TS$$

For example, consider the reaction

$$CaCO_3(s) \rightarrow CaO(s) + CO_2(g)$$

At equilibrium, the pressure and temperature must be the same in all parts of the system. If this were not so, a change would occur as a result of the difference in potential (pressure or temperature). Now suppose that a finite amount of $CaCO_3$ decomposes at a fixed temperature and at equilibrium conditions. Since the system is univariant, the pressure must also remain constant during the process. From the defining equation for free energy, the change ΔF is

$$\Delta F = \Delta H - T \, \Delta S$$

Since the pressure is constant,

$$\Delta H = Q = \int T \, dS = T \, \Delta S$$

Substitution of this expression for ΔH in the previous equation gives

$$\Delta F = 0$$

Thus the free energy may be looked upon as an additional potential, besides the pressure and temperature, that does not vary when a reaction occurs at equilibrium. In this particular case

$$\Delta F = F_{CO_2} + F_{CaO} - F_{CaCO_3} = 0$$

It is important to note the differences between the criteria for phase equilibrium and chemical-reaction equilibrium. In the former (Chap. 12) the temperature and pressure in each phase must be the same, and also the free energy of any component must be the same in all the phases. For a chemical reaction to occur at equilibrium, the temperature and pressure must be the same in all the system, but this time the changes in free energy resulting from the formation of the products and the disappearance of the reactants must be zero.

According to the definition of fugacity [Eqs. (12-19) and (12–11)] the free energy of component A in the *equilibrium* state of the reaction mixture is

$$\bar{F}_A = RT \ln \bar{f}_A + \theta \tag{13-3}$$

Suppose that at the same temperature but at another condition,[1] which may be called the standard state, the free energy of component A is F_A°. Then

$$F_A^\circ = RT \ln f_A^\circ + \theta \tag{13-4}$$

Since the temperature is the same at the two states, θ is eliminated when Eqs. (13-3) and (13-4) are combined, giving

$$\bar{F}_A = F_A^\circ + RT \ln \left(\frac{\bar{f}}{f^\circ}\right)_A \tag{13-5}$$

Equation (13-1) applied to the reaction defined by Eq. (13-2) becomes

$$c\bar{F}_C + d\bar{F}_D - (a\bar{F}_A + b\bar{F}_B) = 0$$

If into this equation are substituted the free-energy expressions like Eq. (13-5) for each component, there results

$$cF_C^\circ + dF_D^\circ - (aF_A^\circ + bF_B^\circ) + RT \ln \frac{(\bar{f}/f^\circ)_C^c (\bar{f}/f^\circ)_D^d}{(\bar{f}/f^\circ)_A^a (\bar{f}/f^\circ)_B^b} = 0$$

or

$$\Delta F^\circ = -RT \ln \frac{(\bar{f}/f^\circ)_C^c (\bar{f}/f^\circ)_D^d}{(\bar{f}/f^\circ)_A^a (\bar{f}/f^\circ)_B^b} \tag{13-6}$$

where ΔF° represents the change in free energy for the reaction when each of the reactants and products is in its standard state.

Equation (13-6) contains two terms, one applying to an equilibrium state and the other to a standard state. The fugacities without the superscript $^\circ$ refer to equilibrium values at the temperature and total pressure of the reaction mixture. The free-energy ΔF° is the difference between the free energies of the products at their standard state (T°K and f° fugacity) and the reactants in their standard state. Similarly, the fugacities with the superscript $^\circ$ pertain to the standard state. Therefore, both ΔF° and the f° values are completely fixed at a definite temperature and are independent of the pressure at equilibrium. Equation (13-6) may be looked upon as a relationship between the fugacities at equilibrium conditions and the state functions ΔF° and f° which are unaffected by the equilibrium state. Its alternative derivation for a gaseous reaction, given later in this section, brings out this point more clearly.

[1] For example, for a gaseous reaction, the equilibrium state would be gas A mixed with B, C, and D at a total pressure p, while the standard state would be pure A at a pressure p°, but at the same temperature.

The ratio of the fugacity at any state to that at the standard state is termed the *activity a*. In terms of activities, Eq. (13-6) may be written

$$\Delta F^\circ = -RT \ln \frac{a_C^c a_D^d}{a_A^a a_B^b} \tag{13-7}$$

The equilibrium constant K of a chemical reaction is defined by the activities of the reactants and products in the equilibrium state as follows:

$$K = \frac{a_C^c a_D^d}{a_A^a a_B^b} \tag{13-8}$$

$K = \frac{[C]}{[A][B]}$

Combination of this definition and Eq. (13-7) results in the basic relationship between the *standard* free-energy change and the equilibrium constant,

$$\Delta F^\circ = -RT \ln K \tag{13-9}$$

If ΔF° is negative, K will be greater than unity; if ΔF° is positive, K will be less than unity. Hence, the equilibrium yield of a reaction is high when the standard free-energy change has a large negative value and low when the free-energy change has a large positive value.

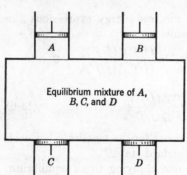

Standard States. Before Eqs. (13-6) to (13-9) can be applied to the calculation of the equilibrium conversion, the standard state of each reactant and product must be specified. The choice is arbitrary, but certain conventions have proved to be more convenient than others. If the standard state for a substance is chosen as the pure component, specification of the temperature and pressure (or fugacity)

FIG. 13-1. Apparatus in which a gaseous reaction occurs at equilibrium (van't Hoff equilibrium box).

Equilibrium mixture of A, B, C, and D

is sufficient to define the state completely. If the standard state chosen for the substance is a solution, the composition must also be specified.

For gases it is most convenient to choose the pure component at the temperature of the reaction and at unit fugacity as the standard state. An advantage of this choice is that the standard-state pressure approaches 1 atm for all gases and is exactly 1 atm for an ideal gas. Free-energy values, and hence ΔF°, are most easily evaluated at this pressure. For this standard state each f° is unity, and Eqs. (13-6) and (13-7) for a gaseous reaction become

$$\Delta F^\circ = -RT \ln \frac{f_C^c f_D^d}{f_A^a f_B^b} = -RT \ln K \tag{13-10}$$

Equation (13-10) is the simplified form of Eq. (13-7) applicable to a gaseous reaction.[1]

When solids, liquids, or solutions are present in the reaction mixture, the standard state of unit fugacity is not convenient and in some cases may be impossible. Therefore Eq. (13-10) is not valid, and the general expression [Eq. (13-7)] must be used for equilibrium calculations.

For solids and liquids the usual standard state is the pure solid or liquid at 1 atm pressure and the temperature of the reaction. A more detailed discussion of standard states is given in Sec. 13-6.

13-3. Effect of Temperature. The standard state is identified by specifying a definite pressure (or fugacity), but the temperature is always that of the reaction mixture at equilibrium. Hence the free-energy values at the standard state, and therefore ΔF° and K, will vary with this temperature. The relationship between K and T depends on the standard heat of reaction and may be developed in the following way:

The general equation for the variation in free energy of a single-component system with temperature and pressure was derived in Chap. 7:

$$dF = v\,dp - S\,dT \qquad (7\text{-}8)$$

At constant pressure the first term on the right disappears so that

$$dF = -S\,dT$$

or

$$\left(\frac{\partial F}{\partial T}\right)_p = -S \qquad (13\text{-}14)$$

---

[1] An alternative derivation of Eq. (13-10) may be more helpful in clarifying the fundamental concepts than the preceding mathematical development. This derivation is based on the concept of a very large vessel containing the reactants and products in equilibrium (van't Hoff equilibrium box).

The vessel is at constant temperature and pressure and is equipped with four piston-cylinder assemblies for adding the two reactants and removing the two products, as shown in Fig. 13-1. The connections between the cylinder and the container are assumed to be semipermeable membranes, permitting in each case only that material in the cylinder to be transferred to or from the vessel.

Suppose that gaseous components are involved in the reaction and that initially there are a moles of A and b moles of B in their respective cylinders, each at the temperature of the equilibrium vessel and at unit fugacity (*i.e.*, at their standard states).

1. First, isothermally compress (or expand, as the case might be) A and B separately to their fugacities, f_A and f_B, which are equal to the equilibrium fugacities in the vessel. The change in free energy for such a process is given by Eq. (12-13),

$$\Delta\mu = \Delta F = RT \ln\frac{f_2}{f_1} \qquad \text{(for 1 mole)}$$

In this case $f_1 = 1$, and f_2 is the equilibrium value in the vessel. Hence

$$\Delta F_1 = RT(a \ln \bar{f}_A + b \ln \bar{f}_B) = RT \ln (\bar{f}_A^a \bar{f}_B^b) \qquad (13\text{-}11)$$

2. The a moles of A and b moles of B are now added to the vessel through the semi-

When applied to a chemical reaction between the standard states of the reactants and products, Eq. (13-14) becomes

$$\frac{d(\Delta F^\circ)}{dT} = -\Delta S^\circ \tag{13-15}$$

The partial notation can be dropped because the standard free-energy change is independent of the pressure at equilibrium by virtue of its definition.[1] The integration of (13-15) will give the desired effect of temperature upon ΔF° and, through Eq. (13-9), upon the equilibrium constant. To carry out the integration, ΔS° may be replaced with its equivalent value in terms of ΔF°. This can be done by applying Eq. (12-2) to the reaction, noting that the temperature is constant for the reaction process itself.

$$\Delta F^\circ = \Delta H^\circ - T\,\Delta S^\circ \tag{13-16}$$

or

$$\Delta S^\circ = \frac{\Delta H^\circ - \Delta F^\circ}{T}$$

---

permeable membranes. Since the fugacities are the same in the cylinder as in the mixture, there is no change in free energy; the process occurs at equilibrium.

$$\Delta F_2 = 0$$

3. Suppose that the reactants in the vessel are converted to c moles of C and d moles of D at equilibrium.

$$\Delta F_3 = 0$$

4. Analogous to step 2, the c moles of C and d moles of D are withdrawn from the vessel at their equilibrium fugacities f_C and f_D.

$$\Delta F_4 = 0$$

5. Finally expand (or compress) these products in their respective cylinders to their standard states of unit fugacity. The change in free energy will be similar to that in step 1, viz.,

$$\Delta F_5 = RT\left(c \ln \frac{1}{f_C} + d \ln \frac{1}{f_D}\right) = -RT \ln\,(f_C^c f_D^d) \tag{13-12}$$

The total change in free energy will be the standard value since the reactants initially were at their standard states and the products ended at their standard states. Therefore

$$\Delta F^\circ = \Delta F_1 + \Delta F_2 + \Delta F_3 + \Delta F_4 + \Delta F_5 = -RT \ln \frac{f_C^c f_D^d}{f_A^a f_B^b} = -RT \ln K \tag{13-13}$$

which is the same as Eq. (13-10).

This derivation emphasizes the fact that there is no change in free energy for the equilibrium step, so that the entire contribution to ΔF° comes from the change from the initial standard states to the final standard states.

[1] The pressure, or fugacity, at the standard state is specified; hence the free-energy change at the standard state cannot depend on the pressure of the reaction mixture at equilibrium.

Substituting in (13-15)

$$\frac{d(\Delta F^\circ)}{dT} = \frac{\Delta F^\circ - \Delta H^\circ}{T} \qquad (13\text{-}17)$$

or

$$\frac{d(\Delta F^\circ)}{dT} - \frac{\Delta F^\circ}{T} = -\frac{\Delta H^\circ}{T}$$

Equation (13-17) is a linear first-order differential equation, which can be integrated after multiplying by the factor

$$e^{\int -(1/T)\,dT} = \frac{1}{T}$$

The integrated form of (13-17) so obtained is

$$\frac{\Delta F^\circ}{T} = -\int \frac{\Delta H^\circ}{T^2}\,dT$$

In terms of the equilibrium constant, using Eq. (13-9),

$$R \ln K = \int \frac{\Delta H^\circ}{T^2}\,dT$$

or

$$\boxed{\frac{d\,(\ln K)}{dT} = \frac{\Delta H^\circ}{RT^2}} \qquad (13\text{-}18)$$

Equation (13-18) gives the effect of temperature upon the equilibrium constant, and hence on the equilibrium yield. It is apparent that if ΔH° is negative, i.e., if the reaction is exothermic, the equilibrium constant will decrease as the temperature increases. Analogously K will increase with T for an endothermic reaction.

If the term ΔH°, which is the standard enthalpy change (heat of reaction), may be assumed constant with respect to temperature, Eq. (13-18) is easily integrable to give

$$\ln \frac{K}{K_1} = -\frac{\Delta H^\circ}{R}\left(\frac{1}{T} - \frac{1}{T_1}\right) \qquad (13\text{-}19)$$

This approximate equation may be used with good results over small temperature ranges, or when ΔH° is nearly constant, to determine the equilibrium constant at a temperature T from the known value at T_1. If $\ln K$ is plotted vs. the reciprocal of the absolute temperature, Eq. (13-19) indicates that a straight line should result. This is a convenient and reasonably accurate method of extrapolating and interpolating equilibrium-constant data.

If molal heat capacities as a function of temperature are known for each chemical species taking part in the reaction, Eq. (13-18) may be integrated rigorously. Suppose the data are available in the form of power functions

$$C_p = \alpha + \beta T + \gamma T^2$$

Then, as shown in Chap. 5, the heat of reaction at any temperature T is given by the expression

$$\Delta H^\circ = \Delta H_0 + \Delta \alpha \, T + \frac{\Delta \beta \, T^2}{2} + \frac{\Delta \gamma \, T^3}{3} \qquad (5\text{-}16)$$

In this equation ΔH_0 is a constant which can readily be evaluated provided the standard heat of reaction is known at a single temperature, e.g., 25°C. With ΔH_0 determined, ΔH° from Eq. (5-16) can be substituted in Eq. (13-18). The integrated result is

$$\ln K = -\frac{\Delta H_0}{RT} + \frac{\Delta \alpha}{R} \ln T + \frac{\Delta \beta}{2R} T + \frac{\Delta \gamma}{6R} T^2 + C \qquad (13\text{-}20)$$

Here C is the constant of integration, which may be evaluated from a knowledge of the equilibrium constant at one temperature.

Either Eq. (13-19) or Eq. (13-20) may be used to evaluate the effect of temperature on the equilibrium constant, the latter being the more accurate but requiring heat-capacity data.

The variation of the standard free-energy change with temperature can be obtained by combining Eqs. (13-20) and (13-9),

$$\Delta F^\circ = \Delta H_0 - \Delta \alpha \, T \ln T - \frac{\Delta \beta}{2} T^2 - \frac{\Delta \gamma}{6} T^3 - IT \qquad (13\text{-}21)$$

where I is a composite constant equal to RC.

13-4. Evaluation of Equilibrium Constants. The equilibrium constant for a given reaction can be calculated at any temperature by Eq. (13-20), provided enough information is known to permit evaluation of the constants ΔH_0 and C. It is presumed that the necessary heat-capacity data are available. The general methods in use and the minimum data necessary for the evaluation of ΔH_0 and C may be listed as follows:

1. K values may be calculated directly by the defining equation for K [Eq. (13-8)] from experimental measurements of composition in the equilibrium mixture. The methods of doing this in practice are taken up in Sec. 13-6. If values of K are known for two temperatures, Eq. (13-20) is written for each temperature and the resulting two equations are solved simultaneously for ΔH_0 and C.

2. If the standard heat of reaction is known for a single temperature, e.g., 25°C, ΔH_0 may be evaluated from Eq. (5-16). Only a single value of K, determined directly from equilibrium measurements, is then needed for an evaluation of C by Eq. (13-20).

3. The last method is probably the most widely used and is the most convenient, because it does not require direct experimental determination of K. The method makes use of thermal data only, usually in the form of a standard heat of reaction ΔH° and a standard free-energy change of reaction ΔF°. The constant ΔH_0 is determined from the standard heat of reaction by Eq. (5-16). The value of ΔF° is then used in Eq. (13-21) to determine I and the constant C is calculated from the relation $C = I/R$.

Only the third method involves no equilibrium measurements. Since these experimental measurements are difficult, the third method is of great importance. It was developed as a result of considerable investigation by famous workers[1] in thermodynamics during the last part of the nineteenth century. Values of ΔF_f° for formation reactions at 25°C are listed in standard references along with the standard heats of formation ΔH_f° (see Table 13-1). Values of ΔF° for other reactions at 25°C are calculated by combining formation reactions exactly in the same way that ΔH° quantities are determined (Chap. 5). The listed values of ΔF° have been calculated from the relation

$$\Delta F^\circ = \Delta H^\circ - T\,\Delta S^\circ \qquad (13\text{-}16)$$

where ΔS° is the standard entropy change of reaction. The determination of ΔS° is based on the third law of thermodynamics. The basic concepts of this law are (1) that the entropy of any substance in its most stable state at absolute zero temperature is zero and (2) that the heat capacity of any substance approaches zero at absolute zero temperature.[2]

One method of applying the third law to calculate the absolute entropy utilizes measured values of the specific heat and latent heats from T to nearly absolute zero (all at constant pressure). At the present time it is impossible to measure C_p at temperatures all the way to absolute zero. However, by carrying the measurements as far as possible (for example, to 10 or 12°K) and utilizing concept 2 of the third law, the C_p vs. T curve can be extrapolated from the limit of the measurements down to $T = 0°K$. From the second law (Chap. 6),

$$dQ = T\,dS$$

If the process occurs at constant pressure, $dQ = C_p\,dT$ (for 1 mole of material) and

$$dS = \frac{C_p\,dT}{T} \qquad (13\text{-}22)$$

---

[1] G. N. Lewis, van't Hoff, and Nernst among others.

[2] For a résumé of the development and significance of the third law see G. N. Lewis and Merle Randall, "Thermodynamics and the Free Energy of Chemical Substances," Chap. XXXI, McGraw-Hill Book Company, Inc., New York, 1923.

Integrating from absolute zero and applying concept 1 of the third law,

$$S_T - S_0 = \int_0^T \frac{C_p \, dT}{T}$$

$$S_T = \int_0^T \frac{C_p \, dT}{T} \tag{13-23}$$

This equation would give the entropy per mole at T provided no phase transitions, such as solid to liquid or solid to solid, occur between 0 and T. As these are present, the heat effects accompanying the changes in phase must be measured. The corresponding entropy increments are equal to ΔH divided by the constant temperature at which the change takes place. Then the general expression for the entropy of a substance at T is

$$S_T = \int_0^T \frac{C_p \, dT}{T} + \sum \frac{\Delta H_i}{T_i} \tag{13-24}$$

Combination of the values of the entropy from Eq. (13-24) for each component taking part in the reaction gives the desired value of $\Delta S°$.

The development of methods of evaluating entropies and enthalpies from spectroscopic data provides an alternative means of obtaining $\Delta F°$ by Eq. (13-16) without requiring low-temperature specific-heat measurements. Although the discussion of this subject is beyond the scope of this text,[1] it is now a most useful procedure for calculating thermodynamic quantities.

Results for many reactions have been obtained by the three methods. (Examples 13-1 to 13-3 illustrate the calculation procedures.) Some of the earlier information has been analyzed by Parks and Huffman[2] and reported in the form of standard free-energy values $\Delta F°$ at 25°C. Information concerning the effect of temperature is also given when available. Useful tables of entropies [applicable in Eq. (13-16) for evaluating $\Delta F°$ and hence K] are given by Wenner[3] and by Kelley.[4] More recent and comprehensive tabulations of standard entropies, enthalpies, and free energies of formation have been developed under the leadership

---

[1] For a discussion of the method of utilizing spectroscopic data for computing thermodynamic quantities see R. R. Wenner, "Thermochemical Calculations," McGraw-Hill Book Company, Inc., New York, 1941. A detailed treatment is also given by S. Glasstone, "Theoretical Chemistry," D. Van Nostrand Company, Inc., Princeton, N.J., 1944.

[2] G. S. Parks and H. M. Huffman, "The Free Energies of Some Organic Compounds," Reinhold Publishing Corporation, New York, 1932.

[3] R. R. Wenner, "Thermochemical Calculations," Chap. VIII, McGraw-Hill Book Company, Inc., New York, 1941.

[4] K. K. Kelley, *U.S. Bur. Mines, Bull.* 476, 1949.

of Rossini.[1]   Table 13-1 showing $\Delta F°$ at 298°K was prepared from this last source.

In concluding the discussion of methods of calculation of free energies and equilibrium constants, it should be mentioned that similarity of structure provides a useful basis for estimation purposes when no experimental data are available. Approximate rules have been developed[2] for predicting the entropy and enthalpy of substances from known information on similar materials. Watson[3,4] and coworkers have suggested a method of estimating entropy, enthalpy, and the constants α, β, and γ in the molal-heat-capacity equation for a wide variety of organic compounds. Their approach is based on the addition of the contributions to the entropy, etc., of each atom or atom group making up the molecule.

A useful principle to remember in estimating thermodynamic quantities for chemical reactions is that free energies, heats of reaction, and entropies are additive. This means that such information can be evaluated for a reaction for which no data exist, provided that the reaction can be obtained by combining related reactions for which experimental data are available.

Example 13-1. The following equilibrium data have been reported for the vapor-phase hydration of ethylene to ethanol at 145 and 320°C.

$t°C$	K	Reference
145	6.8×10^{-2}	H. M. Stanley et al., *J. Soc. Chem. Ind.*, **53**, 205 (1934)
320	1.9×10^{-3}	R. H. Bliss and B. F. Dodge, *Ind. Eng. Chem.*, **29**, 19 (1937)

The molal heat capacities of the reactants and products are given in Table 5-1.

From these data develop general expressions for the equilibrium constant and standard free-energy change as a function of temperature.

Solution. From the two values of K the constants ΔH_0 and C in Eq. (13-20) may be determined. First, values of $\Delta\alpha$, $\Delta\beta$, and $\Delta\gamma$ must be obtained from the heat-capacity data.

$$C_2H_4(g) + H_2O(g) \rightarrow C_2H_5OH(g)$$
$$\Delta = (C_2H_5OH) - (C_2H_4) - (H_2O)$$
$$\Delta\alpha = 6.990 - 2.830 - 7.256 = -3.096$$
$$\Delta\beta = 0.039741 - 0.028601 - 0.002298 = 0.008842$$
$$\Delta\gamma = (-11.926 + 8.726 - 0.283) \times 10^{-6} = -3.483 \times 10^{-6}$$

[1] Selected Values of Chemical Thermodynamic Properties, *Natl. Bur. Standards Circ.* 500, 1952.   Also Selected Values of Properties of Hydrocarbons and Related Compounds, American Petroleum Institute Research Project 44, Carnegie Institute of Technology, Pittsburgh, 1953.

[2] Wenner, *loc. cit.*

[3] J. W. Anderson, G. H. Beyer, and K. M. Watson, *Natl. Petroleum News*, July 5, 1944.

[4] O. A. Hougen and K. M. Watson, "Chemical Process Principles," Part II, Thermodynamics, Chap. XVII, John Wiley & Sons, Inc., New York, 1947.

TABLE 13-1. STANDARD FREE ENERGIES OF FORMATION AT 25°C†

NOTES:

1. The standard free energy of formation $\Delta F^\circ_{f\,298}$ is the change in free energy when the listed compound is formed from its elements with each substance in its standard state at $298°K$ (25°C).

2. Standard states:

   (a) Gases (g): The pure gas at unit fugacity and 25°C

   (b) Liquids (l) and solids (s): The pure substance at atmospheric pressure and 25°C

   (c) Solutes in aqueous solution (aq): The hypothetical 1-molal solution of the solute in water at atmospheric pressure and 25°C

3. The units of ΔF°_f are calories per gram mole of the listed substance.

Substance	Formula	State	$\Delta F^\circ_{f\,298}$
Normal paraffins:			
Methane	CH_4	g	−12,140
Ethane	C_2H_6	g	−7,860
Propane	C_3H_8	g	−5,614
n-Butane	C_4H_{10}	g	−4,100
n-Pentane	C_5H_{12}	g	−2,000
n-Hexane	C_6H_{14}	g	−70
n-Heptane	C_7H_{16}	g	1,920
n-Octane	C_8H_{18}	g	3,920
Increment per C atom above C_8		g	2,010
Normal monoolefins (1-alkenes):			
Ethylene	C_2H_4	g	16,282
Propylene	C_3H_6	g	14,990
1-Butene	C_4H_8	g	17,090
1-Pentene	C_5H_{10}	g	18,960
1-Hexene	C_6H_{12}	g	20,940
Increment per C atom above C_6		g	2,010
Miscellaneous organic compounds:			
Acetaldehyde	C_2H_4O	g	−31,960
Acetic acid	$C_2H_4O_2$	l	−93,800
Acetylene	C_2H_2	g	50,000
Benzene	C_6H_6	g	30,989
Benzene	C_6H_6	l	29,756
1,3-Butadiene	C_4H_6	g	36,010
Cyclohexane	C_6H_{12}	g	7,590
Cyclohexane	C_6H_{12}	l	6,370
Ethanol	C_2H_6O	g	−40,300
Ethanol	C_2H_6O	l	−41,770
Ethylbenzene	C_8H_{10}	g	31,208
Ethylene glycol	$C_2H_6O_2$	l	−77,120
Ethylene oxide	C_2H_4O	g	−2,790
Methanol	CH_4O	g	−38,700
Methanol	CH_4O	l	−39,750
Methylcyclohexane	C_7H_{14}	g	6,520
Methylcyclohexane	C_7H_{14}	l	4,860
Styrene	C_8H_8	g	51,100
Toluene	C_7H_8	g	29,228
Toluene	C_7H_8	l	27,282

TABLE 13-1. STANDARD FREE ENERGIES OF FORMATION AT 25°C† (*Continued*)

Substance	Formula	State	$\Delta F^{\circ}_{f\,298}$
Miscellaneous inorganic compounds:			
Ammonia.................................	NH_3	g	$-3,976$
Ammonia.................................	NH_3	aq	$-6,370$
Calcium carbide.........................	CaC_2	s	$-16,200$
Calcium carbonate.......................	$CaCO_3$	s	$-269,780$
Calcium chloride........................	$CaCl_2$	s	$-179,300$
Calcium chloride........................	$CaCl_2$	aq	$-194,880$
Calcium hydroxide.......................	$Ca(OH)_2$	s	$-214,330$
Calcium hydroxide.......................	$Ca(OH)_2$	aq	$-207,370$
Calcium oxide...........................	CaO	s	$-144,400$
Carbon dioxide..........................	CO_2	g	$-94,260$
Carbon monoxide.........................	CO	g	$-32,808$
Hydrochloric acid.......................	HCl	g	$-22,769$
Hydrogen sulfide........................	H_2S	g	$-7,892$
Iron oxide..............................	Fe_3O_4	s	$-242,400$
Iron oxide..............................	Fe_2O_3	s	$-177,100$
Iron sulfide............................	FeS_2	s	$-39,840$
Nitric acid.............................	HNO_3	l	$-19,100$
Nitric acid.............................	HNO_3	aq	$-26,410$
Nitrogen oxides.........................	NO	g	$20,719$
	NO_2	g	$12,390$
	N_2O	g	$24,760$
	N_2O_4	g	$23,491$
Sodium carbonate........................	Na_2CO_3	s	$-250,400$
Sodium chloride.........................	$NaCl$	s	$-91,785$
Sodium chloride.........................	$NaCl$	aq	$-93,939$
Sodium hydroxide........................	$NaOH$	s	$-90,600$
Sodium hydroxide........................	$NaOH$	aq	$-100,184$
Sulfur dioxide..........................	SO_2	g	$-71,790$
Sulfur trioxide.........................	SO_3	g	$-88,520$
Sulfuric acid...........................	H_2SO_4	aq	$-177,340$
Water...................................	H_2O	g	$-54,635$
Water...................................	H_2O	l	$-56,690$

† Selected mainly from F. D. Rossini et al., Selected Values of Properties of Hydrocarbons and Related Compounds, American Petroleum Institute Research Project 44, Carnegie Institute of Technology, Pittsburgh, 1953. Also loose-leaf supplements. By permission.

Also F. D. Rossini et al., Selected Values of Chemical Thermodynamic Properties, *Natl. Bur. Standards Circ.* 500, 1952. Also loose-leaf supplements, edited by D. D. Wagman.

Substituting these values in Eq. (13-20),

$$R \ln (6.8 \times 10^{-2}) = -\frac{\Delta H_0}{418} - 3.096 \ln 418 + \frac{0.00884}{2} (418)$$
$$- \frac{3.483 \times 10^{-6}}{6} (418)^2 + CR$$

or

$$\frac{\Delta H_0}{418} - CR = -R \ln (6.8 \times 10^{-2}) - 3.096 \ln 418$$
$$+ (0.00442)(418) - (0.580 \times 10^{-6})(418)^2 = -11.59 \quad (A)$$

and

$$\frac{\Delta H_0}{593} - CR = -R \ln (1.9 \times 10^{-3}) - 3.096 \ln 593$$
$$+ (0.00442)(593) - (0.580 \times 10^{-6})(593)^2 = -4.91 \quad (B)$$

Equations (A) and (B) may be solved simultaneously for ΔH_0 and C. The results are

$$\Delta H_0 = -9460 \text{ cal}$$
$$C = -5.56$$

Then the general expression for K as a function of temperature is

$$\ln K = \frac{9460}{RT} - \frac{3.096}{R} \ln T + \frac{0.00442}{R} T - \frac{0.580 \times 10^{-6}}{R} T^2 - 5.56$$

or

$$\boxed{\ln K = \frac{4760}{T} - 1.558 \ln T + 0.00222T - 0.29 \times 10^{-6}T^2 - 5.56}$$

Equation (13-21) for the standard free-energy change is

$$\Delta F^\circ = -9460 + 3.096T \ln T - 0.00442T^2 + 0.580 \times 10^{-6}T^3 + 11.05T$$

Example 13-2. From Stanley's value of K at 145°C and the standard heat of reaction at 298°K, $\Delta H^\circ_{298} = -10,940$ cal, determine equations for the equilibrium constant and free-energy change for the vapor-phase hydration of ethylene. Compare with the results of Example 13-1.

Solution. In this case ΔH_0 can be evaluated according to the method described in Chap. 5. Applying Eq. (5-16) at 298°K,

$$-10,940 = \Delta H_0 - (3.096)(298) + \frac{0.00884}{2} (298)^2 - \frac{3.483 \times 10^{-6}}{3} (298)^3$$
$$\Delta H_0 = -10,940 + 923 - 393 + 30 = -10,380 \text{ cal}$$

Now substitute this value of ΔH_0 and Stanley's value of K in Eq. (13-20):

$$R \ln (6.8 \times 10^{-2}) = \frac{10,380}{418} - 3.096 \ln 418 + (0.00442)(418)$$
$$- (0.580 \times 10^{-6})(418)^2 + CR$$
$$C = -6.67$$

With these values of the constants the equations for K and ΔF° become

$$\ln K = \frac{5220}{T} - 1.558 \ln T + 0.00222T - 0.29 \times 10^{-6}T^2 - 6.67$$
$$\Delta F^\circ = -10,380 + 3.096T \ln T - 0.00442T^2 + 0.58 \times 10^{-6}T^3 + 13.25T$$

The agreement between the two sets of equations (Examples 13-1 and 13-2) may be illustrated by evaluating K at 320°C from the preceding equation for K:

$$\ln K = 8.80 - 9.95 + 1.32 - 0.01 - 6.67 = -6.60$$
$$K = 1.35 \times 10^{-3}$$

This compares with an experimental value of 1.9×10^{-3} determined by Bliss and Dodge. Considering the difficulties involved in experimental measurement of equilibrium constants, the agreement is good. The third method of estimating K, which requires only thermal data, is illustrated in Example 13-3.

Example 13-3. Calculate the equilibrium constant for the vapor-phase hydration of ethylene at 145 and 320°C from the data given in Tables 5-1, 5-3, and 13-1.

Solution. The heat-of-formation data given in Table 5-3 can be combined to give ΔH°_{298} for the hydration reaction

$$\Delta H^\circ_{298} = -10,940 \text{ cal}$$

Similarly the free-energy-of-formation data of Table 13-1 are used to give ΔF°_{298}:

$$\Delta F^\circ_{298} = \Delta F^\circ_{f_{C_2H_5OH}} - (\Delta F^\circ_{f_{C_2H_4}} + \Delta F^\circ_{f_{H_2O}})$$
$$= -40,300 - [16,282 + (-54,635)]$$
$$= -1950 \text{ cal}$$

The constants ΔH_0 and I in Eq. (13-21) can now be evaluated by a procedure similar to that illustrated in Example 13-2. Equation (5-16) is applied at 298°K for the evaluation of ΔH_0. As in Example 13-2 the result is

$$\Delta H_0 = -10,380 \text{ cal}$$

Equation (13-21) is now used in a similar way:

$$-1950 = -10,380 + (3.096)(298) \ln 298 - \frac{0.00884}{2}(298)^2$$
$$+ \frac{3.483 \times 10^{-6}}{6}(298)^3 - 298I$$

or

$$I = \frac{1950 - 10,380}{298} + 3.096 \ln 298 - (0.00442)(298) + (0.58 \times 10^{-6})(298)^2$$
$$= -28.29 + 17.64 - 1.32 + 0.05 = -11.92$$

The general expression for ΔF° as a function of T is therefore

$$\Delta F^\circ = -10,380 + 3.096T \ln T - 0.00442T^2 + 0.580 \times 10^{-6}T^3 + 11.92T$$

At 145°C (418°K)

$$\Delta F^\circ = 1685$$

By Eq. (13-9),

$$\ln K = \frac{-\Delta F^\circ}{RT} = \frac{-1685}{418R} = -2.03$$
$$K = 13.1 \times 10^{-2}$$

At 320°C (593°K)

$$\Delta F^\circ = 6980$$
$$\ln K = -5.94$$
$$K = 2.6 \times 10^{-3}$$

The results of the calculation of equilibrium constants from thermal data as illustrated in this example are compared in the accompanying table with the experimental values given in Example 13-1 and with the result calculated in Example 13-2.

	Experimental data, Example 13-1	Example 13-2	Example 13-3
K at 145°C..............	6.8×10^{-2}	6.8×10^{-2}	13.1×10^{-2}
K at 320°C..............	1.9×10^{-3}	1.35×10^{-3}	2.6×10^{-3}

The agreement between experimental results and the values calculated indirectly from thermal data is fair. This discrepancy has not yet been completely accounted for. However, errors are probably present in both the experimental and calculated values. It should be noted that the experimental K values have been calculated on the assumption that the equilibrium mixture is an ideal gas. Cope[1] has made an exhaustive study of this reaction, and he concludes on the basis of all available evidence that the most likely values for ΔH°_{298} and ΔF°_{298} are somewhat different from the presently accepted ones. His values are

$$\Delta H^\circ_{298} = -10,750 \text{ cal}$$
$$\Delta F^\circ_{298} = -1820 \text{ cal}$$

The discrepancy between experimental and calculated values of K is narrowed by the use of these data.

13-5. Effect of Pressure on the Equilibrium Constant. The equilibrium constant as defined in terms of activities (often called the true equilibrium constant) is not dependent on pressure. As mentioned earlier, this is apparent from Eq. (13-9), since ΔF° is based on fixed initial and final states and is not influenced by the conditions at any intermediate point. On the other hand, the pressure does affect the equilibrium *conversion* for a gas-phase reaction in accordance with the principle that an increase in pressure will increase the conversion if there is a decrease in volume accompanying the reaction. This effect of pressure must be accounted for in the relationship between the equilibrium constant and the equilibrium composition. It may be accurately determined provided the fugacities of the various components in the equilibrium mixture can be related to composition. It was found in Chap. 12 that this relationship was very simple for ideal solutions [Eq. (12-24a)] and that nonideal systems could be studied by introducing the activity coefficient γ. Then

[1] C. S. Cope, "Equilibria in the Hydration of Ethylene at Elevated Pressures and Temperatures," Ph.D. dissertation, Yale University, 1956.

the fugacity of any component in a gaseous mixture is given by the expression

$$\bar{f} = \gamma f y \tag{13-25}$$

where f is the fugacity of the pure component at the temperature and pressure of the equilibrium mixture and y is its mole fraction. With this expression for the fugacity, Eq. (13-10)[1] for K becomes

$$K = \frac{(\gamma f)_C^c (\gamma f)_D^d}{(\gamma f)_A^a (\gamma f)_B^b} \frac{y_C^c y_D^d}{y_A^a y_B^b} = \frac{(\gamma f)_C^c (\gamma f)_D^d}{(\gamma f)_A^a (\gamma f)_B^b} K_y \tag{13-26}$$

where K_y is substituted for the ratio of the mole fractions. This latter quantity is sometimes called an equilibrium constant[2] in terms of composition.

The fugacity of the pure components may be evaluated from volumetric data or from Fig. 12-2 as described in Chap. 12. Since Fig. 12-2 provides values for the ratio of fugacity to pressure (called the fugacity coefficient and given the symbol ϕ), it is convenient to rewrite Eq. (13-26) in terms of the ϕ values:

$$K = \frac{\gamma_C^c \gamma_D^d}{\gamma_A^a \gamma_B^b} \frac{\phi_C^c \phi_D^d}{\phi_A^a \phi_B^b} K_y p^{(c+d-a-b)} \tag{13-27}$$

where p represents the total pressure.

Usually, sufficient data are not available for evaluation of the activity coefficients as a function of composition of the equilibrium mixture, so that γ values must be assumed equal to unity. This is equivalent to assuming that the gas behaves as an ideal solution (not necessarily as an ideal gas; see Chap. 12). The error introduced with this simplification will be a function of the deviation from ideality of the solution. As discussed in Chap. 12, this deviation increases as the dissimilarity of the components in the reaction mixture increases and as the critical point is approached. With this simplification, Eq. (13-27) becomes

$$K = K_\phi K_y p^{(c+d-a-b)} \tag{13-28}$$

where K_ϕ represents the combination of fugacity coefficients as defined in Eq. (13-27).

Since K is independent of pressure, K_y and the equilibrium composition must depend on pressure. If the reaction mixture behaves as an

---

[1] It is appropriate to recall that Eq. (13-10) is valid only for gaseous systems in which the standard states have been taken as the pure gases at unit fugacity. Therefore the limitation to gaseous reactions applies to the remaining equations of this section.

[2] The word *constant* is a misnomer as applied to many of the K's used in equilibrium calculations. Nevertheless it is the universal terminology. K_y, for example, can be constant only under very special circumstances.

ideal gas, this effect becomes immediately evident since all the ϕ values, and hence K_ϕ, become unity. Equation (13-27) then reduces to

$$K = K_y p^{(c+d-a-b)} \qquad (13\text{-}29)$$

This expression indicates quantitatively the effect of a change in pressure on the equilibrium composition. Because K is independent of pressure, variation in the pressure term must be balanced by a corresponding change in K_y, and hence in the composition.

When the ideal-gas law does not apply, the pressure may affect K_y even though the term $c + d - a - b$ is zero. This is due to the fact that K_ϕ [Eq. (13-28)] varies with pressure. However, the effect is usually small.

In gaseous reactions another equilibrium constant K_p is frequently used. It is defined in terms of the mole fractions and total pressure, or in terms of the partial pressures, as follows:

$$K_p = \frac{(y_C p)^c (y_D p)^d}{(y_A p)^a (y_B p)^b} = \frac{\bar{p}_C^c \bar{p}_D^d}{\bar{p}_A^a \bar{p}_B^b} = K_y p^{(c+d-a-b)} \qquad (13\text{-}30)$$

It is understood here that partial pressure is defined as the product of mole fraction and total pressure (Chap. 4).

Comparison of Eqs. (13-27) and (13-30) indicates that the true equilibrium constant K is related to K_p as follows:

$$K = K_\gamma K_\phi K_p \qquad (13\text{-}31)$$

As stated before, K_γ can seldom be evaluated and is usually assumed to be unity, tantamount to the assumption of an ideal solution. With this understanding, Eq. (13-31) assumes the simplified, but approximate, form

$$K = K_\phi K_p \qquad (13\text{-}31a)$$

This expression shows that, although K is independent of pressure, K_p is not. The reason is that the extent of the deviations from ideal-gas behavior, and hence K_ϕ, changes with p. On the other hand if the reaction mixture is an ideal gas, K_ϕ is unity and $K = K_p$.

The value of K_p can be determined experimentally from measurements of total pressure and equilibrium composition, according to Eq. (13-30). Alternatively, it can be evaluated by Eq. (13-31a), provided the assumption of ideal solutions is justified. Figure 13-2 shows K_p as a function of temperature for a number of reactions. These values are valid over a pressure range in which the reaction mixture behaves essentially as an

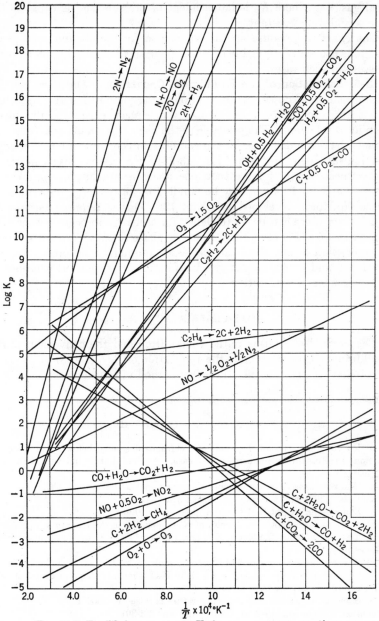

FIG. 13-2. Equilibrium constants K_p for some common reactions.

ideal gas, *i.e.*, where K_p is independent of pressure and is equal to the true equilibrium constant.

The effect of pressure on the conversion for liquid- and solid-phase reactions is usually negligible because of the small change in volume with pressure in such cases.

13-6. Calculation of the Equilibrium Conversion. Once the equilibrium constant is known, the calculation of the composition at equilibrium is a simple process, provided that only one phase exists and this phase is an ideal solution. The principle of the conservation of mass (material balance) and the definition of the equilibrium constant in terms of composition [as, for example, by Eq. (13-28) for a gaseous reaction] are all that is necessary. If more than one phase is present, the problem is more complicated, but it may be handled by introducing the criteria of phase equilibria developed in Chap. 12. This is required because at equilibrium there can be no tendency for a change to occur, either with respect to a transfer of material from one phase to another or with respect to conversion of one chemical species to another. The procedures are developed and illustrated for gas, liquid, and heterogeneous reactions in the remainder of this section.

GAS-PHASE REACTIONS

The method of relating initial composition and the conversion to the equilibrium constant involves the application of Eqs. (13-28) to (13-31a). The following examples illustrate the method of solution:

Example 13-4. The water-gas-shift reaction

$$CO(g) + H_2O(g) \rightarrow CO_2(g) + H_2(g)$$

is carried out under the different sets of conditions described below. Calculate the fraction of the steam decomposed in each case. Assume that the mixture behaves as an ideal gas.

(a) The reactants consist of 1 mole of water vapor and 1 mole of CO. The temperature is 1530°F and the total pressure 1 atm.

(b) Same as (a) except that the total pressure is 10 atm.

(c) Same as (a) except that 2 moles of N_2 is included in the reactants.

(d) The reactants are 2 moles of H_2O and 1 mole of CO. Other conditions are the same as in (a).

(e) The reactants are 2 moles of CO and 1 mole of H_2O.

(f) The initial mixture consists of 1 mole of H_2O, 1 mole of CO, and 1 mole of CO_2. Other conditions are the same as in (a).

(g) Same as (a) except that the temperature is raised to 2500°F.

Solution. From Fig. 13-2, at 1530°F, and Eq. (13-30),

$$K_p = 1.0 = \frac{(p_{CO_2})(p_{H_2})}{(p_{CO})(p_{H_2O})} = K_y p^{(1+1-1-1)} = \frac{(y_{CO_2})(y_{H_2})}{(y_{CO})(y_{H_2O})} \tag{A}$$

Let the moles of H_2 at equilibrium $= z$.

(a)   Moles of CO_2 at equilibrium $= z$ $y_{CO_2} = \dfrac{z}{2}$

        Moles of CO at equilibrium $= 1 - z$ $y_{CO} = \dfrac{1 - z}{2}$

        Moles of H_2O at equilibrium $= \underline{1 - z}$ $y_{H_2O} = \dfrac{1 - z}{2}$

        Total moles $= 2$

Substituting in Eq. (A),

$$1.0 = \frac{z^2}{(1 - z)^2}$$
$$z = 0.50$$
Fraction of steam decomposed $= 0.50$

(b) The total pressure is increased to 10 atm, but since there is no change in the number of moles during reaction and since the mixture is assumed to be an ideal gas, K_y does not change.

        Fraction of the steam decomposed $= 0.50$

(c) In this case the total number of moles $= 2 + 2 = 4$. Since there is no change in the number of moles during reaction, the total number of moles does not affect the result and the fraction of the steam decomposed $= 0.50$.

(d)   Moles of $H_2 = z$
        Moles of $CO_2 = z$
        Moles of $H_2O = 2 - z$
        Moles of CO $= \underline{1 - z}$
        Total $= 3$

$$1.0 = \frac{z^2}{(1 - z)(2 - z)}$$
$$z = 0.667$$
Fraction of steam decomposed $= \dfrac{0.667}{2} = 0.333$

(e) Here the initial moles of CO $= 2$. The equation for z is the same as in (d).

        Fraction of the steam decomposed $= 0.667$

(f) In this case Eq. (A) becomes

$$1.0 = \frac{z(1 + z)}{(1 - z)^2}$$
Fraction of steam decomposed $= 0.333$

(g) From Fig. 13-2, at 2500°F, $K_p = 0.316$.

$$0.316 = \frac{z^2}{(1 - z)^2}$$
$$z = 0.36$$

The conversion decreases (from 0.5 at 1530°F) as the temperature increases because the reaction is exothermic.

Example 13-5. Estimate the maximum conversion of ethylene to alcohol by vapor-phase hydration at 250°C and 500 psia. Use the equilibrium data of Example 13-1, and assume an initial steam-ethylene ratio of 5.

Solution. The equilibrium constant at 250°C can be evaluated from the equation for K developed in Example 13-1.

$$\ln K = \frac{4760}{523} - 1.558 \ln 523 + 0.00222(523) - 0.29 \times 10^{-6}(523)^2 - 5.56$$
$$= -5.13$$
$$K = 5.9 \times 10^{-3}$$

Since there are no partial-volume data available for estimating the activity coefficients, the general equation [Eq. (13-27)] cannot be used. It is necessary to assume that the gas mixture is an ideal solution. Then Eq. (13-28) is applicable:

$$5.9 \times 10^{-3} = K_\phi \frac{y_A}{y_E y_W} p^{-1} \tag{A}$$

The fugacity coefficients of the pure components can be determined from the generalized chart of Fig. 12-1 and are evaluated at the temperature and pressure of the equilibrium mixture.

For ethanol:

$$T_r = \frac{523}{516} = 1.01 \qquad \text{(critical data from Table 4-1)}$$
$$p_r = \frac{500}{(63.0)(14.7)} = 0.54$$
$$\frac{f_A}{p} = 0.84 \qquad \text{(from Fig. 12-1)}$$

For ethylene:

$$T_r = \frac{523}{282} = 1.85$$
$$p_r = \frac{500}{(50.0)(14.7)} = 0.68$$
$$\frac{f_E}{p} = 0.98$$

For water:

$$T_r = \frac{523}{647} = 0.81$$
$$p_r = \frac{500}{(218)(14.7)} = 0.16$$
$$\frac{f_W}{p} = 0.91$$

Substituting these data in Eq. (A),

$$\frac{y_A}{y_E y_W} = 5.9 \times 10^{-3} \frac{(0.98)(0.91)}{0.84} \left(\frac{500}{14.7}\right) = 0.21 \tag{B}$$

The pressure must be in atmospheres, because the standard-state pressure is measured in atmospheres. In proceeding from Eq. (13-7) to Eq. (13-10), the $f°$ values disappeared, because the fugacity in the standard state was chosen equal to 1 atm for each component. Therefore the fugacities in Eq. (13-10) must also be measured in atmospheres, for otherwise the equation would not be dimensionally sound. Note that, in general, K is not dimensionless but has the units of (atmospheres)$^{(c+d-a-b)}$.

If the initial steam-ethylene ratio is 5 and a basis of 1 mole of ethylene is chosen, a material balance gives the following results:

Moles of ethanol at equilibrium $= z$
Moles of ethylene at equilibrium $= 1 - z$
Moles of water at equilibrium $= 5 - z$
Total moles $= 6 - z$

Then

$$y_A = \frac{z}{6 - z}$$

$$y_E = \frac{1 - z}{6 - z}$$

$$y_W = \frac{5 - z}{6 - z}$$

Substituting in Eq. (B),

$$0.21 = \frac{z(6 - z)}{(1 - z)(5 - z)}$$
$$z^2 - 6.0z + 0.868 = 0$$
$$z = 3.0 \pm 2.85 = 5.85 \text{ or } 0.15$$

The first solution is greater than unity and hence is impossible. Therefore, $z = 0.15$ is correct, indicating that 15 per cent of the ethylene could be converted to ethanol, provided that equilibrium were achieved.

In this reaction, increasing the temperature decreases K and therefore the yield. Increasing the pressure increases the yield. From an equilibrium standpoint the operating pressure should be as high as possible (limited by condensation) and the temperature as low as possible. On the other hand, a catalyst is required in order to obtain an appreciable rate. Furthermore, the activity of all the catalysts that have been publicized requires a temperature of at least 150°C in order that the rate be reasonably fast. Even at this temperature the catalysts which have been developed will give no more than 20 to 30 per cent of the equilibrium yield. This is an instance where both equilibrium and reaction rate limit the commercialization of a reaction process.

From the mass-action principle, increasing the steam-ethylene ratio should increase the conversion of ethylene under equilibrium conditions. The results of calculations at various steam-ethylene ratios, and also various pressures and temperatures, are shown in Fig. 13-3. The curves in the figure were obtained by evaluating conversions at various conditions, just as illustrated in this example, except that a slightly different K vs. T relationship was used.

Another point of interest in this example is that the deviations from the ideal-gas law nearly counterbalance each other, as seen from Eq. (B). This means that Eq. (13-29) could have been used with little error. In other words,

$$K_y = \frac{y_A}{y_E y_W} = \frac{K}{p^{(c+d-a-b)}} = \frac{5.9 \times 10^{-3}}{p^{-1}} = 5.9 \times 10^{-3} \frac{500}{14.7} = 0.20$$

in comparison with the value of 0.21 obtained using fugacities.

Example 13-6. In a laboratory investigation, acetylene is catalytically hydrogenated to ethylene at 1220°C and 1 atm total pressure. If the initial mixture consists of 1 mole each of acetylene and hydrogen, what will be the composition of the products at equilibrium?

Solution. The required reaction may be obtained by combining the two formation reactions (rather, their reverse):

$$C_2H_2 \rightarrow 2C + H_2 \tag{1}$$
$$C_2H_4 \rightarrow 2C + 2H_2 \tag{2}$$

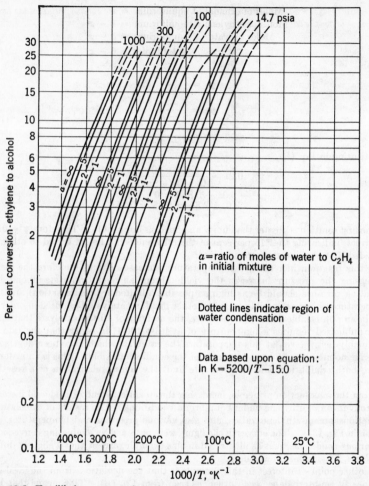

FIG. 13-3. Equilibrium conversion of ethylene to ethyl alcohol in the vapor phase

The difference between reactions (1) and (2) is the desired hydrogenation reaction:

$$C_2H_2 + H_2 \rightarrow C_2H_4$$

Also,

$$\Delta F° = \Delta F_1° - \Delta F_2°$$

By Eq. (13-9),

$$-RT \ln K = -RT \ln K_1 + RT \ln K_2$$

or

$$\ln K = \ln \frac{K_1}{K_2}$$

and

$$K = \frac{K_1}{K_2}$$

The equilibrium constants for reactions (1) and (2) in their most fundamental form are defined in terms of activities by Eq. (13-8):

$$K_1 = \frac{a_{H_2}a_C^2}{a_{C_2H_2}} \quad \text{and} \quad K_2 = \frac{a_{H_2}^2 a_C^2}{a_{C_2H_4}}$$

These expressions may be simplified by the following considerations:

(a) The carbon in reactions (1) and (2) would be present as a separate, essentially pure, phase. Since the standard state of a solid is taken as the pure material at atmospheric pressure and the reaction temperature, the carbon is in its standard state in the equilibrium mixture. Hence its activity is unity, and the equilibrium constants become

$$K_1 = \frac{a_{H_2}}{a_{C_2H_2}} \quad \text{and} \quad K_2 = \frac{a_{H_2}^2}{a_{C_2H_4}}$$

(b) At atmospheric pressure the gas phase will closely follow ideal-gas behavior. Hence the general expression [Eq. (13-27)] for the equilibrium constant reduces to Eq. (13-29). Applied to both reactions, this yields

$$K_1 = K_{y_1} = \frac{y_{H_2}}{y_{C_2H_2}} \quad \text{and} \quad K_2 = K_{y_2}p = \frac{y_{H_2}^2}{y_{C_2H_4}} p$$

For the required reaction,

$$K = \frac{K_1}{K_2} = \frac{y_{C_2H_4}}{y_{H_2}y_{C_2H_2}} p^{-1}$$

Since for ideal gases $K = K_p$ [Eq. (13-30)], the ratio of K_1 and K_2 can be obtained from Fig. 13-2. At 1220°C, $K = 5.2/5.2 = 1.0$.

Since $p = 1$ atm,

$$\frac{y_{C_2H_4}}{y_{H_2}y_{C_2H_2}} = 1.0$$

If $z =$ moles of C_2H_4 at equilibrium,

$$\text{Total number of moles} = z + (1 - z) + (1 - z) = 2 - z$$
$$1.0 = \frac{z(2 - z)}{(1 - z)^2}$$
$$z = 1.71 \text{ or } 0.293$$

Since the first value is impossible, $z = 0.293$, and the equilibrium gases have the following composition:

	Moles	Mole per cent
C_2H_4.............	0.293	17.2
C_2H_2.............	0.707	41.4
H_2...............	0.707	41.4
Total.........	1.707	100.0

Example 13-7. In internal-combustion engines a knowledge of the temperature and pressure at the end of the combustion process is of considerable importance. The type of calculations involved is illustrated by the following simplified example:

Suppose the combustion process in the cylinder takes place at constant volume and is also adiabatic. In a specific case, 0.005 lb mole of fuel (assume this is pure carbon) and 0.03 lb mole of air initially at 77°F are burned in a cylinder volume of 1.0 ft³.

To facilitate the calculations assume that all the gases are ideal.

Compute the following quantities:

(a) The composition and temperature of the products of combustion, provided that equilibrium is attained

(b) The pressure at equilibrium

Solution. In the previous examples the equilibrium temperature was known so that material balances and equilibrium equations were sufficient to yield a solution. In this case the final temperature must be determined by an energy balance.

Since there is an excess of oxygen and the equilibrium constants for the burning of carbon are high, it is safe to assume that all the carbon will be burned. Then the material balances become

$$N_{CO} + N_{CO_2} = 0.005 \quad \text{(carbon balance)}$$
$$\tfrac{1}{2}N_{CO} + N_{CO_2} + N_{O_2} = (0.03)(0.21) = 0.0063 \quad \text{(oxygen balance)}$$

where N_{CO}, etc., represent the number of moles at equilibrium.

Since there is no carbon present at equilibrium, the only pertinent reaction is

$$CO + \tfrac{1}{2}O_2 \rightarrow CO_2$$
$$K_p = \frac{p_{CO_2}}{(p_{CO})(p_{O_2})^{1/2}} \qquad (A)$$
$$p_{CO} = \frac{N_{CO}}{N}\,p$$

where N = total moles
      p = total pressure

$$p_{CO_2} = \frac{0.005 - N_{CO}}{N}\,p$$
$$p_{O_2} = \frac{0.0026 + N_{CO}}{2N}\,p$$

Substituting in Eq. (A),

$$K_p = \frac{0.005 - N_{CO}}{N_{CO}\left(\dfrac{0.0026 + N_{CO}}{2}\right)^{1/2}}\left(\frac{N}{p}\right)^{1/2} = \frac{0.005 - N_{CO}}{N_{CO}\left(\dfrac{0.0026 + N_{CO}}{2}\right)^{1/2}}\left(\frac{V}{RT}\right)^{1/2} \qquad (B)$$

The last equality comes from the fact that for an ideal-gas mixture

$$pV = NRT$$

The final temperature is determined by an energy balance. Since the volume is constant and the process is adiabatic, $\Delta E_{total} = 0$. If this over-all process is considered to take place in two steps, *i.e.*, isothermal reaction followed by heating to the final temperature (see Chap. 5), the energy balance may be written

$$(N\,\Delta E)_{CO} + (N\,\Delta E)_{CO_2} + [(NC_v)_{N_2} + (NC_v)_{CO} + (NC_v)_{CO_2} + (NC_v)_{O_2}]$$
$$(T - 537) = 0 \quad (C)$$

where ΔE_{CO} represents the energy change upon burning carbon to CO at constant volume at 77°F and ΔE_{CO_2} is a similar quantity for burning carbon to CO_2. The terms within the brackets represent the heat required to raise the products of combustion (the equilibrium mixture) from the initial temperature of 537°R to the final value T at constant volume. The molal heat capacities are mean values between 537 and $T°R$.

In Eqs. (B) and (C) there are in essence three unknowns, K_p, N_{CO}, and T. The other equation is the relationship between K_p and T given in Fig. 13-2. It is necessary to solve by a trial-and-error approach.

Assuming $T = 4560°R$,

$$K_p = 18.2 \qquad \text{(from Fig. 13-2)}$$

Then Eq. (B) becomes

$$18.2 = \frac{0.005 - N_{CO}}{N_{CO}\left(\dfrac{0.0026 + N_{CO}}{2}\right)^{1/2}}\left[\frac{1}{(0.73)(4560)}\right]^{1/2}$$

Since the pressure must be in atmospheres, the term V/RT must be in atmospheres. The volume is $1.0 \, ft^3$, and hence the value of R to be used is $0.73 \, (ft^3)(atm)/(lb \, mole)(°R)$.

Solving for N_{CO} yields

$$N_{CO} = 1.3 \times 10^{-4} \text{ mole}$$

The assumed temperature should now be checked by Eq. (C). The values of ΔE may be ascertained from the heats of reaction tabulated in Chap. 5.

$$\Delta E_{CO} = \Delta H - \Delta(pV)$$

The heat of combustion of carbon to form CO is the heat of formation of CO. The $\Delta H°$ value is given in Table 5-3, $\Delta H = (-26,416)(1.8) = -47,550 \text{ Btu/lb mole}$. The $\Delta(pV)$ term for an ideal gas is equal to $\Delta N_{gas} RT$. For the reaction

$$C(s) + \tfrac{1}{2}O_2(g) \rightarrow CO(g)$$
$$\Delta N_{gas} = 1 - \tfrac{1}{2} = \tfrac{1}{2}$$
$$\Delta E_{CO} = -47,550 - (\tfrac{1}{2})(2)(537) = -48,090 \text{ Btu/lb mole}$$

Similarly,

$$\Delta E_{CO_2} = -169,290 - 0 = -169,290 \text{ Btu/lb mole}$$

The mean values of C_v in Eq. (C) can be obtained from the information given in Fig. 5-1 by subtracting R from the C_p values.[1]

Substituting numerical values in (C),

$$1.3 \times 10^{-4}(-48,090) + (0.005 - 0.00013)(-169,290) + [(0.0237)(8.05 - 2) + 1.3$$
$$\times 10^{-4}(8.15 - 2) + (0.00487)(13.25 - 2) + (0.0013)(8.5 - 2)](4560 - 537) = 0$$

or

$$-831 + 834 \cong 0$$

Since the energy balance is essentially satisfied, $4100°F$ is approximately correct for the final temperature.

(a) The composition of the equilibrium mixture is as follows:

	Moles	Mole per cent
CO	0.00013	0.4
CO₂.............	0.00487	16.2
O₂....	0.0013	4.3
N₂...............	0.0237	79.1
Total..........	0.0300	100.0

[1] This simple subtraction of R from C_p to obtain C_v follows from the assumption of ideal gases.

(b) The pressure is given by the equation

$$p = \frac{NRT}{V} = \frac{(0.03)(0.73)(4560)}{1} = 100 \text{ atm}$$

Example 13-8. Estimate the equilibrium conversion of ethyl alcohol to butadiene at 427°C and 1 atm total pressure assuming[1] that the reactions involved are

(I) $C_2H_5OH(g) \rightarrow C_2H_4(g) + H_2O(g)$
(II) $C_2H_5OH(g) \rightarrow CH_3CHO(g) + H_2(g)$
(III) $C_2H_4(g) + CH_3CHO(g) \rightarrow C_4H_6(g) + H_2O(g)$

The standard free-energy changes for these reactions at 427°C are

(I) $\Delta F° = -10{,}850$ cal/g mole
(II) $\Delta F° = -3610$ cal/g mole
(III) $\Delta F° = -1380$ cal/g mole

Solution. From Eq. (13-9) the equilibrium constants are

$$K_I = 2.45 \times 10^3$$
$$K_{II} = 13.5$$
$$K_{III} = 2.69$$

As a basis for the calculations take 1 mole of alcohol. Then suppose that

α = moles of alcohol converted by reaction I
β = moles of alcohol converted by reaction II
ϵ = moles of butadiene formed

At equilibrium the number of moles of each component will be

$$C_4H_6 = \epsilon$$
$$C_2H_5OH = 1 - \alpha - \beta$$
$$C_2H_4 = \alpha - \epsilon$$
$$CH_3CHO = \beta - \epsilon$$
$$H_2O = \alpha + \epsilon$$
$$H_2 = \beta$$
$$\text{Total} = 1 + \alpha + \beta$$

Three equations for α, β, and ϵ can be written using the equilibrium-constant equations. If at 1 atm total pressure the mixture behaves as an ideal gas,

$$K_I = 2.45 \times 10^3 = K_p = \frac{p_{C_2H_4}p_{H_2O}}{p_{C_2H_5OH}} = \frac{(\alpha - \epsilon)(\alpha + \epsilon)}{(1 - \alpha - \beta)(1 + \alpha + \beta)} \quad (A)$$

Similarly,

$$K_{II} = 13.5 = \frac{(\beta - \epsilon)\beta}{(1 - \alpha - \beta)(1 + \alpha + \beta)} \quad (B)$$

$$K_{III} = 2.69 = \frac{(\alpha + \epsilon)\epsilon}{(\beta - \epsilon)(\alpha - \epsilon)} \quad (C)$$

[1] Note that this amounts to postulating a mechanism for the over-all reaction. The important result of this is that it specifies the reaction products which are assumed to be in equilibrium. These are clearly different from what would be present were the reaction to proceed in a single step with no side reactions: $2C_2H_5OH \rightarrow C_4H_6 + 2H_2O + H_2$.

From this point on the problem is simply one in algebra, *i.e.*, solving the three equations (A), (B), and (C) for α, β, and ϵ. Since K_{I} and K_{II} are both relatively large, there will be little unreacted alcohol at equilibrium. This simplifies the solution, for, approximately,

$$\alpha + \beta = 1$$

If α is assumed $= 0.883$, then

$$\beta = 1 - \alpha = 0.117$$

Using these values in Eqs. (I), (II), and (III) to find ϵ values gives essentially the same result, $\epsilon = 0.08$.

At equilibrium:

Moles C_4H_6	0.080
Moles C_2H_5OH	0.000
Moles C_2H_4	0.803
Moles CH_3CHO	0.037
Moles H_2O	0.963
Moles H_2	0.117
Total	2.000

The conversion to butadiene is 8 per cent

LIQUID-PHASE REACTIONS

The problem of calculating the equilibrium composition of liquid-phase reactions is chiefly one of relating the activity to the composition for substitution in Eq. (13-8). The standard states for the components of liquid-phase reactions may be chosen as the pure liquids at 1 atm pressure and the reaction temperature. This is analogous to the choice of standard states for gas-phase reactions.

If the equilibrium mixture is an ideal solution, the fugacity of each component is given by

$$\bar{f} = fx \tag{13-32}$$

where f is the fugacity of the pure component at the reaction pressure and temperature and x is its mole fraction at equilibrium. Since pressure usually has a very small effect on the properties of liquids, f can be replaced by $f°$, the standard-state fugacity, without introducing appreciable error. Hence

$$\bar{f} = f°x \tag{13-33}$$

and the activity is given by

$$a = \frac{\bar{f}}{f°} = x \tag{13-34}$$

Thus for ideal solutions, Eq. (13-8) reduces to

$$K = \frac{x_C^c x_D^d}{x_A^a x_B^b} = K_x \tag{13-35}$$

If the solution is not ideal, the activity coefficient may be introduced, as in Eq. (13-25), to take into account deviations from ideality. The fugacity of each component in the equilibrium mixture is then

$$\bar{f} = \gamma f^\circ x \tag{13-36}$$

and the activity is

$$a = \frac{\bar{f}}{f^\circ} = \gamma x \tag{13-37}$$

The equilibrium constant now becomes

$$K = \frac{\gamma_C^c \gamma_D^d}{\gamma_A^a \gamma_B^b} \frac{x_C^c x_D^d}{x_A^a x_B^b} = \frac{\gamma_C^c \gamma_D^d}{\gamma_A^a \gamma_B^b} K_x \tag{13-38}$$

This is the general relationship for K when the standard states are taken as the pure components at 1 atm.

The practical difficulty with Eq. (13-38) is that data are rarely available for evaluating the activity coefficients, and one usually has no alternative but to assume the solution ideal, so that all the γ's are unity. In other words, when the standard states are taken as the pure components, the approximate equation (13-35) must generally be used. This does not always result in so large an error as might be expected, because the ratio of the γ's in Eq. (13-38) may be nearly unity even when the individual γ's are not.

For components which are known to be present in high concentration, Eq. (13-33) is usually nearly correct, because the Lewis and Randall rule always becomes valid for a component as its concentration approaches $x = 1$. [See Eq. (12-24b). The proof is analogous to Example 12-9.]

For components which are at low concentration in aqueous solution, a different procedure has been widely adopted, because in this case Eq. (13-33) is frequently not even approximately correct. The method is based on the use of fictitious or hypothetical standard states. The standard state of the solute is taken as the hypothetical state which would exist if the solute obeyed Henry's law all the way to a molality of 1. In terms of molality and fugacity, Henry's law is

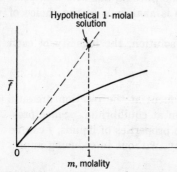

FIG. 13-4. Standard state for dilute aqueous solutions.

$$\bar{f} = km \tag{13-39}$$

and it is always valid for a component whose concentration approaches zero. This hypothetical state is illustrated in Fig. 13-4. The dashed line drawn tangent to the curve at the origin represents Henry's law and is valid in the case shown to a molality much less than unity. However, it is possible to calculate the properties the solute would have if it obeyed Henry's law to a concentration of 1 molal, and this hypothetical state is widely used as a standard state.

The standard-state fugacity is

$$\bar{f}^\circ = km^\circ = k(1) = k$$

Hence, for any component at a concentration low enough for Henry's law to hold

$$\bar{f} = km = \bar{f}^\circ m$$

and

$$a = \frac{\bar{f}}{\bar{f}^\circ} = m \tag{13-40}$$

The obvious advantage of this standard state is that it provides a very simple relationship between activity and concentration for cases where Henry's law is valid. Its range does not commonly extend to a concentration of 1 molal. In the rare case where it does, the standard state is a real state of the solute. This procedure is useful only where ΔF° data are available in terms of the hypothetical 1-molal standard state, for otherwise the equilibrium constant cannot be evaluated from Eq. (13-9).

For solutes in nonaqueous solvents, similar procedures are occasionally used, and this subject is treated in advanced textbooks on chemical thermodynamics. The use of special standard states for components of liquid solutions sometimes allows a more accurate determination of the equilibrium composition, but often at least one component will exist at a concentration outside the range of use of such methods. Recourse is then made to the approximate equations for ideal solutions.

HETEROGENEOUS REACTIONS

When liquid and gaseous phases are both present in a reaction mixture, Eq. (12-1), a requirement of phase equilibrium, must be satisfied along with the equation of chemical-reaction equilibrium. There is considerable choice in the method of treatment of such cases. For example, consider a reaction between gas A and water B to form an aqueous solution of C. The reaction may be assumed to occur entirely in the gas phase with simultaneous transfer of material between phases to maintain phase equilibrium. In this method the equilibrium constant would be evaluated from ΔF° based on the standard state for gases for each component, i.e., unit fugacity at the temperature of the reaction. On the other hand, the reaction may be assumed to occur in the liquid phase, in which case $\Delta F°$ would be determined from the standard states in the liquid phase.   Or the equation might be considered in the following way:

$$A(g) + B(l) = C(aq)$$

in which case the $\Delta F°$ value would be evaluated by considering component C to be in its standard state in a hypothetical solution of 1-molal concentration, component B as a pure liquid at 1 atm pressure, and component A as a pure gas at unit fugacity.   For this choice of standard states, the equilibrium constant would be written (Eq. 13-8)

$$K = \frac{a_C}{a_B a_A} = \frac{m}{(\gamma_B x_B)(f_A)} \tag{13-41}$$

The last term arises from applying Eq. (13-40) to component C, Eq. (13-37) to B, and noting that $a = f$ for the gaseous standard state of A. It is supposed in using Eq. (13-40) for C that Henry's law is valid.   The equilibrium constant in Eq. (13-41) would not be the same as that obtained when the standard state for each component is chosen to be the pure gas at unit fugacity.   However, all the methods theoretically would lead to the same equilibrium composition.   Actually, one particular choice of standard states may simplify the calculations or yield more accurate results because it makes better use of the limited data that are normally available.   The nature of the calculations involved in heterogeneous reactions is illustrated in the following example.

Example 13-9.   Estimate the composition and quantity of the gas and liquid phases in equilibrium when benzene is hydrogenated at 500°K and 30 atm pressure.   Assume that only the three components cyclohexane, benzene, and hydrogen are present. Also determine the over-all conversion of benzene to cyclohexane, and determine the range of values of h_0, the ratio of initial moles of hydrogen to benzene, in order that two phases will be present at equilibrium.   The following data are available:

(a) $\Delta F°_{f500}$, the standard free energy of formation at 500°K for standard states of gas at unit fugacity:[1]

Benzene........... 39,240 cal/g mole
Cyclohexane....... 34,070 cal/g mole

(b) Vapor pressures at 500°K:

Benzene........... 23.0 atm
Cyclohexane....... 19.7 atm

Solution.   First consider the chemical reaction to take place in the gas phase, and choose standard states of unit fugacity at 500°K.

$$C_6H_6(g, f° = 1) + 3H_2(g, f° = 1) \rightarrow C_6H_{12}(g, f° = 1)$$

[1] F. D. Rossini et al., American Petroleum Institute Research Project 44, Carnegie Institute of Technology, Pittsburgh, 1953.

The standard free-energy change for the reaction at 500°K can be obtained by combining the standard free energies of formation for each of the constituents. The result is

$$\Delta F^\circ_{500} = -5170 \text{ cal}$$

Hence

$$\ln K = \frac{-(-5170)}{R(500)} = 5.20$$

and

$$K_{500} = 182$$

Since this constant is based on the reaction in the gas phase, it is related to the composition of the gas phase as follows (for an ideal solution):

$$K = 182 = \frac{\bar{f}_C}{\bar{f}_B \bar{f}_H^3} = \frac{f_C}{f_B f_H^3} \frac{y_C}{y_B y_H^3} \qquad (A)$$

where the subscript C refers to cyclohexane, B to benzene, and H to hydrogen.

The criteria for equilibrium between the gas and liquid phases must be satisfied as well as the criteria of chemical-reaction equilibrium. Therefore the vapor and liquid compositions are related as follows:

$$y_C = K_C x_C \qquad (B)$$
$$y_B = K_B x_B \qquad (C)$$
$$y_H = K_H x_H \qquad (D)$$

where K_C, K_B, and K_H are the phase-equilibrium constants considered in Chap. 12.

In addition, the following two material-balance equations must be satisfied:

Vapor:

$$y_C + y_B + y_H = 1.0 \qquad (E)$$

Liquid:

$$x_C + x_B + x_H = 1.0 \qquad (F)$$

The six equations (A) to (F) are sufficient to determine the solution. The mechanics of solving for the six unknown mole fractions may be approached in many ways. Fortunately, the solution is simplified by noting that hydrogen is very volatile and therefore will be predominantly in the vapor phase at 500°K. Then $K_H = \infty$, and

$$x_H = 0$$

This eliminates one unknown and Eq. (D).

As discussed in Chap. 12, the exact evaluation of the phase-equilibrium constants K_C and K_B requires complete partial-volume data for the system or experimental composition data. On the other hand, an approximate solution can be obtained by assuming that the liquid and gas phases are ideal solutions, in which case K is given by Eq. (12-31),

$$K = \frac{f_L}{f_G}$$

where f_L is the fugacity of the pure component in a liquid phase and f_G the same in a gas phase, both at the temperature and total pressure of the mixture. As shown in Chap. 12, these fugacities can be estimated by evaluating f_L at the vapor pressure (at the given temperature) and f_G at the total pressure, employing Fig. 12-1.[1] Then

---

[1] It should be emphasized that this approach is not rigorous, but is the only method of treatment available when experimental data are lacking.

the constants K_C and K_B may be written as

$$K_C = \left(\frac{f'}{f_a}\right)_C \qquad K_B = \left(\frac{f'}{f_a}\right)_B$$

where the prime refers to a value at the vapor pressure.

Substituting Eqs. (B) and (C) in (A),

$$K = \frac{f_C}{f_B f_H^3} \frac{K_C x_C}{K_B x_B y_H^3} = \frac{f_C}{f_B f_H^3} \frac{(f'x)_C f_B}{(f'x)_B f_C y_H^3}$$

$$K = \frac{(f'x)_C}{(f'x)_B (fy)_H^3} \tag{G}$$

The fugacities of cyclohexane and benzene in the gas phase at the total pressure of the mixture cancel out, leaving only the fugacities at the vapor pressure to be determined. It is of interest at this point to compare Eq. (G) with the equilibrium-constant equation based upon the following standard states, all at 500°K:

C_6H_6 (pure liquid at its vapor pressure) $+ 3H_2$ $(g, f° = 1)$

$\qquad\qquad\qquad\qquad\qquad\qquad \rightarrow C_6H_{12}$ (pure liquid at its vapor pressure)

To use the $\Delta F°$ evaluated from the gas-phase reaction, the free-energy change must be calculated for converting benzene and cyclohexane from liquids at their vapor pressure to gases at unit fugacity. This may be done by first evaporating the liquid at 500°K and then expanding the gas from the vapor pressure to unit fugacity. From the definition of fugacity [Eq. (12-13)] this change in free energy is

$$\Delta F_C = 0 \text{ (for evaporation)} + RT \ln \frac{1}{f'_C} = -RT \ln f'_C$$

$$\Delta F_B = -RT \ln f'_B$$

Then the standard free-energy change $\Delta F°_a$ based on the heterogeneous reaction is as follows:

$$\Delta F°_a = \Delta F° - RT \ln f'_B - (-RT \ln f'_C)$$

where $\Delta F° = -5170$ cal for the gas-phase reaction.

$$-RT \ln K_a = -RT \ln K - RT \ln \frac{f'_B}{f'_C}$$

$$K_a = K \frac{f'_B}{f'_C} \tag{H}$$

From Eq. (13-8),

$$K_a = \frac{a_C}{a_B a_H^3} = \frac{a_C}{a_B f_H^3}$$

since $a = f$ for hydrogen.

If the liquid and gas phases are again assumed to be ideal solutions, the activity is equal to the mole fraction [Eq. (13-34)] so that

$$K_a = \frac{x_C}{x_B f_H^3} = \frac{x_C}{x_B (f_H y_H)^3} \tag{I}$$

Then combining Eqs. (H) and (I) and solving for K gives

$$K = \frac{(xf')_C}{(xf')_B (fy)_H^3}$$

which is the same as Eq. (G). Therefore, the choice of the standard state does not influence the final reaction-equilibrium equation. However, the availability of one type of data and unavailability of another may dictate the choice of standard states.

The numerical solution of Eqs. (A) to (F) or (B) to (G) (the two sets are equivalent) requires evaluation of the phase-equilibrium constants K_C and K_B. Using the critical data of Table 4-1 and the generalized chart, Fig. 12-1,

<table>
<tr><td style="text-align:center">*Cyclohexane*</td><td style="text-align:center">*Benzene*</td></tr>
<tr><td style="text-align:center">$T_r = \dfrac{500}{553} = 0.90$</td><td style="text-align:center">$T_r = \dfrac{500}{562} = 0.89$</td></tr>
</table>

At the vapor pressure,

$$p_r = \frac{19.7}{40.0} = 0.49 \qquad\qquad p_r = \frac{23.0}{48.6} = 0.47$$

$$f' = (0.76)(19.7) = 15.0 \text{ atm} \qquad f' = (0.76)(23.0) = 17.5 \text{ atm}$$

At the total pressure,

$$p_r = \frac{30}{40.0} = 0.75 \qquad\qquad p_r = \frac{30}{48.6} = 0.62$$

$$f = (0.54)(30) = 16.2 \qquad\qquad f = (0.62)(30) = 18.6 \text{ atm}$$

With these fugacities the equations become

$$y_C = \frac{15.0}{16.2} x_C = 0.92 x_C \tag{B}$$

$$y_B = \frac{17.5}{18.6} x_B = 0.94 x_B \tag{C}$$

$$y_C + y_B + y_H = 1.0 \tag{E}$$

$$x_C + x_B = 1.0 \tag{F}$$

$$K = 182 = \frac{15.0 x_C}{(17.5 x_B)(30 y_H)^3} \quad * $$

or

$$\frac{x_C}{x_B y_H^3} = 5.73 \times 10^6 \tag{G}$$

Elimination of x_C and y_H from Eq. (G) yields

$$\frac{1 - x_B}{x_B(0.08 - 0.02 x_B)^3} = 5.73 \times 10^6$$

Since x_B must be very small to satisfy this result,

$$\frac{1}{x_B(0.08)^3} = 5.73 \times 10^6$$

$$x_B = 3.4 \times 10^{-4} \qquad\qquad y_B = (0.94)(3.4 \times 10^{-4}) = 3.2 \times 10^{-4}$$

$$x_C = 1 - 3.4 \times 10^{-4} \cong 1.0 \qquad y_C = (0.92)(1.0) = 0.92$$

$$x_H = 0 \qquad\qquad\qquad y_H = 0.08$$

These results completely determine the phase compositions. To obtain the conversion of benzene to cyclohexane an over-all material balance must be considered.

* Hydrogen at 30 atm and 500°K behaves essentially as an ideal gas. Hence the fugacity f_H of pure hydrogen is equal to the pressure, 30 atm.

If initially there were 1 mole of benzene and h_0 moles of hydrogen, at equilibrium there will be

$$\text{Moles of cyclohexane} = \beta$$
$$\text{Moles of benzene} = 1 - \beta$$
$$\text{Moles of hydrogen} = h_0 - 3\beta$$
$$\text{Total} = h_0 + 1 - 3\beta$$

If N_L represents the moles of liquid at equilibrium, the moles of vapor is

$$N_V = h_0 + 1 - 3\beta - N_L$$

Writing the two additional independent material balances (one has already been used, $N = N_L + N_V$),

Cyclohexane:
$$\beta = 1.0 N_L + 0.92(h_0 + 1 - 3\beta - N_L)$$

Hydrogen:
$$h_0 - 3\beta = 0 + 0.08(h_0 + 1 - 3\beta - N_L)$$

These two equations, involving the three quantities β, N_L, and h_0, indicate that, in general, the over-all conversion and the quantity of each phase depend on the initial hydrogen-benzene ratio. However, in this particular problem the equilibrium constant K was sufficiently high so that essentially all the benzene was reacted; that is, x_B and y_B are very low. Therefore, as seen by adding the two equations,

$$h_0 - 2\beta = N_L + h_0 + 1 - 3\beta - N_L$$
$$\beta = 1$$

Therefore, the conversion to cyclohexane is complete. The quantity of the liquid and gas phases will depend upon the value of h_0, although the range of values of h_0 will be limited by the restriction that two phases be present. If there is to be a liquid phase, N_L must be greater than zero. Hence the maximum permissible values of h_0 may be found by setting $N_L = 0$ in the cyclohexane material balance,

$$1 = N_L + 0.92(h_0 + 1 - 3\beta - N_L)$$
$$= 0.08 N_L + 0.92(h_0 - 2)$$

If $N_L = 0$

$$h_{0,\text{max}} = 2 + \frac{1}{0.92} = 3.09 \text{ moles of } H_2 \text{ per mole of benzene}$$

On the other hand if there is to be a vapor phase present, N_V must be greater than zero. Hence the minimum value of h_0 can be found by placing

$$N_V = 0 = h_0 + 1 - 3\beta - N_L$$

or

$$N_L = h_0 + 1 - 3 = h_0 - 2$$

Then substituting in the cyclohexane material-balance equation,

$$1 = 0.08(h_0 - 2) + 0.92(h_0 - 2) = h_0 - 2$$
$$h_{0,\text{min}} = 3$$

Therefore, the hydrogen-benzene mole ratio must be between 3 and 3.09 if two phases are to be present at equilibrium. For example, if $h_0 = 3.05$,

$$0.92(h_0 - 2) = 1 - 0.08N_L$$
$$N_L = \frac{1 - (0.92)(3.05 - 2)}{0.08} = 0.42 \text{ mole}$$
$$N_V = 3.05 + 1 - 3 - 0.42 = 0.63 \text{ mole}$$

Then for this case the quantity and composition of each phase are as summarized in the accompanying table.

	Liquid		Vapor	
	Moles	Mole per cent	Moles	Mole per cent
H_2............	0.0	0.0	0.05	8.0
C_6H_{12}.........	0.42	100.0	0.58	92.0
C_6H_6..........	0.0	0.0	0.0	0.0
Total........	0.42	100.0	0.63	100.0

This solution illustrates the method of combining chemical and phase-equilibria equations for the solution of heterogeneous problems. The assumptions involved should be clearly understood. First, the liquid and vapor phases were assumed to behave as ideal solutions. Second, the phase-equilibrium constants were evaluated from Fig. 12-1, based upon the law of corresponding states and on assumptions regarding the fugacity of a pure component in an unstable state. Third, the solubility of hydrogen in the liquid phase was neglected. This third assumption did not affect the general equations but simplified their solution. Finally, the equilibrium constant for the reaction chosen was sufficiently large that complete conversion was obtained. This also simplified the numerical solution but did not affect the method of approach and the general equations.

PROBLEMS

1. If the values of K_p for the synthesis of ammonia from nitrogen and hydrogen at 500°C are 0.00381 and 0.00651 atm^{-1} at 10 and 600 atm, respectively, calculate K and K_y at each pressure. What conclusions can be drawn from the results?

2. Using data from Tables 5-1, 5-3, and 13-1 with reference to the ammonia synthesis reaction,

(a) Calculate the standard free-energy change and the equilibrium constant at 500°C.

(b) Estimate the values of K_p and K_y if the total pressure is 250 atm.

3. Using the results of Prob. 2, compute the maximum percentage conversion of nitrogen to ammonia at 500°C and 250 atm with a feed gas having a hydrogen-nitrogen molal ratio of 3. What would be the conversion and composition of the equilibrium gas if this ratio were 4.5?

4. Water vapor is 1.85 mole per cent dissociated at 2000°C and 1 atm total pressure. Calculate the dissociation at 25°C and 1 atm.

5. The final step in the process for producing 1,3-butadiene from petroleum fractions is the dehydrogenation of butylenes. Estimate the temperature at which the dehydrogenation process must operate in order that a conversion of 40 per cent be possible. Assume that the operating pressure is 20 psia and that 15 moles of steam per mole of butylenes is added as a diluent. Assume also that the butylene stream is made up entirely of 1-butene.

6. If the initial mixture in Prob. 5 consisted of 50 mole per cent steam and 50 mole per cent 1-butene, how would the required temperature be affected?

7. Calculate the dissociation pressure of Ag_2O at 200°C. Use the following data:

$$\text{At } 25°C, \ \Delta H° = 6950 \text{ cal/g mole}$$
$$\text{At } 25°C, \ \Delta F° = 2230 \text{ cal/g mole}$$
$$\text{For Ag: } C_p = 5.60 + 1.5 \times 10^{-3}T$$
$$Ag_2O: C_p = 13.87 + 8.9 \times 10^{-3}T \qquad T = °K$$
$$O_2: C_p = 6.50 + 1.0 \times 10^{-3}T$$

8. In the Deacon process for the manufacture of chlorine, hydrochloric acid is oxidized with 95 per cent pure oxygen according to the reaction

$$4HCl(g) + O_2 \rightarrow 2H_2O(g) + 2Cl_2$$

The remaining 5 per cent of the oxygen stream is nitrogen, which does not take part in the reaction. The reaction occurs at 1 atm and at temperatures between 450 and 650°C. The other variable involved is the ratio of reactants. Determine:

(a) A general equation relating ln K to the absolute temperature of reaction

(b) The composition of the equilibrium mixture at both 450 and 650°C for feed ratios of both 4 and 12 moles HCl per mole O_2

(c) The purity of the chlorine produced on an HCl-free and H_2O-free basis for each of the conditions of part (b)

(d) The conversion of HCl for each of the conditions of part (b)

9. Consider the two gas-phase reactions:

(a) $A + B \rightarrow C + D$

(b) $A + C \rightarrow 2E$

At the temperature of reaction $K_{p_a} = 2.667$ and $K_{p_b} = 3.200$. The pressure in the reactor is to be 10 atm, and the feed consists of 2 moles of A to 1 mole of B. Calculate the composition of the reaction mixture if equilibrium is reached with respect to both reactions.

10. Ethylene oxide is an important organic intermediate in the chemical industry. The standard free-energy change at 25°C for the reaction $C_2H_4(g) + \frac{1}{2}O_2(g) \rightarrow C_2H_4O(g)$ is $-19,070$ cal/g mole. This large negative value of $\Delta F°$ indicates that equilibrium is far to the right at 25°C. However, the direct oxidation of ethylene must be promoted by a catalyst selective to this reaction to prevent the complete combustion of ethylene to carbon dioxide and water. Even with such a catalyst, it is thought that the reaction will have to be carried out at a temperature of about 550°K in order to obtain a reasonable reaction rate. Since the reaction is exothermic, an increase in temperature will have an adverse effect on the equilibrium. Is the reaction feasible (from an equilibrium standpoint) at 550°K, assuming that a suitable catalyst selective for this reaction is available? The following data are available:

Heat of formation of C_2H_4 at 25°C = 12,500 cal/g mole

Heat of formation of C_2H_4O at 25°C = $-12,190$ cal/g mole

Heat-capacity equations for the temperature range involved [C_p in cal/(g mole)(°K), T in degrees Kelvin]:

$$C_2H_4O: C_p = 1.57 + 0.0332T$$
$$C_2H_4: C_p = 3.68 + 0.0224T$$
$$O_2: C_p = 6.37 + 0.0021T$$

11. One method for the manufacture of "synthesis gas" depends on the vapor-phase catalytic reaction of methane with steam according to the equation

$$CH_4 + H_2O(g) \rightarrow CO + 3H_2$$

The only other reaction which ordinarily occurs to an appreciable extent is the "water-gas-shift" reaction

$$CO + H_2O(g) \rightarrow CO_2 + H_2$$

The following heats and free energies of formation are available in calories per gram mole:

	$\Delta H°$ at 600°K	$\Delta H°$ at 1300°K	$\Delta F°$ at 600°K	$\Delta F°$ at 1300°K
CH$_4$............	$-19,890$	$-21,920$	$-5,490$	$+12,500$
H$_2$O(g)...........	$-58,490$	$-59,620$	$-51,150$	$-42,020$
CO.............	$-26,330$	$-27,210$	$-39,360$	$-54,240$
CO$_2$.............	$-94,120$	$-94,460$	$-94,440$	$-94,680$

Assume equilibrium to be attained for both of the above reactions for all parts of this problem.

(a) Would it be better to carry out the manufacture of synthesis gas at 1 atm or at 100 atm? Why?

(b) Would it be better to carry out the manufacture of synthesis gas so that the maximum temperature reached in the reactor is 600 or 1300°K? Why?

(c) Using the conditions selected as preferable in parts (a) and (b), *estimate* the molal ratio of hydrogen to carbon monoxide in the synthesis gas produced if a feed consisting of 1 mole of steam to 1 mole of methane is used.

(d) Repeat part (c) if a feed consisting of 2 moles of steam to 1 mole of methane is used.

(e) How would you alter the feed composition to obtain a lower ratio of hydrogen to carbon monoxide in the synthesis gas than is obtained in part (c) for the same conditions of temperature and pressure?

(f) Calculate the heat requirement for the reactor under conditions of part (d) if both the methane and the steam are preheated to 600°K.

(g) Is there any danger that carbon will be deposited by the reaction $2CO \rightarrow C + CO_2$ under the conditions of part (c)? Part (d)? If so, how would you alter the feed composition so that carbon deposition would be impossible?

12. Calculate the equilibrium per cent conversion of ethylene oxide to ethylene glycol at 25°C and 1 atm total pressure if the initial molal ratio of ethylene oxide to water is 3.0. Assume the free-energy change for the reaction with the following standard states is -1870 cal per gram mole of glycol:

$$C_2H_4O \ (g, \text{ unit fugacity}) + H_2O \text{ (pure liquid)}$$
$$\rightarrow (CH_2OH)_2 \text{ (1- molal aqueous solution)}$$

To simplify the calculations assume that the gas phase is an ideal-gas mixture, that Raoult's law is valid for the water in the liquid phase, and that Henry's law is valid for the ethylene oxide in the liquid phase. The vapor pressure of pure water at 25°C is 0.46 psia, and the partial pressure of ethylene oxide over aqueous solutions containing glycol may be taken as

$$p \text{ (psia)} = 60x \qquad (x = \text{mole fraction of dissolved ethylene oxide})$$

Consider the definition of molality to be the gram moles of a component in the solution per 1000 g of water regardless of the other components present. The vapor pressure of pure ethylene glycol at 25°C is approximately 0.3 mm Hg.

APPENDIX: STEAM TABLES

Table A-1. Saturated Steam†

Absolute pressure = atmospheric pressure − vacuum.

Barometer and vacuum columns may be corrected to mercury at 32°F by subtracting $0.00009 \times (t - 32) \times$ column height, where t is the column temperature in degrees Fahrenheit.

One inch of mercury at 32°F = 0.4912 lb/sq in.

Example

Barometer reads 30.17 in. at 70°F.

Vacuum column reads 28.26 in. at 80°F.

Absolute pressure = $(30.17 - 0.00009 \times 38 \times 30.17) - (28.26 - 0.00009 \times 48 \times 28.26) = 1.93$ in. of mercury at 32°F.

Saturation temperature (from table) = 100°F.

v = specific volume, ft³/lb$_m$
H = specific enthalpy, Btu/lb$_m$
S = specific entropy, Btu/(lb$_m$)(°R)

Temp t, °F	Absolute pressure p		Specific volume			Enthalpy			Entropy		
	Psia	In. Hg (32°F)	Sat. liquid v_f	Evap. v_{fg}	Sat. vapor v_g	Sat. liquid H_f	Evap. H_{fg}	Sat. vapor H_g	Sat. liquid S_f	Evap. S_{fg}	Sat. vapor S_g
32	0.0886	0.1806	0.01602	3305.7	3305.7	0	1075.1	1075.1	0	2.1865	2.1865
34	0.0961	0.1957	0.01602	3060.4	3060.4	2.01	1074.0	1076.0	0.0041	2.1755	2.1796
36	0.1041	0.2120	0.01602	2836.6	2836.6	4.03	1072.9	1076.9	0.0082	2.1645	2.1727
38	0.1126	0.2292	0.01602	2632.2	2632.2	6.04	1071.7	1077.7	0.0122	2.1533	2.1655
40	0.1217	0.2478	0.01602	2445.1	2445.1	8.05	1070.5	1078.6	0.0162	2.1423	2.1585

42	0.1315	0.2677	0.01602	2271.8	2271.8	10.06	1069.3	1079.4	0.0203	2.1314	2.1517
44	0.1420	0.2891	0.01602	2112.2	2112.2	12.06	1068.2	1080.3	0.0242	2.1207	2.1449
46	0.1532	0.3119	0.01602	1965.5	1965.5	14.07	1067.1	1081.2	0.0282	2.1102	2.1384
48	0.1652	0.3364	0.01602	1829.9	1829.9	16.07	1065.9	1082.0	0.0322	2.0995	2.1317
50	0.1780	0.3624	0.01602	1704.9	1704.9	18.07	1064.8	1082.9	0.0361	2.0891	2.1252
52	0.1918	0.3905	0.01603	1588.4	1588.4	20.07	1063.6	1083.7	0.0400	2.0786	2.1186
54	0.2063	0.4200	0.01603	1482.4	1482.4	22.07	1062.5	1084.6	0.0439	2.0684	2.1123
56	0.2219	0.4518	0.01603	1383.5	1383.5	24.07	1061.4	1085.5	0.0478	2.0582	2.1060
58	0.2384	0.4854	0.01603	1292.7	1292.7	26.07	1060.2	1086.3	0.0517	2.0479	2.0996
60	0.2561	0.5214	0.01603	1208.1	1208.1	28.07	1059.1	1087.2	0.0555	2.0379	2.0934
62	0.2749	0.5597	0.01604	1129.7	1129.7	30.06	1057.9	1088.0	0.0594	2.0278	2.0872
64	0.2949	0.6004	0.01604	1057.1	1057.1	32.06	1056.8	1088.9	0.0632	2.0180	2.0812
66	0.3162	0.6438	0.01604	989.6	989.6	34.06	1055.7	1089.8	0.0670	2.0082	2.0752
68	0.3388	0.6898	0.01605	927.0	927.0	36.05	1054.5	1090.6	0.0708	1.9983	2.0691
70	0.3628	0.7387	0.01605	868.9	868.9	38.05	1053.4	1091.5	0.0745	1.9887	2.0632
72	0.3883	0.7906	0.01606	814.9	814.9	40.04	1052.3	1092.3	0.0783	1.9792	2.0575
74	0.4153	0.8456	0.01606	764.7	764.7	42.04	1051.2	1093.2	0.0820	1.9697	2.0517
76	0.4440	0.9040	0.01607	718.0	718.0	44.03	1050.1	1094.1	0.0858	1.9603	2.0461
78	0.4744	0.9659	0.01607	674.4	674.4	46.03	1048.9	1094.9	0.0895	1.9508	2.0403
80	0.5067	1.032	0.01607	633.7	633.7	48.02	1047.8	1095.8	0.0932	1.9415	2.0347
82	0.5409	1.101	0.01608	595.8	595.8	50.02	1046.6	1096.6	0.0969	1.9321	2.0290
84	0.5772	1.175	0.01608	560.4	560.4	52.01	1045.5	1097.5	0.1006	1.9230	2.0236
86	0.6153	1.253	0.01609	527.6	527.6	54.01	1044.4	1098.4	0.1042	1.9139	2.0181
88	0.6555	1.335	0.01609	497.0	497.0	56.00	1043.2	1099.2	0.1079	1.9047	2.0126
90	0.6980	1.421	0.01610	468.4	468.4	58.00	1042.1	1100.1	0.1115	1.8958	2.0073

TABLE A-1. SATURATED STEAM† (*Continued*)

Temp t, °F	Absolute pressure p		Specific volume			Enthalpy			Entropy		
	Psia	In. Hg (32°F)	Sat. liquid v_f	Evap. v_{fg}	Sat. vapor v_g	Sat. liquid H_f	Evap. H_{fg}	Sat. vapor H_g	Sat. liquid S_f	Evap. S_{fg}	Sat. vapor S_g
92	0.7429	1.513	0.01611	441.7	441.7	59.99	1040.9	1100.9	0.1151	1.8867	2.0018
94	0.7902	1.609	0.01611	416.7	416.7	61.98	1039.8	1101.8	0.1187	1.8779	1.9966
96	0.8403	1.711	0.01612	393.2	393.2	63.98	1038.7	1102.7	0.1223	1.8692	1.9915
98	0.8930	1.818	0.01613	371.3	371.3	65.98	1037.5	1103.5	0.1259	1.8604	1.9863
100	0.9487	1.932	0.01613	350.8	350.8	67.97	1036.4	1104.4	0.1295	1.8517	1.9812
102	1.0072	2.051	0.01614	331.5	331.5	69.96	1035.2	1105.2	0.1330	1.8430	1.9760
104	1.0689	2.176	0.01614	313.5	313.5	71.96	1034.1	1106.1	0.1366	1.8345	1.9711
106	1.1338	2.308	0.01615	296.5	296.5	73.95	1033.0	1107.0	0.1401	1.8261	1.9662
108	1.2020	2.447	0.01616	280.7	280.7	75.94	1032.0	1107.9	0.1436	1.8179	1.9615
110	1.274	2.594	0.01617	265.7	265.7	77.94	1030.9	1108.8	0.1471	1.8096	1.9567
112	1.350	2.749	0.01617	251.6	251.6	79.93	1029.7	1109.6	0.1506	1.8012	1.9518
114	1.429	2.909	0.01618	238.5	238.5	81.93	1028.6	1110.5	0.1541	1.7930	1.9471
116	1.512	3.078	0.01619	226.2	226.2	83.92	1027.5	1111.4	0.1576	1.7848	1.9424
118	1.600	3.258	0.01620	214.5	214.5	85.92	1026.4	1112.3	0.1610	1.7767	1.9377
120	1.692	3.445	0.01620	203.45	203.47	87.91	1025.3	1113.2	0.1645	1.7687	1.9332
122	1.788	3.640	0.01621	193.16	193.18	89.91	1024.1	1114.0	0.1679	1.7606	1.9285
124	1.889	3.846	0.01622	183.44	183.46	91.90	1023.0	1114.9	0.1714	1.7526	1.9240
126	1.995	4.062	0.01623	174.26	174.28	93.90	1021.8	1115.7	0.1748	1.7446	1.9194
128	2.105	4.286	0.01624	165.70	165.72	95.90	1020.7	1116.6	0.1782	1.7368	1.9150
130	2.221	4.522	0.01625	157.55	157.57	97.89	1019.5	1117.4	0.1816	1.7289	1.9105

132	2.343	4.770	0.01626	149.83	149.85	99.89	1018.3	1118.2	0.1849	1.7210	1.9059
134	2.470	5.029	0.01626	142.59	142.61	101.89	1017.2	1119.1	0.1883	1.7134	1.9017
136	2.603	5.300	0.01627	135.73	135.75	103.88	1016.0	1119.9	0.1917	1.7056	1.8973
138	2.742	5.583	0.01628	129.26	129.28	105.88	1014.9	1120.8	0.1950	1.6980	1.8930
140	2.887	5.878	0.01629	123.16	123.18	107.88	1013.7	1121.6	0.1984	1.6904	1.8888
142	3.039	6.187	0.01630	117.37	117.39	109.88	1012.5	1122.4	0.2017	1.6828	1.8845
144	3.198	6.511	0.01631	111.88	111.90	111.88	1011.3	1123.2	0.2050	1.6752	1.8802
146	3.363	6.847	0.01632	106.72	106.74	113.88	1010.2	1124.1	0.2083	1.6678	1.8761
148	3.536	7.199	0.01633	101.82	101.84	115.87	1009.0	1124.9	0.2116	1.6604	1.8720
150	3.716	7.566	0.01634	97.18	97.20	117.87	1007.8	1125.7	0.2149	1.6530	1.8679
152	3.904	7.948	0.01635	92.79	92.81	119.87	1006.7	1126.6	0.2181	1.6458	1.8639
154	4.100	8.348	0.01636	88.62	88.64	121.87	1005.5	1127.4	0.2214	1.6384	1.8598
156	4.305	8.765	0.01637	84.66	84.68	123.87	1004.4	1128.3	0.2247	1.6313	1.8560
158	4.518	9.199	0.01638	80.90	80.92	125.87	1003.2	1129.1	0.2279	1.6241	1.8520
160	4.739	9.649	0.01639	77.37	77.39	127.87	1002.0	1129.9	0.2311	1.6169	1.8480
162	4.970	10.12	0.01640	74.00	74.02	129.88	1000.8	1130.7	0.2343	1.6098	1.8441
164	5.210	10.61	0.01642	70.79	70.81	131.88	999.7	1131.6	0.2376	1.6029	1.8405
166	5.460	11.12	0.01643	67.76	67.78	133.88	998.5	1132.4	0.2408	1.5958	1.8366
168	5.720	11.65	0.01644	64.87	64.89	135.88	997.3	1133.2	0.2439	1.5888	1.8327
170	5.990	12.20	0.01645	62.12	62.14	137.89	996.1	1134.0	0.2471	1.5819	1.8290
172	6.272	12.77	0.01646	59.50	59.52	139.89	995.0	1134.9	0.2503	1.5751	1.8254
174	6.565	13.37	0.01647	57.01	57.03	141.89	993.8	1135.7	0.2535	1.5683	1.8218
176	6.869	13.99	0.01648	54.64	54.66	143.90	992.6	1136.5	0.2566	1.5615	1.8181
178	7.184	14.63	0.01650	52.39	52.41	145.90	991.4	1137.3	0.2598	1.5547	1.8145
180	7.510	15.29	0.01651	50.26	50.28	147.91	990.2	1138.1	0.2629	1.5479	1.8108

TABLE A-1. SATURATED STEAM† (*Continued*)

Temp t, °F	Absolute pressure p		Specific volume			Enthalpy			Entropy		
	Psia	In. Hg (32°F)	Sat. liquid v_f	Evap. v_{fg}	Sat. vapor v_g	Sat. liquid H_f	Evap. H_{fg}	Sat. vapor H_g	Sat. liquid S_f	Evap. S_{fg}	Sat. vapor S_g
182	7.849	15.98	0.01652	48.22	48.24	149.92	989.0	1138.9	0.2661	1.5412	1.8073
184	8.201	16.70	0.01653	46.28	46.30	151.92	987.8	1139.7	0.2692	1.5346	1.8038
186	8.566	17.44	0.01654	44.43	44.45	153.93	986.6	1140.5	0.2723	1.5280	1.8003
188	8.944	18.21	0.01656	42.67	42.69	155.94	985.3	1141.3	0.2754	1.5213	1.7967
190	9.336	19.01	0.01657	40.99	41.01	157.95	984.1	1142.1	0.2785	1.5147	1.7932
192	9.744	19.84	0.01658	39.38	39.40	159.95	982.8	1142.8	0.2816	1.5081	1.7897
194	10.168	20.70	0.01659	37.84	37.86	161.96	981.5	1143.5	0.2847	1.5015	1.7862
196	10.605	21.59	0.01661	36.38	36.40	163.97	980.3	1144.3	0.2877	1.4951	1.7828
198	11.057	22.51	0.01662	34.98	35.00	165.98	979.0	1145.0	0.2908	1.4885	1.7793
200	11.525	23.46	0.01663	33.65	33.67	167.99	977.8	1145.8	0.2938	1.4822	1.7760
202	12.010	24.45	0.01665	32.37	32.39	170.01	976.6	1146.6	0.2969	1.4759	1.7728
204	12.512	25.47	0.01666	31.15	31.17	172.02	975.3	1147.3	0.2999	1.4695	1.7694
206	13.031	26.53	0.01667	29.99	30.01	174.03	974.1	1148.1	0.3029	1.4633	1.7662
208	13.568	27.62	0.01669	28.88	28.90	176.04	972.8	1148.8	0.3059	1.4570	1.7629
210	14.123	28.75	0.01670	27.81	27.83	178.06	971.5	1149.6	0.3090	1.4507	1.7597
212	14.696	29.92	0.01672	26.81	26.83	180.07	970.3	1150.4	0.3120	1.4446	1.7566
215	15.591	......	0.01674	25.35	25.37	183.10	968.3	1151.4	0.3165	1.4352	1.7517
220	17.188	......	0.01677	23.14	23.16	188.14	965.2	1153.3	0.3239	1.4201	1.7440
225	18.915	......	0.01681	21.15	21.17	193.18	961.9	1155.1	0.3313	1.4049	1.7362

230	20.78	...	0.01684	19.371	19.388	198.22	958.7	1156.9	0.3386	1.3900	1.7286
235	22.80	...	0.01688	17.761	17.778	203.28	955.3	1158.6	0.3459	1.3751	1.7210
240	24.97	...	0.01692	16.307	16.324	208.34	952.1	1160.4	0.3531	1.3607	1.7138
245	27.31	...	0.01696	15.010	15.027	213.41	948.7	1162.1	0.3604	1.3462	1.7066
250	29.82	...	0.01700	13.824	13.841	218.48	945.3	1163.8	0.3675	1.3320	1.6995
255	32.53	...	0.01704	12.735	12.752	223.56	942.0	1165.6	0.3747	1.3181	1.6928
260	35.43	...	0.01708	11.754	11.771	228.65	938.6	1167.3	0.3817	1.3042	1.6859
265	38.54	...	0.01713	10.861	10.878	233.74	935.3	1169.0	0.3888	1.2906	1.6794
270	41.85	...	0.01717	10.053	10.070	238.84	931.8	1170.6	0.3958	1.2770	1.6728
275	45.40	...	0.01721	9.313	9.330	243.94	928.2	1172.1	0.4027	1.2634	1.6661
280	49.20	...	0.01726	8.634	8.651	249.06	924.6	1173.7	0.4096	1.2500	1.6596
285	53.25	...	0.01731	8.015	8.032	254.18	921.0	1175.2	0.4165	1.2368	1.6533
290	57.55	...	0.01735	7.448	7.465	259.31	917.4	1176.7	0.4234	1.2237	1.6471
295	62.13	...	0.01740	6.931	6.948	264.45	913.7	1178.2	0.4302	1.2107	1.6409
300	67.01	...	0.01745	6.454	6.471	269.60	910.1	1179.7	0.4370	1.1980	1.6350
305	72.18	...	0.01750	6.014	6.032	274.76	906.3	1181.1	0.4437	1.1852	1.6289
310	77.68	...	0.01755	5.610	5.628	279.92	902.6	1182.5	0.4505	1.1727	1.6232
315	83.50	...	0.01760	5.239	5.257	285.10	898.8	1183.9	0.4571	1.1587	1.6158
320	89.65	...	0.01765	4.897	4.915	290.29	895.0	1185.3	0.4637	1.1479	1.6116
325	96.16	...	0.01771	4.583	4.601	295.49	891.1	1186.6	0.4703	1.1356	1.6059
330	103.03	...	0.01776	4.292	4.310	300.69	887.1	1187.8	0.4769	1.1234	1.6003
335	110.31	...	0.01782	4.021	4.039	305.91	883.2	1189.1	0.4835	1.1114	1.5949
340	117.99	...	0.01788	3.771	3.789	311.14	879.2	1190.3	0.4900	1.0994	1.5894
345	126.10	...	0.01793	3.539	3.557	316.38	875.1	1191.5	0.4966	1.0875	1.5841
350	134.62	...	0.01799	3.324	3.342	321.64	871.0	1192.6	0.5030	1.0757	1.5787

TABLE A-1. SATURATED STEAM† (Continued)

Temp t, °F	Absolute pressure p		Specific volume			Enthalpy			Entropy		
	Psia	In. Hg (32°F)	Sat. liquid v_f	Evap. v_{fg}	Sat. vapor v_g	Sat. liquid H_f	Evap. H_{fg}	Sat. vapor H_g	Sat. liquid S_f	Evap. S_{fg}	Sat. vapor S_g
355	143.58	......	0.01805	3.126	3.144	326.91	866.8	1193.7	0.5094	1.0640	1.5734
360	153.01	......	0.01811	2.940	2.958	332.19	862.5	1194.7	0.5159	1.0522	1.5681
365	162.93	......	0.01817	2.768	2.786	337.48	858.2	1195.7	0.5223	1.0406	1.5629
370	173.33	......	0.01823	2.607	2.625	342.79	853.8	1196.6	0.5286	1.0291	1.5577
375	184.23	......	0.01830	2.458	2.476	348.11	849.4	1197.5	0.5350	1.0176	1.5526
380	195.70	......	0.01836	2.318	2.336	353.45	844.9	1198.4	0.5413	1.0062	1.5475
385	207.71	......	0.01843	2.189	2.207	358.80	840.4	1199.2	0.5476	0.9949	1.5425
390	220.29	......	0.01850	2.064	2.083	364.17	835.7	1199.9	0.5540	0.9835	1.5375
395	233.47	......	0.01857	1.9512	1.9698	369.56	831.0	1200.6	0.5602	0.9723	1.5325
400	247.25	......	0.01864	1.8446	1.8632	374.97	826.2	1201.2	0.5664	0.9610	1.5274
405	261.67	......	0.01871	1.7445	1.7632	380.40	821.4	1201.8	0.5727	0.9499	1.5226
410	276.72	......	0.01878	1.6508	1.6696	385.83	816.6	1202.4	0.5789	0.9390	1.5179
415	292.44	......	0.01886	1.5630	1.5819	391.30	811.7	1203.0	0.5851	0.9280	1.5131
420	308.82	......	0.01894	1.4806	1.4995	396.78	806.7	1203.5	0.5912	0.9170	1.5082
425	325.91	......	0.01902	1.4031	1.4221	402.28	801.6	1203.9	0.5974	0.9061	1.5035
430	343.71	......	0.01910	1.3303	1.3494	407.80	796.5	1204.3	0.6036	0.8953	1.4989
435	362.27	......	0.01918	1.2617	1.2809	413.35	791.2	1204.6	0.6097	0.8843	1.4940
440	381.59	......	0.01926	1.1973	1.2166	418.91	785.9	1204.8	0.6159	0.8735	1.4894
445	401.70	......	0.01934	1.1367	1.1560	424.49	780.4	1204.9	0.6220	0.8626	1.4846
450	422.61	......	0.01943	1.0796	1.0990	430.11	774.9	1205.0	0.6281	0.8518	1.4799

455	444.35	. . . .	0.0195	1.0256	1.0451	435.74	769.3	1205.0	0.6342	0.8410	1.4752
460	466.97	. . . .	0.0196	0.9745	0.9941	441.42	763.6	1205.0	0.6403	0.8303	1.4706
465	490.43	. . . .	0.0197	0.9262	0.9459	447.10	757.8	1204.9	0.6463	0.8195	1.4658
470	514.70	. . . .	0.0198	0.8808	0.9006	452.84	751.9	1204.7	0.6524	0.8088	1.4612
475	539.90	. . . .	0.0199	0.8379	0.8578	458.59	745.9	1204.5	0.6585	0.7980	1.4565
480	566.12	. . . .	0.0200	0.7972	0.8172	464.37	739.8	1204.2	0.6646	0.7873	1.4519
485	593.28	. . . .	0.0201	0.7585	0.7786	470.18	733.6	1203.8	0.6706	0.7766	1.4472
490	621.44	. . . .	0.0202	0.7219	0.7421	476.01	727.3	1203.3	0.6767	0.7658	1.4425
495	650.59	. . . .	0.0203	0.6872	0.7075	481.90	720.8	1202.7	0.6827	0.7550	1.4377
500	680.80	. . . .	0.0204	0.6544	0.6748	487.80	714.2	1202.0	0.6888	0.7442	1.4330
505	712.19	. . . .	0.0206	0.6230	0.6436	493.8	707.5	1201.3	0.6949	0.7334	1.4283
510	744.55	. . . .	0.0207	0.5932	0.6139	499.8	700.6	1200.4	0.7009	0.7225	1.4234
515	777.96	. . . .	0.0208	0.5651	0.5859	505.8	693.6	1199.4	0.7070	0.7116	1.4186
520	812.68	. . . .	0.0209	0.5382	0.5591	511.9	686.5	1198.4	0.7132	0.7007	1.4139
525	848.37	. . . .	0.0210	0.5128	0.5338	518.0	679.2	1197.2	0.7192	0.6898	1.4090
530	885.20	. . . .	0.0212	0.4885	0.5097	524.2	671.9	1196.1	0.7253	0.6789	1.4042
535	923.45	. . . .	0.0213	0.4654	0.4867	530.4	664.4	1194.8	0.7314	0.6679	1.3993
540	962.80	. . . .	0.0214	0.4433	0.4647	536.6	656.7	1193.3	0.7375	0.6569	1.3944
545	1003.6	. . . .	0.0216	0.4222	0.4438	542.0	648.9	1191.8	0.7436	0.6459	1.3895
550	1045.6	. . . .	0.0218	0.4021	0.4239	549.3	640.9	1190.2	0.7498	0.6347	1.3845
555	1088.8	. . . .	0.0219	0.3830	0.4049	555.7	632.6	1188.3	0.7559	0.6234	1.3793
560	1133.4	. . . .	0.0221	0.3648	0.3869	562.2	624.1	1186.3	0.7622	0.6120	1.3742
565	1179.3	. . . .	0.0222	0.3472	0.3694	568.8	615.4	1184.2	0.7684	0.6006	1.3690
570	1226.7	. . . .	0.0224	0.3304	0.3528	575.4	606.5	1181.9	0.7737	0.5890	1.3627
575	1275.7	. . . .	0.0226	0.3143	0.3369	582.1	597.4	1179.5	0.7810	0.5774	1.3584

TABLE A-1. SATURATED STEAM† (Continued)

Temp t, °F	Absolute pressure p		Specific volume			Enthalpy			Entropy		
	Psia	In. Hg (32°F)	Sat. liquid v_f	Evap. v_{fg}	Sat. vapor v_g	Sat. liquid H_f	Evap. H_{fg}	Sat. vapor H_g	Sat. liquid S_f	Evap. S_{fg}	Sat. vapor S_g
580	1326.1	......	0.0228	0.2989	0.3217	588.9	588.1	1177.0	0.7872	0.5656	1.3528
585	1378.1	......	0.0230	0.2840	0.3070	595.7	578.6	1174.3	0.7936	0.5538	1.3474
590	1431.5	......	0.0232	0.2699	0.2931	602.6	568.8	1171.4	0.8000	0.5419	1.3419
595	1486.5	......	0.0234	0.2563	0.2797	609.7	558.7	1168.4	0.8065	0.5297	1.3362
600	1543.2	......	0.0236	0.2432	0.2668	616.8	548.4	1165.2	0.8130	0.5175	1.3305
605	1601.5	......	0.0239	0.2306	0.2545	624.1	537.7	1161.8	0.8196	0.5050	1.3246
610	1661.6	......	0.0241	0.2185	0.2426	631.5	526.6	1158.1	0.8263	0.4923	1.3186
615	1723.4	......	0.0244	0.2068	0.2312	638.9	515.3	1154.2	0.8330	0.4795	1.3125
620	1787.0	......	0.0247	0.1955	0.2202	646.5	503.7	1150.2	0.8398	0.4665	1.3063
625	1852.4	......	0.0250	0.1845	0.2095	654.3	491.5	1145.8	0.8467	0.4531	1.2998
630	1919.8	......	0.0253	0.1740	0.1993	662.2	478.8	1141.0	0.8537	0.4394	1.2931
635	1989.0	......	0.0256	0.1638	0.1894	670.4	465.5	1135.9	0.8609	0.4252	1.2861
640	2060.3	......	0.0260	0.1539	0.1799	678.7	452.0	1130.7	0.8681	0.4110	1.2791
645	2133.5	......	0.0264	0.1441	0.1705	687.3	437.6	1124.9	0.8756	0.3961	1.2717
650	2208.8	......	0.0268	0.1348	0.1616	696.0	422.7	1118.7	0.8832	0.3809	1.2641
655	2286.4	......	0.0273	0.1256	0.1529	705.2	407.0	1112.2	0.8910	0.3651	1.2561
660	2366.2	......	0.0278	0.1167	0.1445	714.4	390.5	1104.9	0.8991	0.3488	1.2479
665	2448.0	......	0.0283	0.1079	0.1362	724.5	372.1	1096.6	0.9074	0.3308	1.2382
670	2532.4	......	0.0290	0.0991	0.1281	734.6	353.3	1087.9	0.9161	0.3127	1.2288
675	2619.2	......	0.0297	0.0904	0.1201	745.5	332.8	1078.3	0.9253	0.2933	1.2186

680	....	2708.4	0.0305	0.0810	0.1115	757.2	310.0	1067.2	0.9352	0.2720	1.2072
685	....	2800.4	0.0316	0.0716	0.1032	770.1	284.5	1054.6	0.9459	0.2485	1.1944
690	....	2895.0	0.0328	0.0617	0.0945	784.2	254.9	1039.1	0.9579	0.2217	1.1796
695	....	2992.7	0.0345	0.0511	0.0856	801.3	219.1	1020.4	0.9720	0.1897	1.1617
700	....	3094.1	0.0369	0.0389	0.0758	823.9	171.7	995.6	0.9904	0.1481	1.1385
705	....	3199.1	0.0440	0.0157	0.0597	870.2	77.6	947.8	1.0305	0.0661	1.0966
705.34‡	....	3206.2	0.0541	0	0.0541	910.3	0	910.3	1.0645	0	1.0645

† Reproduced by permission from "Steam Tables: Properties of Saturated and Superheated Steam," copyright 1940, Combustion Engineering, Inc.

‡ Critical temperature.

TABLE A-2. SUPERHEATED STEAM†

Abs. press., psia (sat. temp.)		Sat. water	Sat. steam	\multicolumn{14}{Temperature, °F}													
				200	250	300	350	400	450	500	600	700	800	900	1000	1100	1200
1 (101.76)	v	0.0161	333.79	392.5	422.5	452.1	482.1	511.7	541.8	571.3	630.9	690.6	750.2	809.8	869.4	929.1	988.7
	H	69.72	1105.2	1149.2	1171.9	1194.4	1217.3	1240.2	1263.5	1286.7	1333.9	1382.1	1431.0	1480.8	1531.4	1583.0	1635.4
	S	0.1326	1.9769	2.0491	2.0822	2.1128	2.1420	2.1694	2.1957	2.2206	2.2673	2.3107	2.3512	2.3892	2.4251	2.4592	2.4918
5 (162.25)	v	0.0164	73.600	78.17	84.24	90.21	96.26	102.19	108.23	114.16	126.11	138.05	149.99	161.91	173.83	185.80	197.72
	H	130.13	1130.8	1148.3	1171.1	1193.6	1216.6	1239.8	1263.0	1286.1	1333.5	1381.8	1430.8	1480.6	1531.3	1582.9	1635.3
	S	0.2347	1.8437	1.8710	1.9043	1.9349	1.9642	1.9920	2.0182	2.0429	2.0898	2.1333	2.1738	2.2118	2.2478	2.2820	2.3146
10 (193.21)	v	0.0166	38.462	38.88	41.96	44.98	48.02	51.01	54.04	57.02	63.01	68.99	74.96	80.92	86.89	92.88	98.85
	H	161.17	1143.3	1146.7	1170.2	1192.8	1216.0	1239.3	1262.5	1285.8	1333.3	1381.6	1430.6	1480.5	1531.2	1582.8	1635.2
	S	0.2834	1.7876	1.7928	1.8271	1.8579	1.8875	1.9154	1.9416	1.9665	2.0135	2.0570	2.0975	2.1356	2.1716	2.2058	2.2384
14.696 (212.00)	v	0.0167	26.828		28.44	30.52	32.61	34.65	36.73	38.75	42.83	46.91	50.97	55.03	59.09	63.19	67.25
	H	180.07	1150.4		1169.2	1192.0	1215.4	1238.9	1262.1	1285.4	1333.0	1381.4	1430.5	1480.4	1531.1	1582.7	1635.1
	S	0.3120	1.7566		1.7838	1.8148	1.8446	1.8727	1.8989	1.9238	1.9709	2.0145	2.0551	2.0932	2.1292	2.1634	2.1960
15 (213.03)	v	0.0167	26.320		27.86	29.90	31.94	33.95	35.98	37.97	41.98	45.97	49.95	53.93	57.91	61.91	65.89
	H	181.11	1150.7		1169.2	1192.0	1215.4	1238.9	1262.1	1285.4	1333.0	1381.4	1430.5	1480.4	1531.1	1582.7	1635.1
	S	0.3135	1.7548		1.7816	1.8126	1.8424	1.8705	1.8967	1.9216	1.9687	2.0123	2.0529	2.0910	2.1270	2.1612	2.1938
20 (227.96)	v	0.0168	20.110		20.81	22.36	23.91	25.43	26.95	28.45	31.46	34.46	37.44	40.43	43.42	46.43	49.41
	H	196.16	1156.1		1168.0	1191.1	1214.8	1238.4	1261.6	1285.0	1332.7	1381.2	1430.3	1480.2	1531.0	1582.6	1635.1
	S	0.3356	1.7315		1.7485	1.7799	1.8101	1.8384	1.8646	1.8896	1.9368	1.9805	2.0211	2.0592	2.0952	2.1294	2.1620
25 (240.07)	v	0.0169	16.321		16.58	17.84	19.08	20.30	21.53	22.73	25.15	27.55	29.94	32.33	34.73	37.14	39.52
	H	208.41	1160.4		1166.3	1190.2	1214.1	1237.9	1261.1	1284.6	1332.4	1381.0	1430.1	1480.0	1530.9	1582.5	1635.0
	S	0.3532	1.7137		1.7221	1.7570	1.7875	1.8160	1.8422	1.8673	1.9146	1.9584	1.9990	2.0371	2.0732	2.1074	2.1400
30 (250.34)	v	0.0170	13.763			14.82	15.87	16.89	17.91	18.92	20.94	22.94	24.94	26.93	28.93	30.94	32.93
	H	218.83	1164.0			1189.2	1213.4	1237.4	1260.6	1284.2	1332.1	1380.8	1429.9	1479.9	1530.8	1582.4	1634.9
	S	0.3680	(1.6992)			1.7335	1.7643	1.7930	1.8192	1.8444	1.8918	1.9357	1.9763	2.0145	2.0506	2.0848	2.1174

35 (259.28)	v	0.0171		11.907	12.66	13.57	14.45	15.33	16.20	17.94	19.66	21.36	23.08	24.79	26.52	28.22
	H	227.92		1167.0	1188.2	1212.7	1236.9	1260.1	1283.8	1331.9	1380.6	1429.8	1479.8	1530.7	1582.3	1634.8
	S	0.3807		1.6869	1.7156	1.7468	1.7758	1.8020	1.8274	1.8750	1.9189	1.9596	1.9978	2.0339	2.0681	2.1007
40 (267.24)	v	0.0172		10.506	11.04	11.84	12.62	13.40	14.16	15.68	17.19	18.69	20.18	21.68	23.20	24.69
	H	236.02		1169.7	1187.1	1211.9	1236.4	1259.6	1283.4	1331.6	1380.4	1429.6	1479.6	1530.6	1582.2	1634.8
	S	0.3919		1.6763	1.6997	1.7313	1.7606	1.7868	1.8123	1.8600	1.9040	1.9447	1.9829	2.0191	2.0533	2.0860
45 (274.45)	v	0.0172		9.408	9.785	10.50	11.20	11.89	12.57	13.93	15.27	16.60	17.94	19.27	20.62	21.95
	H	243.38		1172.0	1185.9	1211.1	1235.8	1259.1	1283.0	1331.3	1380.1	1429.4	1479.4	1530.5	1582.1	1634.7
	S	0.4019		1.6668	1.6854	1.7175	1.7471	1.7734	1.7990	1.8468	1.8908	1.9315	1.9697	2.0059	2.0401	2.0728
50 (281.01)	v	0.0173		8.522	8.777	9.430	10.06	10.69	11.30	12.53	13.74	14.93	16.14	17.34	18.55	19.75
	H	250.09		1174.0	1184.6	1210.3	1235.2	1258.6	1282.6	1331.0	1379.9	1429.3	1479.3	1530.4	1582.0	1634.6
	S	0.4110		1.6583	1.6724	1.7051	1.7349	1.7613	1.7870	1.8349	1.8790	1.9198	1.9580	1.9942	2.0284	2.0611
55 (287.07)	v	0.0173		7.792	7.950	8.553	9.130	9.703	10.26	11.38	12.48	13.57	14.67	15.76	16.86	17.95
	H	256.30		1175.8	1183.2	1209.4	1234.6	1258.2	1282.2	1330.7	1379.7	1429.1	1479.2	1530.3	1581.9	1634.5
	S	0.4193		1.6506	1.6604	1.6938	1.7240	1.7507	1.7764	1.8244	1.8685	1.9093	1.9475	1.9837	2.0179	2.0512
60 (292.71)	v	0.0174		7.179	7.260	7.821	8.353	8.882	9.398	10.42	11.44	12.44	13.44	14.44	15.45	16.45
	H	262.10		1177.5	1181.8	1208.5	1234.0	1257.7	1281.8	1330.4	1379.5	1428.9	1479.0	1530.2	1581.8	1634.4
	S	0.4271		1.6437	1.6494	1.6834	1.7139	1.7407	1.7665	1.8146	1.8588	1.8996	1.9378	1.9741	2.0083	2.0410
65 (297.97)	v	0.0174		6.654	6.674	7.202	7.696	8.187	8.665	9.614	10.55	11.48	12.40	13.33	14.26	15.19
	H	267.51		1179.1	1180.7	1207.6	1233.4	1257.2	1281.4	1330.1	1379.3	1428.8	1478.9	1530.1	1581.7	1634.4
	S	0.4342		1.6374	1.6391	1.6738	1.7047	1.7316	1.7575	1.8057	1.8500	1.8909	1.9291	1.9654	1.9996	2.0323
70 (302.92)	v	0.0175		6.210		6.671	7.132	7.592	8.036	8.920	9.791	10.65	11.51	12.37	13.24	14.10
	H	272.61		1180.5		1206.7	1232.8	1256.7	1281.0	1329.9	1379.0	1428.6	1478.7	1530.0	1581.6	1634.3
	S	0.4409		1.6314		1.6647	1.6960	1.7230	1.7490	1.7974	1.8416	1.8826	1.9208	1.9572	1.9914	2.0241
75 (307.60)	v	0.0175		5.820		6.210	6.644	7.076	7.492	8.319	9.133	9.938	10.74	11.54	12.36	13.16
	H	277.44		1181.9		1205.8	1232.2	1256.2	1280.6	1329.6	1378.8	1428.4	1478.6	1529.8	1581.5	1634.2
	S	0.4472		1.6260		1.6563	1.6879	1.7150	1.7411	1.7896	1.8339	1.8749	1.9132	1.9495	1.9837	2.0164

TABLE A-2. SUPERHEATED STEAM† (Continued)

Abs. press., psia (sat. temp.)		Sat. water	Sat. steam	340	360	380	400	420	450	500	600	700	800	900	1000	1100	1200
80 (312.03)	v	0.0176	5.476	5.720	5.889	6.055	6.217	6.384	6.623	7.015	7.793	8.558	9.313	10.07	10.82	11.58	12.33
	H	282.02	1183.1	1200.0	1211.0	1221.2	1231.5	1240.3	1255.7	1280.2	1329.3	1378.5	1428.2	1478.4	1529.7	1581.4	1634.1
	S	0.4532	1.6209	1.6424	1.6560	1.6683	1.6804	1.6905	1.7077	1.7339	1.7825	1.8268	1.8679	1.9062	1.9426	1.9768	2.0095
85 (316.25)	v	0.0176	5.169	5.368	5.528	5.685	5.839	5.995	6.226	6.594	7.329	8.050	8.762	9.472	10.18	10.90	11.61
	H	286.40	1184.3	1198.5	1210.0	1220.5	1230.7	1239.7	1255.1	1279.7	1329.0	1378.3	1428.0	1478.2	1529.6	1581.3	1634.0
	S	0.4587	1.6159	1.6339	1.6481	1.6608	1.6728	1.6831	1.7003	1.7266	1.7754	1.8198	1.8609	1.8992	1.9357	1.9699	2.0026
90 (320.27)	v	0.0177	4.898	5.055	5.208	5.357	5.504	5.653	5.869	6.220	6.916	7.599	8.272	8.943	9.626	10.29	10.96
	H	290.57	1185.4	1197.3	1209.0	1219.8	1230.0	1239.1	1254.5	1279.3	1328.7	1378.1	1427.9	1478.1	1529.5	1581.2	1634.0
	S	0.4641	1.6113	1.6264	1.6408	1.6538	1.6658	1.6763	1.6935	1.7200	1.7689	1.8134	1.8546	1.8929	1.9294	1.9636	1.9964
95 (324.13)	v	0.0177	4.653	4.773	4.921	5.063	5.205	5.346	5.552	5.886	6.547	7.195	7.834	8.481	9.117	9.751	10.38
	H	294.58	1186.4	1196.0	1208.0	1219.0	1229.3	1238.6	1254.0	1278.9	1328.4	1377.8	1427.7	1478.0	1529.4	1581.1	1633.9
	S	0.4692	1.6070	1.6191	1.6339	1.6472	1.6593	1.6700	1.6872	1.7138	1.7628	1.8073	1.8485	1.8869	1.9234	1.9576	1.9904
100 (327.83)	v	0.0177	4.433	4.520	4.663	4.801	4.936	5.070	5.266	5.589	6.217	6.836	7.448	8.055	8.659	9.262	9.862
	H	298.43	1187.3	1194.9	1207.0	1218.3	1228.4	1238.6	1253.7	1278.6	1327.9	1377.5	1427.5	1478.0	1529.2	1581.0	1633.7
	S	0.4741	1.6028	1.6124	1.6273	1.6409	1.6528	1.6645	1.6814	1.7080	1.7568	1.8015	1.8428	1.8814	1.9177	1.9520	1.9847
105 (331.38)	v	0.0178	4.232	4.292	4.429	4.562	4.691	4.820	5.007	5.316	5.916	6.507	7.090	7.670	8.245	8.819	9.391
	H	302.13	1188.2	1193.5	1205.9	1217.2	1227.6	1237.5	1252.9	1278.0	1327.6	1377.4	1427.3	1477.7	1529.2	1580.9	1633.7
	S	0.4787	1.5988	1.6055	1.6208	1.6344	1.6466	1.6580	1.6752	1.7020	1.7511	1.7960	1.8372	1.8757	1.9122	1.9464	1.9791
110 (334.79)	v	0.0178	4.050	4.084	4.217	4.345	4.469	4.592	4.773	5.069	5.643	6.208	6.765	7.319	7.869	8.417	8.963
	H	305.69	1189.0	1192.2	1204.9	1216.4	1226.9	1236.9	1252.4	1277.5	1327.4	1377.1	1427.1	1477.5	1529.1	1580.8	1633.6
	S	0.4832	1.5950	1.5990	1.6147	1.6286	1.6410	1.6525	1.6698	1.6966	1.7460	1.7908	1.8321	1.8706	1.9072	1.9414	1.9742
115 (338.08)	v	0.0179	3.882	.....	4.022	4.146	4.266	4.384	4.558	4.843	5.393	5.935	6.469	6.999	7.525	8.049	8.572
	H	309.13	1189.8	.....	1203.8	1215.6	1226.2	1236.3	1251.9	1277.1	1327.1	1376.9	1427.0	1477.4	1528.9	1580.7	1633.6
	S	0.4875	1.5915	.....	1.6088	1.6230	1.6355	1.6471	1.6645	1.6915	1.7410	1.7859	1.8273	1.8658	1.9023	1.9366	1.9695

(p) t (t_sat)		Sat.															
120 (341.26)	»	0.0179	3.728		3.845	3.963	4.079	4.194	4.361	4.635	5.165	5.685	6.197	6.705	7.210	7.713	8.215
	H	312.46	1190.6		1202.7	1214.7	1225.4	1235.7	1251.4	1276.7	1326.8	1376.7	1426.8	1477.2	1528.8	1580.6	1633.5
	S	0.4916	1.5879		1.6028	1.6173	1.6299	1.6417	1.6592	1.6863	1.7359	1.7809	1.8223	1.8608	1.8974	1.9317	1.9646
125 (344.34)	»	0.0179	3.586		3.680	3.796	3.908	4.019	4.181	4.445	4.954	5.454	5.947	6.435	6.920	7.403	7.885
	H	315.69	1191.3		1201.6	1213.7	1224.5	1235.0	1250.8	1276.3	1326.5	1376.4	1426.6	1477.1	1528.7	1580.5	1633.4
	S	0.4956	1.5846		1.5973	1.6119	1.6246	1.6367	1.6544	1.6817	1.7314	1.7764	1.8179	1.8565	1.8931	1.9274	1.9603
130 (347.31)	»	0.0180	3.455		3.528	3.641	3.750	3.857	4.013	4.268	4.760	5.242	5.716	6.186	6.653	7.117	7.581
	H	318.81	1192.0		1200.4	1212.7	1223.6	1234.3	1250.3	1275.8	1326.1	1376.1	1426.4	1476.9	1528.6	1580.4	1633.3
	S	0.4995	1.5815		1.5918	1.6066	1.6194	1.6317	1.6496	1.6769	1.7267	1.7718	1.8134	1.8520	1.8887	1.9230	1.9559
135 (350.21)	»	0.0180	3.333		3.388	3.497	3.603	3.707	3.859	4.105	4.580	5.045	5.502	5.955	6.405	6.853	7.303
	H	321.86	1192.7		1199.2	1211.7	1222.7	1233.6	1249.7	1275.4	1325.8	1375.9	1426.2	1476.8	1528.5	1580.3	1633.2
	S	0.5032	1.5784		1.5864	1.6015	1.6144	1.6269	1.6449	1.6724	1.7223	1.7674	1.8090	1.8476	1.8843	1.9186	1.9515
140 (353.03)	»	0.0180	3.220		3.258	3.364	3.467	3.567	3.715	3.954	4.413	4.862	5.303	5.741	6.175	6.607	7.037
	H	324.83	1193.3		1198.0	1210.6	1221.8	1232.8	1249.1	1275.0	1325.5	1375.7	1426.0	1476.6	1528.4	1580.2	1633.2
	S	0.5069	1.5755		1.5813	1.5965	1.6097	1.6225	1.6406	1.6683	1.7183	1.7635	1.8051	1.8437	1.8804	1.9147	1.9476
145 (355.76)	»	0.0181	3.114		3.136	3.240	3.340	3.438	3.581	3.812	4.257	4.692	5.119	5.541	5.961	6.378	6.794
	H	327.71	1193.9		1196.7	1209.5	1220.9	1232.2	1248.5	1274.5	1325.1	1375.4	1425.8	1476.5	1528.3	1580.1	1633.1
	S	0.5104	1.5726		1.5760	1.5914	1.6048	1.6178	1.6360	1.6638	1.7139	1.7592	1.8009	1.8396	1.8763	1.9106	1.9435
150 (358.43)	»	0.0181	3.016			3.124	3.221	3.317	3.456	3.681	4.112	4.533	4.946	5.355	5.761	6.164	6.567
	H	330.53	1194.4			1208.4	1220.0	1231.4	1248.0	1274.1	1324.9	1375.1	1425.6	1476.3	1528.1	1580.0	1633.0
	S	0.5138	1.5698			1.5865	1.6002	1.6133	1.6319	1.6598	1.7101	1.7553	1.7970	1.8357	1.8724	1.9068	1.9397
155 (361.02)	»	0.0181	2.921			3.015	3.110	3.203	3.340	3.558	3.976	4.384	4.785	5.181	5.574	5.964	6.354
	H	333.27	1195.0			1207.2	1219.1	1230.7	1247.5	1273.6	1324.5	1374.9	1425.4	1476.2	1528.0	1579.9	1632.9
	S	0.5172	1.5671			1.5818	1.5958	1.6091	1.6279	1.6558	1.7062	1.7516	1.7933	1.8321	1.8688	1.9032	1.9361
160 (363.55)	»	0.0182	2.834			2.913	3.006	3.097	3.230	3.443	3.849	4.245	4.633	5.018	5.398	5.777	6.155
	H	335.95	1195.5			1206.0	1218.3	1230.0	1246.9	1273.2	1324.1	1374.7	1425.2	1476.0	1527.9	1579.8	1632.8
	S	0.5204	1.5646			1.5772	1.5917	1.6052	1.6241	1.6522	1.7026	1.7482	1.7899	1.8287	1.8655	1.8999	1.9328

TABLE A-2. SUPERHEATED STEAM† (Continued)

Temperature, °F

Abs. press., psia (sat. temp.)		Sat. water	Sat. steam	400	420	440	460	480	500	550	600	700	800	900	1000	1100	1200
165 (366.01)	v	0.0182	2.752	2.909	2.997	3.084	3.170	3.251	3.334	3.533	3.729	4.114	4.491	4.864	5.234	5.601	5.967
	H	338.55	1195.9	1217.4	1229.3	1241.1	1251.8	1262.4	1272.8	1298.5	1323.8	1374.5	1425.0	1475.9	1527.8	1579.7	1632.7
	S	0.5236	1.5619	1.5874	1.6011	1.6144	1.6262	1.6376	1.6486	1.6747	1.6991	1.7448	1.7865	1.8254	1.8622	1.8966	1.9295
170 (368.42)	v	0.0182	2.674	2.816	2.903	2.988	3.071	3.151	3.232	3.426	3.617	3.991	4.357	4.720	5.079	5.436	5.791
	H	341.11	1196.3	1216.5	1228.4	1240.5	1251.3	1261.8	1272.3	1298.2	1323.5	1374.2	1424.9	1475.7	1527.6	1579.6	1632.7
	S	0.5266	1.5593	1.5832	1.5969	1.6105	1.6224	1.6337	1.6448	1.6711	1.6955	1.7412	1.7831	1.8219	1.8587	1.8931	1.9261
175 (370.77)	v	0.0182	2.601	2.730	2.814	2.897	2.979	3.057	3.136	3.325	3.510	3.875	4.231	4.584	4.932	5.279	5.625
	H	343.61	1196.7	1215.6	1227.6	1239.9	1250.8	1261.3	1271.9	1297.8	1323.2	1374.0	1424.7	1475.6	1527.5	1579.5	1632.6
	S	0.5296	1.5569	1.5793	1.5931	1.6069	1.6189	1.6302	1.6414	1.6677	1.6922	1.7380	1.7799	1.8185	1.8553	1.8897	1.9227
180 (373.08)	v	0.0183	2.532	2.648	2.731	2.812	2.892	2.968	3.045	3.229	3.410	3.765	4.112	4.455	4.794	5.132	5.468
	H	346.07	1197.2	1214.6	1226.8	1239.2	1250.2	1260.8	1271.5	1297.4	1322.8	1373.7	1424.5	1475.5	1527.4	1579.4	1632.5
	S	0.5325	1.5545	1.5751	1.5891	1.6030	1.6151	1.6265	1.6378	1.6641	1.6886	1.7345	1.7765	1.8154	1.8522	1.8866	1.9196
185 (375.34)	v	0.0183	2.466	2.570	2.651	2.731	2.809	2.884	2.958	3.139	3.315	3.661	3.999	4.333	4.664	4.992	5.319
	H	348.47	1197.6	1213.7	1226.0	1238.4	1249.6	1260.3	1271.0	1297.1	1322.4	1373.4	1424.3	1475.3	1527.3	1579.3	1632.4
	S	0.5354	1.5522	1.5712	1.5853	1.5992	1.6115	1.6230	1.6343	1.6611	1.6853	1.7312	1.7733	1.8122	1.8491	1.8835	1.9165
190 (377.55)	v	0.0183	2.404	2.496	2.576	2.654	2.731	2.804	2.877	3.053	3.225	3.563	3.893	4.218	4.540	4.860	5.179
	H	350.83	1198.0	1212.7	1225.1	1237.7	1249.0	1259.8	1270.5	1296.6	1322.1	1373.1	1424.1	1475.2	1527.1	1579.2	1632.3
	S	0.5382	1.5501	1.5674	1.5817	1.5959	1.6083	1.6199	1.6312	1.6577	1.6823	1.7282	1.7703	1.8093	1.8461	1.8806	1.9136
195 (379.70)	v	0.0184	2.344	2.426	2.505	2.581	2.656	2.728	2.799	2.972	3.140	3.470	3.791	4.109	4.423	4.735	5.046
	H	353.13	1198.4	1211.7	1224.2	1237.0	1248.3	1259.3	1270.0	1296.2	1321.8	1372.9	1423.9	1475.0	1527.0	1579.1	1632.2
	S	0.5409	1.5479	1.5636	1.5780	1.5924	1.6048	1.6166	1.6279	1.6545	1.6792	1.7252	1.7673	1.8063	1.8432	1.8777	1.9107
200 (381.82)	v	0.0184	2.288	2.360	2.437	2.512	2.585	2.656	2.726	2.895	3.059	3.381	3.697	4.005	4.311	4.616	4.919
	H	355.40	1198.7	1210.8	1223.7	1236.3	1247.9	1258.7	1269.4	1295.6	1321.4	1372.5	1423.9	1474.9	1526.6	1579.0	1632.1
	S	0.5436	1.5457	1.5599	1.5748	1.5889	1.6017	1.6133	1.6245	1.6511	1.6761	1.7221	1.7646	1.8035	1.8402	1.8749	1.9079

	1	2	3	4	5	6	7	8	9	10	11	12	13	14	15	16
205 (383.89) v	0.0184	2.235	2.297	2.372	2.446	2.518	2.587	2.656	2.821	2.982	3.297	3.604	3.906	4.205	4.502	4.798
H	357.61	1199.0	1209.7	1222.5	1235.4	1247.1	1258.2	1269.0	1295.4	1321.0	1372.4	1423.5	1474.7	1526.8	1578.9	1632.1
S	0.5462	1.5436	1.5562	1.5709	1.5854	1.5983	1.6102	1.6216	1.6484	1.6731	1.7194	1.7616	1.8007	1.8377	1.8722	1.9052
210 (385.93) v	0.0184	2.183	2.237	2.311	2.384	2.454	2.522	2.589	2.751	2.909	3.216	3.516	3.812	4.104	4.395	4.683
H	359.80	1199.4	1208.8	1221.8	1234.7	1246.5	1257.7	1268.5	1295.0	1320.7	1372.1	1423.3	1474.6	1526.6	1578.8	1632.0
S	0.5488	1.5417	1.5527	1.5676	1.5821	1.5951	1.6071	1.6185	1.6454	1.6702	1.7165	1.7588	1.7980	1.8349	1.8695	1.9025
215 (387.93) v	0.0185	2.134	2.179	2.252	2.324	2.393	2.460	2.526	2.685	2.839	3.140	3.433	3.722	4.008	4.292	4.574
H	361.95	1199.6	1207.8	1221.0	1234.0	1245.9	1257.2	1268.0	1294.6	1320.4	1371.9	1423.1	1474.4	1526.5	1578.7	1631.9
S	0.5513	1.5395	1.5491	1.5643	1.5789	1.5920	1.6042	1.6156	1.6426	1.6675	1.7139	1.7562	1.7954	1.8324	1.8670	1.9000
220 (389.89) v	0.0185	2.086	2.124	2.196	2.267	2.335	2.400	2.465	2.621	2.772	3.067	3.354	3.637	3.916	4.193	4.469
H	364.05	1199.9	1206.8	1220.1	1233.2	1245.2	1256.7	1267.5	1294.1	1320.0	1371.6	1422.9	1474.2	1526.4	1578.6	1631.8
S	0.5538	1.5376	1.5457	1.5610	1.5757	1.5889	1.6013	1.6127	1.6397	1.6647	1.7112	1.7536	1.7928	1.8298	1.8644	1.8974
225 (391.81) v	0.0185	2.042	2.072	2.142	2.212	2.279	2.344	2.407	2.560	2.708	2.997	3.278	3.555	3.828	4.100	4.369
H	366.11	1200.2	1205.8	1219.2	1232.3	1244.5	1256.2	1267.1	1293.7	1319.6	1371.4	1422.7	1474.1	1526.3	1578.5	1631.7
S	0.5562	1.5358	1.5423	1.5577	1.5724	1.5858	1.5984	1.6099	1.6369	1.6619	1.7086	1.7510	1.7902	1.8272	1.8618	1.8948
233 (393.70) v	0.0186	1.9989	2.021	2.091	2.160	2.226	2.289	2.352	2.502	2.647	2.930	3.205	3.477	3.744	4.010	4.274
H	368.16	1200.4	1204.9	1218.3	1231.6	1243.8	1255.6	1266.7	1293.3	1319.3	1371.1	1422.5	1474.0	1526.2	1578.4	1631.6
S	0.5585	1.5337	1.5390	1.5544	1.5693	1.5827	1.5954	1.6071	1.6341	1.6592	1.7059	1.7484	1.7877	1.8247	1.8593	1.8923
235 (395.56) v	0.0186	1.9573	1.973	2.042	2.110	2.175	2.237	2.298	2.446	2.589	2.866	3.136	3.402	3.664	3.924	4.182
H	370.17	1200.7	1203.9	1217.5	1230.8	1243.2	1255.0	1266.2	1292.9	1319.0	1370.9	1422.3	1473.8	1526.0	1578.3	1631.6
S	0.5609	1.5320	1.5357	1.5513	1.5662	1.5798	1.5925	1.6043	1.6314	1.6566	1.7034	1.7459	1.7852	1.8222	1.8568	1.8899
240 (397.40) v	0.0186	1.9176	......	1.995	2.062	2.126	2.187	2.247	2.392	2.532	2.805	3.069	3.330	3.586	3.841	4.095
H	372.16	1200.9	......	1216.6	1230.0	1242.5	1254.4	1265.7	1292.5	1318.6	1370.5	1422.1	1473.6	1525.9	1578.2	1631.5
S	0.5632	1.5301	......	1.5482	1.5633	1.5770	1.5898	1.6017	1.6289	1.6541	1.7009	1.7435	1.7828	1.8199	1.8545	1.8876
245 (399.20) v	0.0186	1.8797	......	1.950	2.015	2.078	2.139	2.198	2.341	2.479	2.746	3.006	3.261	3.513	3.762	4.011
H	374.11	1201.1	......	1215.6	1229.1	1241.8	1253.8	1265.2	1292.0	1318.3	1370.3	1421.9	1473.5	1525.8	1578.1	1631.4
S	0.5654	1.5283	......	1.5450	1.5602	1.5742	1.5871	1.5991	1.6263	1.6517	1.6985	1.7411	1.7805	1.8176	1.8522	1.8853

461

Temperature, °F

Abs. press., psia (sat. temp.)		Sat. water	Sat. steam	420	440	460	480	500	520	550	600	700	800	900	1000	1100	1200
250 (400.97)	v	0.0187	1.8431	1.9065	1.9711	2.0334	2.0932	2.1515	2.2085	2.2920	2.4272	2.6897	2.9444	3.1949	3.4416	3.6867	3.9299
	H	376.04	1201.4	1214.6	1228.3	1241.0	1253.2	1264.7	1274.5	1291.6	1317.9	1370.0	1421.7	1473.3	1525.6	1578.0	1631.3
	S	0.5677	1.5267	1.5419	1.5573	1.5713	1.5844	1.5965	1.6066	1.6238	1.6492	1.6961	1.7388	1.7782	1.8153	1.8500	1.8831
255 (402.71)	v	0.0187	1.8079	1.8686	1.9286	1.9899	2.0489	2.1065	2.1626	2.2447	2.3776	2.6354	2.8855	3.1313	3.3733	3.6138	3.8524
	H	377.91	1201.6	1213.7	1227.5	1240.3	1252.6	1264.2	1274.2	1291.2	1317.5	1369.8	1421.5	1473.2	1525.5	1577.9	1631.2
	S	0.5698	1.5249	1.5388	1.5543	1.5684	1.5816	1.5938	1.6041	1.6212	1.6466	1.6937	1.7364	1.7759	1.8130	1.8477	1.8808
260 (404.43)	v	0.0187	1.7742	1.8246	1.8876	1.9482	2.0063	2.0631	2.1185	2.1991	2.3299	2.5833	2.8289	3.0701	3.3077	3.5437	3.7778
	H	379.78	1201.8	1212.8	1226.6	1239.5	1252.0	1263.6	1273.8	1290.8	1317.1	1369.5	1421.3	1473.0	1525.4	1577.8	1631.1
	S	0.5720	1.5233	1.5359	1.5514	1.5656	1.5790	1.5912	1.6017	1.6188	1.6442	1.6914	1.7342	1.7737	1.8109	1.8456	1.8787
265 (406.12)	v	0.0187	1.7416	1.7858	1.8481	1.9080	1.9654	2.0213	2.0759	2.1554	2.2840	2.5331	2.7744	3.0114	3.2446	3.4761	3.7061
	H	381.62	1202.0	1211.9	1225.7	1238.7	1251.2	1263.0	1273.4	1290.4	1316.8	1369.3	1421.1	1472.9	1525.3	1577.7	1631.1
	S	0.5741	1.5217	1.5330	1.5485	1.5628	1.5762	1.5886	1.5993	1.6164	1.6419	1.6892	1.7320	1.7715	1.8087	1.8434	1.8765
270 (407.79)	v	0.0188	1.7101	1.7486	1.8101	1.8692	1.9259	1.9810	2.0350	2.1131	2.2399	2.4847	2.7219	2.9548	3.1838	3.4112	3.6370
	H	383.43	1202.2	1211.0	1224.9	1238.0	1250.6	1262.5	1273.0	1290.0	1316.4	1369.0	1420.9	1472.7	1525.1	1577.6	1631.0
	S	0.5761	1.5200	1.5301	1.5457	1.5601	1.5736	1.5861	1.5969	1.6140	1.6395	1.6869	1.7298	1.7693	1.8065	1.8413	1.8744
275 (409.44)	v	0.0188	1.6798	1.7127	1.7735	1.8318	1.8879	1.9422	1.9956	2.0725	2.1973	2.4382	2.6714	2.9002	3.1253	3.3486	3.5704
	H	385.22	1202.3	1210.0	1224.1	1237.3	1250.0	1262.0	1272.6	1289.5	1316.1	1368.7	1420.7	1472.6	1525.0	1577.5	1630.9
	S	0.5782	1.5183	1.5271	1.5429	1.5574	1.5711	1.5837	1.5946	1.6116	1.6373	1.6847	1.7277	1.7673	1.8045	1.8393	1.8724
280 (411.06)	v	0.0188	1.6504	1.6780	1.7381	1.7957	1.8512	1.9048	1.9575	2.0334	2.1562	2.3932	2.6226	2.8475	3.0688	3.2883	3.5062
	H	386.99	1202.5	1209.0	1223.2	1236.5	1249.4	1261.5	1272.2	1289.1	1315.7	1368.5	1420.5	1472.4	1524.9	1577.4	1630.8
	S	0.5802	1.5167	1.5241	1.5401	1.5547	1.5686	1.5813	1.5923	1.6093	1.6350	1.6826	1.7256	1.7652	1.8024	1.8372	1.8703
285 (412.66)	v	0.0188	1.6232	1.6446	1.7040	1.7610	1.8157	1.8687	1.9207	1.9955	2.1165	2.3499	2.5756	2.7968	3.0143	3.2300	3.4443
	H	388.74	1202.7	1208.0	1222.3	1235.6	1248.7	1260.9	1271.8	1288.6	1315.4	1368.2	1420.3	1472.2	1524.7	1577.3	1630.7
	S	0.5822	1.5153	1.5214	1.5375	1.5521	1.5662	1.5790	1.5902	1.6071	1.6330	1.6806	1.7237	1.7633	1.8005	1.8353	1.8684

290 (414.24)	v	0.0189	1.5947	1.6122	1.6710	1.7273	1.7815	1.8338	1.8853	1.9590	2.0783	2.3080	2.5302	2.7478	2.9616	3.1738	3.3844
	H	390.47	1202.9	1207.0	1221.4	1234.8	1248.0	1260.4	1271.4	1288.2	1315.0	1367.9	1420.1	1472.1	1524.6	1577.2	1630.6
	S	0.5841	1.5137	1.5184	1.5346	1.5493	1.5635	1.5766	1.5879	1.6048	1.6307	1.6784	1.7215	1.7612	1.7984	1.8332	1.8663
295 (415.80)	v	0.0189	1.5684	1.5809	1.6391	1.6948	1.7484	1.8001	1.8510	1.9236	2.0413	2.2677	2.4863	2.7004	2.9108	3.1195	3.3267
	H	392.17	1203.0	1206.1	1220.5	1234.0	1247.4	1259.8	1271.0	1287.8	1314.7	1367.6	1419.9	1472.0	1524.5	1577.1	1630.5
	S	0.5861	1.5122	1.5157	1.5319	1.5467	1.5611	1.5742	1.5857	1.6026	1.6286	1.6763	1.7195	1.7593	1.7965	1.8313	1.8644
300 (417.33)	v	0.0189	1.5426	1.5506	1.6082	1.6634	1.7164	1.7677	1.8172	1.8896	2.0056	2.2286	2.4447	2.6547	2.8634	3.0670	3.2707
	H	393.85	1203.2	1205.2	1219.5	1233.4	1246.6	1259.2	1270.5	1287.4	1314.4	1367.4	1419.7	1471.8	1524.4	1577.0	1630.4
	S	0.5879	1.5107	1.5130	1.5291	1.5443	1.5585	1.5718	1.5834	1.6004	1.6265	1.6742	1.7175	1.7572	1.7945	1.8294	1.8625
310 (420.35)	v	0.0189	1.4938	....	1.5495	1.6036	1.6555	1.7054	1.7546	1.8246	1.9375	2.1541	2.3631	2.5675	2.7682	2.9671	3.1645
	H	397.16	1203.5	....	1217.8	1231.5	1245.3	1258.0	1269.6	1286.4	1313.5	1366.5	1419.3	1471.5	1524.1	1576.8	1630.3
	S	0.5917	1.5079	....	1.5240	1.5391	1.5539	1.5673	1.5793	1.5962	1.6224	1.6705	1.7138	1.7536	1.7909	1.8258	1.8590
320 (423.29)	v	0.0190	1.4479	....	1.4943	1.5473	1.5982	1.6472	1.6954	1.7637	1.8737	2.0844	2.2874	2.4857	2.6804	2.8735	3.0648
	H	400.40	1203.8	....	1216.0	1229.9	1244.0	1256.8	1268.6	1285.6	1312.8	1366.3	1418.9	1471.2	1523.8	1576.6	1630.1
	S	0.5953	1.5052	....	1.5189	1.5342	1.5494	1.5629	1.5751	1.5922	1.6185	1.6667	1.7102	1.7501	1.7874	1.8224	1.8556
330 (426.16)	v	0.0190	1.4048	....	1.4424	1.4944	1.5445	1.5925	1.6397	1.7064	1.8138	2.0189	2.2163	2.4090	2.5981	2.7855	2.9712
	H	403.56	1204.0	....	1214.1	1228.2	1242.5	1255.5	1267.6	1284.7	1312.1	1365.8	1418.4	1470.8	1523.6	1576.4	1630.0
	S	0.5988	1.5023	....	1.5136	1.5291	1.5445	1.5582	1.5707	1.5879	1.6144	1.6628	1.7063	1.7463	1.7837	1.8187	1.8520
340 (428.96)	v	0.0191	1.3640	....	1.3935	1.4446	1.4936	1.5409	1.5872	1.6525	1.7573	1.9572	2.1493	2.3368	2.5206	2.7027	2.8831
	H	406.65	1204.2	....	1212.2	1226.5	1241.0	1254.2	1266.6	1283.8	1311.4	1365.2	1418.0	1470.5	1523.3	1576.2	1629.8
	S	0.6023	1.4997	....	1.5086	1.5243	1.5399	1.5538	1.5666	1.5839	1.6106	1.6591	1.7027	1.7428	1.7802	1.8152	1.8485
350 (431.71)	v	0.0191	1.3255	....	1.3472	1.3976	1.4460	1.4923	1.5377	1.6016	1.7041	1.8991	2.0863	2.2687	2.4475	2.6246	2.8000
	H	409.70	1204.4	....	1210.3	1224.8	1239.5	1252.9	1265.5	1282.9	1310.6	1364.7	1417.6	1470.2	1523.0	1576.0	1629.6
	S	0.6057	1.4972	....	1.5038	1.5197	1.5355	1.5496	1.5626	1.5801	1.6069	1.6556	1.6993	1.7395	1.7769	1.8120	1.8453
360 (434.39)	v	0.0192	1.2889	....	1.3035	1.3532	1.4008	1.4463	1.4909	1.5536	1.6538	1.8441	2.0266	2.2044	2.3784	2.5506	2.7213
	H	412.67	1204.5	....	1208.5	1223.1	1238.0	1251.5	1264.5	1282.0	1309.9	1364.1	1417.2	1469.9	1522.8	1575.8	1629.4
	S	0.6090	1.4946	....	1.4991	1.5151	1.5311	1.5453	1.5587	1.5763	1.6033	1.6521	1.6960	1.7362	1.7737	1.8088	1.8421

TABLE A-2. SUPERHEATED STEAM† (Continued)

Abs. press., psia (sat. temp.)		Sat. water	Sat. steam	Temperature, °F 460	480	500	520	540	560	580	600	700	800	900	1000	1100	1200
370 (437.01)	v	0.0192	1.2545	1.3111	1.3579	1.4028	1.4466	1.4881	1.5286	1.5675	1.6063	1.7921	1.9703	2.1435	2.3131	2.4809	2.6471
	H	415.58	1204.6	1221.4	1236.5	1250.2	1263.4	1275.2	1286.7	1298.3	1309.1	1363.6	1410.8	1469.6	1522.5	1575.6	1629.2
	S	0.6122	1.4921	1.5106	1.5268	1.5412	1.5548	1.5667	1.5781	1.5894	1.5997	1.6488	1.6928	1.7331	1.7706	1.8058	1.8391
380 (439.59)	v	0.0193	1.2217	1.2711	1.3173	1.3614	1.4045	1.4452	1.4850	1.5232	1.5612	1.7428	1.9168	2.0859	2.2512	2.4148	2.5768
	H	418.45	1204.7	1219.8	1235.0	1248.8	1262.3	1274.2	1286.0	1297.5	1308.4	1363.0	1416.4	1469.2	1522.2	1575.4	1629.1
	S	0.6154	1.4897	1.5063	1.5226	1.5371	1.5510	1.5630	1.5747	1.5859	1.5963	1.6455	1.6896	1.7299	1.7675	1.8027	1.8361
390 (442.11)	v	0.0193	1.1904	1.2332	1.2788	1.3222	1.3647	1.4046	1.4436	1.4812	1.5184	1.6961	1.8661	2.0311	2.1925	2.3521	2.5101
	H	421.27	1204.8	1218.0	1233.4	1247.4	1261.2	1273.2	1285.1	1296.7	1307.7	1362.5	1416.0	1468.9	1522.0	1575.2	1628.9
	S	0.6184	1.4872	1.5017	1.5183	1.5330	1.5472	1.5593	1.5711	1.5824	1.5929	1.6423	1.6865	1.7269	1.7646	1.7998	1.8332
400 (444.58)	v	0.0193	1.1609	1.1972	1.2422	1.2849	1.3269	1.3660	1.4042	1.4413	1.4777	1.6522	1.8179	1.9796	2.1367	2.2926	2.4475
	H	424.02	1204.9	1216.5	1231.6	1245.9	1259.9	1272.4	1284.3	1295.8	1307.0	1362.1	1415.5	1468.6	1521.5	1574.8	1628.8
	S	0.6215	1.4850	1.4977	1.5140	1.5290	1.5434	1.5561	1.5678	1.5790	1.5897	1.6393	1.6835	1.7240	1.7615	1.7968	1.8304
410 (447.00)	v	0.0194	1.1327	1.1628	1.2071	1.2494	1.2906	1.3291	1.3669	1.4033	1.4390	1.6095	1.7722	1.9297	2.0837	2.2359	2.3864
	H	426.74	1205.0	1214.6	1230.2	1244.5	1258.8	1271.1	1283.5	1295.1	1306.2	1361.4	1415.1	1468.3	1521.4	1574.8	1628.6
	S	0.6244	1.4828	1.4933	1.5101	1.5252	1.5399	1.5524	1.5646	1.5759	1.5865	1.6362	1.6806	1.7212	1.7589	1.7943	1.8277
420 (449.38)	v	0.0194	1.1058	1.1300	1.1738	1.2156	1.2561	1.2942	1.3312	1.3671	1.4021	1.5693	1.7285	1.8826	2.0332	2.1819	2.3290
	H	429.42	1205.0	1213.0	1228.6	1243.1	1257.5	1270.2	1282.6	1294.3	1305.4	1360.8	1414.6	1468.0	1521.2	1574.6	1628.4
	S	0.6273	1.4805	1.4892	1.5060	1.5213	1.5361	1.5489	1.5612	1.5726	1.5832	1.6331	1.6776	1.7184	1.7561	1.7915	1.8249
430 (451.72)	v	0.0195	1.0800	1.0986	1.1419	1.1834	1.2233	1.2607	1.2972	1.3326	1.3670	1.5309	1.6869	1.8377	1.9850	2.1305	2.2742
	H	432.05	1205.0	1211.2	1227.0	1241.7	1256.3	1269.1	1281.8	1293.5	1304.6	1360.3	1414.2	1467.6	1520.9	1574.4	1628.2
	S	0.6302	1.4782	1.4850	1.5020	1.5175	1.5326	1.5455	1.5581	1.5695	1.5801	1.6303	1.6748	1.7156	1.7534	1.7888	1.8222
440 (454.01)	v	0.0195	1.0554	1.0688	1.1116	1.1524	1.1918	1.2288	1.2648	1.2996	1.3334	1.4943	1.6472	1.7949	1.9390	2.0814	2.2220
	H	434.63	1205.0	1209.6	1225.3	1240.2	1255.0	1268.0	1280.9	1292.6	1303.9	1359.7	1413.8	1467.3	1520.6	1574.1	1628.0
	S	0.6330	1.4762	1.4812	1.4981	1.5138	1.5291	1.5422	1.5550	1.5664	1.5772	1.6275	1.6722	1.7130	1.7508	1.7862	1.8197

Press. (Sat. temp.)																	
450 (456.27)	»	0.0195	1.0318	1.0401	1.0824	1.1230	1.1617	1.1982	1.2337	1.2681	1.3013	1.4593	1.6092	1.7539	1.8951	2.0345	2.1720
	H	437.18	1205.0	1207.9	1223.7	1238.7	1253.8	1266.9	1280.0	1291.8	1303.1	1359.1	1413.4	1467.0	1520.3	1573.9	1627.8
	S	0.6357	1.4739	1.4771	1.4941	1.5099	1.5255	1.5387	1.5517	1.5632	1.5740	1.6245	1.6694	1.7103	1.7481	1.7836	1.8171
460 (458.48)	»	0.0196	1.0092	......	1.0545	1.0946	1.1329	1.1690	1.2039	1.2379	1.2706	1.4258	1.5729	1.7147	1.8530	1.9896	2.1243
	H	439.69	1205.0	......	1222.0	1237.2	1252.5	1265.8	1279.0	1291.0	1302.3	1358.6	1413.0	1466.6	1520.0	1573.7	1627.7
	S	0.6384	1.4719	......	1.4902	1.5062	1.5220	1.5354	1.5485	1.5602	1.5710	1.6217	1.6667	1.7076	1.7455	1.7811	1.8146
470 (460.66)	»	0.0196	0.9875	......	1.0278	1.0676	1.1053	1.1410	1.1755	1.2091	1.2412	1.3937	1.5381	1.6772	1.8127	1.9465	2.0785
	H	442.17	1205.0	......	1220.2	1235.7	1251.2	1264.7	1278.0	1290.0	1301.5	1358.0	1412.5	1466.3	1519.8	1573.5	1627.5
	S	0.6411	1.4699	......	1.4862	1.5025	1.5185	1.5321	1.5453	1.5570	1.5680	1.6189	1.6639	1.7050	1.7429	1.7785	1.8120
480 (462.80)	»	0.0197	0.9668	......	1.0021	1.0416	1.0789	1.1141	1.1482	1.1813	1.2131	1.3630	1.5049	1.6413	1.7742	1.9054	2.0347
	H	444.60	1205.0	......	1218.6	1234.2	1249.9	1263.5	1277.0	1289.1	1300.8	1357.5	1412.1	1466.0	1519.5	1573.3	1627.3
	S	0.6436	1.4679	......	1.4825	1.4989	1.5151	1.5288	1.5422	1.5539	1.5650	1.6161	1.6612	1.7023	1.7402	1.7758	1.8093
490 (464.91)	»	0.0197	.9466	......	0.9774	1.0166	1.0535	1.0884	1.1220	1.1548	1.1860	1.3335	1.4729	1.6067	1.7371	1.8659	1.9927
	H	447.00	1204.9	......	1217.0	1232.7	1248.4	1262.3	1276.0	1288.3	1300.0	1356.9	1411.7	1465.6	1519.2	1573.1	1627.1
	S	0.6462	1.4659	......	1.4789	1.4954	1.5116	1.5256	1.5392	1.5511	1.5622	1.6135	1.6588	1.6999	1.7379	1.7736	1.8071
500 (467.00)	»	0.0197	0.9274	......	0.9538	0.9926	1.0290	1.0636	1.0969	1.1292	1.1600	1.3051	1.4417	1.5735	1.7016	1.8280	1.9532
	H	449.40	1204.9	......	1215.3	1231.4	1246.6	1261.1	1275.0	1287.3	1299.3	1356.3	1411.2	1465.1	1518.8	1572.9	1626.9
	S	0.6488	1.4641	......	1.4752	1.4922	1.5079	1.5225	1.5363	1.5482	1.5596	1.6110	1.6564	1.6975	1.7356	1.7714	1.8052
510 (469.05)	»	0.0198	0.9090	......	0.9310	0.9695	1.0056	1.0397	1.0727	1.1046	1.1350	1.2780	1.4127	1.5418	1.6675	1.7915	1.9135
	H	451.75	1204.8	......	1213.5	1229.6	1245.6	1259.9	1274.0	1286.6	1298.4	1355.7	1410.9	1465.0	1518.7	1572.6	1626.8
	S	0.6513	1.4621	......	1.4714	1.4883	1.5048	1.5192	1.5332	1.5454	1.5566	1.6082	1.6538	1.6951	1.7332	1.7689	1.8026
520 (471.07)	»	0.0198	0.8912	......	0.9091	0.9472	0.9829	1.0169	1.0494	1.0810	1.1110	1.2519	1.3844	1.5113	1.6347	1.7565	1.8763
	H	454.07	1204.7	......	1211.8	1228.1	1244.2	1258.6	1272.9	1285.6	1297.6	1355.1	1410.4	1464.6	1518.4	1572.4	1626.6
	S	0.6537	1.4601	......	1.4677	1.4849	1.5015	1.5160	1.5302	1.5425	1.5539	1.6057	1.6514	1.6928	1.7310	1.7668	1.8005
530 (473.05)	»	0.0199	0.8741	......	0.8879	0.9258	0.9612	0.9948	1.0269	1.0582	1.0878	1.2267	1.3571	1.4818	1.6031	1.7228	1.8402
	H	456.35	1204.6	......	1210.0	1226.5	1242.8	1257.3	1271.8	1284.8	1296.8	1354.6	1410.0	1464.3	1518.1	1572.2	1626.4
	S	0.6562	1.4584	......	1.4642	1.4816	1.4984	1.5130	1.5274	1.5400	1.5514	1.6035	1.6493	1.6908	1.7290	1.7648	1.7985

TABLE A-2. SUPERHEATED STEAM† (Continued)

Abs. press, psia (sat. temp.)	v H S	Sat. water	Sat. steam	Temperature, °F 500	520	540	560	580	600	650	700	750	800	900	1000	1100	1200
540 (475.02)	v	0.0199	0.8576	0.9051	0.9401	0.9736	1.0054	1.0363	1.0655	1.1356	1.2025	1.2671	1.3309	1.4535	1.5727	1.6903	1.8056
	H	458.62	1204.5	1225.0	1241.4	1256.1	1270.7	1283.8	1296.0	1325.6	1354.0	1382.1	1409.4	1463.9	1517.8	1572.0	1626.2
	S	0.6585	1.4565	1.4781	1.4950	1.5098	1.5243	1.5370	1.5486	1.5759	1.6009	1.6246	1.6469	1.6884	1.7266	1.7625	1.7962
550 (476.94)	v	0.0199	0.8416	0.8851	0.9198	0.9530	0.9846	1.0151	1.0441	1.1132	1.1791	1.2428	1.3055	1.4262	1.5434	1.6590	1.7724
	H	460.83	1204.4	1223.4	1240.0	1254.8	1269.6	1282.9	1295.2	1324.9	1353.5	1381.6	1409.2	1463.6	1517.5	1571.7	1626.0
	S	0.6609	1.4548	1.4748	1.4919	1.5068	1.5215	1.5344	1.5461	1.5735	1.5987	1.6224	1.6447	1.6862	1.7244	1.7603	1.7940
560 (478.85)	v	0.0200	0.8263	0.8658	0.9003	0.9332	0.9644	0.9947	1.0233	1.0917	1.1566	1.2193	1.2810	1.3998	1.5151	1.6289	1.7403
	H	463.04	1204.3	1221.8	1238.5	1253.5	1268.5	1282.0	1294.4	1324.2	1352.9	1381.1	1408.7	1463.2	1517.2	1571.5	1625.8
	S	0.6632	1.4530	1.4714	1.4886	1.5038	1.5187	1.5318	1.5436	1.5711	1.5964	1.6202	1.6425	1.6841	1.7224	1.7584	1.7921
570 (480.73)	v	0.0200	0.8114	0.8472	0.8814	0.9141	0.9450	0.9749	1.0033	1.0708	1.1348	1.1966	1.2575	1.3744	1.4879	1.5998	1.7093
	H	465.22	1204.1	1220.2	1236.9	1252.2	1267.3	1281.0	1293.5	1323.5	1352.3	1380.6	1408.3	1462.9	1517.0	1571.3	1625.6
	S	0.6655	1.4512	1.4681	1.4853	1.5008	1.5156	1.5291	1.5410	1.5686	1.5940	1.6179	1.6403	1.6820	1.7204	1.7564	1.7901
580 (482.58)	v	0.0201	0.7968	0.8291	0.8631	0.8956	0.9263	0.9558	0.9839	1.0506	1.1137	1.1747	1.2347	1.3498	1.4616	1.5714	1.6794
	H	467.37	1204.0	1218.6	1235.5	1250.9	1266.1	1280.0	1292.6	1322.8	1351.6	1380.0	1407.8	1462.5	1516.7	1571.0	1625.4
	S	0.6677	1.4494	1.4648	1.4822	1.4978	1.5128	1.5264	1.5384	1.5662	1.5916	1.6156	1.6381	1.6799	1.7183	1.7543	1.7881
590 (484.41)	v	0.0201	0.7831	0.8116	0.8455	0.8778	0.9082	0.9373	0.9653	1.0310	1.0934	1.1535	1.2128	1.3262	1.4360	1.5442	1.6505
	H	469.50	1203.8	1217.0	1234.0	1249.6	1265.0	1278.9	1291.8	1322.1	1351.0	1379.5	1407.4	1462.2	1516.4	1570.8	1625.3
	S	0.6699	1.4477	1.4616	1.4791	1.4949	1.5101	1.5236	1.5359	1.5638	1.5894	1.6134	1.6360	1.6778	1.7162	1.7522	1.7861
600 (486.21)	v	0.0201	0.7695	0.7945	0.8284	0.8605	0.8907	0.9194	0.9471	1.0123	1.0738	1.1332	1.1915	1.3032	1.4115	1.5179	1.6224
	H	471.59	1203.6	1215.6	1232.5	1248.3	1263.7	1278.1	1290.9	1321.4	1350.5	1379.0	1407.0	1461.8	1516.0	1570.5	1625.0
	S	0.6721	1.4460	1.4586	1.4760	1.4920	1.5072	1.5212	1.5334	1.5615	1.5871	1.6112	1.6339	1.6757	1.7141	1.7502	1.7841
610 (487.99)	v	0.0202	0.7565	0.7781	0.8120	0.8436	0.8736	0.9022	0.9296	0.9942	1.0548	1.1135	1.1708	1.2809	1.3878	1.4928	1.5964
	H	473.67	1203.5	1213.8	1230.9	1246.9	1262.5	1276.8	1290.0	1320.6	1350.0	1378.5	1406.5	1461.5	1515.8	1570.3	1624.9
	S	0.6743	1.4444	1.4552	1.4728	1.4890	1.5044	1.5183	1.5309	1.5591	1.5850	1.6091	1.6318	1.6738	1.7123	1.7484	1.7823

620 (489.75)	v	0.0202	0.7438	0.7622	0.7960	0.8275	0.8572	0.8856	0.9127	0.9765	1.0364	1.0943	1.1505	1.2596	1.3648	1.4677	1.5707
	H	475.72	1203.3	1212.2	1229.5	1245.5	1261.3	1275.8	1289.1	1319.9	1349.3	1377.9	1406.1	1461.2	1515.5	1570.1	1624.7
	S	0.6764	1.4427	1.4520	1.4698	1.4860	1.5016	1.5157	1.5284	1.5568	1.5827	1.6068	1.6296	1.6717	1.7102	1.7464	1.7803
630 (491.49)	v	0.0202	0.7316	0.7466	0.7802	0.8117	0.8413	0.8694	0.8963	0.9595	1.0187	1.0757	1.1312	1.2387	1.3423	1.4445	1.5449
	H	477.75	1203.1	1210.6	1227.8	1244.1	1260.1	1274.7	1288.3	1319.2	1348.7	1377.4	1405.7	1460.8	1515.2	1569.9	1624.5
	S	0.6785	1.4410	1.4488	1.4665	1.4830	1.4988	1.5130	1.5260	1.5545	1.5805	1.6047	1.6276	1.6697	1.7083	1.7445	1.7784
640 (493.21)	v	0.0203	0.7197	0.7317	0.7651	0.7963	0.8258	0.8537	0.8804	0.9429	1.0015	1.0578	1.1124	1.2187	1.3210	1.4213	1.5193
	H	479.79	1202.9	1209.0	1226.3	1242.7	1258.9	1273.6	1287.4	1318.5	1348.2	1376.8	1405.2	1460.5	1515.0	1569.7	1624.3
	S	0.6806	1.4394	1.4458	1.4636	1.4802	1.4962	1.5105	1.5236	1.5523	1.5785	1.6026	1.6256	1.6678	1.7065	1.7427	1.7766
650 (494.90)	v	0.0203	0.7082	0.7171	0.7504	0.7816	0.8107	0.8384	0.8648	0.9269	0.9846	1.0404	1.0944	1.1988	1.2999	1.3987	1.4958
	H	481.73	1202.7	1207.3	1224.8	1241.3	1257.6	1272.5	1286.6	1317.8	1347.6	1376.3	1404.7	1460.1	1514.7	1569.4	1624.1
	S	0.6826	1.4379	1.4427	1.4607	1.4774	1.4935	1.5080	1.5213	1.5501	1.5764	1.6006	1.6236	1.6659	1.7046	1.7408	1.7748
660 (496.58)	v	0.0204	0.6969	0.7031	0.7361	0.7672	0.7962	0.8237	0.8499	0.9113	0.9686	1.0234	1.0769	1.1803	1.2797	1.3774	1.4727
	H	483.77	1202.5	1205.7	1223.2	1240.0	1256.4	1271.4	1285.5	1317.1	1347.0	1375.8	1404.3	1459.7	1514.4	1569.2	1624.0
	S	0.6847	1.4363	1.4396	1.4576	1.4746	1.4908	1.5054	1.5188	1.5479	1.5742	1.5985	1.6216	1.6639	1.7027	1.7390	1.7730
670 (498.23)	v	0.0204	0.6861	0.6892	0.7224	0.7531	0.7820	0.8093	0.8354	0.8963	0.9527	1.0072	1.0599	1.1617	1.2600	1.3560	1.4603
	H	485.61	1202.3	1204.0	1221.7	1238.7	1255.1	1270.2	1284.5	1316.3	1346.3	1375.3	1403.9	1459.4	1514.1	1569.0	1623.8
	S	0.6867	1.4349	1.4367	1.4549	1.4721	1.4883	1.5030	1.5166	1.5459	1.5723	1.5968	1.6200	1.6624	1.7012	1.7376	1.7716
680 (499.87)	v	0.0204	0.6757	……	0.7089	0.7397	0.7663	0.7954	0.8212	0.8814	0.9375	0.9912	1.0432	1.1440	1.2408	1.3357	1.4283
	H	487.64	1202.1	……	1220.2	1237.3	1253.9	1269.1	1283.6	1315.6	1345.8	1374.7	1403.4	1459.0	1513.8	1568.7	1623.6
	S	0.6886	1.4332	……	1.4519	1.4692	1.4856	1.5004	1.5142	1.5437	1.5703	1.5947	1.6179	1.6603	1.6992	1.7356	1.7697
690 (501.49)	v	0.0205	0.6652	……	0.6956	0.7263	0.7549	0.7818	0.8075	0.8675	0.9225	0.9758	1.0272	1.1267	1.2223	1.3162	1.4075
	H	489.56	1201.8	……	1218.5	1235.8	1252.5	1268.0	1282.7	1314.9	1345.1	1374.2	1402.8	1458.7	1513.6	1568.5	1623.4
	S	0.6906	1.4316	……	1.4488	1.4663	1.4828	1.4978	1.5118	1.5415	1.5681	1.5927	1.6159	1.6586	1.6975	1.7339	1.7680
700 (503.09)	v	0.0205	0.6552	……	0.6830	0.7133	0.7419	0.7687	0.7941	0.8534	0.9084	0.9608	1.0117	1.1096	1.2043	1.2965	1.3870
	H	491.49	1201.6	……	1217.1	1234.7	1251.3	1266.8	1281.9	1314.3	1344.6	1373.7	1402.5	1458.2	1513.4	1568.2	1623.3
	S	0.6925	1.4301	……	1.4461	1.4638	1.4803	1.4953	1.5097	1.5396	1.5663	1.5908	1.6141	1.6567	1.6958	1.7321	1.7663

Temperature, °F

Abs. press., psia (sat. temp.)		Sat. water	Sat. steam	520	540	560	580	600	620	650	700	750	800	900	1000	1100	1200
725 (507.01)	v	0.0206	0.6314	0.6524	0.6827	0.7109	0.7373	0.7624	0.7864	0.8203	0.8740	0.9250	0.9745	1.0697	1.1612	1.2511	1.3383
	H	496.2	1200.9	1212.8	1230.9	1248.0	1264.0	1279.1	1293.8	1312.3	1343.0	1372.3	1401.3	1457.4	1512.5	1567.7	1622.7
	S	0.6973	1.4263	1.4385	1.4568	1.4737	1.4892	1.5036	1.5173	1.5342	1.5612	1.5859	1.6094	1.6522	1.6913	1.7279	1.7621
750 (510.83)	v	0.0207	0.6091	0.6237	0.6538	0.6818	0.7080	0.7326	0.7561	0.7896	0.8419	0.8918	0.9399	1.0326	1.1212	1.2078	1.2928
	H	500.8	1200.2	1208.8	1227.4	1244.9	1261.0	1276.6	1291.4	1310.5	1341.5	1371.0	1400.2	1456.5	1511.8	1567.1	1622.3
	S	0.7019	1.4225	1.4313	1.4501	1.4674	1.4830	1.4979	1.5117	1.5291	1.5564	1.5813	1.6049	1.6479	1.6871	1.7237	1.7580
775 (514.57)	v	0.0208	0.5882	0.5969	0.6268	0.6545	0.6803	0.7047	0.7278	0.7607	0.8119	0.8606	0.9073	0.9977	1.0838	1.1676	1.2505
	H	505.3	1199.5	1204.7	1223.7	1241.5	1258.2	1271.9	1289.0	1308.6	1340.0	1369.7	1399.0	1455.6	1511.1	1566.6	1621.8
	S	0.7064	1.4189	1.4242	1.4434	1.4610	1.4772	1.4902	1.5062	1.5241	1.5518	1.5769	1.6006	1.6438	1.6832	1.7200	1.7543
800 (518.20)	v	0.0209	0.5685	0.5714	0.6013	0.6288	0.6545	0.6785	0.7013	0.7336	0.7838	0.8313	0.8770	0.9648	1.0486	1.1302	1.2105
	H	509.7	1198.8	1200.3	1220.0	1238.2	1255.3	1271.4	1286.5	1306.8	1338.4	1368.5	1397.8	1454.9	1510.5	1566.0	1621.4
	S	0.7108	1.4155	1.4170	1.4369	1.4549	1.4715	1.4868	1.5009	1.5195	1.5473	1.5727	1.5964	1.6400	1.6794	1.7162	1.7506
825 (521.75)	v	0.0210	0.5500		0.5774	0.6046	0.6300	0.6539	0.6763	0.7081	0.7573	0.8038	0.8483	0.9338	1.0155	1.0950	1.1727
	H	514.0	1198.0		1216.1	1234.9	1252.1	1268.5	1284.0	1304.8	1336.8	1367.0	1396.6	1453.8	1509.7	1565.4	1620.8
	S	0.7152	1.4121		1.4304	1.4490	1.4657	1.4813	1.4958	1.5148	1.5430	1.5685	1.5925	1.6362	1.6758	1.7127	1.7471
850 (525.23)	v	0.0210	0.5326		0.5545	0.5817	0.6070	0.6306	0.6528	0.6841	0.7323	0.7779	0.8213	0.9048	0.9845	1.0619	1.1375
	H	518.3	1197.2		1212.4	1231.5	1249.1	1265.7	1281.4	1302.9	1335.2	1365.7	1395.4	1452.8	1509.0	1564.8	1620.4
	S	0.7194	1.4087		1.4240	1.4429	1.4600	1.4758	1.4905	1.5101	1.5386	1.5643	1.5883	1.6321	1.6720	1.7090	1.7435
875 (528.62)	v	0.0211	0.5162		0.5327	0.5601	0.5851	0.6085	0.6305	0.6615	0.7087	0.7535	0.7960	0.8773	0.9554	1.0306	1.1045
	H	522.4	1196.4		1208.4	1228.0	1246.0	1263.0	1279.0	1300.9	1333.5	1364.4	1394.2	1451.9	1508.3	1564.3	1619.9
	S	0.7236	1.4056		1.4177	1.4371	1.4546	1.4708	1.4858	1.5058	1.5345	1.5606	1.5847	1.6287	1.6687	1.7058	1.7403
900 (531.94)	v	0.0212	0.5006		0.5123	0.5394	0.5644	0.5876	0.6094	0.6399	0.6856	0.7304	0.7720	0.8516	0.9277	1.0010	1.0727
	H	526.6	1195.6		1204.0	1224.2	1242.6	1260.0	1276.5	1298.6	1331.8	1363.0	1392.9	1451.1	1507.8	1563.7	1619.3
	S	0.7276	1.4022		1.4106	1.4306	1.4484	1.4649	1.4803	1.5004	1.5296	1.5559	1.5801	1.6245	1.6647	1.7017	1.7362

Pressure (Sat. temp.)		C1	C2	C3	C4	C5	C6	C7	C8	C9	C10	C11	C12	C13	C14	C15
925 (535.20)	v	0.0213	0.4858	0.4927	0.5199	0.5448	0.5678	0.5894	0.6196	0.6655	0.7085	0.7494	0.8272	0.9014	0.9731	1.0432
	H	530.6	1194.7	1200.8	1220.8	1239.6	1257.0	1273.9	1296.7	1330.2	1361.7	1391.7	1450.0	1506.9	1563.1	1618.9
	S	0.7316	1.3991	1.4044	1.4250	1.4433	1.4599	1.4757	1.4965	1.5260	1.5526	1.5769	1.6214	1.6618	1.6990	1.7337
950 (538.38)	v	0.0214	0.4717	0.4741	0.5014	0.5262	0.5491	0.5705	0.6003	0.6456	0.6877	0.7277	0.8039	0.8766	0.9465	1.0148
	H	534.6	1193.8	1195.8	1217.0	1236.4	1254.1	1271.3	1294.5	1328.5	1360.3	1390.5	1449.1	1506.1	1562.6	1618.5
	S	0.7355	1.3960	1.3980	1.4190	1.4378	1.4547	1.4708	1.4920	1.5220	1.5488	1.5733	1.6180	1.6584	1.6958	1.7305
975 (541.50)	v	0.0215	0.4583		0.4835	0.5083	0.5311	0.5524	0.5820	0.6266	0.6680	0.7073	0.7820	0.8533	0.9214	0.9880
	H	538.5	1192.9		1213.0	1233.0	1251.2	1268.7	1292.1	1326.7	1358.8	1389.2	1448.2	1505.4	1562.0	1618.0
	S	0.7393	1.3929		1.4128	1.4322	1.4495	1.4659	1.4873	1.5178	1.5449	1.5695	1.6145	1.6551	1.6926	1.7274
1000 (544.56)	v	0.0216	0.4456		0.4665	0.4914	0.5141	0.5351	0.5639	0.6085	0.6492	0.6879	0.7611	0.8306	0.8974	0.9626
	H	542.4	1191.9		1208.8	1229.4	1248.2	1265.8	1289.6	1324.9	1357.2	1388.0	1447.3	1504.7	1561.3	1617.5
	S	0.7431	1.3899		1.4066	1.4266	1.4445	1.4610	1.4827	1.5138	1.5411	1.5660	1.6113	1.6520	1.6895	1.7244
1025 (547.57)	v	0.0217	0.4334		0.4498	0.4751	0.4978	0.5188	0.5479	0.5913	0.6314	0.6695	0.7413	0.8095	0.8746	0.9384
	H	546.1	1191.0		1204.5	1225.9	1245.2	1263.0	1287.6	1323.1	1355.7	1386.8	1446.4	1504.1	1560.6	1617.0
	S	0.7468	1.3871		1.4004	1.4212	1.4396	1.4562	1.4787	1.5100	1.5375	1.5627	1.6082	1.6491	1.6866	1.7216
1050 (550.52)	v	0.0218	0.4219		0.4345	0.4596	0.4822	0.5031	0.5320	0.5749	0.6143	0.6519	0.7223	0.7892	0.8531	0.9154
	H	550.0	1190.0		1200.5	1222.4	1241.9	1260.2	1285.1	1321.3	1354.2	1385.6	1445.4	1503.4	1560.0	1616.5
	S	0.7504	1.3839		1.3942	1.4155	1.4341	1.4512	1.4739	1.5058	1.5336	1.5590	1.6047	1.6458	1.6833	1.7184
1075 (553.42)	v	0.0219	0.4108		0.4195	0.4446	0.4672	0.4879	0.5169	0.5592	0.5980	0.6349	0.7042	0.7696	0.8322	0.8933
	H	553.7	1188.9		1196.3	1218.7	1238.8	1257.2	1282.8	1319.4	1352.6	1384.1	1444.3	1502.5	1559.3	1615.9
	S	0.7540	1.3810		1.3883	1.4100	1.4292	1.4464	1.4698	1.5020	1.5300	1.5555	1.6015	1.6428	1.6804	1.7156
1100 (556.26)	v	0.0219	0.4002		0.4054	0.4304	0.4530	0.4736	0.5027	0.5445	0.5828	0.6190	0.6871	0.7511	0.8125	0.8724
	H	557.4	1187.8		1192.3	1214.9	1235.6	1254.5	1280.6	1317.8	1351.3	1383.0	1443.6	1501.7	1558.7	1615.4
	S	0.7575	1.3780		1.3824	1.4044	1.4241	1.4418	1.4656	1.4984	1.5267	1.5523	1.5986	1.6398	1.6776	1.7128
1125 (559.07)	v	0.0220	0.3902			0.4167	0.4392	0.4598	0.4883	0.5301	0.5678	0.6036	0.6706	0.7333	0.7938	0.8524
	H	561.0	1186.7			1211.3	1232.2	1251.5	1277.7	1315.9	1349.6	1381.7	1442.6	1500.8	1558.2	1614.9
	S	0.7610	1.3752			1.3991	1.4190	1.4370	1.4610	1.4946	1.5231	1.5491	1.5956	1.6369	1.6749	1.7101

Temperature, °F

Abs. press., psia (sat. temp.)		Sat. water	Sat. steam	580	600	620	640	660	680	700	720	750	800	900	1000	1100	1200
1150 (561.81)	v	0.0221	0.3804	0.4035	0.4259	0.4468	0.4659	0.4839	0.5005	0.5165	0.5317	0.5537	0.5889	0.6549	0.7166	0.7760	0.8333
	H	564.6	1185.6	1207.4	1228.7	1248.6	1266.9	1284.4	1299.5	1314.1	1327.9	1348.1	1380.4	1441.7	1500.2	1557.8	1614.5
	S	0.7644	1.3723	1.3934	1.4137	1.4323	1.4491	1.4649	1.4783	1.4910	1.5028	1.5197	1.5458	1.5926	1.6341	1.6723	1.7075
1175 (564.54)	v	0.0222	0.3710	0.3911	0.4133	0.4339	0.4530	0.4708	0.4874	0.5032	0.5183	0.5400	0.5747	0.6396	0.7005	0.7586	0.8149
	H	568.2	1184.4	1203.6	1225.4	1245.4	1264.6	1281.5	1297.3	1312.1	1326.1	1346.4	1379.0	1440.6	1499.4	1557.0	1614.0
	S	0.7678	1.3694	1.3880	1.4088	1.4275	1.4451	1.4603	1.4743	1.4872	1.4991	1.5161	1.5425	1.5896	1.6313	1.6694	1.7048
1200 (567.19)	v	0.0223	0.3620	0.3793	0.4013	0.4219	0.4408	0.4585	0.4750	0.4907	0.5056	0.5271	0.5613	0.6251	0.6853	0.7423	0.7975
	H	571.7	1183.2	1200.2	1222.1	1242.6	1261.5	1279.2	1295.3	1310.3	1324.4	1345.0	1377.7	1439.5	1499.0	1556.6	1613.6
	S	0.7712	1.3667	1.3831	1.4040	1.4232	1.4405	1.4565	1.4707	1.4838	1.4958	1.5131	1.5395	1.5867	1.6289	1.6671	1.7025
1225 (569.82)	v	0.0224	0.3534	0.3669	0.3895	0.4102	0.4290	0.4466	0.4631	0.4786	0.4934	0.5146	0.5483	0.6113	0.6702	0.7264	0.7806
	H	575.1	1182.0	1195.6	1218.6	1239.7	1258.8	1276.7	1293.3	1308.3	1322.7	1343.3	1376.4	1438.6	1498.0	1556.0	1613.0
	S	0.7745	1.3640	1.3771	1.3990	1.4188	1.4363	1.4524	1.4671	1.4802	1.4925	1.5097	1.5365	1.5840	1.6262	1.6646	1.7000
1250 (572.39)	v	0.0225	0.3453	0.3549	0.3782	0.3991	0.4177	0.4354	0.4517	0.4672	0.4817	0.5027	0.5360	0.5980	0.6558	0.7113	0.7644
	H	578.6	1180.8	1190.9	1215.0	1236.7	1256.0	1274.5	1291.2	1306.6	1321.0	1341.9	1375.2	1437.7	1497.1	1555.4	1612.6
	S	0.7777	1.3612	1.3710	1.3939	1.4142	1.4319	1.4486	1.4634	1.4768	1.4891	1.5066	1.5335	1.5813	1.6235	1.6620	1.6975
1275 (574.93)	v	0.0226	0.3371	0.3437	0.3672	0.3881	0.4068	0.4244	0.4406	0.4560	0.4705	0.4912	0.5241	0.5852	0.6420	0.6966	0.7488
	H	582.0	1179.5	1186.5	1211.2	1233.5	1253.3	1272.0	1289.0	1304.6	1319.4	1340.3	1373.9	1436.7	1496.3	1554.7	1612.0
	S	0.7809	1.3584	1.3651	1.3887	1.4095	1.4277	1.4445	1.4596	1.4732	1.4858	1.5033	1.5305	1.5785	1.6207	1.6594	1.6950
1300 (577.43)	v	0.0227	0.3294	0.3329	0.3567	0.3776	0.3965	0.4140	0.4301	0.4453	0.4598	0.4803	0.5127	0.5730	0.6290	0.6826	0.7340
	H	585.4	1178.3	1182.0	1207.7	1230.3	1250.6	1269.6	1287.0	1302.8	1317.8	1338.9	1372.6	1435.8	1495.7	1554.2	1611.6
	S	0.7840	1.3557	1.3593	1.3837	1.4049	1.4235	1.4406	1.4560	1.4698	1.4826	1.5002	1.5275	1.5758	1.6183	1.6570	1.6926
1325 (579.89)	v	0.0228	0.3220	....	0.3463	0.3673	0.3863	0.4037	0.4200	0.4350	0.4493	0.4696	0.5016	0.5611	0.6162	0.6689	0.7195
	H	588.7	1177.0	....	1203.8	1227.0	1247.8	1267.0	1285.0	1300.8	1315.9	1337.1	1371.2	1434.8	1494.9	1553.4	1611.0
	S	0.7871	1.3530	....	1.3785	1.4002	1.4193	1.4366	1.4525	1.4663	1.4792	1.4971	1.5246	1.5731	1.6158	1.6545	1.6903

		0.0229	0.3147		0.3363	0.3576	0.3766	0.3940	0.4105	0.4252	0.4393	0.4594	0.4911	0.5497	0.6042	0.6559	0.7057
1350 (582.32)	v	0.0229	0.3147	....	0.3363	0.3576	0.3766	0.3940	0.4105	0.4252	0.4393	0.4594	0.4911	0.5497	0.6042	0.6559	0.7057
	H	592.1	1175.8	....	1200.0	1223.8	1245.0	1264.6	1283.2	1299.1	1314.2	1335.8	1370.0	1433.8	1494.3	1552.8	1610.6
	S	0.7902	1.3504	....	1.3734	1.3957	1.4151	1.4328	1.4492	1.4631	1.4760	1.4941	1.5218	1.5705	1.6134	1.6521	1.6881
1375 (584.71)	v	0.0230	0.3078	....	0.3266	0.3480	0.3670	0.3847	0.4007	0.4154	0.4295	0.4494	0.4808	0.5387	0.5922	0.6432	0.6922
	H	595.3	1174.5	....	1195.8	1220.2	1242.0	1262.1	1280.7	1296.8	1312.3	1334.1	1368.6	1432.8	1493.2	1552.0	1609.9
	S	0.7932	1.3477	....	1.3680	1.3908	1.4108	1.4289	1.4453	1.4593	1.4726	1.4908	1.5188	1.5678	1.6107	1.6496	1.6856
1400 (587.07)	v	0.0231	0.3011	....	0.3172	0.3388	0.3581	0.3760	0.3914	0.4063	0.4203	0.4401	0.4711	0.5283	0.5811	0.6313	0.6795
	H	598.6	1173.2	....	1191.8	1216.9	1239.2	1260.1	1278.2	1294.9	1310.6	1332.8	1367.4	1431.9	1492.7	1551.7	1609.6
	S	0.7963	1.3452	....	1.3629	1.3863	1.4068	1.4256	1.4416	1.4562	1.4696	1.4882	1.5162	1.5654	1.6086	1.6476	1.6836
1425 (589.40)	v	0.0232	0.2947	....	0.3081	0.3297	0.3491	0.3668	0.3825	0.3972	0.4112	0.4308	0.4616	0.5180	0.5701	0.6195	0.6671
	H	601.8	1171.8	....	1187.7	1213.2	1236.2	1257.2	1275.8	1292.9	1308.9	1331.1	1366.1	1431.0	1491.8	1551.0	1609.1
	S	0.7992	1.3425	....	1.3576	1.3814	1.4025	1.4215	1.4379	1.4528	1.4665	1.4850	1.5134	1.5629	1.6061	1.6453	1.6814
1450 (591.70)	v	0.0233	0.2885	....	0.2991	0.3211	0.3405	0.3580	0.3739	0.3885	0.4025	0.4220	0.4524	0.5082	0.5597	0.6083	0.6552
	H	605.0	1170.5	....	1183.2	1209.7	1233.1	1254.3	1273.5	1290.6	1307.0	1329.7	1364.8	1430.1	1491.3	1550.4	1608.6
	S	0.8022	1.3401	....	1.3521	1.3769	1.3984	1.4175	1.4345	1.4493	1.4634	1.4824	1.5108	1.5606	1.6041	1.6432	1.6794
1475 (593.97)	v	0.0234	0.2824	....	0.2903	0.3126	0.3318	0.3495	0.3654	0.3801	0.3939	0.4129	0.4435	0.4986	0.5493	0.5973	0.6439
	H	608.2	1169.1	....	1178.7	1206.2	1229.7	1251.5	1271.0	1288.8	1305.0	1327.4	1363.5	1429.1	1490.3	1549.8	1608.4
	S	0.8052	1.3375	....	1.3466	1.3723	1.3939	1.4135	1.4308	1.4463	1.4601	1.4789	1.5081	1.5582	1.6016	1.6410	1.6774
1500 (596.20)	v	0.0235	0.2765	....	0.2817	0.3044	0.3236	0.3413	0.3573	0.3721	0.3856	0.4042	0.4349	0.4894	0.5396	0.5869	0.6332
	H	611.4	1167.7	....	1174.2	1202.5	1226.4	1248.5	1268.6	1286.8	1303.0	1325.4	1362.1	1428.1	1489.8	1549.3	1608.4
	S	0.8081	1.3350	....	1.3411	1.3676	1.3895	1.4094	1.4272	1.4431	1.4569	1.4757	1.5054	1.5558	1.5995	1.6390	1.6757
1525 (598.41)	v	0.0236	0.2708	....	....	0.2962	0.3158	0.3335	0.3495	0.3642	0.3777	0.3965	0.4265	0.4804	0.5299	0.5766	0.6218
	H	614.5	1166.2	....	....	1198.6	1223.5	1245.8	1266.2	1284.7	1301.2	1324.1	1360.7	1427.0	1488.9	1548.6	1607.4
	S	0.8109	1.3323	....	....	1.3626	1.3855	1.4055	1.4236	1.4397	1.4538	1.4730	1.5026	1.5532	1.5971	1.6367	1.6732
1550 (600.59)	v	0.0237	0.2653	....	....	0.2883	0.3084	0.3261	0.3420	0.3567	0.3702	0.3891	0.4185	0.4719	0.5208	0.5669	0.6113
	H	617.7	1164.8	....	....	1194.5	1220.5	1243.3	1264.0	1282.7	1299.6	1323.0	1359.4	1426.2	1488.3	1548.2	1607.0
	S	0.8138	1.3298	....	....	1.3576	1.3814	1.4020	1.4203	1.4365	1.4510	1.4706	1.5001	1.5511	1.5951	1.6348	1.6713

TABLE A-2. SUPERHEATED STEAM† (Continued)

Abs. press., psia (sat. temp.)	v H S	Sat. water	Sat. steam	620	640	660	680	700	720	740	760	780	800	900	1000	1100	1200
1575 (602.74)	v	0.0238	0.2599	0.2804	0.3008	0.3186	0.3345	0.3492	0.3627	0.3755	0.3877	0.3993	0.4105	0.4633	0.5117	0.5573	0.6010
	H	620.8	1163.4	1190.3	1216.9	1240.3	1261.3	1280.5	1297.6	1313.5	1328.8	1343.5	1357.8	1424.9	1487.3	1547.4	1606.2
	S	0.8166	1.3273	1.3524	1.3768	1.3979	1.4165	1.4332	1.4478	1.4612	1.4738	1.4858	1.4972	1.5485	1.5927	1.6325	1.6691
1600 (604.87)	v	0.0239	0.2548	0.2730	0.2935	0.3114	0.3274	0.3421	0.3555	0.3682	0.3802	0.3919	0.4031	0.4554	0.5032	0.5482	0.5914
	H	623.9	1161.9	1186.3	1213.7	1237.6	1258.9	1278.4	1295.7	1311.8	1327.3	1342.2	1356.7	1424.1	1486.8	1547.0	1605.8
	S	0.8195	1.3249	1.3477	1.3728	1.3943	1.4132	1.4302	1.4449	1.4585	1.4713	1.4834	1.4950	1.5465	1.5909	1.6308	1.6674
1625 (606.97)	v	0.0240	0.2497	0.2656	0.2864	0.3044	0.3203	0.3348	0.3484	0.3610	0.3729	0.3845	0.3957	0.4474	0.4948	0.5391	0.5816
	H	627.0	1160.4	1182.1	1210.2	1234.5	1256.2	1275.9	1293.5	1310.0	1325.5	1340.6	1355.2	1423.0	1486.0	1546.3	1605.2
	S	0.8222	1.3223	1.3425	1.3683	1.3902	1.4094	1.4266	1.4416	1.4555	1.4683	1.4806	1.4923	1.5440	1.5887	1.6287	1.6652
1650 (609.05)	v	0.0241	0.2448	0.2583	0.2794	0.2976	0.3136	0.3280	0.3417	0.3542	0.3661	0.3776	0.3887	0.4399	0.4867	0.5305	0.5724
	H	630.0	1158.8	1177.6	1206.8	1231.7	1253.7	1273.6	1291.8	1308.4	1324.1	1339.3	1354.0	1422.1	1485.3	1545.7	1604.7
	S	0.8250	1.3198	1.3373	1.3641	1.3865	1.4060	1.4233	1.4389	1.4528	1.4658	1.4782	1.4899	1.5420	1.5867	1.6268	1.6634
1675 (611.10)	v	0.0242	0.2401	0.2511	0.2726	0.2909	0.3069	0.3214	0.3350	0.3474	0.3592	0.3706	0.3817	0.4324	0.4787	0.5220	0.5634
	H	633.1	1157.2	1173.1	1203.2	1228.2	1251.0	1271.5	1289.7	1306.2	1322.2	1337.5	1352.5	1420.9	1484.4	1545.0	1604.1
	S	0.8278	1.3173	1.3321	1.3597	1.3827	1.4024	1.4203	1.4358	1.4499	1.4629	1.4754	1.4874	1.5396	1.5846	1.6248	1.6615
1700 (613.12)	v	0.0243	0.2354	0.2441	0.2659	0.2844	0.3006	0.3152	0.3286	0.3411	0.3528	0.3641	0.3750	0.4254	0.4711	0.5139	0.5549
	H	636.1	1155.7	1168.1	1199.4	1225.7	1248.4	1269.4	1287.8	1304.7	1320.7	1336.2	1351.2	1420.1	1483.7	1544.4	1603.9
	S	0.8304	1.3147	1.3262	1.3549	1.3786	1.3987	1.4170	1.4327	1.4469	1.4602	1.4728	1.4848	1.5374	2.5825	1.6227	1.6597
1725 (615.13)	v	0.0244	0.2309	0.2384	0.2593	0.2780	0.2943	0.3088	0.3222	0.3346	0.3463	0.3575	0.3684	0.4183	0.4636	0.5058	0.5464
	H	639.1	1154.1	1165.2	1195.6	1222.4	1245.8	1266.8	1285.5	1302.7	1318.9	1334.5	1349.5	1419.0	1482.9	1543.7	1603.4
	S	0.8332	1.3123	1.3226	1.3505	1.3747	1.3954	1.4136	1.4296	1.4441	1.4575	1.4702	1.4822	1.5352	1.5806	1.6208	1.6579
1750 (617.11)	v	0.0245	0.2265	0.2329	0.2529	0.2718	0.2882	0.3028	0.3162	0.3285	0.3402	0.3514	0.3622	0.4116	0.4564	0.4982	0.5383
	H	642.1	1152.5	1162.0	1191.7	1219.2	1243.1	1264.5	1283.6	1300.9	1317.4	1333.1	1348.3	1418.1	1481.2	1543.3	1603.0
	S	0.8359	1.3099	1.3187	1.3460	1.3708	1.3919	1.4105	1.4269	1.4414	1.4550	1.4678	1.4800	1.5333	1.5780	1.6192	1.6562

1775 (619.07)	p	0.0246	0.2222	....	0.2466	0.2657	0.2822	0.2968	0.3102	0.3225	0.3340	0.3452	0.3559	0.4049	0.4493	0.4906	0.5302
	H	645.0	1150.9		1187.6	1216.0	1240.4	1262.1	1281.5	1299.0	1315.5	1331.5	1346.8	1416.9	1481.3	1542.5	1602.3
	S	0.8386	1.3076		1.3413	1.3669	1.3885	1.4074	1.4239	1.4387	1.4523	1.4653	1.4775	1.5311	1.5767	1.6173	1.6544
1800 (621.00)	p	0.0247	0.2180		0.2405	0.2598	0.2764	0.2912	0.3045	0.3168	0.3283	0.3393	0.3499	0.3986	0.4425	0.4834	0.5224
	H	648.0	1149.3		1183.7	1212.7	1237.6	1259.8	1279.6	1297.4	1313.9	1329.9	1345.3	1416.0	1480.6	1542.0	1601.8
	S	0.8412	1.3051		1.3367	1.3628	1.3848	1.4041	1.4211	1.4360	1.4497	1.4627	1.4750	1.5290	1.5748	1.6155	1.6526
1825 (622.92)	p	0.0248	0.2139		0.2345	0.2540	0.2708	0.2855	0.2991	0.3112	0.3225	0.3335	0.3441	0.3924	0.4357	0.4763	0.5147
	H	650.9	1147.7		1179.5	1209.4	1234.9	1257.3	1277.8	1295.6	1312.2	1328.3	1343.9	1415.0	1479.6	1541.3	1601.1
	S	0.8439	1.3028		1.3319	1.3589	1.3815	1.4009	1.4185	1.4334	1.4471	1.4602	1.4727	1.5270	1.5728	1.6137	1.6508
1850 (624.82)	p	0.0249	0.2099		0.2285	0.2482	0.2651	0.2799	0.2936	0.3056	0.3170	0.3279	0.3384	0.3863	0.4293	0.4695	0.5075
	H	653.9	1145.9		1175.1	1205.8	1231.8	1254.8	1275.6	1293.5	1310.5	1326.7	1342.4	1413.9	1479.0	1540.8	1600.8
	S	0.8465	1.3002		1.3269	1.3546	1.3776	1.3976	1.4154	1.4305	1.4445	1.4577	1.4703	1.5248	1.5710	1.6120	1.6492
1875 (626.69)	p	0.0251	0.2060		0.2225	0.2427	0.2597	0.2746	0.2882	0.3003	0.3115	0.3224	0.3328	0.3804	0.4229	0.4626	0.5003
	H	656.9	1144.2		1170.5	1202.3	1229.0	1252.3	1273.5	1291.8	1308.7	1325.2	1340.8	1412.9	1478.0	1540.2	1600.3
	S	0.8491	1.2977		1.3218	1.3504	1.3741	1.3943	1.4124	1.4278	1.4418	1.4552	1.4677	1.5227	1.5689	1.6101	1.6475
1900 (628.55)	p	0.0252	0.2022		0.2165	0.2371	0.2543	0.2694	0.2828	0.2950	0.3063	0.3171	0.3274	0.3747	0.4170	0.4562	0.4934
	H	659.9	1142.4		1165.6	1198.8	1225.9	1249.8	1271.0	1289.7	1307.0	1323.5	1339.4	1411.9	1477.5	1539.7	1599.8
	S	0.8517	1.2951		1.3163	1.3462	1.3702	1.3910	1.4091	1.4249	1.4392	1.4526	1.4653	1.5207	1.5672	1.6084	1.6457
1925 (630.38)	p	0.0253	0.1985		0.2107	0.2317	0.2491	0.2642	0.2776	0.2898	0.3010	0.3118	0.3221	0.3690	0.4109	0.4497	0.4864
	H	662.8	1140.6		1160.9	1195.0	1223.1	1247.3	1268.7	1287.7	1305.1	1321.8	1337.8	1410.7	1476.6	1538.9	1599.0
	S	0.8543	1.2926		1.3111	1.3419	1.3667	1.3878	1.4061	1.4221	1.4364	1.4500	1.4628	1.5185	1.5652	1.6065	1.6438
1950 (632.20)	p	0.0254	0.1949		0.2049	0.2264	0.2440	0.2591	0.2726	0.2848	0.2960	0.3067	0.3170	0.3636	0.4052	0.4436	0.4800
	H	665.8	1138.8		1155.8	1191.3	1220.0	1244.8	1266.5	1285.8	1303.4	1320.2	1336.3	1409.7	1476.0	1538.4	1598.8
	S	0.8569	1.2901		1.3056	1.3376	1.3630	1.3846	1.4031	1.4194	1.4339	1.4476	1.4604	1.5165	1.5635	1.6048	1.6424
1975 (634.00)	p	0.0256	0.1913		0.1992	0.2212	0.2391	0.2544	0.2678	0.2798	0.2910	0.3016	0.3117	0.3581	0.3994	0.4376	0.4737
	H	668.7	1137.0		1150.5	1187.5	1217.0	1242.4	1264.4	1283.6	1301.5	1318.3	1334.4	1408.4	1475.1	1537.8	1598.4
	S	0.8595	1.2877		1.3000	1.3334	1.3595	1.3816	1.4004	1.4165	1.4313	1.4450	1.4579	1.5144	1.5617	1.6032	1.6409

Temperature, °F

Abs. press., psia (sat. temp.)		Sat. water	Sat. steam	660	680	700	720	740	760	780	800	820	850	900	1000	1100	1200
2000 (635.78)	v	0.0257	0.1879	0.2162	0.2344	0.2498	0.2633	0.2752	0.2862	0.2966	0.3067	0.3165	0.3305	0.3528	0.3940	0.4319	0.4678
	H	671.7	1135.2	1183.7	1214.3	1240.0	1262.4	1281.8	1299.6	1316.4	1332.7	1348.6	1371.1	1407.2	1473.5	1537.4	1598.6
	S	0.8620	1.2851	1.3289	1.3560	1.3783	1.3975	1.4138	1.4285	1.4422	1.4552	1.4677	1.4851	1.5132	1.5592	1.6015	1.6395
2025 (637.54)	v	0.0258	0.1845	0.2112	0.2296	0.2452	0.2587	0.2707	0.2816	0.2919	0.3020	0.3116	0.3257	0.3478	0.3887	0.4262	0.4617
	H	674.7	1133.3	1179.9	1211.1	1237.5	1260.3	1280.1	1297.9	1314.8	1331.3	1347.1	1370.1	1406.2	1473.8	1537.0	1598.1
	S	0.8646	1.2826	1.3246	1.3523	1.3752	1.3947	1.4114	1.4261	1.4398	1.4530	1.4654	1.4832	1.5103	1.5582	1.6001	1.6380
2050 (639.29)	v	0.0259	0.1812	0.2062	0.2248	0.2405	0.2541	0.2661	0.2769	0.2872	0.2972	0.3067	0.3208	0.3428	0.3833	0.4205	0.4556
	H	677.6	1131.4	1175.8	1207.7	1234.6	1257.9	1278.0	1295.9	1313.0	1329.5	1345.3	1368.6	1405.1	1472.8	1536.2	1597.4
	S	0.8671	1.2800	1.3199	1.3483	1.3717	1.3916	1.4085	1.4233	1.4372	1.4504	1.4628	1.4808	1.5082	1.5562	1.5982	1.6362
2075 (641.02)	v	0.0261	0.1780	0.2013	0.2200	0.2358	0.2494	0.2615	0.2724	0.2828	0.2927	0.3022	0.3161	0.3374	0.3782	0.4151	0.4499
	H	680.5	1129.5	1171.5	1204.3	1231.6	1255.7	1275.7	1294.0	1311.5	1328.1	1344.0	1367.3	1403.1	1472.1	1535.7	1597.0
	S	0.8697	1.2776	1.3154	1.3445	1.3682	1.3884	1.4056	1.4208	1.4350	1.4483	1.4608	1.4788	1.5056	1.5546	1.5967	1.6348
2100 (642.73)	v	0.0262	0.1748	0.1964	0.2152	0.2310	0.2447	0.2568	0.2679	0.2783	0.2882	0.2977	0.3114	0.3319	0.3730	0.4096	0.4441
	H	683.4	1127.6	1167.3	1200.4	1228.2	1252.2	1273.0	1292.0	1309.6	1326.4	1342.6	1365.8	1400.8	1471.0	1534.8	1596.4
	S	0.8722	1.2751	1.3108	1.3401	1.3643	1.3848	1.4023	1.4180	1.4323	1.4458	1.4585	1.4764	1.5027	1.5525	1.5947	1.6330
2125 (644.43)	v	0.0263	0.1716	0.1918	0.2108	0.2268	0.2406	0.2527	0.2637	0.2739	0.2838	0.2933	0.3070	0.3290	0.3682	0.4045	0.4386
	H	686.3	1125.6	1163.0	1197.3	1225.7	1250.2	1271.3	1290.2	1307.8	1324.8	1341.2	1364.7	1400.8	1470.5	1534.5	1596.0
	S	0.8747	1.2726	1.3060	1.3364	1.3611	1.3820	1.3994	1.4151	1.4294	1.4430	1.4559	1.4740	1.5011	1.5505	1.5929	1.6311
2150 (646.11)	v	0.0265	0.1685	0.1872	0.2064	0.2225	0.2364	0.2485	0.2594	0.2695	0.2793	0.2889	0.3026	0.3240	0.3633	0.3993	0.4331
	H	689.2	1123.5	1158.6	1193.7	1222.7	1247.7	1269.1	1288.1	1305.7	1322.7	1339.4	1363.2	1400.5	1469.4	1533.8	1595.3
	S	0.8773	1.2700	1.3015	1.3326	1.3578	1.3792	1.3972	1.4129	1.4272	1.4408	1.4540	1.4723	1.5003	1.5492	1.5918	1.6300
2175 (647.77)	v	0.0266	0.1655	0.1828	0.2018	0.2182	0.2321	0.2442	0.2552	0.2654	0.2752	0.2847	0.2983	0.3196	0.3587	0.3943	0.4279
	H	692.0	1121.5	1154.3	1189.7	1219.8	1244.9	1266.5	1286.1	1304.0	1321.3	1338.0	1361.9	1399.4	1468.9	1533.1	1595.0
	S	0.8798	1.2676	1.2971	1.3284	1.3546	1.3760	1.3942	1.4104	1.4250	1.4388	1.4519	1.4704	1.4985	1.5478	1.5903	1.6288

2200 (649.42)	»	0.0267	0.1626	0.1773	0.1972	0.2138	0.2277	0.2399	0.2509	0.2612	0.2710	0.2804	0.2939	0.3151	0.3540	0.3893	0.4226
	H	695.0	1119.4	1148.0	1185.8	1216.2	1241.8	1263.8	1283.6	1302.9	1319.5	1336.2	1360.3	1398.0	1467.9	1532.3	1594.3
	S	0.8823	1.2649	1.2906	1.3239	1.3504	1.3723	1.3907	1.4072	1.4229	1.4362	1.4494	1.4679	1.4962	1.5458	1.5884	1.6269
2225 (651.06)	»	0.0269	0.1597	0.1727	0.1931	0.2097	0.2237	0.2360	0.2471	0.2574	0.2671	0.2765	0.2900	0.3109	0.3495	0.3847	0.4175
	H	697.9	1117.4	1142.7	1182.1	1213.3	1239.1	1261.7	1282.0	1300.5	1318.0	1335.2	1359.2	1397.0	1467.0	1531.9	1593.7
	S	0.8848	1.2625	1.2852	1.3201	1.3472	1.3693	1.3883	1.4051	1.4201	1.4341	1.4476	1.4661	1.4944	1.5441	1.5871	1.6255
2250 (652.67)	»	0.0270	0.1569	0.1680	0.1889	0.2055	0.2197	0.2320	0.2432	0.2535	0.2632	0.2726	0.2860	0.3066	0.3449	0.3800	0.4125
	H	700.8	1115.3	1137.2	1178.0	1209.7	1236.5	1259.2	1279.8	1298.6	1316.3	1333.5	1357.8	1395.5	1465.8	1531.2	1593.1
	S	0.8873	1.2599	1.2795	1.3156	1.3432	1.3661	1.3852	1.4022	1.4175	1.4317	1.4452	1.4640	1.4922	1.5421	1.5854	1.6239
2275 (654.27)	»	0.0272	0.1542	0.1630	0.1848	0.2018	0.2159	0.2281	0.2393	0.2496	0.2594	0.2688	0.2821	0.3026	0.3407	0.3755	0.4077
	H	703.8	1113.2	1130.8	1174.3	1207.1	1233.9	1256.7	1277.6	1296.8	1314.8	1332.1	1356.5	1394.4	1465.1	1530.7	1592.8
	S	0.8898	1.2573	1.2731	1.3116	1.3401	1.3630	1.3822	1.3995	1.4151	1.4295	1.4431	1.4619	1.4903	1.5405	1.5839	1.6225
2300 (655.87)	»	0.0274	0.1514	0.1580	0.1807	0.1980	0.2120	0.2241	0.2353	0.2457	0.2556	0.2649	0.2781	0.2986	0.3365	0.3709	0.4029
	H	706.7	1111.0	1124.2	1169.9	1204.0	1230.9	1253.9	1275.0	1294.5	1312.9	1330.3	1354.9	1393.2	1464.3	1529.9	1592.2
	S	0.8923	1.2547	1.2665	1.3070	1.3366	1.3596	1.3790	1.3964	1.4123	1.4270	1.4407	1.4597	1.4884	1.5388	1.5823	1.6210
2325 (657.74)	»	0.0275	0.1488	0.1530	0.1766	0.1941	0.2083	0.2207	0.2319	0.2423	0.2520	0.2613	0.2744	0.2948	0.3324	0.3665	0.3983
	H	709.7	1108.8	1117.1	1165.7	1200.4	1228.2	1252.0	1273.3	1293.0	1311.5	1329.0	1353.6	1392.1	1463.5	1529.2	1591.7
	S	0.8948	1.2521	1.2595	1.3025	1.3327	1.3565	1.3765	1.3941	1.4101	1.4249	1.4387	1.4577	1.4866	1.5372	1.5807	1.6196
2350 (659.00)	»	0.0277	0.1462	0.1479	0.1725	0.1901	0.2046	0.2172	0.2285	0.2389	0.2484	0.2576	0.2706	0.2910	0.3282	0.3621	0.3936
	H	712.6	1106.5	1109.7	1161.2	1196.6	1225.2	1249.8	1271.7	1291.6	1309.8	1327.3	1352.1	1391.0	1462.3	1528.3	1590.9
	S	0.8974	1.2495	1.2524	1.2980	1.3287	1.3532	1.3739	1.3920	1.4082	1.4227	1.4365	1.4557	1.4848	1.5354	1.5791	1.6180
2375 (660.55)	»	0.0278	0.1436	……	0.1686	0.1863	0.2010	0.2137	0.2250	0.2353	0.2450	0.2541	0.2671	0.2873	0.3244	0.3580	0.3892
	H	715.6	1104.0	……	1156.9	1193.0	1222.4	1247.5	1269.5	1289.6	1308.3	1325.8	1350.8	1389.8	1461.7	1527.8	1590.4
	S	0.9000	1.2467	……	1.2935	1.3249	1.3501	1.3712	1.3893	1.4057	1.4207	1.4344	1.4537	1.4830	1.5340	1.5777	1.6166
2400 (662.09)	»	0.0280	0.1410	……	0.1646	0.1824	0.1974	0.2101	0.2214	0.2317	0.2415	0.2506	0.2636	0.2836	0.3205	0.3538	0.3848
	H	718.5	1101.4	……	1152.2	1189.1	1219.4	1244.7	1267.1	1287.3	1306.5	1324.2	1349.6	1388.5	1460.8	1526.9	1589.8
	S	0.9025	1.2438	……	1.2887	1.3208	1.3467	1.3680	1.3865	1.4030	1.4183	1.4323	1.4519	1.4810	1.5323	1.5761	1.6152

TABLE A-2. SUPERHEATED STEAM† (*Continued*)

| Abs. press., psia (sat. temp.) | v H S | Sat. water | Sat. steam | \multicolumn{14}{c}{Temperature, °F} |
				680	700	720	740	760	780	800	820	850	900	950	1000	1100	1200
2450 (665.12)	v	0.0283	0.1360	0.1567	0.1750	0.1902	0.2032	0.2147	0.2250	0.2347	0.2440	0.2569	0.2766	0.2954	0.3130	0.3458	0.3764
	H	724.6	1096.3	1142.3	1181.3	1212.9	1239.5	1262.8	1283.5	1302.9	1321.4	1347.1	1386.3	1423.8	1459.0	1525.6	1588.9
	S	0.9076	1.2381	1.2787	1.3127	1.3397	1.3620	1.3813	1.3981	1.4136	1.4282	1.4481	1.4774	1.5045	1.5290	1.5732	1.6125
2500 (668.10)	v	0.0287	0.1313	0.1488	0.1680	0.1834	0.1967	0.2083	0.2188	0.2285	0.2375	0.2503	0.2700	0.2884	0.3058	0.3381	0.3683
	H	730.7	1091.0	1131.9	1173.9	1206.8	1234.5	1258.6	1280.1	1299.9	1318.3	1344.2	1384.3	1421.8	1457.3	1524.2	1587.9
	S	0.9127	1.2322	1.2683	1.3048	1.3329	1.3562	1.3761	1.3936	1.4095	1.4240	1.4440	1.4740	1.5011	1.5258	1.5701	1.6097
2550 (671.03)	v	0.0291	0.1264	0.1408	0.1606	0.1766	0.1902	0.2020	0.2125	0.2223	0.2315	0.2440	0.2634	0.2817	0.2989	0.3308	0.3604
	H	736.7	1085.6	1120.0	1164.7	1199.8	1228.9	1254.0	1276.0	1296.5	1315.6	1341.5	1381.8	1419.8	1455.6	1522.9	1586.7
	S	0.9179	1.2265	1.2568	1.2957	1.3257	1.3502	1.3709	1.3888	1.4052	1.4202	1.4402	1.4704	1.4979	1.5228	1.5674	1.6070
2600 (673.91)	v	0.0295	0.1219	0.1323	0.1541	0.1706	0.1842	0.1961	0.2066	0.2164	0.2256	0.2380	0.2573	0.2754	0.2924	0.3237	0.3530
	H	743.1	1080.1	1106.0	1157.0	1194.0	1223.9	1249.7	1272.2	1293.1	1312.6	1338.9	1379.7	1418.1	1454.2	1521.6	1585.8
	S	0.9232	1.2205	1.2433	1.2877	1.3193	1.3444	1.3657	1.3840	1.4008	1.4161	1.4364	1.4670	1.4947	1.5199	1.5645	1.6044
2650 (676.75)	v	0.0300	0.1173	0.1235	0.1469	0.1640	0.1782	0.1903	0.2009	0.2108	0.2200	0.2322	0.2514	0.2691	0.2859	0.3169	0.3458
	H	749.5	1074.5	1090.1	1146.8	1186.4	1218.3	1245.1	1268.3	1289.9	1309.9	1336.2	1377.5	1415.9	1452.2	1520.2	1584.7
	S	0.9287	1.2147	1.2284	1.2777	1.3116	1.3384	1.3606	1.3794	1.3967	1.4125	1.4328	1.4637	1.4914	1.5167	1.5618	1.6018
2700 (679.54)	v	0.0305	0.1123	......	0.1402	0.1581	0.1725	0.1846	0.1954	0.2053	0.2147	0.2269	0.2458	0.2632	0.2798	0.3105	0.3389
	H	756.1	1068.3	......	1137.5	1179.7	1213.0	1240.3	1264.5	1286.5	1307.2	1334.0	1375.7	1414.0	1450.6	1519.2	1583.8
	S	0.9342	1.2082	......	1.2684	1.3045	1.3325	1.3550	1.3747	1.3923	1.4086	1.4293	1.4606	1.4882	1.5137	1.5592	1.5993
2750 (682.28)	v	0.0310	0.1077	......	0.1335	0.1520	0.1670	0.1794	0.1902	0.2000	0.2094	0.2215	0.2402	0.2576	0.2740	0.3043	0.3322
	H	763.0	1061.8	......	1127.1	1172.2	1207.4	1236.0	1260.8	1283.0	1304.2	1331.4	1373.3	1412.2	1449.2	1518.0	1582.8
	S	0.9399	1.2016	......	1.2583	1.2969	1.3265	1.3501	1.3703	1.3881	1.4048	1.4258	1.4572	1.4853	1.5110	1.5566	1.5969
2800 (684.98)	v	0.0316	0.1032	......	0.1267	0.1461	0.1615	0.1741	0.1851	0.1950	0.2045	0.2166	0.2351	0.2521	0.2685	0.2983	0.3258
	H	770.0	1054.6	......	1115.9	1164.5	1201.3	1231.3	1257.0	1279.8	1301.7	1329.3	1371.5	1410.4	1447.9	1517.0	1581.9
	S	0.9458	1.1944	......	1.2476	1.2892	1.3203	1.3449	1.3658	1.3840	1.4013	1.4226	1.4542	1.4823	1.5084	1.5542	1.5945

Pressure (Sat. temp)																
2850 (687.65)	v	0.0322	0.0986	0.1198	0.1404	0.1563	0.1690	0.1801	0.1903	0.1995	0.2117	0.2298	0.2469	0.2629	0.2925	0.3197
	H	777.5	1046.6	1103.5	1156.6	1195.8	1226.5	1252.9	1276.9	1298.4	1326.8	1368.9	1408.7	1446.0	1515.8	1581.1
	S	0.9521	1.1866	1.2359	1.2813	1.3143	1.3397	1.3611	1.3803	1.3973	1.4192	1.4507	1.4795	1.5055	1.5517	1.5923
2900 (690.26)	v	0.0329	0.0941	0.1126	0.1348	0.1511	0.1641	0.1754	0.1855	0.1949	0.2069	0.2250	0.2418	0.2578	0.2870	0.3138
	H	785.2	1038.1	1089.2	1148.3	1189.5	1221.6	1249.1	1273.3	1295.7	1324.2	1367.1	1406.9	1444.8	1514.8	1580.2
	S	0.9586	1.1785	1.2228	1.2733	1.3080	1.3345	1.3569	1.3762	1.3939	1.4159	1.4480	1.4767	1.5032	1.5495	1.5902
2950 (692.83)	v	0.0337	0.0895	0.1052	0.1292	0.1460	0.1593	0.1708	0.1809	0.1902	0.2023	0.2202	0.2369	0.2527	0.2815	0.3081
	H	793.6	1028.9	1073.2	1139.5	1183.1	1216.6	1245.1	1269.8	1292.5	1321.7	1364.9	1405.1	1443.2	1513.5	1579.4
	S	0.9655	1.1697	1.2080	1.2647	1.3014	1.3290	1.3522	1.3720	1.3898	1.4124	1.4448	1.4738	1.5004	1.5469	1.5879
3000 (695.37)	v	0.0346	0.0849	0.0972	0.1236	0.1410	0.1546	0.1661	0.1763	0.1856	0.1978	0.2155	0.2322	0.2478	0.2763	0.3027
	H	802.6	1019.3	1054.0	1130.3	1176.4	1211.4	1240.6	1266.0	1289.0	1319.0	1362.5	1403.4	1441.7	1512.4	1578.9
	S	0.9731	1.1607	1.1907	1.2559	1.2947	1.3236	1.3474	1.3677	1.3858	1.4090	1.4416	1.4711	1.4978	1.5447	1.5860
3050 (697.84)	v	0.0357	0.0804	0.0868	0.1183	0.1361	0.1499	0.1617	0.1719	0.1812	0.1935	0.2111	0.2275	0.2431	0.2712	0.2973
	H	812.9	1007.7	1025.0	1121.2	1169.6	1205.9	1236.3	1262.4	1285.7	1316.4	1360.4	1401.3	1440.2	1511.1	1577.9
	S	0.9818	1.1501	1.1650	1.2472	1.2879	1.3179	1.3437	1.3635	1.3819	1.4056	1.4386	1.4681	1.4952	1.5422	1.5837
3100 (700.29)	v	0.0372	0.0752		0.1128	0.1312	0.1456	0.1576	0.1680	0.1771	0.1891	0.2068	0.2231	0.2385	0.2663	0.2921
	H	824.6	994.0		1110.8	1162.4	1200.9	1232.5	1259.4	1282.7	1313.4	1358.2	1399.5	1438.7	1509.9	1577.0
	S	0.9916	1.1376		1.2374	1.2808	1.3126	1.3383	1.3599	1.3782	1.4019	1.4355	1.4653	1.4926	1.5398	1.5815
3150 (702.69)	v	0.0392	0.0691		0.1075	0.1266	0.1410	0.1532	0.1636	0.1729	0.1850	0.2024	0.2187	0.2341	0.2615	0.2871
	H	841.3	976.3		1100.3	1155.3	1194.7	1227.6	1254.9	1279.2	1310.5	1355.5	1397.5	1437.2	1508.6	1576.1
	S	1.0056	1.1217		1.2276	1.2738	1.3064	1.3331	1.3550	1.3741	1.3983	1.4320	1.4623	1.4900	1.5373	1.5792
3200 (705.04)	v	0.0443	0.0596		0.1024	0.1217	0.1368	0.1493	0.1596	0.1687	0.1810	0.1985	0.2145	0.2296	0.2570	0.2822
	H	871.3	946.6		1089.8	1146.9	1189.3	1223.4	1251.1	1275.2	1307.7	1353.8	1395.7	1435.2	1507.6	1575.3
	S	1.0311	1.0958		1.2180	1.2660	1.3011	1.3288	1.3510	1.3699	1.3950	1.4296	1.4598	1.4874	1.5353	1.5774
3206.2‡ (705.34)	v	0.0541	0.0541		0.1018	0.1211	0.1363	0.1488	0.1591	0.1682	0.1805	0.1980	0.2140	0.2290	0.2564	0.2816
	H	910.3	910.3		1088.5	1145.8	1188.5	1222.9	1250.6	1274.8	1307.3	1353.4	1395.3	1434.8	1507.3	1575.1
	S	1.0645	1.0645		1.2170	1.2652	1.3005	1.3284	1.3506	1.3696	1.3947	1.4293	1.4596	1.4872	1.5351	1.5773

† Reproduced by permission from "Steam Tables: Properties of Saturated and Superheated Steam," copyright 1940, Combustion Engineering, Inc.

‡ Critical pressure.

477

NAME INDEX

Amagat, E. H., 23, 98

Bacon, Francis, 20
Barr-David, F. H., 361, 364
Beattie, J. A., 92
Benedict, M., 92, 351
Benger, H., 216
Berthelot, D., 92
Bichowsky, F. R., 142
Black, Joseph, 20
Bliss, H., 415
Boyle, Robert, 20, 64
Bridgeman, O. C., 92

Carnot, Sadi, 179
Chilton, T. H., 129
Clausius, Rudolf, 15
Colburn, A. P., 129
Colding, A., 20
Comings, E. W., 86, 202
Coriolis, G. G., 14
Cramer, E., 216

Davy, Humphry, 20
Denbigh, K., 43
De Priester, C. L., 369, 370
Dieterici, C., 92
Dodds, W. S., 214
Dodge, B. F., 360, 383

Edmister, W. C., 369

Galileo, 14
Gibbs, J. Willard, 42, 343, 381
Glasstone, S., 195
Greenhaus, L. R., 169
Greenkorn, R. A., 96, 112, 220, 221

Helmholtz, H. von, 20
Hou, Y. C., 92

Hougen, O. A., 96, 112, 220, 221, 354
Hunsaker, J. C., 238
Hurd, C. O., 214

Ibl, N. V., 383
Ingersoll, A. C., 238

Joule, J. P., 19, 20, 24

Kay, W. B., 106
Keenan, J. H., 286
Kelley, K. K., 128, 130
Kelvin, Lord, 15, 179, 181
Keyes, F. G., 7, 92
Kister, A. T., 384
Kistiakowsky, W., 132
Kobe, K. A., 98
Koch, A. V., 216
Kuenen, J. P., 360
Kwong, J. N. S., 92

Lacey, W. N., 205, 348
Landsbaum, E. M., 214
Lewis, G. N., 346, 349
Lewis, W. K., 372
Lydersen, A. L., 96, 112, 220, 221
Lynn, R. E., Jr., 98

McCabe, W. L., 164
McCracken, P. G., 362
Margules, M., 389
Martin, J. J., 92
Matthews, C. S., 214
Mayer, J. R. von, 20
Mohr, K. F., 20

Newton, Isaac, 20, 314

479

SUBJECT INDEX

481